McGRAW-HILL SERIES IN HEALTH SCIENCE

Amos Christie, M.D., Consulting Editor

The Commonsense Psychiatry of Dr. Adolf Meyer

THE COMMONSENSE PSYCHIATRY OF DR.

FIFTY-TWO SELECTED PAPERS

EDITED, WITH BIOGRAPHICAL NARRATIVE,

BY ALFRED LIEF

FIRST EDITION

McGRAW-HILL BOOK COMPANY, INC.

NEW YORK   TORONTO   LONDON   1948

THE COMMONSENSE PSYCHIATRY OF DR. ADOLF MEYER

Frontispiece photograph by Bachrach.

To
Alfred B. Kastor
In Friendship

Foreword

When I first met Dr. Meyer in his Baltimore home and told him of my desire to preserve and present his basic papers, he put a fresh log on the fire, seated himself near by, and folded his hands in his lap. He suggested that the book be an expression of my own needs and urges. Like many others who regard the world as a post-graduate education in life, I had been seeking clarity on the subject of psychiatry. The literature contained many illuminating answers attributed to Adolf Meyer. From the footnotes I turned to the sources. There, distinct from a psychiatry on a basis of psychoanalysis, was his concept of mind and behavior and organs as a biological whole. I looked for a complete statement, for a textbook, or at any rate a full-bodied volume, in which possibly he unfolded his findings; but though he had written close to two hundred papers, there was no such book.

"The main thing," the doctor continued, "is that your point of reference should always be life itself and not the imagined cesspool of the unconscious."

He said he himself had never been weaned from an interest in ordinary daily life and daily observation by either theological or scientific dogmatism.

I wondered whether intense revulsion from dogma—marked in his conversation by such epithets as "pseudoscience," "psycho-physical parallelism," and "psychosomatic nonsense"—had kept him from preparing an authoritative text. He spoke of a particular treatise as an act of "washing one's hands" of a subject. A further clue was his professional habit of refraining from imposing a decision upon a patient, but instead using the patient's collaboration and offering only indications to suit specific wants and capacities.

For there was no universal answer. In his teaching he had not offered Truth but ways of finding truths. By avoiding finality he kept the channels of thought clear for fresh discovery and new growth. The work called for an open mind, patience, and preparedness for further assimilation.

"My struggle in this country," he told me, "has been with a false conception of science." Mistaken science, using test tube and microscope as its symbols, talked about and claimed to know more and more about less and less, such as the alleged importance of the smallness of cell nuclei. "Psychiatry has to be found in the function and the life of the people."

In 1933 the late Dr. William Alanson White had written in his memoirs

In many respects Dr. Meyer has been the outstanding influence in the development of psychiatry in this country for about forty years, and practically no major enterprise has been projected in the field of psychiatry which he has not influenced in some way.

The years had added up to fifty by the time Dr. Meyer retired from his professorship at The Johns Hopkins University Medical School.

The doctor sat placidly in his chair and reflected, "I never wanted to be the leader of American psychiatry. Power did not interest me. I did not want to be called the dean of American psychiatrists."

It was important to me to trace the origins and consequences of his principles.

He said, "When it comes to psychobiology, I wish it were possible to get rid of the words and get the sense to unprejudiced readers." A fresh start seemed to him essential. I would have to break through the incrustation of "the pseudoerudition of present-day popular slang and the formal effort of available renderings." What he hoped I would convey was "a sense for the human person expressed as behavior in situations and efforts aiming at satisfactions and meeting one's needs." In that way I would satisfy my own urge.

On subsequent visits to Dr. Meyer, heightened in pleasure by the presence and helpfulness of Mrs. Meyer, his commonsense approach to the problems of psychiatry was always the keynote. In all his work he had proceeded from the experiences of ordinary life, using concrete material instead of venturing into fatalistic realms.

"I am not particularly interested in data concerning which I have to accept the fact that the dice have already been cast and that life is practically nothing but the dance of factors largely settled by heredity and constitution."

He objected to the Freudian pattern into which each one was fitted. "Instead of leaving the impression that in most cases we have to probe at once into the sex life when we suspect 'mental factors' to be playing a role, I should emphasize the fact that after all practically every fundamental function can take a lead in the personality"—the gastro-intestinal, for instance. "It is always wisest to pay attention to the whole range of factors."

He did not believe in applying a "ready-made code in terms of complexes and mechanisms." Instead of making a mystery of the unconscious, he said, "There is very little difference between the conscious and the unconscious." He preferred to speak of "more or less" consciousness, the less conscious material being things that did not immediately come to mind; less accessible to scrutiny because they were dissociated from the general trend. This material consisted of tendencies rather than outspoken performance, but was as clearly active or potent.

He said he did not believe in participating in controversies. "I never got much satisfaction out of fighting. I am not a bitter-ender." When there was personal opposition, he took it as he did the weather. He hoped this book would not make a contrast of personalities but concentrate the readers' attention upon the data.

But he saw a persistence of Barnumism in America: showmanship, advertising to create an impression of importance and implant false ideas. Anything more than twenty-five years old was considered unimportant; many psychiatrists thought nothing had happened before they made the acquaintance of Freudianism. If they overlooked psychobiology, perhaps this was because it did not have enough glamour to make the front page.

Frequently in these conversations he described himself as a meliorist. "I am not an optimist and not a pessimist. I look for opportunities to make improvements rather than sins to be overcome." Again, "I do not believe in perfection or omniscience but in doing one's best." He also called himself a pragmatist and a pluralist and a naturalist. "What I want for service is real life and performance, that which has objective validity but works with subjective self-referring function."

A patient was not a mere summing-up of cells and organs, but a human being in need of readjustment to the demands of life. In his time psychiatry had reached out from hospital administration to respect for the patient as a unique individual, not as a type; for the individual as a person in difficulty, not as a disease. Meyer gave a new meaning to psychology: "I mean by it the behavior of the person and the reactions and the feelings and the impulses, and not only the sensations." He developed personality-studies to see how one functioned in the long run and how disturbances of special functions were apt to affect those long-term adjustments. Thus it was possible to determine where lay the miscarriages and what were the patient's assets that could best be used for management and redirection into happier activity.

Ordinarily a physician concentrated on physiological disturbances—the handling of injuries and malfunction of special organs. At the other extreme was the minister and the problems which confronted him. "These extremes are intimately connected," Dr. Meyer said. The physician must now add to the disturbances of part-functions those of person-function and the story of life. Concerning the tendency of medicine to speak of psychosomatic considerations as if the two components were separate and contrasting, he observed, "As a matter of fact, there is a wide range of inadequacy of the person and the individual organs, so that today we demand that the student of man learn to pay attention to all these aspects of disease, which are interrelated—attention to the whole person."

And here he stressed differentiation as man's peculiar quality. "I put my emphasis on specificity. It is 'the story' that counts in a person."

Prophylaxis became possible when mental disorder was understood as the pathology of function. But prophylaxis consisted not only of giving a black mark to potentially harmful factors and heeding the danger signals of anxiety, fear, and fatalism with its note of blame and moping and defeatism. It meant also "preparedness for what is practicable and conducive to the result that we call health." It meant "the positive tendency to live in harmony with what you know is within the reach of your choice and your available assets."

At our final conference on this book Dr. Meyer pointed out, "As long as there is life there are positive assets—action, choice, hope—not in the imagination but in a clear understanding of the situation, goals, and possibilities." As against running away from things, there should be "a positive selection of the sensible, workable resources . . . attention to what can be brought into one's life and what is attainable, and not merely an optimism with its counterpart in defeatism."

He called for "frank work with a clear evaluation of one's status and workable responsibilities in the direction of more and more insight and natural leaning toward the choice of the better." He cautioned against the belittlement implied in comparison and exaggeration. "We do not want to make the better the enemy of the good, but to help promotion of the better."

Objective evaluation was the goal of wisdom and of real health and success. "To see life as it is, to tend toward objectivity, is one of the fundamentals of my philosophy, my attitude, my preference. It is something that I would recommend if it can be kept free of making itself a pest to the self and to the others."

In this book I have undertaken, as Dr. Meyer put it, "to give the average person a better practical understanding of my material"—as a help to himself and myself and "the many I should like to be helpful to." He has given me the liberty to make such use of it as will "aid in the receptivity of the reader."

Fifty-two selections are presented here in a setting meant to portray the evolution of a psychiatrist and of his thinking and work. It is an exposition of American psychiatry and at the same time a picture of a physician in action. The papers have been edited with a view to integration and abridged where necessary to avoid repetition and preserve continuity. As a whole, it may stand as Dr. Meyer's declaration of independence from dogma. I also hope it fulfills his expectation that I would produce "very much what is needed to awaken in others a respect for the person and his behavior."

Social workers, educators, clergymen, personnel directors, nurses, all who are interested in man, and all who are interested in medicine will find in Meyer, as I have found, a source of growth and a stimulating, steadying philosophy. I am especially interested in reaching the general practitioner, for Meyer has always kept in mind the fact that psychiatry is a branch of medicine and the intention that its fruits should return to the general body of medicine.

Grateful acknowledgment of permissions to reprint is made to: American Education Fellowship, American Eugenics Society, *American Journal of Psychology*, American Medical Association, American Psychiatric Association, American Psychological Association, American Psychopathological Association, Association of American Medical Colleges, British Medical Association, Child Study Association of America, Mrs. Ethel S. Dummer, Harper & Brothers, Paul B. Hoeber, Inc., Johns Hopkins Press, *Journal of Mental Science*, *Medical Times*, National Committee for Mental Hygiene, National Conference of Social Work, National Research Council, *Nervous and Mental Disease Monographs*, *The Psychiatric Quarterly*, Survey Associates, Inc., and The Williams & Wilkins Company.

Warm thanks are given also to Dr. Solomon Katzenelbogen, of St. Elizabeths Hospital, Washington, D. C., whose bibliography covering 1891-1936 was an accurate guide; to Dr. Oskar Diethelm, director of the Payne Whitney Clinic of The New York Hospital, for permitting me virtually to inhabit the Clinic's library for more than two years; to Dr. John C. Whitehorn, director of the Henry Phipps Psychiatric Clinic of The Johns Hopkins Hospital, for the use of its library; to Mrs. J. G. Nichols, librarian of Cornell University Medical College; to Drs. William L. Russell, A. A. Brill, and Harold W. Lovell, all of New York. I am especially grateful to Dr. Lovell, who read this book in manuscript.

For her faith, encouragement, and communicable zest for life, I thank my wife, Zola.

ALFRED LIEF

NEW YORK, N. Y.
February, 1948

Contents

Introduction

THE CONTRIBUTIONS OF PSYCHIATRY TO THE UNDERSTANDING OF LIFE PROBLEMS

From an address by Dr. Meyer at the celebration of the 100th anniversary of Bloomingdale Hospital, May 26, 1921, at White Plains, N. Y.; in A Psychiatric Milestone, *privately published.*

Of all the divisions of medicine, psychiatry has suffered longest from man's groping for a conception of his own nature. Psychiatry means, literally, the healing of souls. What then do we actually mean by soul or by psyche? The question has too long been treated as a disturbing puzzle.

Today we feel that modern psychiatry has found itself—through the discovery that, after all, the uncritical commonsense view of mind and soul is not so far remote from a critical commonsense view of the individual life and its activity, freed from the forbidding and confusing assumptions through which the concept of mind and soul has been held in bewildering awe.

Strange to say, good old Aristotle was nearer an understanding than most of the wise men and women that have succeeded him for these more than two thousand years. He saw in the psyche

1

what he called the form and realization or fulfillment of the human
organism; he would probably now say with us, the activity and
function of an individual or person.

Through the disharmonies and inevitable disruption of a self-
disorganizing civilization, the Greek and Roman world was
plunged into the dark centuries during which the perils of the
soul and the sacrificial attainment of salvation by monastic life and
crusades threatened to overshadow all other concern. This had
some inevitable results: it favored all those views through which
the soul became like a special thing or substance, in contrast to and
yet a counterpart of the physical body. As long as there was no
objective experimental science, the culminating solution of life
problems had to be entrusted to that remarkable development of
religious philosophy which arose from the blending of Hebrew
religion and tradition and the loftiest products of the Greek mind,
in the form which St. Paul and the early Church fathers gave to
the teachings of Christ. From being the form and activation, or
function, of the organism in life, the soul feature of man was given
an appearance in which it could neither be grasped nor understood,
nor shaped, nor guided by man when it got into trouble. From the
Middle Ages there arose an artificial soul and an artificial world
of souls presented as being in eternal conflict with the evil of the
flesh—*and thus the house of human nature was divided against
itself.*

Science of the nineteenth century came nearer bringing mind
and body together again. The new astronomical conception of the
world and the objective experimental science gradually began to
command confidence, and from being a destroyer of excessively
dogmatic notions, science began to rise to its modern constructive
and creative position. But the problem of *mind* remained on a
wrong basis and still does so even with most scientists. Too much
had been claimed for the psyche, and because of the singling-out
of a great world of spirit, the world of fact had been compromised
and left cold and dry and unattractive and unpromising. No doubt
it was necessary that the scientist should become hardened and
weaned from all misleading expectation, and shy of all the spurious
claims of sordid superstition and of childish fancy. He may have

been unduly radical in cutting out everything that in any way recalled the misleading notions. In the end, we had to go through a stage of psychology without a "soul," and lately even a psychology without "consciousness," so that we might be safe from unscientific pretensions. All the gyrations no doubt tended to retard the wholesome practical attack upon the problems in the form in which we find them in our commonsense life.

The first effort at a fresh start tried to explain everything rather one-sidedly out of the meager knowledge of the body. Spinoza had said in his remarkable *Ethics* (III, Prop. II, Schol.): "Nobody has thus far determined what the body can do, *i.e.*, nobody has as yet shown by experience and trial what the body can do by the laws of nature alone in so far as nature is considered merely as corporeal and extended, and what it cannot do save when determined by mind."

This challenge of Spinoza's had to be met. With some investigators this seemed very literally all there was to be done about the study of man—to show how far the body could explain the activity we call "the mind." The unfortunate feature was that they thought they had to start with a body not only with mind and soul left out but also with practical disregard of the whole natural setting. They studied little more than corpses and experimental animals, and many a critic wondered how such a corpse or a frog could ever show any mind, normal or abnormal. To get things balanced again, the vision of man had to expand to take a sane and practical view of all of human life—not only its machinery.

The human organism can never exist without its setting in the world. All we are and do is of the world and in the world. The great mistake of an overambitious science has been the desire to study man altogether as a mere sum of parts, if possible of atoms, or now of electrons, and as a machine, detached, by itself, because at least some points in the simpler sciences could be studied to the best advantage with this method of the so-called elementalist. It was a long time before willingness to see the large group of facts, in their broad relations as well as in their inner structure, finally gave us the concept and vision of integration which now fits man as a live unit and transformer of energy into the world of fact and makes him frankly a consciously integrated psycho-biological individual and member of a social group.

It is natural enough that man should want to travel on the road he knows and likes best. The philosopher uses his logic and analysis and synthesis. The introspectionist wants to get at the riddle of the universe by crawling into the innermost depth of his own self-scrutiny, even at the risk—to use a homely phrase—of drawing the hole in after him and losing all connection with the objective world. The physicist follows the reverse course. He gives us the appreciation of the objective world around and in us. The chemist follows out the analytic and synthetic possibilities of his atoms and elements, and the biologist the growth and reproduction and multiplication of cells. Each sees an open world of possibilities and is ready to follow as far as facts will carry and as far as the imagination will soar. Each branch has created its rules of the game culminating in the concept of objective science, and the last set of facts to bring itself under the rules of objective science, and to be accepted, has been man as a unit and personality.

The mind and the soul of man have indeed had a hard time. To this day, investigators have suffered under the dogma that mind must be treated as a purely subjective entity, something that can be studied only by introspection, or at least only with ultra-accurate instruments—always with the idea that commonsense is all wrong in its psychology. Undoubtedly it was, so long as it spoke of a mind and soul as if what was called so had to be, even during life, mysterious and inaccessible, something quite different from any other fact of natural-history study.

The great step was taken when all of life was seen again in its broad relations, without any special theory but frankly as com-monsense finds it, *viz.*, as the activities and behavior of definite individuals—very much as Aristotle had put it—"living organisms in their 'form' or activity and behavior." Psychology had to wake up to studying other minds as well as one's own. Commonsense has always been willing to study other persons besides our own selves, and that exactly as we study single organs—for what they are and do and for the conditions of success and failure. Nor do we have to start necessarily from so-called elements. Progress cannot be made merely out of details. It will not do merely to pile up fragments and to expect the aggregates to form themselves. It also takes a friend of facts with the capacity for mastering and unifying them, as the general musters his army. Biology had to have evolutionists and its Darwin to get on a broad basis to start with, and human biology, the life of man, similarly had to be conceived in a new spirit, with a clear recognition of the opportunities for the study of detail about the brain and about the conditions for its working and its proper support, but also with a clear vision of the whole man and all that his happiness and efficiency depended upon.

All this evolution is strongly reflected in the actual work of psychiatry and medicine. For a time, it looked to the physician as if the physiology and pathology of the body had to make it their ambition to make wholly unnecessary what traditional psychology had accumulated, by turning it all into brain physiology. The "psychological" facts involved were undoubtedly more difficult to control, so much so that one tried to cut them out altogether. As if foreshadowing the later academic "psychology without soul and consciousness," the venerable superintendent of Utica, Dr. John Purdue Gray, was very proud when in 1870 he had eliminated the "mental and moral" causes from his statistics of the Utica State Hospital, hiding behind the dogma that "mind cannot become diseased, but only the body." Today "mental and moral causes" are recognized again in truer form—no longer as mere ideas and uninvestigated suppositions taken from uncritical histories, but as concrete and critically studied life situations and life factors and life problems. Our patients are sick not merely in an abstract mind, but by actually living in ways which put their mind and the entire organism and its activity in jeopardy, and we are now free to see how this happens—since we study the biography and life history, the resources of adaptation and of shaping the life to success or to failure.

The study of life problems always concerns itself with the interaction of an individual organism with life situations. The first result of a recognition of this fact was a more wholehearted and practical concept of personality.

In 1903 I put together for the first time my analysis of the neurotic personality [see page 103], which was soon followed by a series of studies on the influences of the mental factors, and in 1908 a paper on "What Do Histories of Cases of Insanity Teach Us Concerning Preventive Mental Hygiene During the Years of School Life?" [see page 233]. All this was using for psychiatry the growing appreciation of a broad biological viewpoint in its concrete application. It was a reaction against the peculiar fear of studying the facts of life simply and directly as we find and experience them—scoffed at because it looked as if one was not dealing with dependable and effective data. Many of the factors mentioned as causes do not have the claimed effects with sufficient regularity. It is quite true that not everybody is liable to any serious upset by several of the handicaps sometimes found to be disastrous during the years of development; but we have learned to see more clearly why the one person does and the other does not suffer. Evidently, not everybody who is reserved and retiring need be in danger of mental disorder, yet there are persons of just this type of make-up who are less able than others to stand the strains of isolation, of inferiority feeling, of exalted ambitions and one-sided longings, intolerable desires, etc. The same individual difference of susceptibility holds even for alcohol. With this recognition we came to lay stress again on the specific factors which make for the deterioration of habits, for tantrums with imaginations, and for drifting into abnormal behavior, and conditions incompatible with health.

After studying in each patient all the nonmental disorders such as infections, intoxications, and the like, we can now also attack the problems of life which can be understood only in terms of plain and intelligible human relations and activities, and thus we have learned to meet on concrete ground the real essence of mind and soul—the plain and intelligible human activities and relations to self and others. There are in the life records of our patients certain ever-returning tendencies and situations which a psychiatry of exclusive brain speculation, autointoxications, focal infections, and internal secretions could never have discovered.

Much is gained by the frank recognition that man is fundamentally a social being. There are reactions in us which only contacts and relations with other human beings can bring out. We must study men as mutual reagents in personal affections and aversions and their conflicts; in the desires and satisfactions of the simpler appetites for food and personal necessities; in the natural interplay of anticipation and fulfillment of desires and their occasional frustration; in the selection of companionship which works helpfully or otherwise—for the moment or more lastingly throughout the many vicissitudes of life. All through we find situations which create a more or less personal bias and chances for success or failure, such as simpler types of existence do not produce. They create new problems, and produce some individuals of great sensitiveness and others with immunity—and in this great field nothing will replace a simple study of the life factors and the social and personal life problems and their working—the study of the real mind and the real soul—*i.e.*, human life itself.

Looking back then, we see that this practical turn has changed greatly the general view as to what should be the chief concern of psychology. One only need take up a book on psychology to see what a strong desire there always was to contrast a pure psychology and an applied psychology, and to base a new science directly on the new acquisitions of the primary sciences such as anatomy and histology of the nervous system. There was a quest for the elements of mind and their immediate correlation with the latest discoveries in the structure of the brain. The center theory and the cell-and-neuron theory seemed obligatory starting points. Today we have become shy of such postulates of one-sided, not sufficiently functional materialism. We now call for an interest in psychobiological facts in terms of critical common-sense and in their own right—largely a product of psychiatry. There always is a place for elements, but there certainly is also a place for the large momentous facts of human life just as we find and live it.

Thus psychiatry has opened to us new conceptions and understandings of the relation of child and mother, child and father, the child as a reagent to the relations between mother and father, brothers and sisters, companions and community—in the competitions of real concrete life. It has furnished a concrete setting for the interplay of emotions and their effects.

It has led us from a cold dogma of blind heredity and a wholesale fatalistic asylum scheme, to an understanding of individual, familiar, and social adjustments, and a grasp on the factors which we can consider individually and socially modifiable. We have passed from giving mere wholesale advice to a conscientious study of the problems of each unit, and at the same time we have developed a new and sensible approach to mental hygiene and prevention, as expressed in the comprehensive surveys of state and community work and even more clearly in the development of helps to individuals in finding themselves, and in the work in schools to reach those who need a special adaptation of aims and means. To the terrible emergency of the war it was possible to bring experienced men and women as physicians and nurses, and how much was done only those can appreciate who have seen the liberality with which all the hospitals, and Bloomingdale among the first, contributed more than their quota of help, and all the assistance that could possibly be offered to returning victims for their readjustment.

It is natural enough that psychiatry should have erred in some respects. We had forced upon us the herding together of larger numbers of patients than can possibly be handled by one human working unit or working group. The consequence was that there arose a narrowing routine and wholesale classifications and a loss of contact with the concrete needs of the individual case; that very often progress had to come from one-sided enthusiasts or even outsiders, who lost the sense of proportion and magnified points of relative importance until they were supposed to explain everything and to be cure-alls. We are all inclined to sacrifice at the altar of excessive simplicity, especially when it suits us; we become "single taxers" and favor wholesale legislation and exclusive state care when our sense for democratic methods has gone astray. Human society has dealt with the great needs of psychiatry about as it has dealt with the objects of charity, only in some ways more stingily, with a shrewd system and unfortunately often with a certain dread of the workers themselves and of their enthusiasm and demands. Law and prejudice surround a great share of the work with notions of stigma and hopelessness and weirdness—while to those who see the facts in terms of life problems there can be but few more inspiring tasks than watching the unfolding of the problematic personality, seeking and finding its proper settings, and preventing the clashes and gropings in maladjustments and flounderings of fancy and the faulty use and nutrition of the brain and of the entire organism.

What a difference between the history of a patient reported and studied and advised by the well-trained psychiatrist of today and the account drawn up by the statistical-minded researcher or the physician who wants to see nothing but infections or chemistry and hypotheses of internal secretion! What a different chance for the patient in his treatment, in contrast to what the venerable John M. Galt of Virginia reports as the conception of treatment recommended by a great leader of a hundred years ago [Benjamin Rush]:

Mania in the first stage, if caused by study, requires separation from books. Low diet and a few gentle doses of purging physic; if pulse tense, ten or twelve ounces of blood [not to be given but to be taken!]. In the high grade, catch the patient's eye and look him out of countenance. Be always dignified. Never laugh at or with them. Be truthful. Meet them with respect. Act kindly toward them in their presence. If these measures fail, coercion if necessary. Tranquilizing chair. Strait waistcoat. Pour cold water down their sleeves. The shower bath for fifteen or twenty minutes. Threaten them with death. Chains seldom and the whip never required. Twenty to forty ounces of blood, unless fainting occurs previously . . .

Today an understanding of the life history, of the patient's somatic and functional assets and problems, likes and dislikes, the problem presented by the family, etc.!

So much for the change within and for psychiatry. How about psychiatry's contribution beyond its own narrower sphere? It has led us on in philosophy, it has brought about changes in our attitude toward ethics, toward social study, toward religion, toward law, and toward life in general. Psychiatric work has undoubtedly intensified the hunger for a more objective and yet melioristic and really idealistic philosophical conception of reality, such as has been formulated in the modern concept of integration.

Philosophical tradition, logic, and epistemology alike had all conspired to make as great a puzzle as possible of the nature of mental life, of life itself, and of all the fundamental principles, so much so that as a result anything resembling or suggesting philosophy going beyond the ordinary traditions has got into poor repute in our colleges and universities and among those of practical intelligence. The consequence is that the student and the physician are apt to be hopeless and indifferent concerning any effort at orderly thinking on these problems.

Most of us grew up with the attitude of a fatalistic intellectual hopelessness. How could we ever be clear on the relation of mind and body? How could mind and soul ever arise out of matter? How can we harmonize strict science with what we try to do in our treatment of patients? How can we, with our mechanistic science, speak of effort, and of will to do better? How can we meet the invectives against the facts of matter on the part of the opposing idealistic philosophies and their uncritical exploitations in "New Thought"—*i.e.*, really the revival of archaic thought? It is not merely medical usefulness that forced these broad issues on many a thinking physician, but having to face the facts all the time in dealing with a living human world. The psychopathologist had to learn to do more than the so-called elementalist who always goes back to the elements and smallest units and then is apt to shirk the responsibility of making an attempt to solve the concrete problems of greater complexity.

The psychiatrist has to study individuals and groups as wholes, as complex units, as the "you" or "he" or "she" or "they" we have to work with. We recognize that throughout nature we have to face the general principle of unit formation, and the fact that the new units need not be like a mere sum of the component parts but can be an actually new entity not wholly predictable from the component parts and known only through actual experience with the specific product. Hydrogen and oxygen, it is true, can form simple mixtures, but when they make an actual chemical integration we get a new specific type of substance, water, behaving and dividing according to its own laws and properties in a way not wholly predictable from just what we know of hydrogen and oxygen as such. Analogy prompts us to see in plants and animals products of physics and chemistry and organization, although the peculiarity of the product makes us recognize certain specificities of life not contained in the theory of mere physics and chemistry.

All the facts of experience prompt us to see in mentation a biological function, and we are no longer surprised to find this product of integration so different from the nature and functions of all the component parts. All the apparent discontinuities in the intrinsic harmony of facts, on the one hand, and the apparent impossibility of accounting for new features and peculiarities of the new units, are shown to be a general feature of nature and of facts; integration is not mere summation, but a creation of ever-new types and units, with superficial discontinuities and with their own new denominators of special peculiarities; hence there is no reason to think of an insurmountable and unique feature in the origin of life, nor even of mentally integrated life; no need of special mystical sparks of life, of a mysterious spirit, etc.; but—and this is the important point—also no need of denying the existence of all the evidence there may be of facts which we imply when we use the deeply felt concepts of mind and soul. In other words, we do not have to be mind-shy or body-shy any longer.

The inevitable problem of having to study other persons as well as ourselves necessarily leads us on to efforts at solution of other philosophical problems, the problem of integrating materialism and idealism, mechanism and relative biological determinism and purpose, etc. Man has to live with the laws of physics and chemistry unbroken and in harmony with all that is implied in the laws of heredity and growth and function of a biological organism. Yet what might look like a limitation is really his strength and safe foundation and stability. On this ground, man's biological make-up has a legitimate sphere of growth and expansion shared by no other type of being. We pass into every new moment of time with a preparedness shown in adaptive and constructive activity as well as structure, most plastic and far-reaching in the greatest feat of man, that of imagination. Imagination is not a mere duplication of reality in consciousness and subjectivity; it is a substitute in a way, but actually an amplification, and often a real addition to what we might otherwise call the "crude world," integrated in the real activities of life, a new creation, an ever-new growth, seen in its most characteristic form in choice and in any new volition. Hence the liberating light which integration and the concepts of growth and time throw on the time-honored problem of absolute and relative determinism and on the relation of an ultrastrict "science" with commonsense.

In logic, too, we are led to special assertions. We are forced to formulate "open definitions," *i.e.*, we have to insist on the open formulation of tendencies rather than "closed definitions." We deal with rich potentialities, never completely predictable.

This background and the demands of work in guiding ourselves and others thus come to lead us also into practical ethics, with a new conception of the relation of actual and experimental determinism and of what "free will" we may want to speak of, with a new emphasis on the meaning of choice, of effort, and of new creation out of new possibilities presented by the ever newly created opportunities of ever-new time. We get a right to the type of voluntaristic conception of man which most of us live by—with a reasonable harmony between our science and our pragmatic needs and critical commonsense.

The extent to which we can be true to the material foundations, and yet true to a spiritual goal, ultimately measures our health and natural normality and the value of our morality. *Nature shapes her aims according to her means.* Would that every man might realize this simple lesson and maxim—there would be less call for a rank and wanton hankering for relapses into archaic but evidently not wholly outgrown tendencies to the assumption of "omnipotence of thought," revived again from time to time as "New Thought." Psychiatry restores to science and to the practical mind the right to reinclude rationally and constructively what a narrower view of science has, for a time at least, handed over unconditionally to uncritical fancy. But the only way to make unnecessary astrology and phrenology and playing with mysticism and with Oliver Lodge's fancies of the revelation of his son Raymond is to recognize the true needs and yearnings of man and to show nature's real ways of granting appetites and satisfactions that are wholesome.

Hereby we have indeed a contribution to biologically sound idealism: a clearer understanding of how to blend fact and ambition, nature and ideal—an ability to think scientifically and practically and yet idealistically of matters of real life.

To come back to more concrete problems again, a wider grasp of what psychiatry may well furnish us helps toward a new ethical goal in our social conscience. The nineteenth century brought us the boon and the bane of industrialism. More and more of the pleasures and satisfactions of creation and production and of the natural rewards of the daily labor drifted away from the sight and control of the worker, who now rarely sees the completed result of his work as the farmer or the artisan used to do. Few workers have the experience of getting satisfaction from direct pride in the end result; as soon as the product is available, a set of traders carries it to the markets and a set of financiers determines, in fact may already have determined, the reward—just as the reward of the farmer is often settled for him by astounding speculations long before the crop is at hand. There is a field for a new conscience heeding the needs of fundamental satisfactions of man so well depicted by Carlton Parker, and psychiatric study furnishes much concrete material for this new conscience in industrial relations—with a better knowledge of the human needs of all the participants in the great game of economic life.

Psychiatry gives us also a new appreciation of the religious life and needs of our race. Man's religion shows in his capacity to feel and grasp his relations and responsibility toward the largest unit or force he can conceive, and his capacity for faith and hope in a deeper and more lasting interdependence of individual and race with the Ruler or rules of the universe. Whatever form it may take expresses his capacity to feel himself in humility and faith, and yet with determination, a more or less responsible part of the greatest unit he can grasp. The form this takes is bound to vary individually. As physicians we learn to respect the religious views of our fellow beings, whatever they may be; because we are sure that we have the essentials in common; and with this emphasis on what we have in common, we can help in attaining the individually highest attainable truth without having to be destructive. We all recognize relations that go beyond individual existence, lasting and "more than biological" relations, and it is the realization of these conceptions intellectually and emotionally true to our individual and group nature that constitutes our various religions and faiths. Emphasizing what we have in common, we become tolerant of the idea that probably the points on which we differ are, after all, another's best way of expressing truths which our own nature may picture differently but would not want to miss in, or deny to, the other.

One of the evidences of the great progress of psychiatry is that we have learned to be more eager to see what is sane and strong and constructively valuable even in the strange notions of our patients, and less eager to call them queer or foolish. A delusion may contain another person's attempt at stating truth. The goal of psychiatry and of sound commonsense is truth free of distortion. Many a strange religious custom and fancy has been brought nearer our understanding and appreciation since we have learned to respect the essential truth and individual and group value of fancy and feeling even in the myths and in the religious conceptions of all races.

Among the most interesting formulations and potential contributions of psychiatry are those reaching out toward jurisprudence. Psychiatry deals preeminently with the variety and differences of human personalities. To correct or supplement a human system apparently enslaved by concern about precedent and baffling rules of evidence inherited from the days of cruel and arbitrary kings, the demand for justice has called for certain remedies. Psychiatry still plays a disgraceful role in the so-called expert testimony, largely a prostitution of medical authority in the service of legal methods.

Yet out of it all there has arisen the great usefulness of the psychiatrist in the juvenile and other courts. There it is shown that if psychiatry is to help, it should be taken for granted that the person indicted on a charge should thereby become subject to a complete and unreserved study of all the facts, subject to cross-examination, to be sure, but before all accessible to complete and unreserved study. This would mean a substantial participation of law in the promotion of knowledge of facts and constructive activity, and a conception of indeterminate sentence not merely in the service of leniency but in the service of the best protection of the public, and, if necessary, lasting detention of those who cannot be reformed, before they have had to do their worst. Whoever is clearly indicted for breaking the laws of social compatibility should not merely invite a spirit of revenge, but should, through the indictment, surrender automatically to legalized authority endowed with the right and duty of unlimited investigation of the facts as they are.

Looking back then, you can see how the history of the human thought about what we call mind and psyche displayed some strange reactions of the practical man, the scientist, the philosopher, and the theologian toward one of the most important and practical problems. It is difficult to realize what it means to arrive at ever-more-workable formulations and methods of approach. We do not have to be mind-shy *or* body-shy any longer. Today we can attack the facts as we find them, without that disturbing obsession of having to translate them first into something artificial before we can really study them and work with them. Since we have reached a sane pluralism with a justifiable conviction of the fundamental consistency of it all, a satisfaction with what we modestly call formulation rather than definition and with an appreciation of relativity, we have at last an orderly and natural field and method from which nobody need shy.

I

Preparation in Europe

In the Swiss parish of Niederweningen, about five miles from Zürich, harmonies of tolerance and neighborliness obtained among the thousand inhabitants. No fissures of denominationalism divided them, and no one claimed to have the doctrine of exclusive salvation. Rural occupations, the tending of cattle and vineyards, provided the pattern of a stable daily life. Darwinism came without fanfare: the people saw the logic of evolution, and it certainly upset no household gods in the rectory of Rudolf Meyer, the Zwinglian minister. Here was a man who got his religion from life. He used the Bible for its wealth of illustrative material and not as a source of formal dogmatism. Nor did it occur to him to consider himself the mouthpiece of his congregation.

In the parish house a son was born on September 13, 1866, to grow up in an atmosphere of liberalism and reflection. Instead of a burden of sins to be atoned for, young Adolf acquired a sense of opportunities ahead. His even-tempered mother was devoted to her three children (Anna was a year older than Adolf, Hermann was younger) but did not tie them to her apron string. It was easy enough to keep an eye on them: their playground was the churchyard. The years that laid Adolf's foundations were, as he recalled, "diversified, happy, and helpful." From the rectory in the heart of the village it was only a short walk to a Catholic community in the next canton and in the opposite direction to a Jewish settlement. This gave him early a recognition of humanity's variety. He had natural curiosity to a strong degree and also preserved an open mind. At confirmation, accepting the creed with mental reservation, he said under his breath, "If that is so."

There was no feeling of compulsion in democratic Swiss life. "Compulsory education" was simply taken to mean universal opportunity. And a curious lad had his own special urges for knowledge. On one furtive quest he removed a volume on the philosophy of the unconscious from his father's library and carefully shifted the other books on the shelf to fill the accusing gap. Somehow he could not openly ask his father for answers to the imponderables but relied instead on impressions of what he thought his father thought. What was death, for example? "In our last conversation I should have liked to ask him about his belief in immortality, but I desisted, not wanting to embarrass him."

In the secondary school Adolf did not take Latin and Greek because of a greater interest in living languages, French and English, as part of the world around him. While attending gymnasium at Zürich, he boarded out, and walked home for week ends. On Sundays he played the organ in the parish church. As a student he rated the first of four groups except in composition, where he was second, and he had an excellent memory, except for poetry. His accuracy in dates would sometimes discomfit the history teacher. In his third year he really blossomed, and this is how it happened: Given the choice of a topic to write on, Adolf presented an autobiography that was not a mere recital of events but an account of his general attitudes and the feelings he experienced. The professor pronounced it outstanding and put him in the first group. But the important thing to Adolf was the acceptance of this emphasis on what counted in a person: the appreciation of thinking and feeling, rather than ability to repeat. The incident impressed on him the value of a biographical sketch in getting at the core of an individual, and he was to make good use of the method later in life. With a glow he set to work in making up the requirements of the gymnasium examination and accomplished three years of Latin and one of Greek in his last year.

In trying to find himself Adolf had sought to learn about mankind, and this brought him to a difficult problem: whether to follow in his father's clerical footsteps or to choose the profession of his mother's brother, who was a physician. He felt that the ministry dealt with only a part of man. There were many questions which a thirsty youth needed answered and which also the practice of medicine seemed to fail to cover. Having to decide between going into the cultural sciences or the natural sciences, he wanted both. "I wanted all the science there was as far as my moderate intellect would be able to cope with it and would be able to make use of it." He was more interested "in the man that I can know than in man the unknown." Then, one day, he wrote in his diary, "I am glad that I have decided to study the whole of man."

His choice of medicine, made while his father was still living, led him into the orbit of Professor August Forel at the University of Zürich. Forel had a lively spirit, a genius for patient observation, and a practical bent. Famous for his youthful achievement of a classic work on the ants of Switzerland and subsequent studies on brain anatomy and the basis of the neuron theory, Forel acquired his psychiatric training in the clinic at Munich under Von Gudden. In Zürich he soon became chief at the Burghölzli Hospital for the Insane and took the chair of psychiatry at the University at the age of twenty-nine.

Forel had become familiar to Meyer in gymnasium days in association with hypnotism and through espousal of total abstinence from alcohol. The professor appeared at a *Kommers* [beer fest] of the entire university student body; he drank a toast to a nonalcoholic beverage—and the students did not howl him down. While Forel's lectures did not attract Meyer, his clinical demonstrations were something else again. These demonstrations consisted of a trinity of patient, student, and doctor, with Forel so vivacious that a stranger peeking in at the door could not have told which was the patient.

Meyer's teacher of neurology was Constantin von Monakow, who gave the course on anatomy of the brain. Though not as critical as Forel, he had a quality that marked him as a neurobiologist rather than a neurophysiologist, a difference which in time became more important to this student.

After passing his state examination in 1890, entitling him to practice medicine, Meyer sought knowledge beyond the frontiers of Switzerland. With expenses defrayed in part by a fellowship, in part by money from his father, he took a year's study in Paris, Edinburgh, and London, covering all fields of medicine but culminating in neurology.

He counted as the most significant thing that happened to him in that *Wanderjahr* his contact with "British soil and British thought." A warmhearted young surgeon, Francis M. Caird, introduced him in London to the great names in medicine and made the Swiss fledgling feel at home among the citizens of his professional world. Meyer was struck with the biological approach of Dr. John Hughlings Jackson, the Queen Square Hospital neurologist, and with the work and mind of the scientist Thomas Huxley. Their concepts traveled along functional lines in contrast to Continental static finalities and "hangovers of ghost lore and tradition-ridden metaphysics." Meyer had shown no affinity for the German influence on Swiss education and the German condensation of reality "into an either-or of materialism or idealism." He welcomed the British workers' vista of a dynamic human organism making adjustments to life. It was an invitation to explore.

But what occurred to Meyer was that Hughlings Jackson missed something in failing to apply his interest in psychology to neurology. It seemed a grave omission that the patient's disease held attention to the exclusion of the patient. In a clinical discussion in Edinburgh he heard Sir Thomas Grainger Stewart give a "more than archeological review of the temperaments, constitutions and dispositions" and heard Dr. Thomas Clouston lecture on "The Neuroses of Development." In his Paris semester with Jean Charcot, the Déjerines, and other French masters, Meyer had come upon references to constitutional types—a topic which the Germans had neglected for the study of disease of tissues and infective agents. This very year of 1890 saw the publication of a monograph by Meyer's former urology professor, Alexander Peyer, on frustrated sex stimulation in anxiety reactions. Here was a whole new world of medicine.

Meyer was fascinated by the precise workmanship of the men he saw in action. Attending William R. Gowers' dispensary for epileptics in London, he watched him take down case histories in shorthand so as to avoid missing anything. Dr. Gowers' textbook on the anatomy of the spinal cord was a model of accuracy and clarity, inspiring Meyer to attempt a doctoral thesis which would do the same for the brain. On his way home to Zürich he resolved to attain this by research on the more complex parts of the nervous system and to apply to Professor Forel for a topic of cerebral anatomy.

He knew what a man of spirit Forel was. Now he obtained firsthand experience. The professor blustered: No! young candidates were forever biting off pieces too big for them and making him finish the job. Silent, Meyer was sure the storm would subside if he lasted it out, and he endured ten minutes of verbal lightning and grumbling. The sky cleared and Forel led him into his laboratory and opened a cabinet containing chameleon brains. Find out how the chameleon's nervous system permits its eyes to look in different directions at the same time!

The student was not satisfied. He did not like the stained sections and did not like the limitations of the subject. What he wanted was to study in general the forebrain of reptiles. Forel fumed—and let him have his way. That way was thorough and determined. Meyer made a point of acquiring live specimens of reptiles and sent off to the Hamburg Zoo for some; then proceeded to prepare the sections by a method which Forel disapproved.

The doctoral candidate, left alone in the laboratory, did not bother the master, and the master in turn invaded the quiet no more than twice, for a quarter-hour or so, to finish a paper he was writing and, in passing, to scold Meyer for using a different staining method. "At that point my spirit of independence made me start my own laboratory at home, where I completed my thesis work."

When the thesis was done (*Über das Vorderhirn einiger Reptilien*, 1892) they became good friends, and remained so "notwithstanding the fact that I never became a militant total ab-

stainer, as Forel would have liked. Yet he respected my independence." On the other hand, Meyer deeply respected Forel's
exacting discipline and "nondogmatic, open-minded science." One
of the joys of this period had been an opportunity to study his
published papers along with the original sections on which they
were based. Forel was "a naturalist through and through," a man
of action, an idealist, a vigorous pacifist—a great model and
impetus! His philosophic perspective was also important for
Meyer "in my search for a functional concept of the nature of
man that could contain the phenomenon of consciousness."

Meyer pursued his neurological studies. He was not interested
in practicing psychiatry, even though he took pains in a report
to his Swiss colleagues (*Medizinische Studien in Paris, Edinburg
und London*, 1891, his first publication) to describe the organization of the care of mental patients in Scotland. In spare time
and on summer vacations he had assisted his uncle at an institution for demented women, which was conducted as a small
cotton factory; and while he attended them for their intercurrent
ailments, he made no effort to learn about them as personalities.
This would have seemed irrelevant to him, despite a natural sympathy and his need of seeing broader relationships. After all, he
was called to treat bronchitis and gastro-intestinal upsets, not to
consider aggressive mental symptoms and hallucinations. Meyer
relates:

How was it that a practical vision of psychiatry took shape with
me so slowly? Psychiatry became real to me only when the concepts
and the experiences with its facts and problems became clearer and
more concretely related to my life interests; and especially when I
had to handle patients whom I also had known without the mental
disorder and who were viewed not as mere derelicts but as persons
to be readjusted. No doubt the interest became more insistent when
my coming to this country helped, with many other factors, to precipitate a serious depression of three years' duration in my own mother,
who had always appeared as one of the sanest persons in my experience
and who recovered against the expectations of my old teacher [Forel],
giving me many an opportunity to incorporate well-known human
facts in my more strictly medical thought of the time. The full urge

started with concrete work, when I obliged myself to treat and to study patients and to discuss with my colleagues what we had before us.[1] *

In 1892, when he received his medical degree at the age of twenty-six, the pressing problem was where to take the next step. The limitations of his uncle's practice did not appeal to him after his contacts abroad. He now regarded himself as a student in the broad sense and wanted to function in an environment equal to his capacity. He would have liked teaching as an adjunct to continued research, and he had set his heart on the post of assistant to the professor of medicine at Zürich, despite a strong dislike for the man. But having been refused the place, and considering that remaining in his country practice would only make him an assistant to his uncle—and feeling also that the English-speaking world was open to him—he decided to go to the United States. Family life was already broken up. His father had died. His sister Anna had also died, and his brother Hermann had left home for business training in French Switzerland.

He had no definite idea where in America he would settle (two sons of a neighbor were established physicians in St. Paul and Minneapolis), but he vaguely hoped to be able to support himself somewhere by part-time practice while devoting most of his attention to studies in comparative and clinical neurology. Institutional work did not appeal to him because it usually blotted out any prospect of working with sufficient independence and growth. An academic connection, however, would be very desirable. "I thought of chances at Johns Hopkins, Clark University and Chicago—but I got them in reverse order."

After five months in Vienna and Berlin medical centers in preparation for practice, Meyer made a second stay in Paris for another month's work with the Déjerines. While in Paris he read in the *Boston Transcript*, borrowed from a fellow pensionnaire, that the entire biology department of Clark University at Worcester, Mass., had migrated to Rockefeller's University of Chicago, which was to open that year (1892). This might be

* See Reference Notes at end of book.

the chance. He wrote to G. Stanley Hall, the president of Clark, for the position of assistant professor of neurology vacated by Henry H. Donaldson, who had studied under Von Monakow in Zürich. President Hall, in the midst of a financial crisis, replied that Donaldson was still at Clark. Someone was in error. In Edinburgh again, Meyer met an American whom he remembered as a silent graduate student in Von Monakow's course. This was Donaldson, and he said that the place was indeed vacant.

Since it was useless to arrive in the States before early October, Meyer took time to attend the Second International Psychological Congress in London. "There I saw the whole psychological world represented. It got me into contact with psychology from a practical point of view." He went also to the Nottingham meeting of the British Medical Association, which Professor William Osler of Baltimore's Johns Hopkins University was taking in on his honeymoon. Someone offered to introduce him to Dr. Osler and chose an inopportune moment. Osler was courteous but forbidding: he had no job for Meyer at Johns Hopkins. (Years later Osler asked, "Why did you get introduced by that old humbug?")

Meyer decided to try Chicago. He would find Donaldson there.

BRITISH INFLUENCES

IN PSYCHIATRY

From the Fourteenth Maudsley Lecture: "British Influences in Psychiatry and Mental Hygiene," delivered by Dr. Meyer before the Royal Medico-Psychological Association, London, May 17, 1933; Journal of Mental Science, 79:435 (July, 1933).

To the son of a Swiss Zwinglian minister and nephew of a medical practitioner the problem of the nature of man—of mind and body and of their integration—was not a mere abstract problem; nor was it altogether easy, or just casually treated; nor would it have shaped itself as it did without British influence.

The early helps that happened to be available in my father's library were in the direction of the rigid psychophysical trend of German science, as laid down in the works of two leaders who had both for a time been professors at the University of Zürich— Lange, the historian and critic of materialism, whose book gave me valuable historical foundations but no working solution, and Wundt, Lange's successor, who in 1874 was called from the chair of *physiology* at Heidelberg to that of *philosophy* at Zürich, but was soon called further to Leipzig, where he founded the first psychophysical laboratory and became the leader of German psychology along the lines initiated by the psychologically inspired physicist Fechner.

Somehow both Lange's and Wundt's essays had failed me in my quest for a satisfactory understanding of life and psyche—of what the philosophy of my environment and those speaking of psychology and psychiatry emphasize by the prefix "psycho," the soul and the soul concept, which I met in my extracurricular browsing. I saw myself before a decision between theology, with perhaps a philosophical and linguistic-historical preference related to my father's interests, and medicine, with the possibility of a naturalistic career closer to the physician's world, as suggested by my maternal uncle. Eduard von Hartmann's *Philosophy of the Unconscious*, which I also found among my father's books, furnished me with the first live insight into basic studies of comparative-experimental physiology (in contrast to the elemental materialism reviewed by Lange), but also a provocative, critical review of human—supposedly idealistic—illusions, somehow without leading me into either agnosticism or pessimism. It offered a bold but vital philosophical presentation of a psychophysical parallelism linking physiology and psychology together on a common functional ground, and it must have aroused in me a sense of real possibilities in naturalistic interests, since evidently its pessimism did not overwhelm me, as might readily have been possible from such reading during one's teens.

The positive naturalistic interests won out in favor of medicine, but without eclipsing the problem of the psyche during the practical years of medical study. Even with my premedical and early medical interests I was too practical-minded and too familiar with hypnosis, as viewed from the start as a simple process of suggestion, to be quite satisfied with Forel's strongly monistic but unduly neurologizing neurokyme formulation of hypnosis and mental function. It was a neurophysiological, psychophysical attempt at solution that still left me unsatisfied, especially under the peculiar subjectivistic wave of the later eighties, that struck even the physicists in the form of Kantian epistemology as revived by Mach.

A much more decisive constructive step forward in dealing with the pertinent issues came to me through the reading of Thomas Huxley's essays and Hughlings Jackson's neurological writings, through which an important aspect of British thought came to exert a definite, more than merely epistemological, influence upon

today it is almost unintelligibly obsessed by epistemological dogmatism. I remember that even in 1892 I definitely rejected the advice to take up psychiatry in Switzerland because I felt it required much more ability than I had for verbal expression, rather than opportunity for concrete demonstration through action.

The methods and techniques actually used were rapport, understanding, advice, reassurance and guidance of activity and of fancy and emotional life, and suggestion or explanation, with or without hypnosis, and with or without reference to the beginnings of neurological localization initiated by Broca, Hughlings Jackson, Hitzig, and demonstrated and so vividly brought before me by Horsley and Ferrier and Henschen at the 1892 Psychological Congress. Neither the hypnosis nor the localization concept was primarily and especially introduced or developed by psychiatrists, or perhaps directly important for them; but as problems of correlation they formed a challenge especially under my energetic and critically aggressive teacher, Professor Forel, the successor of Von Gudden and of Hitzig at Zürich, and in the British influences mentioned, and in Carl Hauptmann's critique of the brain-physiological concepts from the Avenarius angle—all of which played a real role in the efforts to find oneself philosophically, scientifically, and humanly.

Somehow a really vital sense for the human individual or person was coming into its rights, and that especially through the English emphasis on biology in a scientific naturalism and the living unit, rather than an excessive assertion of selves of supernatural origin. Under the broadening contacts, man began to attain a biological naturalness approaching a pluralism rather than a Cartesian dualism with its parallelistic fear of "interaction." We no longer worked with a body that also happened to be complicated by a mind, or a mind that also happened to be hampered by a body. There was a growing sense of an intrinsic belonging together, notwithstanding the traditional contrasts, and a question why the terms "mind" and "soul" should continue to suggest substances or entities so disparate from the rest of our experience. Since that time there has been a steady urge for a unitary biological conception, with the result that today it is much more natural to think in terms of a live organism, the "he" or "she," or "you" or "I," asleep or awake, at rest or in action, in that "more or less" of a specific "state of function" we know as consciousness (comparable to a fluid "state of matter").

That the resulting conditions and functions had features not evident in the parts of the brain did not have to appear strange in a product of integration. We have come to speak of mind or soul as the person's *nature and function*, not as if we meant something detached; nor were we or are we necessarily overawed by the terms "mind" and "soul" as suggesting "things" rather than functions, as long as we see in them the kind of traditional language which we also use when speaking of sunrise and sunset, guided by practical considerations of relativity or relationism, and out of respect for tradition. We sense a *complete person* with flesh and blood, a product of growth, cerebrally and functionally integrated, an active entity, exhibiting what was spoken of by Charles Mercier even in the nineties as *conduct*, and later by William McDougall and others as *behavior*. The subjective economizing functioning of this entity we then came to call *mentation* (*i.e.*, the minding-function) rather than "a mind" (or quasi substance); while the term "soul" was used as applying to ultrabiological or supra-biological religious-eschatological relationships, perhaps with more of simple tradition and dogma behind them than a full and critical use of the really objective "facts"—the kind which would have to satisfy the demand of all science, *i.e.*, direct or indirect accessibility to the critical experience of all adequately trained and competent workers.

There were beginnings of a naturalization of man, different from the schism of materialism and idealism and the old Cartesian contrast of body and soul, with the pineal body as the main point of contact of two worlds; a naturalization also different from a culturally destructive iconoclastic and aggressively agnostic materialism, and equally different from the later Watsonian behaviorism unnecessarily excluding subjective experience from objective consideration. There was no pejoristic tendency in such a conception as there would have been in a reduction to "mere matter," nor any exaltation as in a reduction to "mere mind."

We were learning to see how the structural and functional segregation of receptor-function and effector-function provides room in the delayed reflex for the differentiation of that wealth of symbolization or contact of consciousness, *i.e.*, sign- and meaning-function, which allows us to incorporate all that which is accessible to the senses, imagination, and memory, and equally that which consists in preparedness for action, as part of the attitude, reaction or action of the moment as well as of the personality, as spread over the lifetime, allowing us thus to consider the whole of man's nature, including his religious, moral, and evaluating capacities. Man's sense, involving both sensory and motor function, came to appear as if in a *solution,* a time-consuming flux, in a flow of more or less content or differentiation of consciousness that stands simultaneously for the now and here, and the past, and the future, and for fancy and emotion and reason through the general inherent function of *symbolization.* Symbolization or sign-function or meaning-function begins to be more than a mere logical figure; it becomes itself the characteristic psychobiological function and activity that we call mentation or "a mind" in varying degrees of overt performance.

In the nineties, to be interested (as a psychologist) in what everybody (and not only the introspectionist closeted by himself) might observe and sense as objective reality, in another man's or one's own nature, was not yet done or accepted as practicable, yet the problem and ways of solution answered more and more affirmatively the question: "Does not all this bring knowing and being and feeling and fancy within the range of our life-function, of our *biological performance?*" Or is it left outside? Why make a puzzle of it? Why not "go to it," study it for what it is and does, as behavior, and as mentation or implicit function where it occurs as such, in the sense of meaning-function, *i.e.*, something to be understood by its specific context, its causes and reasons, and its consequences and bearings and suggestive significance? If too much dissection into sensations and neurons gets the facts too far from life, why not turn to the events that *are* life, a specific kind of order of meaningful function that will make experience telling and effective again if rearoused (if we just take sufficiently telling developments), sometimes as a mere hint or thought, or fancy, or story or a dramatization, or a sufficiently obvious action in its setting?

These are conceptions which I am fairly certain would not have had an easy development on the European continent, or perhaps later if I had lived only in America, without the influence of the British understanding of biology, that of mind, as not making of life and of mind something mysterious, but dealing frankly with living things to be accepted as found, and studied for what they are and do, without either dogmatic vitalistic obsession and/or dogmatic mechanistic arbitrary or negativistic limitation.

Commonsense was naturally inclined toward such a practical and unifying attitude in a nondogmatic Swiss atmosphere as any-where else—I feel as if I never really would have thought differ-ently; but when approached with scientific ambition in Continental academic thought, this really biological functioning somehow had to be harnessed in a physiologizing, actually psycho*physical* paral-lelism, leaving us with a stipulation of merely ghostlike mental epiphenomena, a kind of shadow of the real man in action, with all the supposed horrors of a forbidden interaction.

Somehow in earlier German and French thought the idea of development and evolution had played a role that proved some-what premature in the hands of keen but not naturalistically trained thinkers. It was based on the principle of plausibility, over-elaborate and dialectical, and with the German temperament it was destined to become a *Naturphilosophie, i.e.,* a system formation running ahead of the facts or of experimental proof. A peculiar conservatism gave British thought that sober and critical progres-sion from Baconian principles to the Darwinian method of collect-ing data, seeing and seeking long-term developments, with that world-embracing range of inquiry possible only to the trained traveler and collector, not only of dead museum specimens but also of events and their observations and records. It is easy to see how, and with what results, Germany and France developed their physi-ologists bent on physics and chemistry, leaving man to various philosophies and systems, and the English their physiology with physics and chemistry in natural biological settings. While German thought shaped its concept of parallelism as the way forward from Cartesian dualism, as a truce in matters of mind and matter and of man and nature, the thought of the English-speaking naturalists had in the *biological* principle a frame which did not make for a premature dogmatism and a premature rigidity, nor a demand for panpsychologizing. It helped us to harmonize man and nature in a natural conception, without passing a large part of human nature to what would either belong to the realm of agnosticism, or at least to a segregated instead of an integrated world.

A good share of the problem of readjustment depends on the type of plasticity and dependability of the rank and file of the people. The English-speaking world has a record of stability and progressiveness in many directions. It has removed, within one century, one of the most deeply rooted and tenacious medieval creations, that of the duel, radically expunged from the British code of honor, of manhood and of valor. When we come to freedom of belief, and to disposition to be hospitable and fair to new experience and new concepts, I am willing to give my confidence to the liberal tendencies—a biological social phenomenon or tendency of the first order.

I was strongly impressed by this inclusiveness and experiential preparedness having a sense for balance and correlation with normal phenomena in a problematic field when in 1892, at the Second International Psychological Congress in London, it frankly and inquiringly admitted the section for Psychic Research. Today this plays a much greater role among Germans, in the same quarters which also gave biology the stamp of aggressive vitalism in Driesch, with all the German urge for system formation and assumption of "psychons," etc. Why can we not study human nature as we study nature generally? Why not be prepared to determine where we find facts? Is it because we are not willing or allowed to give nature credit that we are willing to give only to powers from which we expect magic in a highly anthropomorphic sense, satisfying the human capacity for anticipation by symbolization and resulting wish?

In all this we owe a great debt to Hughlings Jackson—the foremost representative of those who rose to the principle which Spencer made the central thought of his philosophy, and which reflected British scientific thought and work from the middle of the nineteenth century. Hughlings Jackson's capacity for observation, his use of the principle of evolution and dissolution rather than of a narrower concept of structure and function, and his caution in the use of psychological terms and concepts, all put a premium on observation, of great importance, and especially natural under conditions in which autopsy could not be obligatorily practiced. Jackson was the functional pathologist *par excellence*, whose work had to be, and could quite naturally be, supplemented by the experimental physiologists without perpetuation of a mind-body split, and was a real experimental psychology and ordinary commonsense. His clearness in a recognition of several levels appealed to me. With my interest in structure I was prompted to give the Jacksonian formulations also a structural expression as far as facts permitted with structural experimental methods, and yet in the end with a functional anatomy of the nervous system, willing to accept a truly "functional organicism," if such a blending of concepts is permitted. It *is* permissible—provided that we distinguish (physiological) part-functions and (psychobiological) total-functions.

My entrance into psychiatry was through the autopsy room, but with the temperament of the practitioner of medicine from my early clinical training, and through the functional thought of Jackson, supplemented by a frank acceptance also of the biographic relations of function or behavior. I might sum it up in this way: Following up the stimulus from Gowers, and my earlier impressions from Forel and Von Monakow and the Déjerines, put me in a mood or *capacity to assimilate a special structural, and at the same time also a functional, orientation with a place also for the psychobiological data or ergasias*, structural under the Von Gudden and Forel influence, and the impression of Roux's *Entwicklungsmechanik* [mechanics of evolution], but definitely also with an open-minded interest in Hughlings Jackson's concerns and their application. In the psychological and general scientific orientation the influence of the empirocritical philosophy of Hume, Riehl and Avenarius played a role.

I agreed with Hughlings Jackson in keeping from loose identification of psychological and neurological data and concepts, but I saw a solution in the cultivation of objectivity in the field, also of psychology, and especially also in a need of a concrete and when necessary historical objectivity, rather than too complete a satisfaction with ever-ready analogy in either the post-Darwinian trend of British and early American psychiatry, or later in their ultimate, perhaps too exclusive and ready surrender to what, devoid of claims either to omniscience or to aggressive agnosticism, I consider as too mechanized and overspecialized and too exclusive a "psychopathology of the unconscious." We may easily run into the effects of too-ready and final hitching of one's wagon to a star, which then, when adjustments are needed, makes the realities look pale, and invites the cultivation of a realm of the supernatural as extranatural, or as open only to analogizing inference from the unusual or pathological or the occult.

Binding oneself to be true to (1) structure when dealing with structure and to (2) structure-function when dealing with physiology or function of parts, gives free hand and free use of one's best experimentally tried sense in dealing also with a third set of relations, the total-functions and the intrafunctional relations of the live organism, the individual, the person and the group, and therewith came a socializable objective psychobiology and psychopathology doing justice also to all the objectively demonstrable subjectivity.

2

The American Setting

Crazy. Inmate. Asylum. In the nineteenth century these words commonly expressed the hopeless incarceration of the mentally afflicted, whom society had to get out of the way for its own protection and for theirs. Like wickedness and punishment, the issue was a legal rather than a medical one. Corralled from attics and almshouses and jails, the victims were virtually abandoned by the medical profession to public custody and to time. It was characteristic of a moralizing community, when mental disorder occurred, not to study and observe—for this would require patience —but to regulate.

Recognition that there was an ailment at work came only after the danger or nuisance point had been reached. Only then was medical consideration given, and this solely to establish whether the individual was *compos mentis* [of sound mind]; whether or not deserving of segregation. Insanity was thus something vulgarly sensational, horror and stigma attending legal procedure, and the physician who had the temerity to tackle it assumed the role of alienist in the courtroom or, more bravely, undertook administrative burdens as superintendent of a crowded, prisonlike asylum. There the inmate was crudely classified for statistical and custodial purposes, and left to whimper. If he stormed, he was chained and even beaten.

Medical science was incurious. The prevailing idea was that mind was something apart from medicine. In the first place, "mental" and "physical" were separated in the orthodox manner of the scientific world of that time. In addition, the multidenominational religious structure of American society made "soul" an untouchable, thereby raising another barrier to investigation. Man could not be regarded as a person—except in the domains of religion, philosophy, and education. He was simply a body—to be examined for its parts and for the difficulties of its organs. Therefore the doctors who organized the Association of Medical Superintendents of American Institutions for the Insane in 1844 (the forerunner of the American Psychiatric Association) concerned themselves merely with management.

Outside the asylums were the neurologists, devoted to disorders of the nervous system, and the families that could afford to consult them for a genteel handling of a case found them focusing on the brain. The only pathology that developed in the field of behavior problems was pursued along the lines of physiology. Psychology was crowded out—an unnecessary and unwarranted complication. Science cast its hopeful eye on post-mortems for brain lesions.

This was the picture of American psychiatry until far into the nineties. It was limited to cases who needed to be committed and controlled. It interested itself little in what was normal in disturbed people and more in legal rights and restrictions. It left out the entirety of man, his functioning as a person; made no attempt to seek the principles of the processes going on within him.

Holding center-stage in this picture, Dr. John Purdue Gray, the superintendent of the New York State Lunatic Asylum at Utica, kept the skirts of psychiatry clear of psychological probing. There must be brain impairment, he maintained. Imported European theories as to the possibility of mental causes of mental disorders he denounced as a device to shield depravity. When later he rediscovered the ancient principle of mind-body unity, he misunderstood it as meaning body-over-mind. Gray thought he saw interaction but did not conceive of integration. To him and those he dominated in this specialty, insanity was a physical disease recognizable by mental phenomena.

The views of Gray and twenty-two other doctors called by the prosecution were aired at the trial of Charles Guiteau, assassin of President James Garfield in 1881. Here was a prisoner with a history of extreme religious enthusiasm, who had acted under the delusion of divine inspiration to "remove the President"—a mission exerting an irresistible impulse and causing "a grinding pressure," as Guiteau put it. Only one medical witness testified that he was insane—a young neurologist from New York, Dr. Edward C. Spitzka, who had not yet been born when Gray started handling insanity. But Gray, the dean of alienists, found no indication of a disease of the brain.

Although Gray's old reports at Utica had classified cases by "physical" and "moral" causes, he had an answer when confronted with these reports on the witness stand: "There were persons at that time who believed, as my predecessors did, that griefs and anxiety and religious excitement, religious worry, fright, and so forth might produce an insanity without the intervention of the brain," but he was convinced that in every instance the subject previously had been physically ill. And now he asserted: "I do not believe in moral insanity." He called it a wicked term, nonexistent in medical science, but used loosely to excuse outrageous conduct.

Guiteau broke in: "It shows that these experts don't know much about the business after all. . . . The idea that a man cannot be insane without he has got a diseased brain is all nonsense, according to the Savior. . . . There is no brainology in this case, but it is spiritology. Spirits get into a man and make him do this and that thing, and that is insanity!"

It took a patriotic jury just one hour to return a verdict of guilty and provide a patriotic public with a hanging. To the very end, Guiteau was stubborn: "I say the Deity killed the President and not me."

Despite the fact that the Dr. Grays of that period forestalled a nonorganic approach to psychiatry, they served a good purpose. These precursors of scientific research made it possible to rescue "insanity" from the nonmedical control of metaphysicians and lodge it where it belonged—with physicians. On the other hand, if Gray had pronounced Guiteau insane, how could he—by the brain-disease theory—prove it while the man was still alive? And yet the doctor had no trouble at all when he returned from the trial and a Turkish-bath attendant in Utica fired a bullet through his cheeks. Confronted with a practical example of person against person, Gray was quick to declare his assailant insane.

The notion that a deranged person was possessed by a spirit—preferably an evil spirit that had to be ejected forcibly—was an heirloom from colonial times, when exorcism by fire was once the therapy applied to witchcraft. A less misguided age considered such people irksome and hauled them off to hospital cells, where iron shackles were as common as beds. When Dr. Benjamin Rush, of Revolutionary War fame, was called to Pennsylvania General Hospital in Philadelphia in 1783, to take charge of its basement population, he pioneered in advocating kindness and medical treatment. Bleeding, blistering, and purging were the medical remedies in vogue, and they fitted into his concept of insanity as an arterial disease that required a check on "the impetus of the blood towards the brain." Rivaling the inventiveness of that other Philadelphian, Benjamin Franklin, Rush designed the "tranquilizing chair" as an instrument of humane restraint, and a gyrator, which induced evacuation, exhaustion, and blessed sleep. Both of these mechanisms continued long in use.

The cellar was a favorite hospital spot for confining mental patients whose families could pay for what passed for private care. Of specialized private asylums there were only a few in the early eighteen hundreds, among them Bloomingdale (a division of the New York Hospital), on Bloomingdale Road in New York City. For dependent persons there were no facilities; they were herded with miscellaneous paupers, idiots, orphans, and dissolute characters wherever local communities could house them, and some were auctioned off by the county for day labor, sometimes at a profit to the county.

Social conscience evolved the maxim that the insane were the wards of the state, and a reform movement was carried on for the establishment of state hospitals. Massachusetts responded with Worcester Lunatic Asylum in 1833; other states followed, including New York with its Utica asylum in 1843. The accommodations of every institution soon proved inadequate; they never sufficed for the growing numbers of tortured souls and twisted minds, so that the vile almshouses became crowded again.

This era shone with the resplendent one-woman campaign of a retired Boston schoolteacher, frail but strenuous Dorothea Lynde Dix, who was angered by the inhumane conditions she found in the East Cambridge jail. Beginning in 1841, Miss Dix centered her sense of shame and duty on a publicity crusade to shock legislatures into voting appropriations. After succeeding in getting Worcester enlarged, she moved on to other states, always certain of witnessing deplorable neglect, which she vividly publicized; always drawing up petitions and arguing ultimate economy; almost always winning her way. The people of ten states owed their new or bigger asylums to her energized indignation.

The building wave was renewed by a wave of optimism as reports of a high rate of recovery were issued. Then came reaction, the natural sequel to exaggeration. Criticism assailed the asylums and their superintendents. Reformers decried political control, ex-inmates exposed cruelty and mismanagement, and within the profession neurologists accused the institutional psychiatrists of misdirection and torpor. A leading Civil War neurologist, Dr. S. Weir Mitchell, who studied nerve injuries of Union soldiers, but not mental disorders, developed a new therapy in his private practice—his "fat and blood" cure. Shades of Benjamin Rush! Where Rush blamed excessive blood supply of the brain, Mitchell ordered overfeeding, massage, and complete rest to cure *anemia* of the brain.

Psychiatry still traveled the road of physiology and failed to take a cue that Rush, as a teacher, had given his medical students: to relate medicine to daily living. The research undertaken in a flourish of scientific activity continued to be limited to autopsies. It started with the dead patient and ended there.

Why was no attention paid to the sick person as an individual? Psychology was ostracized: too subjective for science. The psychiatrist did not think of putting himself in the place of the patient but stayed in the position of an attendant, looking only for symptoms and tissue changes. Another handicap was the national habit of thinking in terms of extremes, contrasts, right or wrong, sane or insane, either-or. The vast scale of differentiation, wherein each person had his specific quality, was blurred by "sophisticated error."

A modest beginning in truly psychiatric emphasis was made in the state hospital at Kankakee, Ill., by a young man shortly after his arrival from Switzerland in 1892. By inclination and training he thought in terms of more-or-less. He looked for the differences among men. To Adolf Meyer, human experience was a concern of medicine.

3

Action in Kankakee

Here in America were evolutionary currents favoring freedom to develop a young physician's strong urge to study the whole of man, not merely physical or cultural pieces. True, he would encounter rigid traditions as capable of hardening the arteries of thought as the arbitrary European four-faculty scheme of learning, but there were liberalizing traditions as well. American philosophy was beginning to take the form of a willingness to deal with experience. Adolf Meyer's chief quest was a better solution of "the mind problem," a functional understanding. The mind should not be declared a mystery or treated with finality. He had no taste for "wholly imaginary superaccuracy of argument and definitions of irrelevant detail." Conditions in this country would enable him to take the facts "as one actually meets them and as one uses them" and yet remain free "from the frequently narrowing tendency to turn one small region of the world's knowledge into a system that would make everything else unnecessary and unwanted."

A unique immigrant, he arrived to treat the New World as a place to break new scientific ground. His plan for self-support was rather naïve, as he himself admitted. In Chicago he found the new university's biology department housed in improvised quarters and obliged to reject a project of work although it would have required only a modest outlay; but through H. H. Donaldson he obtained an honorary fellowship which carried no stipend. In one of the city's medical centers far from the heart of Chicago he found two days' work a week taking charge of a neurological dispensary. He rented a flat near by, on the city side of the branching-off of

43

Ninety-eighth Avenue at West Madison Street (an hour's streetcar ride from the university), and hung out his sign.

On the second floor over a shoe store, his quarters looked more like a workshop than a doctor's office. Bottles and jars containing brains and spinal cords of a variety of animals were arranged along the mantelpiece of his sitting room. There were several small tables on which he spread his work—books, papers, microscope, measuring instruments—and in his waiting room stood a newly bought piano. All around his consultation room bottles and jars were lined up, on shelves and floor, tall ones, short ones, wide and narrow. They were both his work and his relaxation. To a visitor he puckishly hinted of a live opossum in one of the closets.

Chicago was stimulating if not financially or professionally satisfying. Of private practice there was little to speak. The only progress was an appointment by the university as docent in neurology, and Donaldson gave him the privilege of conducting an elective course in the comparative anatomy of the nervous system. The real ferment was in friendships. Through Paul Carus, editor of *The Monist,* he became acquainted with the philosophy of Charles S. Peirce, which encouraged "independence of thought, scientific logic, and a welcome objectivity in contrast to the subjectiveness of all science." William James had recently published his two-volume *Principles of Psychology,* positing a dynamic basis. John Dewey came on to Chicago from Michigan in 1894 and began a lasting intellectual companionship with Meyer. These philosophers justified in Meyer his sense for pluralism—"a recognition that nature is not just one smooth continuity in which isolated particles could tell us all there is to be known." George Herbert Mead, Charles Horton Cooley, and James Hayden Tufts provided other fruitful contacts. In addition, he met the people of Hull-House, whose social work was anchored in realities.

His first winter there (February, 1893) Meyer read a paper before the Chicago Pathological Society, describing psychoneuroses observed at the dispensary and in practice. He felt that pathologists should know more than the end product of their subject, and he turned their attention to the proper use of time in some helpful activity as the fundamental issue in the treatment of any neuropsychiatric case. "I thought primarily of occupation therapy, of getting the patient to do things, and getting the things going which did not work but which could work with proper straightening out." Then he asked his new colleagues for suggestions suitable to the tastes and inclinations of American patients: "Can you tell me what types of occupation will arouse and hold the interest of Americans when they become self-concerned and neurotic?" This was his initial public expression on psychotherapy.

A member of that society, Dr. Ludvig Hektoen, who had just obtained a professorship after serving as assistant physician at the state mental hospital at Kankakee, called one evening at Meyer's rooms and was amused to find a tidy, small-scale neurological institute ensconced over the shoe store. Hektoen told him that this hospital, the second largest of its kind, with 2,200 patients, wanted to engage a pathologist, and while it was Hektoen's opinion that nowhere in the Middle West was there a position affording work at Meyer's best level, at least this would be a good springboard.

Of course, Meyer was avid. He would get systematic access to brains. A pathologist was a new kind of special job in state hospitals —one they did not have in Zürich, where every hospital physician had received laboratory training and could do his own research, having only an average of 130 patients to attend. In this country, with 300 or more asylum patients per physician, medical work could be improved by the introduction of a pathologist (an argument useful also in dealing with state authorities loath to appropriate money for additional physicians). Despite Meyer's eagerness to go to the Illinois Eastern Hospital for the Insane at Kankakee, he did not picture himself confined within the boundaries of a laboratory, out of contact with the wards; laboratory work and clinical work must be done in perfect harmony and toward the same ends. For all he knew, the superintendent might have a limited idea of a pathologist's duties. Meyer certainly had one of his own.

He sent an application to the trustees with references from Forel, Donaldson, J. J. Déjerine of Paris, and E. C. Spitzka of New York. At the same time Hektoen wrote Superintendent Richard Dewey of the applicant's rare qualifications. Neither received an answer.

The young Swiss did not know he was lost in the mesh of

American politics. Illinois, for the first time in twenty-five years, had voted Democratic in the Cleveland landslide. The new governor, John P. Altgeld, was under pressure to make a house cleaning of Republican officeholders, and on the pretext that the management of the asylums was rotten, he had his new trustees dismiss Dr. Dewey, Kankakee's capable administrator since its beginning. Dewey received Hektoen's letter the very week of the upheaval. He turned it over to his successor, Dr. Shobal V. Clevenger, with as strong a recommendation as the circumstances permitted.

Anxious Meyer was unaware of the change. He bought a railroad ticket for the sixty-mile trip to Kankakee in April, 1893, to give inaction a good push. He was surprised to find Clevenger, whom he knew as a Chicago neurologist, at Dewey's desk. As a matter of fact, Clevenger had hardly got over his own surprise: he did not know Governor Altgeld and had not been active in politics; but at a time when Altgeld had been a superior court judge, Clevenger had testified before him as an alienist and made such a good impression that apparently he was well remembered. With a friendly grin Clevenger picked up the long-neglected letter, conversed a bit more with Meyer, and gave him the job at $1,200 a year, to start May 1.

Life stretched out before him. So did the 200 acres of plains that comprised the hospital grounds on the bank of the Kankakee River. Numerous limestone buildings were disposed around a broad square dominated by the tower of a large administration building. Avenues cut through this area of houses, most of which were two-story detached wards. The whole effect was that of a self-contained village on forty acres, the rest of the land being used for farming. And Meyer found the hospital, as built up by Dewey, superior to any similar institution he had seen in Europe. It meant much to him to have his start here with this example of achievement.

Politics was still at work. Clevenger at once balked at politicians' orders to hire incompetents and at demands to sign checks without examining bills, and in less than four months he was forced to resign. With the arrival of the new superintendent, Dr. Clarke Gapen, the payroll was revised and by some mischance Meyer's name was omitted. One of the trustees summoned him, stared at him, and asked, "What's a pathologist?"

Gapen wondered with Meyer what could be done about it, and they reached an agreement: Meyer would stay on at half pay. With board and lodging provided, and with the supplementary income from teaching at the university, the pathologist was sure he could survive. After all, wasn't work what he wanted?

And Superintendent Gapen helped. At first the space available for Meyer's analytical service was small, poorly lit to boot. Later two rooms were cleared in the tower of the central building, and here the Illinois State Pathological Laboratory was set up under his direction, Gapen encouraging him with new equipment and authorizing him to buy some coveted apparatus exhibited by the German government at the World's Fair.

"I found the medical staff hopelessly sunk into routine and perfectly satisfied with it. A comfortable existence seemed to be an issue preceding that of medical ambition." [2] Meyer could have passed muster with similar perfunctory performance, but it irked him to have to make autopsies without a background of satisfactory clinical observations. It was discouraging not to be able to put your findings of pathoanatomical research on a solid foundation. A growing literature, "fragmentary and homeless," was being published. For himself he set high standards in writing reports for the *American Journal of Insanity*, the quarterly organ of the superintendents' national association, and for other professional periodicals.

Urging fellow scientists to be more scientific, he lamented time wasted in the haphazard examination of a spinal cord without the accompanying brain and spinal ganglia and a part of the peripheral nerves. He harped on accuracy and completeness of clinical records, without which a pathoanatomist worked blindly. The laboratory must be related to the living patient.

Since established routines have a way of resisting change, Meyer chose an informal approach to the problem of obtaining adequate case records. In the recreation period after lunch he held physical examinations of new patients with the staff doctors—"quite unofficially." He then carefully analyzed their methods and conclusions.

The descriptive terms used in the record, which was dictated, were criticized for their accuracy or their ambiguity, and the same held for the final formulation of the diagnosis. It was easy to see that the methods of the various assistants varied considerably, that their dictation was not uniformly accurate, and that their reasoning for diagnosis followed rather general impressions than definite and precise statements of fact, and failed to make a sufficiently clear distinction between what was actually found and what was merely supposed to exist.[2]

When it came to examining for the mental condition, Meyer was faced with extreme indifference. "The main trouble seemed to be the general idea that any agreement on this point could not be reached, that every book and every alienist had his own plan. Hence the unwillingness to really collect facts needed for diagnostic decisions." In this respect at Kankakee he was virtually helpless, although he devised forms for history taking to make the anamnesis specific and put the accent on the evolution of the illness. "I saw clearly that the existence of a pathologist in a hospital for the insane was a poor remedy for that which was actually needed."

One day, at the autopsy of a Kankakee patient who had dropped dead after a hearty meal, Meyer was showing the coroner's jury that the man had succumbed to the rupture of a diseased heart muscle. The foreman, a physician himself, satisfied with the demonstration of the cause of death, watched Meyer examine the brain, and he asked, "Now, doctor, show us what you find in the mind."

Meyer assured him that, meager as the life record of the case was, there were more mental findings in the history than in the brain.

Only a few other state hospitals had a full-time pathologist studying neurological material after autopsy. Not for a lack of interest in science, Meyer felt; American doctors needed to know a simple way of preserving brains and cords and to be satisfied that the material would reach careful, trained hands. In a plea for cooperation from practitioners he wrote an article explaining a safe and easy procedure. By way of scientific progress he pointed out that chairs of pure neurology had been founded at the University of Chicago and at Clark University; that the New York State Legislature had recently recommended the establishment of a Pathological Institute to serve the state's hospitals—which sounded promising. In addition, President Hall of Clark had inspired Dr. Edward Cowles of McLean Hospital (then at Somerville, Mass.) to add to McLean's cluster of laboratories one relating psychology to psychiatry.

Not a single medical school in the West at this time afforded facilities for the practical study of mental disease. The zealot from Zürich saw his opportunity to remedy this lack. Superintendent Gapen was ambitious, and the trustees were sensitive to political criticism; they endorsed Meyer's plan for a summer course in neurology and psychiatry for outside physicians and medical students. He was to give daily lectures and supervise laboratory and ward work. The immediate benefit would be the training of men for positions as hospital assistants, thus building up an efficient state service. Unfortunately the announcement of the course came too late to attract outsiders, and Meyer concentrated on Kankakee's staff. However, "a thoroughly unspoiled inquirer," Dr. Albert Moore Barrett, came over from Iowa State Hospital for special training in the technique of studying the brain at autopsy.

In his tower setting Meyer received Julia Lathrop. She commented on the doves in the cotes and the snakes in boxes. Miss Lathrop came as a visitor for the State Board of Charities and Correction, open-minded, deeply concerned in her work, and interested in Meyer as a European who could answer her questions about social service abroad, particularly child welfare. (Twenty years later she became the first head of the Federal Children's Bureau.) She introduced him to Jane Addams, another vibrant woman who was doing a share of the world's work, and to Governor Altgeld. When Meyer slipped and injured himself on a visit to the Fair, Miss Lathrop had him put up for a week at Hull-House, which was an excellent point of orientation in sociology.

He did not hear the scolding that S. Weir Mitchell meted out to asylum men for scientific unproductiveness—a symptom of their torpor, Mitchell called it. The Philadelphian was a guest speaker at the semicentennial meeting of the American Medico-Psychological Association (the new name of the superintendents' organization, itself unchanged for all the "Psychological"). At this meeting in Philadelphia in the spring of 1894, Mitchell charged the state-hospital men, preoccupied as they were with building and administration problems, with isolating themselves from the main stream of medicine in a "monastery of madness." The famous doctor, a novelist in his own right, demanded competent original work and did not spare the neurological rod. "We ask you experts, what have you taught us of these ninety-one thousand insane whom you see or treat?"

Meyer was eager for his chief's return from the convention, and Gapen brought home a piece of the storm. Meyer accepted Mitchell's strictures as a personal challenge. Obtaining copies of the speech, he found it a rhapsodic recitation of a bard, lofty in notion, weak on facts. Apparently Mitchell was unaware of "some of us lesser known and less favored beginners." The Kankakee pathologist had an idea: he sent a copy of the rebuke to Governor Altgeld and, through Miss Lathrop, induced him to give the Illinois hospital physicians a chance to express their own views and visions. Telling the Governor that while criticism from without was a spur, even more profitable discussion might come from the hospital workers themselves, Meyer suggested that Altgeld invite them to write reports. In this way a compilation of them was published by the State Board, and it served as a vehicle for Meyer.

He described his own work as being more than the usual performance of autopsies, for it included staff studies with the physicians and demonstrations from the 192 specimens in his private collection. His classes brought the doctors up to date, gave a livelier interest in the purely medical questions, and reviewed systematically "what to look out for in the examination of patients." Here was a fair start, Meyer told the Governor, "in a movement that is not generally recognized yet by outside neurologists, but which will grow steadily and rapidly."

One result of the publication of the report was that Miss Lathrop was able, with help, to persuade the State Board to hold a competitive examination in 1895—the first of its kind in the United States—for medical internships in state hospitals. Meyer was one of the examiners.

Another achievement was an outgrowth of his vacation trip in 1894. He used the holiday for a visit to other institutions, and his contact with an active clinical staff at Battle Creek Sanitarium gave him the determination to organize the medical workers—in distinction to the superintendents—into an Association of Assistant Physicians of Hospitals for the Insane. These upstarts included men in Illinois, Michigan, and Iowa who needed a forum which would not be loaded down with administrative discussions. "The saddest thing," Meyer wrote at this time, "would be if we should submit to the idea that we knew enough. It will be our duty to collect systematically whatever may give us a clue for progress and for formulating distinct problems." [3]

As he lost himself in his work—now also giving the regular course in brain anatomy at the University of Chicago—he found himself. Deep inside was a concern over the possible share his venturing away from home had had in his mother's depression— "something that left a lasting wish that I might pay back and give some compensation during her life, something more than gratitude."

So it was consistent that the son should ponder the factors preceding a mental disturbance and take pains to gather pre-hospital histories for constitutional and psychogenic data and turn his mind to the experiences of formative years and evolution. In 1894 he pioneered in child psychology "as part of the study of life." He joined the Illinois Association for Child-Study, founded by William O. Krohn (assistant professor of psychology at the University of Illinois and a former pupil of Stanley Hall). For the first number of its journal Meyer wrote the opening article.

The roots of a person's good qualities as well as evil anomalies could be found in "the period of plasticity," with its early surroundings and lasting impressions. Too much was made of heredity; the significant thing was that "the child of abnormal parents is apt to be exposed from birth to acquire unconsciously habits of a morbid character." [4] Meyer cautioned educators against misinterpreting symptoms of aberrations; any symptom might be observed isolated in a normal person; its measurement was in the power to overcome it and in its connection with other symptoms. The ideal examination of a child would be one that was capable of revealing all his possibilities, powers, defects. "Such an estimate of an individual is, at the present time at least, an impossibility."

But Meyer was hewing a way to personality-studies, to a scrutiny of life situations and dynamic developments.

TREATMENT OF THE INSANE

From a report by Dr. Meyer to the Governor of Illinois (March 20, 1895), in response to a circular letter to the superintendents of the state's hospitals for the insane.

The times are gone when the insane were considered to be demoniac and were the objects of religious adoration, or were treated worse than criminals, as enemies of society. Traces of views of the past are, however, very frequent in the form of prejudices against the insane, the cured insane, and even their relatives. The wishes of the people at large are much influenced by the remnants of traditions which must not be underrated. The voice of the physician who professes that mental diseases are not essentially different from other diseases is received with some aversion even by the unprejudiced.

There is, indeed, enough ground for this aversion, for practical reasons. *Legally* an insane person is thought to be altogether different from the sane. The responsibility of the person is considered to be diminished and his acts are not worth more than those of a person under age. But the relation is not that of the minority of a child. The sphere of interest is greater; the family is no longer to be considered altogether competent in decisions with regard to the person and his property, and the state steps in as a guardian. The range of competence of the family and of the state varies considerably in the different codices.

According to the law of the State of Illinois a person "comes under the act of lunacy who by reason of unsoundness of mind is incapable of managing or caring for his own estate, or is dangerous to self or others if permitted to go at large, or is in such condition of mind or body as to be a fit subject for care or treatment in a hospital or asylum for the insane, except idiots or persons whose mental development was arrested by disease or physical injury occurring prior to the age of puberty, and epileptics unless dangerous." There is no provision made for cases where the state should step in in order to give the patient the best chances of recovery, where he himself or his friends are unable or unwilling to recognize what is best for the patient. This could be done so that neglect in this line would be open to legal prosecution.

The insane may be in the care of the state or of the county, or of both. For reasons of convenience the county judge is the legal authority for his district and keeps the record of the insane of his county. The care and treatment, however, is in the hands of the state and of the county. State and county take their share, the state furnishing hospitals for the acute and dangerous cases, the county furnishing the clothes for all the pauper cases and annexes of poorhouses for the chronic and harmless patients, or even for the acute forms.

QUALIFICATIONS OF THE PHYSICIAN

According to the laws of most European countries, it is not sufficient that a physician should have only the degree of a university, but he has to pass a state examination. Whereas the study of mental diseases does not form an intrinsic part of the curriculum of many universities, it forms an object in the examination for the license.

According to the Swiss laws, a candidate is obliged to attend a practical course in mental diseases in one of the recognized clinics during at least one semester. The instruction is given only by first-class alienists. In this country most students leave college without having any idea about mental diseases. The instruction is given by men who would like to practice in nervous diseases and have perhaps at one time been interns of some asylum. Considering the fact that residence in an asylum of several years' duration does not make necessarily a proficient alienist and much less a teacher, we have to admit that even the little that students get is utterly deficient. This holds for the so-called better colleges. What conditions will we find in the small colleges?

The consequence is that very few physicians can be considered qualified to act in the most difficult of all kinds of diseases.

Here we come across a very serious side of the regulations on the practice of medicine. As soon as the patient is considered to be insane, the state assumes the right and the duty of caring for him. Whereas individuals are not blamed for choosing incompetent physicians, the state should know better and become more responsible. The state should therefore require a thorough training from medical advisers. In Switzerland every physician who obtains a license has fulfilled certain requirements in this direction. The state does not protect the interests of the state alone, but also those of the individuals. In Germany we find two classes of physicians. The physician who merely obtained the *Staatsexamen* may practice anywhere, although an examination in mental disease was not passed in every case. Those physicians, however, who fill government positions have to prove that they did satisfactory work in connection with the care of the insane. The self-protection of the state goes, therefore, further than the protection of the individual. I cannot help thinking that the plan adopted in Switzerland—compulsory education in mental diseases a condition for obtaining a license—is the one which a democratic form of government can recognize.

This rule can be carried out by

1. Erection of clinics of mental diseases in the medical centers.

2. Extension of the facilities for clinical study in the asylums.

3. Courses in one of the two classes of institutions (at a college or an asylum) for obtaining a license.

Moreover, the state should consider whether courses offered by colleges reach a standard worth having. At present this could not be said of any educational institution—either on account of lack of patients or on account of lack of trained teachers.

For the period of transition the attempt is made in Kankakee to lay the foundation for a school for mental diseases, with regard to both theory and practice.

One of the most important duties of the state would be to see that every insane person should have the benefit of treatment and supervision by a competent physician.

TREATMENT IN THE HOME OF THE PATIENT

With the exception of very mild forms of disease, most cases are profited much more when brought into altogether changed circumstances. Some treatment is very unsatisfactory because so often one of the causes of the disturbance is in the surroundings, and the first task would be to attack those. As a rule, removal from home into the care of competent nurses is the best initial remedy. It is very probable that in a great number of cases the situation in this respect brings much harm.

In a small number of chronic cases there is some justification for keeping patients at home. Whereas, however, this can be done rather frequently in the quiet and steady condition of old settlements, the frequent changes in the life of a family here make it preferable that even those patients should be taken care of, both in their own and in the community's interests.

The same holds for the boarding-out system. Valuable for the community and the patient in Scotland and other countries of a rather conservative life, it would scarcely be practicable here.

There must, however, be a provision, in case for some reason an individual receives merely home treatment or treatment in a family.

The American Medico-Psychological Association has been trying to introduce instruction in mental diseases in every medical college. Although I would not venture to give a judgment of the attempts made, I should say that the so-called clinics and lectures on mental diseases in one of the best Chicago medical colleges is of no value in itself and of harm to the students. Good teachers in this line are not numerous enough to supply all the colleges; and it is therefore desirable that an attempt be made, without any connection with the college, in the way of a special school, which would not, however, require a great financial effort from the state.

There is no doubt but that such a step forward will have its beneficial effects. If one institution begins, its success will encourage others and call for competition. Wherever there are students, teachers cannot afford to do bad work, and the standard will be raised in a measure as the number of critical pupils and observers increases. The state should make such courses compulsory, at least for those who are in official contact with cases of insanity (county physicians), and in the period of transition give preference to those who have fulfilled the requirements.

TREATMENT OF THE PATIENT

There is a great deal of difference in the treatment of the insane here and abroad, in perfect concordance with the tendencies of the people and the medical world. The public here believe in drugs and consider prescription as the aim and end of medical skill, whereas in Germany and in many other places the people feel that drugs are quite as great an affliction as the disease itself and therefore wish to get through with no more than absolutely indicated. Still, day and night change the same way as here, and the diseases run their course with hygienic treatment as well as under the complication of drugs, and the main point is that the conscience of all the parties is soothed by the idea of superiority of therapeutic skill. I do not venture to subject various forms of treatment to a careful examination. I should only say this, that any method merits much praise if it does not do any harm, either directly or in making the attendants and physicians believe that a drug can do away with more time-taking care. There is always some danger that the patient may get tonics instead of good desirable food, sedatives instead of rest or distractive occupation, and avoiding irritation instead of administering a simple bath, etc. It is especially dangerous to keep standing formulas for sedative and hypnotic purposes, because the attendants or even the physicians may be tempted to use what is ready, without going into the trouble of individualizing.

Under all circumstances the history of the patient must be kept so that the clinical symptoms justify in every case the prescription. It must contain the indications and every prescription given. This is probably the best self-control for the physician, the best preventive against useless and misleading treatment.

The ideal of an asylum or hospital for the insane should furnish the patients most of the advantages of the homes and avoid the petty and irritating features of many small circles or families. Still, that is not all. It must, moreover, have all the facilities of an ordinary hospital. The attendants shall be nurses, not supervisors; they shall live like the patients, eat the same food, have the same rooms, do any kind of work that a patient would be asked to do, share the recreations and amusements with the patients with as little "bossing" as possible. Everything that suggests detention in prison or in houses for correction must be strictly avoided.

Where treatment is necessary, it must be based on experience and not on misleading theories. Dr. Henry M. Hurd describes (quoted from Paetz) in an article on the minor treatment of insane patients (*Alienist and Neurologist*, 1883) his practice with regard to rest, building it on theories that are somewhat misleading, because they prevent him from investigating matters more carefully. For him the horizontal position in bed is the leading point in the bed treatment of acute cases, and therefore he does not hesitate to enforce this position with covered beds and cribs; or he is afraid of the horizontal in maniacs because the hyperemia of the brain is increased by it and because the restriction of physical activity increases the molecular activity of the diseased ganglion cells and hastens the destructive changes.

I cannot help thinking that Dr. Hurd's unpleasant experience with the bed treatment in mania has something to do with the restraint, because elsewhere experience has shown that just mania (and allied excited conditions) was favorably influenced by bed treatment without restraint, or at least without systematic restraint.

There is, of course, a great danger for the alienist who is in seclusion from the rest of the world himself, to fall into routine, to cultivate hobbies, and to become dogmatical. The conviction that drugs should be restricted to a minimum should never deprive a patient of their benefit when they are required; the dislike of restraint should not lead to dangerous ridiculous experiments, and the recognition of the advisability of restraint should not make the field for restraint wider than necessary. It is difficult to find a remedy against hobbies; the best one is perhaps the daily contact with critical pupils and cultivation of truly professional spirit among them.

Occupation is, with good right, called the most essential side of hygienic treatment of most insane patients. The last thirty years have brought great and practical investigations in this field.

In my introductory remarks on the qualifications of physicians, I made a few remarks on the medical management of asylums abroad. Our task here is modified very much by the standard of medical education. Whereas the medical man in Germany and other countries has the highest and widest education, we find here the average medical man below the capacity of the average business man. More than any other physician, the alienist must have a broad general education, a good knowledge of the life and social condition of the patients, and a very thorough clinical training. Insane patients are largely like children; they mislead and oppose instead of helping the physician, and it requires much skill and also a great amount of self-criticism and systematic will to work against a tendency toward superficial and loose work. Moreover, rational study of mental diseases requires a solid foundation of psychological knowledge and talent of observation, besides numerous personal qualities. All that can be taught is taught at European universities, whereas here the young assistant has to acquire his learning first in the active hospital work. He has, therefore, to consider his first year as little more than apprenticeship; he has to go to school for the special work and must be initiated by the senior physicians. In the old plan the junior assistant was in charge of chronic patients only, and forced to do the most demoralizing routine work, without any supervision or stimulation. According to the new plan of subdivision of work at Kankakee, the junior assistant will work, under the direct supervision of the senior assistant, among recent and chronic cases. He will, moreover, get instruction in clinical courses and thus be enabled to do independent and systematic work by and by.

Another excellent feature will be the advancement of the senior physician to a post of general supervisor of the medical work. This takes much unnecessary work from the hands of the superintendent and gives him more time for general supervision and the administrational work. Moreover, it gives the physicians a chance for more frequent consultation with headquarters, which is now practically impossible because of the tremendous accumulation of work in the hands of the superintendent. The first decided progress will be made when every new case can be demonstrated to the whole staff and his treatment discussed. Every physician will then be familiar with what is going on and he will also profit by the advice of the colleagues. This requires, of course, practice; but, if once introduced for some time, can be done without much, if any, loss of time.

The pathological laboratory, which is just now developing, will bring a severe control of clinical accuracy into the field of work. It has certainly brought some fruits so far and it must do much more as soon as the physicians have enough help to do their work accurately, to keep scientific records.

MENTAL ABNORMALITIES

IN CHILDREN

From Transactions, *Illinois Society for Child-Study, p.* 48 (1895), *"Mental Abnormalities in Children During Primary Education,"* by Dr. Meyer, dated Feb. 28, 1895.

From the point of view of the alienist, education has a twofold end: the formation of a steady character and the acquirement of such training and knowledge as the struggle of life requires from all and allows to a child of certain talent and ability. In school education the personal disposition of the child is unfortunately but little considered practically. On the whole, education is imposed on the child without much consideration of the individual needs, because the whole plan of education so far has been guided largely by the theoretic question, "What should the average individual know in order to be successful?" The most important and most difficult question, the question of the disposition of the child, is answered by a conventional standard of so-called experience.

School reform and school hygiene have done much in the line of study of *defects* of old systems. This new enterprise seems to be more radical; it seems to be not merely critical but an attempt to construct an altogether new foundation for the work, based on scientific, exact methods and prepared on the most extensive scale I know of. The problem as initiated by Professor Krohn is not merely the question, "How can we mend the old system?" but it means, "What can we do in order to obtain a solid basis and scientific data for the study of the mental development of the growing child, to collect facts that show exactly what the child's mind is able to do and where educational efforts might begin to do harm?"

It is a fact that no child can digest the whole modern curriculum. In earlier days, when one teacher with a moderate education led all the classes from the first steps through all the branches of the curriculum, the requirements in specialization were less exacting. Now the work has been divided among special teachers because a man who teaches a limited number of branches only should become experienced in methods that make tasks easier by directing the exertion on the side of the pupil. This is, however, not always the case. Every special teacher wants to make a show of his own department and he cannot help doing this at the expense of other departments and especially of the pupils. It seems more advisable to return to the old method of having only one teacher who would exactly know how the child works, would have to do the same work himself and tire himself out with the same work as the child. The rivalry of specialists is one of the greatest dangers of our public school; for the competition at the end of the term is too often carried on by goading on the already overtaxed pupil.

My object is to outline a number of types that require special attention of the teacher for a rational primary education up to, but not including, the years of puberty. I cannot enter on the abnormalities of character or the distinct forms of defectiveness, such as idiots and children that are excluded from public schools, nor do I think it wise to enter upon more elaborate studies of complicated forms of psychical abnormalities that would interest only the alienist and criminologist. I restrict myself to those children who might require special attention in the ordinary school course. It is a part of school hygiene that has been scarcely developed, but deserves as much attention as the nourishment of the child, the construction of the schoolrooms, the seats, etc.

Every teacher of experience has seen that quite a number of those pupils who seemed to be the best at one time proved to be a failure in later life, and that many who were, at least in their first years, among the *unnoticed* or even the dull pupils proved finally to become more or less advanced or prominent. Should it not be desirable to find out reasons for this and to classify them?

Further: in our age, where insanity seems to be spread over a much greater proportion of families than formerly, we lack altogether statistics about the predisposing features that show through the years of education at school, and we rarely see attempts to find and to correct it. Yet, would there be any task more urgent than the prevention of this most ruinous scourge of society? This latter point is, of course, difficult. First, for practical reasons. The degenerative processes in children have their chief encouragement in the equally defective home surroundings, and to make a statistical attempt worth anything these conditions at home would have to be watched. This is, of course, impracticable; it would rouse much animosity, if it were known, that records are taken at school which throw a bad light on methods used in families. This can, perhaps, be done some day when home education too is a less haphazard business than in our day. The other reason is that the teacher cannot be expected to be overburdened with too much statistical work; his interests must remain with the school, within the domain of education of the pupils, and we cannot ask him to do what the overwhelming number of alienists do *not* do with their patients; *i.e.*, give them a thorough psychological examination.

In classification we must strictly differentiate between primary abnormality of the mental constitution due to primary disorders of the mind and the mental substratum of the psychical functions, and secondly, abnormality due to disorders of the organs of perception or of expression. The latter does not necessarily belong to the class of mental degenerates; two or three children of a family might be thus hampered in their mental development and still we should not have a reason to call the family a family of mental degenerates, because removal of the accidental cause alone will restore it to its old position. On the other hand, slight mental defects—perversity of feelings, precocious sexual feelings, etc.—without external cause, will make us class a child, and perhaps the family, among the neurotic and psychopathic.

What will help us to make an early diagnosis of secondary, symptomatic, mental weakness?

One considerable and typical group has lately been described by Dr. Victor Lange in Copenhagen. Most of you have probably seen children with a rather dull, often stupid and vacant expression, with staring eyes and open mouth, children who have difficulty in breathing through the nose, who have a thick, frequently indistinct, stammering pronunciation, and defective power of hearing. The child seems brighter at times; at other times it scarcely hears at all. Pronounced degrees of this symptom complex attract, of course, the attention of the family, and the child is put under the care of a physician; but slight degrees are frequently overlooked; the boy is punished for manifestations of a bad spell because at times he shows that he *can* work and hear.

It is certain that most of these children are suffering from adenoid vegetations in the pharynx and posterior nasal cavity, and many of them show enlarged tonsils. At times the swelling is little marked; the child breathes more freely, the head on the whole feels more free; the ears are, as it were, open again; the child will be relatively bright. But at other times the ears have a kind of damper that may be removed for a little while by sneezing; the nose does not let the air pass, and besides the defect of hearing you find that mental dullness which catarrh of the nose produces. All this is due to the facility with which these granulations swell, cover the Eustachian tubes and occlude the nasal air passages. If these spells go over into a chronic condition, the child deteriorates not only because the defect of hearing prevents it from learning, but because the full feeling due to the occlusion of the nose has a depressing effect on the spontaneous mental activity. Last but not least, the moral effect on the child is very strong; the child becomes accustomed to be blamed unjustly and develops an unpleasant disposition because it is at a disadvantage compared with the companions. It is not rare to see these vegetations disappear in adult life; but then it is generally too late. Not to remove them in time means spoiling the child's education and future.

The same holds probably for other defects of hearing and for defects of sight, with the only difference that the latter are of a less intermittent character. Correction of the anomalies will be followed by nearly complete recovery of the mental loss.

How do the primary abnormalities show? We may differentiate between the various degrees of obvious defectiveness—imbecility —and the more concealed forms that seem to be little more than predispositions but, under close observation, become perfectly distinct abnormalities.

The child who comes to school has already a great number of experiences registered in the cerebral cortex: impressions from home, from early companions, from a more or less free life with a limited number of pleasures, dangers, desires, and fears. Generally the fate of a child, whether it will show abnormal or normal tendencies, is decided before it is taken to school for the first time.

We have to consider two classes of children that show intellectual defects during the years of primary education:

1. Children who are by inheritance and early education in an abnormal nervous condition, and get worse or better under the influence of school.

2. Children who do not show any abnormality primarily but who suffer under the life and overwork of school.

In the former group we would differentiate between the mentally weak child and the apparently normal or more than normally developed child. As we have seen, we have no right to classify a child among the mentally weak before a careful examination by a physician who is familiar with school diseases and diseases of development has shown that the mental weakness is primary, not secondary. It is natural that this group before all makes the institution of a regular medical school inspector most advisable. No child should lose a chance to be treated for what might be the primary cause of the arrest of development; and, with a cause beyond reach, no teacher should be allowed to entertain useless hopes and useless efforts at the expense of those who deserve attention.

I do not know how far the plan of a few German states merits imitation, where special classes are provided for the weak. We must not forget that the moral feelings of both parents and child are apt to be hurt unless such a separation can be made with much tact. Children, always ready to make comparisons, will be apt to look down upon a weak companion, and the weak child may grow up with the feeling of humiliation and develop many unpleasant or even serious antipathies. I do not know how this unpleasant side of the practice in Baden is made to lose its sharp edge. If it can be done, it will certainly be of advantage to keep a weak child away from the failure in competition with highly talented and abnormally gifted children as soon as competition loses its beneficent influence, becoming a grave danger on account of overwork or of hopeless unfavorable comparisons.

Now, the abnormally bright child. I do not speak of the young genius—those marvels are too rare to deserve special attention here —but of all those parentally-dubbed "geniuses" who are expected to be the most promising part of the rising generation. The symptom complex of which I am going to speak shows largely between the years preceding the entrance to school; but in school you have to observe the outcome of it and also more persistent types.

I mention first the nervous temperament. Unlike pronounced nervous abnormalities, the nervous temperament shows itself *at times* only, following more or less obvious incidents and plausible and rational causes which are known to everybody as exciting factors. Among others, we find pain the cause of excitement; sometimes a deep impression, or fright, or digestive disorders may cause nightmares, vomiting, convulsions, outbreaks of anger and screaming. At school you would recognize these children by the temporary restlessness and distraction, inattention and lack of power of concentration—all this without a perfectly adequate reason, but usually passing by when the child has rested. In others this condition, exceedingly frequent in children from three to five, becomes more constant. The child is bright, at least reacting quickly, but unsteady in its application to the work. It knows how to cover defects of its work by little deceptions and to keep a place higher than it deserves; it responds to repeated stimuli much less by fatigue than by excitement and restlessness, capricious, impulsive manners, fits of crying or hilarity. A number of little things which at first seem to be nothing but the normal unrestrained reaction of the child accumulate and grow more constant, until you finally have the hysterical boy or girl.

These children are very difficult to manage. Generally the home surroundings are the cause of the condition—foolish parents or relatives who cannot distinguish superficial brilliancy and natural brightness. A teacher who can lead such children to a more quiet and steady disposition deserves high praise for tact and ability.

The next step is the development of a pronounced hysterical attitude, most observed in girls between eight and twelve. They are extremely impressionable and make a show of everything, cry and laugh over the least trifles and show a remarkable imagination and intelligence. They distinguish themselves in everything that can be done with imitation, drawing, music, recitations, even in mathematics, as long as nothing original is asked from them. Disappointments produce strong reaction, pressure and pain over forehead, pain in the eyes, with or without obvious exaggeration of the complaints, and finally all that lamentable series of hysterical symptoms that belong more to the age of adolescence.

In boys the following course of development of neurotic conditions is more frequently observed: The parents discover special faculties in the boy and encourage him to stay away from the companions of the same age to cultivate those accomplishments and to associate with those that can help him, *i.e.*, with people older than himself. Thus we find an ardent ambition to excel hidden under a show of industry and strong will power. The curriculum at school is not wide enough; private lessons often seem to be necessary for the especially bright boy. The wonderful elasticity of the child stands this for a while; then symptoms of fatigue show, first without disturbing the sleep, later on with headaches, restless sleep, or sleeplessness—and finally the boy drifts into a marked condition of neurasthenia as soon as the period of puberty comes.

Both groups, the neurasthenic and the hysterical, show one marked feature: the great contrast between knowledge and the ability of application; further, the inability to react in time by the inattention which preserves a normal child from being overburdened. The perfectly normal child will relax in time, before the brain suffers; inattention will be the healthy remedy. To overcome the inattention of fatigue means to set up a condition of irritability and excitement which will do harm in the long run. This is why so many of the very best teachers injure their pupils, by not doing justice to inattention as a normal sign of fatigue.

What can the school do for children who show the nervous symptoms described?

It is easy to say that it has to implant steadiness of purpose, steadiness of character, which might prevent the excesses mentioned. Unfortunately the home of the children is the vulnerable point in most institutions, and the good which the children get from beneficial school discipline is too quickly undone by ignorant parents. It will probably be best to let the parents know that it would be desirable to have a medical examination of the child, to give them through the physician the necessary advice and to enforce the order and rules of the school with such caution as seems necessary.

Another very important point is this: School and home should impress the child with the *moral* law that physical and mental welfare is a gift deserving the greatest respect; and that disregard of one's health is always a mean, immoral neglect which does not merit any sympathy.

As far as I am aware, there is more work done in the schools here than abroad, where, at least in the higher grades, most of the time is nothing but recitation of the work done at home and dictation of the new tasks to be studied at home. Whereas it may be good to keep certain individuals busy a little longer than the ordinary school time, homework seems to me to be a considerable danger; the pupil becomes accustomed to *irregularity of work*, which should never be cultivated. Try to find out how much work a child can do every day; let the child do such work at school and let it feel that it leaves the school as a business man would his office with the business done and the satisfaction of well-deserved rest. Moreover, the work at home creates that *martyr spirit* with which abnormally conscientious pupils pride themselves on having so much work to do, and on having to avoid company and society; these children crave for admiring sympathy, and do this later on in life to the disadvantage of those who live up to more rational and sanitary rules. I know quite well that homework cannot be altogether left out from the school plan. But the teacher should keep control over it; he should exert his influence on the families and see that the work should always be done in order within a certain time, and without encroaching in the least on the time of recreation.

The work at home can be greatly reduced by omitting so-called exercises of memory. It is a great illusion, the idea that learning by heart improves memory. Experiments show that things learnt by heart mechanically disappear rapidly from memory. Simple learning by heart should therefore be condemned mercilessly. If you wish children to remember poetry and similar things, you may repeat it before them, or rather make them enjoy the poetry frequently. Those who have facilities to learn it will learn it thus without mechanical pressure; others would carry it anyhow as an undigested stone in their memory, and forget it as soon as they had a chance.

Whereas the types of children with whom we have been dealing so far were largely such as to bring their defects to school when they enter it, I should now like to draw your attention to another class exposed to mental abnormality worth much study—to children who return to school after sickness. It is a popular experience that children who have suffered from diphtheria, scarlet fever, smallpox, etc., sometimes undergo a deep intellectual change. It would be of very great interest to have notes on the time that children require for complete recovery from the consequences of these diseases. As a rule they are sent to school too soon, at a time when they are rapidly tired out. They have to fill up gaps of memory, have extra work to make up for what they missed, and do, moreover, nearly all the work that the class is doing. I know of a number of young people whose serious mental disorders must be attributed to this experience. The questions will be: "When shall a child be allowed after sickness to take up the classes again? What measure should be taken to prevent overwork after sickness without putting the child to the inconvenience of losing a whole year?" It seems to me that a prolonged rest and gradual private instruction in the essential points should precede the entrance in school and should be insisted upon emphatically.

In connection with this I might mention the attitude toward children that suffer from chorea. I should not wonder if sometimes the symptoms of chorea show first in the mental faculties; in the course of the disease the mind and intellect are certainly much affected. Here we must insist upon discontinuation of attendance at school and a long period of convalescence. Moreover, chorea is a disease which seems to become epidemic. Another important disease is epilepsy. It would be interesting to know how many children are affected by it and whether a state school for epileptics would be a desirable institution.

Let me sum up my conclusions:

1. It would be desirable that the teachers engaged in the study undertaken by this congress be assisted by competent physicians. An attempt of a few years would show how much could be done among those children that suffer merely from symptomatic mental weakness due to disease of extracranial organs, and also by advice for the *purely* nervous child.

2. In the investigation of the teachers special attention should be paid to the forms of fatigue shown in various children, to the inattention and to the directions of the stage of excitement and irritability and to the most frequent causes of fatigue at various times of the day.

3. Combination of various kinds of work and recreation should be tried with a view to the least possible exhaustion.

4. Provision should be made for the weak and for those who have been kept from school through sickness.

5. The schools should be invited to furnish satisfactory statistics for the nervous affections, especially of headache, chorea, epilepsy, etc., and to have them controlled by a physician.

EARLY PREVENTION OF

DANGER

From Handbook, *Illinois Society for Child-Study*, p. 53 (1895), "*Schedule for the Study of Mental Abnormalities in Children*," by Dr. Meyer, dated Feb. 28, 1895.

Mental abnormalities and mental diseases in childhood have been little studied so far. It is partly because parents accept the disposition of the child as a gift that must be taken without grumbling, partly because parents as a rule do not like to be advised as to the education of the character of their children. This is not true with regard to the intellectual training; there they avail themselves of the teachers quite often. But if a child is a liar, or a thief, or is cruel, ungrateful, disobedient, regardless of others, especially of authority, parents do not like to be advised; the fact touches a tender spot in the natural love of their children. They do not like to speak or consult on the subject. People continually, and perhaps fortunately, make allowances for children. In reality the child portrays fairly well the future adult; appearances may change; the true nature of the individual, however, may be restrained by education but is never lost and still breaks forth at times. Yet we think the child's life and conduct is of little account.

Our aim must be to collect careful observations of children who show abnormalities. Well-established mental disease, aside from idiocy and imbecility, is not frequent among children; but how often do we find mental abnormalities that form the basis for mental difficulties later in life, or even mental derangement? How often are children, through inheritance from parents, in danger of insanity and nervousness, and to what extent do they show abnormalities? What forms characterize the borderland between a normal and an abnormal mind in childhood?

We need a great number of careful observations so as to work them up in a way that will become useful not only for the specialist in mental diseases, but above all to parents and teachers, in preventing danger.

Remember always that one symptom does not make a disease of itself, but that it suggests dangers in certain directions when it is associated with many others in a peculiar way. Theory cannot help us to find out the relative importance of such symptoms. The only way to obtain clearness is to collect a great number of individual cases and to follow them through the years.

The intellectual faculties are on the whole most easily studied.

Lack of attention can be seen in the infant and is throughout childhood the most important sign of intellectual disorder. Attend first to diseases of the sense organs, especially of the eyes and ears. Sight and hearing form the chief channels through which the world reaches the mental life. Defective sight or hearing may cause mental defects and apparent weakness of the mind. But a child that has good mental possibilities (*i.e.*, suffers merely from defective development of a really normal brain) will improve when the obstacle in vision or hearing is removed, while a child with genuine weakness of mind (*i.e.*, defective brain) has only a limited chance for education.

Attention may be vivid but unsteady, fleeting; in a nervous child during the excitement of fatigue it may lead to real incoherence of thought and action. Restlessness becomes so excessive that the child loses the control of self completely. Stupor is less frequently the result of fatigue.

Many children take a great, explosive fancy to a thing and drop their interest all of a sudden in order to admire something else, it being often difficult to account for the sudden change.

Every child is moody in this respect, but there are degrees which are decidedly abnormal.

Where the intellectual development is one-sided—abnormal talent in special directions or utter deficiency in others—we deal with conditions frequently observed in the history of the nervous patients of our hospital and also (we may say for the comfort of those concerned) in the biographies of many famous people.

Notice deficiency in abstract thought; do not confound the repetition of expressions learned by heart, and not digested, with abstract ideation. This becomes evident in reproduction of somewhat difficult thoughts. Does the pupil use freely chosen expressions or merely repetition of the same words?

In connection with these you find abnormal degrees of the power of learning by heart verses or prose, altogether different from the power of repeating freely the contents of the matter learned by heart. All this is more or less common in all children, but excessive cases should attract attention.

Excessive imagination. Normally children can reproduce voluntarily all sorts of mental pictures in the dark. This becomes abnormal when the mental pictures become an obsession, *i.e.,* cannot be suppressed. Especially pictures that create fear and unpleasant feelings are apt to become excessively strong.

Excessive imagination may lead to the construction of lies and the irresistible impulse to play them on others. This becomes abnormal where the desire for deception is irrational, becomes an obsession and leads to actions that bring self or others into great calamities. It may oftener accompany criminal disposition (stealing), but it has been described as a characteristic entity in juvenile mental disorders.

Imperative conceptions and impulses are very frequent. A child has to walk on certain figures of the carpet only, must touch all corners of the tables, must make certain movements just so many times before doing something else, must keep rhythm.

Mysophobia (fear of contamination of dirt, fear of metals, etc.), morbid hesitation and scruples belong in a similar category, especially as long as the individual is conscious of the strange irresistible character of the impulses.

Excessive fear in children is not infrequent. Where it is not founded on experience of threatening dangers, but is unreasonable, it may affect the whole disposition of the child. *Morbid bashfulness,* blushing very easily, and especially long durations of sad impressions, *brooding over being slighted,* etc., mark a large class of morbid children and should be looked into before they have undermined the whole disposition.

One of the most important features of certain aberrations is *cruelty,* either as excessive egotism or as positive pleasure in the suffering of others.

Precocious development of sexual feelings is a very frequent companion of other symptoms of a neurotic disposition and is unfortunately, under the present system of making a mystery of everything connected with it, a problem almost beyond control.

Sometimes the formation of very intimate friendships and seclusion from classmates, desire for being alone, etc., is of importance and should be noted.

Pronounced forms of temporary derangements are better known, such as delirium (especially during febrile affections or after exhaustion), furor (sudden outbreak of anger without adequate cause, observed even in children who would wake all of a sudden with such derangement, quite different from somnambulism), ecstasis (for instance, through religious overexcitement), nightmares, various degrees of somnambulism, laughing and crying spells, etc.

Finally, we may mention several characteristic habits of nervous children: chewing of fingernails, incontinence of urine during daytime or night, breathing through the mouth, etc., headaches, convulsions, sleeplessness, chorea; further, concurrence with deformities and hereditary influences.

These remarks cannot be closed without an earnest word of warning to the observer:

Do not let the child feel that you observe. If you wish to find peculiar symptoms in a child you can always produce them by simply rousing the intense desire for mimicry and the suggestibility of the child. Thus you may do the child harm and deceive yourself and others.

Child study in the hands of people who make the child feel its importance may do more harm than good, and should be left to those who have tact enough to guide their intelligence.

Do not speak of, or intimate in the presence of children, the result of your observation; do not train morbid self-observation, hypochondria, pleasure in suffering, and other hysterical disorders.

Do not overrate the importance of one symptom but pay special attention to the connection of symptoms and causation.

4

Action in Worcester

The Kankakee pathologist, far from being a cloistered researcher, liked making contacts with other centers of activity and other workers. On his 1894 vacation he took a boat through the Great Lakes from Chicago to Buffalo and visited several upstate New York hospitals. (In Buffalo he made the acquaintance of another American institution, the minstrel show.) The next summer, as an associate member of the American Medico-Psychological Association, Meyer went to its annual meeting in Denver in place of Superintendent Gapen, and his baggage included brain sections from epilepsy cases. What mainly happened in Denver was that he heard the presidential address of Edward Cowles, of the McLean Hospital, he read a paper of his own on brain pathology, and he was looked over by Dr. Cowles as possible material for the State Lunatic Hospital staff at Worcester, Mass. After the meeting, Cowles asked him if he would consider making a change.

Kankakee was not satisfying. It had taught him that the division of labor into practical routine and scientific work tended to "create corners that are never swept." Although Gapen had accepted Meyer's idea for developing the scientific and clinical work of the hospital, he held back from giving him the participation Meyer needed, and Meyer was determined to "make the living patient the center of my interest, with all the controls which conditions would permit."

His view was strengthened by the talk which Superintendent P. M. Wise of the St. Lawrence State Hospital at Ogdensburg,

N. Y., gave at the association meeting. Dr. Wise made an appeal for improved ward work; he said it should not be separated from pathological research, and deprecated the adoption of special pathologists. Meyer stood up and agreed. He hoped that some day the old type of pathologist would not be needed.

At Worcester, he understood, conditions were better and might bring him nearer the realization of his expectations. There was a progressive spirit, leavened by President Hall of Clark University, who held weekly clinics with hospital patients for his psychology students—inadequate though it was to pick out curiosities as morbid exhibits.

Soon after the chat with Cowles, Meyer received a letter from Worcester's superintendent, Dr. Hosea M. Quinby, which was a joy to digest, for Quinby thought along his lines: Most hospitals confined their scientific work to post-mortems and chemical analyses of blood and urine; Worcester required someone qualified to combine pathology, neurology, and psychology, one who could help make the hospital, in connection with Clark, a training school for those interested in nervous diseases; who could train the hospital's assistant physicians and attract a more desirable type of young doctor. To make the opportunity more inviting, Quinby wrote that the pathologist to be engaged would be relieved of the obligation of making the rounds of patients; he would be a supervisor, while clinical assistants took case histories and kept records, and he need select only interesting cases for himself. There were abundant materials and exceptional facilities, Quinby said: "We only lack the man to organize it."

Meyer reflected, "I shall go on the Clark faculty at last." He answered Quinby and in return received an offer to try his hand with the 1,200 patients—a free hand.

In the fall of 1895 he left the steppingstone of Kankakee. (First he applied for naturalization papers in Chicago, where the court clerk solemnly asked him if he forswore allegiance to "the Duke of Switzerland.") Stopping in New York, Meyer met Dr. Ira Van Gieson, histologist, newly appointed as the first director of the Pathological Institute. This was a project intended to serve as the nucleus of the laboratory work of all the state's hospitals. Van Gieson was going to develop what he termed, in a booklet he gave Meyer, a "correlation of sciences." The booklet listed forty-eight neurological and biological problems to be worked out, and Meyer noticed two "fatal gaps"—there was no place for man in it, no place for psychiatry at work. A mentally sick person, after all, was not the sum of the elements of disease but a specific functioning unit.

It seemed to Meyer that Van Gieson's abstract correlation was just another move to get along without psychiatry. The Institute director expounded the theory that toxic substances, acting on nerve cells, produced changes in them, which in turn disturbed the functioning of the brain, and that insanity was simply the expression of such a disturbance. Van Gieson struck Meyer as being "quasi-intoxicated" with neurons and with the notion that he could "outflank the plain work of the hospital physicians."

The McLean plan was also fallacious. Cowles had staffed laboratories on pathology, physiology, psychology, and biochemistry with able men, but handled clinical psychiatry by itself and by himself. The Worcester plan, as Meyer was formulating it, would have the laboratory's line of work suggested by the work on the wards, and this could not be done if pathology were kept out of contact with clinical activity. Meyer recalled:

I might have yielded to the temptation to occupy a throne of privilege, with the risk of splendid isolation, but my first concern was the creation of a sounder average level of the medical and psychiatric work as a whole. I did not feel as if I could claim such insight as would enable me to choose from cases in an initial stage those that would necessarily prove interesting when they had reached the end stage.[1]

Although engaged as a pathologist, he laid out a program which put chief stress on a careful study of the patient's symptoms and needs and on the laboratory as a help for doing justice to the daily-increasing complexity of diagnostic and therapeutic problems. Without these aids clinical medicine could not exist, much less progress. The practical work with the rank and file of the staff would thus become the foundation as well as the goal of the laboratory.

Before he arrived at Worcester and reorganized the entire medical work of the hospital, data on patients had been gathered in a slipshod manner, written up days or weeks after observation. These records were of little practical value. They gave no adequate medical picture of the disorder, furnished no basis for diagnosis, indicated no procedure or result of treatment. Meyer regarded as the best fruit of his two-and-a-half-year Kankakee "novitiate" (so he called it) a determination to "study the facts as I might find them and for the factors at work in them."

As the first task he gave himself at Worcester was not to select cases but to set dependable standards, it was necessary to evolve a technique for preparing comprehensive clinical histories, all of one cast. Meyer obtained four assistants. He instructed them in case taking and in accurate, concise recording. He outlined a uniform method of making a thorough mental and physical examination of each patient upon admission and a guide for use in subsequent observation. Notes were to be taken at the bedside and later edited or dictated to a stenographer for typing. Nothing like this had been done before.

After a year's operation of the new system a workmanlike record and study of all recent cases was in hand and the histories of old ones had been compiled as well as possible. Nobody thought of returning to the slapdash ways, Meyer reported, though the assistants were hard pressed to make the minute observation of their allotted patients which was essential to a careful elaboration of each case. To meet the excuse of lack of time he acquired a corps of four interns to assist the assistants.

My plea was that where efficiency of work is an issue, it is necessary to have a correct ratio between working force and accepted working plan, and that a comparison of payrolls with different standards is a poor way of looking into the actual needs.[2]

"How do you keep the boys busy?" a medical visitor asked superciliously after this seeming extravagance was inaugurated. Meyer's worry was different: how to give them "a sense of satisfaction with their work, some fruitions and results, some happiness out of psychiatry." On his junior staff for a year was Albert M.

Barrett, whose interest in the brain branched out into intensive clinical concerns. Other assistants included George H. Kirby, Charles B. Dunlap, George M. Kline, Henry A. Cotton, Isador H. Coriat, and Peter Bassoe.

In time Meyer received the title of clinical director. He made regular rounds, covering the entire hospital each week, and conducted daily staff meetings which "raised the level of growing interest in the wide range of real cases." In addition, he gave a series of lectures on the nervous system (anatomy in particular) and another on laboratory methods. As docent in psychiatry at Clark, he took over from Stanley Hall the clinical demonstrations of various symptom complexes and saw to it that the hospital men also attended.

With this course at Clark to graduate students in psychology, he put the subject on a ground of biology, and from their number came a group who figured largely in the later creation of the profession of clinical psychologist. It was not wholly desirable, however, that the biological influence should come from teaching with pathological material, Meyer realized.

His labors attracted the critical attention of Dr. Bernard Sachs, of New York, another neurologist whom the American Medico-Psychological Association bravely invited to its sessions. Sachs's address marked a milestone beyond Weir Mitchell's. The New Yorker praised Meyer's work as worthy of emulation by other pathologists; asylum physicians were endeavoring to solve the mysteries of the morbid anatomy of insanity, Sachs said, and asylum reports were fast becoming storehouses of useful investigations. Yet as late as January, 1899, a writer in the *American Journal of Insanity* observed that few hospitals were provided with pathologists and, despite the promise of scientific productiveness, "nothing denoting marked originality of thought or thoroughness of work has emanated."

But Meyer found his Worcester period "sound and solidly useful." He aimed to gather from experience, systematically and conscientiously, all that might benefit medical science in treating mental patients. And this aim incidentally became a plan for research work, in the same sense that every practitioner would mean to use his experience for the future, except that here at Worcester were ten physicians in cooperation, all employing the same methods, striving for the same end, and therefore likely to be more fortunate in research results than one man alone could expect for himself.

For as long as he remained at Worcester, Meyer succeeded in staving off Superintendent Quinby's project of a special laboratory building to be constructed away from the hospital's central offices. He kept staff and laboratories close together, for the latter were meant to serve as a staff center, "not a mere mortuary nor a scientific side show."

Quinby and the board of trustees were pleased enough with his progress to give him a five-month leave for a tour of European centers. In the spring of 1896 he sailed for Genoa on the *Kaiser Wilhelm II.* (A fellow passenger who looked unmistakably distinguished turned out to be the Massachusetts judge, Oliver Wendell Holmes, Jr.) At Turin he would see Cesare Lombroso, who was making a doctrine of "degeneracy," and Angelo Mosso, the physiologist who wrote on fear. After covering Italian hospitals he would visit Switzerland and proceed to Germany, that stronghold of misconception of the science of man, oriented on the mind-body split. The lodestone was Dr. Emil Kraepelin's clinic at Heidelberg, which had been conceived on psychological principles.

When Meyer had first tackled the problems of psychiatry he found the textbooks inadequate. They did not touch on salient points which arose face to face with patients. They were arbitrary in their classification of mania, melancholia, paranoia, and dementia. "I thought that the only way in which I could get any satisfaction would be to carefully describe what seemed to be essential in all cases that I could possibly observe and then try to get a picture quite independently of the books." As with the study of internal medicine, an unprejudiced study of the facts was indicated: here the attitudes and behavior of the person and his life situations. "I decided to work pragmatically with the best possible use of critical commonsense. I was ready to put aside all preconceived traditional classification; I wanted to take the facts and group them without adulteration or suppression of any available data." [5]

Professor Kraepelin seemed promising. His textbook was helpful but did not give a full idea of his principles, and Meyer had to see them at work. En route, the full-fledged American visited his Swiss mother and found her recovered from her depression in spite of Forel's pessimism.

Meyer spent six weeks at the small hospital in Heidelberg with Kraepelin—a rare bird who had not stumbled into psychiatry by accident but had marched into it. Kraepelin was quite different from Forel, the agnostic who was ever ready to say, "I do not know." Kraepelin had singled out symptom complexes as evidencing specific disease entities and set up his own classifications, such as dementia praecox, abolishing terminal dementia, and later added manic-depressive psychosis. He propounded disease processes after noting what the patients were before and after the disorder developed; he followed them up for years within the community, and thus arrived at apparent standards of prognosis. The outcome was assumed to be the result of a definite course, originating in some physical cause (a lesion, or perhaps a toxic agent?).

Meyer was attracted by this look beyond mere description, hoping to find a dynamic key to mental ailments, but was dismayed to discover psychology snowed under nosology, or groupings. Kraepelin kept devising and revising classifications; types replaced persons; the patients' constitutional factors were minimized, their experiences ignored.

While Meyer was at Heidelberg the fifth edition of Kraepelin's book was published. He reviewed it in the *American Journal of Insanity* and expressed misgivings. For Kraepelin had postulated suggestive disease processes, whereas the facts of each case were more important than prognosis, or divining the future. Just as Meyer had revolted against the finalities in classical teachings that his own observations disproved (as in his study of aphasia cases at Worcester), he now kept a sharp eye on "new" science. Nevertheless, Kraepelin's system of classification was an improvement on the old, and Meyer was the first to adopt it outside of Heidelberg when recasting the statistical accounts of the Worcester hospital— "in a mitigated form." He took from Kraepelin's principles only what was acceptable, wary of fortunetelling pigeonholes. Though stimulated, he was not swayed into "any idolatry of dogmatic nosology."

The Kraepelinian concept was slow of adoption, but after taking root it attained a supremacy that subdued the psychological approach. The scientific world still acted on the assumption that reality was divisible into physical and mental spheres which must stay separate. Thus, Cowles at McLean regarded insanity as a physiological process. Van Gieson in New York clung to toxic origin and committed the further error of keeping his superior research institute aloof from the hospitals and including everything except work with living patients. At the other pole the danger was a predilection for fads. Many doctors facing psychological manifestations in their patients came close to mystical notions. "The psychology of hypnotism, of hysteria, even that of aphasia, give good instances of such tendencies," Meyer pointed out at Clark University's decennial celebration.[6]

Stanley Hall, who had what Meyer called a genetic conception of the study of man, staged the anniversary event with brilliant innovation. He brought to Worcester in 1899 a number of scientists from Europe and invited guests from all the American universities to hear their lectures. Professor Mosso, of Turin, was one of the speakers; another was Professor S. Ramon y Cajal, histologist and pathologist, of Madrid. Forel, who had given up Burghölzli to conserve his health for work as an active scholar in social movements, tapped two of his many reservoirs of knowledge and drew a lecture from each: ant life and hypnotism. Meyer wished Forel had spoken also on alcoholism for the benefit of the alienists in the audience (and later persuaded him to write such an article, which Meyer translated for the *Journal*).

His own contribution to the celebration was a departmental report on psychopathology, looking forward to closer integration of psychology with biology. "Medicine, barely deserving the attribute of an applied science, is not rich in literature breathing the biological spirit." He used the occasion for launching the idea of a psychiatric clinic and research station to be set up by the state and university jointly. No course in psychopathology was worthy of its name if the students lacked sound biological training. And without an all-embracing clinic, psychiatry could not gather enough facts to put a check on hasty speculation.

But the necessary appropriations for this project were not forthcoming. Meyer simply had to wait—wait and advocate. He confided to his colleagues:

I see myself before a mountain which is overwhelming and crushing at certain periods of one's work. The greatest difficulty has not been in the work itself but in the energy that must be exercised to overcome the feeling that things are improperly done. When we are speaking of the progress of psychiatry this is a very important point which I have experienced. If we want to succeed we must bear in mind that we are doing something which has not been done before now.[7]

In seven years at Worcester, with his exact fact-finding system running in good order within its limitations, and with a mind open to grasp the data, Meyer was able to make realistic groupings of psychiatric pictures and to perceive their meanings. Behind each cluster of symptoms he recognized dynamic forces driving a patient into illness.

I was constantly confronted with the evolution of constitutional factors. It was my urge to understand and guide, not only to describe and dissect, the patient. I was also personally sensitized [referring to his mother's attack of depression] concerning the blending and differentiation of possible hereditary and constitutional factors with definitely psychogenic, *i.e.*, life-experienced, and somatic ones, and so I was bound to cultivate a very concrete and intimate concern for the genetic-dynamic developments in the individual patient and life situations.[8]

And this was only a part of the vision. Psychiatry must also protect the health of the healthy. So he scrutinized the patients' past to see how influences might have been modified and destiny diverted. He took stock of the present to appraise the potentialities or dangers in a person's mode of living—with a view to giving it proper direction.

This broad concept needed a broader arena than the one which Massachusetts authorities were willing to afford—a somewhat costly organization, Meyer admitted. He was ripe for another change.

Meanwhile, in 1901, while again visiting Europe, he went to Scotland to represent Clark University at the 250th anniversary exercises of the University of Glasgow. Andrew Carnegie, emerging from the castle that marked his triumph over a Scottish boy's poverty, saw this fellow American receive the honorary degree of doctor of laws.

THE BIOLOGICAL APPROACH

TO PSYCHIATRY

From "*A Short Sketch of the Problems of Psychiatry,*" read by Dr. Meyer before the *Worcester District Medical Society*, March 10, 1897; American Journal of Insanity, 53:538 (*April,* 1897).

Owing to the marvelous change of thought in this century we have learned that man is not so different from the rest of creation as was formerly thought. We are subject to the same laws of the universe with all other creations. We are the outcome of a slow, gradual development of the living world, different from the rest in degree only. We all grow from fertilized egg cells. Division of cell after cell takes place, and differentiation of cells; the egg, as it lives and grows to be a fetus, grows to be a moving, active being; action becomes more and more differentiated, in a measure, as the body differentiates itself, and we say that we recognize in the fetus and in the child a body and its function, the objects of anatomy and physiology. The infant goes on growing, and with the development of the brain gives evidence of what we call sentient or conscious life, a feature common to all higher animals at least, expressed in various motions and actions, and in man more especially in his language, the most differentiated movements of expression.

Thus we have three fields of observation in the higher animals—anatomy, physiology, and psychology; they study the respective sides of what developed from the one fertilized egg cell, and with all that, there is nowhere a gap through which we might say life crept into the cell and, just as little, a gap through which mind might have crept in. (This implies that the fertilized egg cell, as long as it lives, is not purely "matter" but includes the elements of vital processes and among them of the psychical processes, whatever they may be. What we see as "matter" is not more real than what we recognize as its physiological and psychical life. Materialism claims that we know matter to be the only real thing and everything else is an attribute of it. This view seems untenable; it is an undue exaggeration of the importance of our tactile senses which forces us unnecessarily into dualistic difficulties.)

As I say, this holds for all higher animals, but owing to the slow and highly differentiated development of our brain, we reach a degree which makes us eminently gifted with the ability of seeing behind us a past to learn from, and before us stages of higher development, and, owing to this ability, we are under the moral obligation to aspire to an ideal more than any other living creature. All this develops from the fertilized ovum of a mother. The body and its mechanical and chemical functions, and the mental life associated with it, make out the biological unit, the person, as we would say in the case of a man. In this unit the development of the mind goes hand in hand with the anatomical and physiological development, not merely in a parallelism but as a oneness with several aspects.

To make myself understood by a simile from inorganic nature (which has for centuries been able to get along without mystic spirits), I would refer you to a red-hot iron. That the iron is the same iron, whether it is hot or cold, gray, red, or white, nobody would doubt. But it undergoes changes by absorbing heat. It becomes hot—we feel this by the sense of temperature; it changes its color—we see this with our eyes; it becomes larger—we appreciate that with considerations on the ground of the sense of space. We know that the iron is one, but our senses are so organized that we recognize several aspects in the one iron; the heat is to be studied with the methods of the theory of heat, the color with the methods of optics, the expansion with the methods of measurement of space, and yet we never think for a moment that anything but one iron is before us. In an analogous and more complicated way we see in the living person the body with its mechanical and chemical functions, and further, the mental aspect, and this one person is to be studied with methods of anatomy, physiology, and psychology.

The fundamental principle on which the psychiatry of today is built is undoubtedly this biological conception of man. From the purely materialistic conception of the middle of this century this biological view has developed which does better justice to our entire experience, not solving the ultimate problems, to be sure, but furnishing a rational working basis.

This genetic view of man is altogether borne out by the reverse process, the destruction. Clinical and pathological studies have furnished satisfactory evidence to the effect that the brain is the "bearer of mental activity," and that destruction of certain parts of the brain is identical with destruction of certain mental functions, or even more or less extended domains of mental life.

All life is reaction, either to stimuli of the outside world or of the various parts of the organism. We recognize death by the absolute absence of these reactions. In our mental life these reactions are pictured as if in a mirror. But not every reaction appears in this mirror, *i.e.*, becomes conscious. Most of the reactions during sleep, all during epileptic fits, during syncope, remain unconscious, *i.e.*, we do not remember having been aware of them and do not give any evidence of consciousness at the time. In our daily life, in walking and working, we heed many things without thinking of them. Further, many reactions take place in our mind which are not expressed. They take the form of "simple" thought. They seem, indeed, purely mental, and create the appearance on which the idea of mind independent from the body is built. Will this shake our biological conception? Hardly.

We do not see direct evidence of the process of digestion, of action of sensory nerves, not even of the flowing of the blood on hasty examination. On the other hand, the work of Mosso and others has shown that accurate methods of observing changes of blood pressure, variations of the pupils, of respiration, in the rhythm of the heartbeat, give us physiological evidence of reactions which were formerly believed to be purely psychical. One might ask further, How is it that there are so many physiological reactions of which we are not conscious? Would not this rather speak for the independence of the mind? We find in normal man that a stimulus, in order to be noticed, must produce a sufficient change in the equilibrium to become conscious at all. Not all reactions become conscious, but largely those which mean a change in the relations between the whole individual and the outside world. In other words, the circle of consciousness is limited largely to those reactions which we say make up the personality.

In this lies the essence of the possibility of concentration of thought and reactions generally in the so-called mental realm. The greater part of our nervous system works automatically. Those nerve-cell mechanisms, however, which present reactions of the individual as a whole, that is the personality, have a physiological and psychological aspect. The extensive development of just these mechanisms subserving the personality is characteristic of man as compared to animals. I need hardly point out that what we say of mind has absolutely nothing to do with soul; soul is a concept which cannot be an object of biology. If we give the concept "soul" a proper definition, the idea of its persistence and immortality meets absolutely no objection in biology; but our principles of biology say that a persistence of the *biological* phenomenon "mind" is inconceivable without the coexistence and persistence of the living body.

With this we imply also that all mental reaction is one aspect of a process which must have its physiological aspect; and we must further claim that a purely psychic disorder, commonly called functional, is just as well a disorder of the life of the brain as any organic lesion; and although we have not learned yet to see the changes in the cells and their processes we must admit that a functional disorder can be just as serious, and is as actual, as an "organic" one.

The biological working hypothesis forces us at once to recognize a fact very important in the method of study of psychiatry. As long as the view of an independence of mind and body could be maintained, the alienist was allowed to work largely in the field of mental symptoms, with little care about the physiological or, rather, pathological condition of the physical side. Those were the days when the professor of philosophy felt himself called upon to write on the diseases of the mind in preference to the physician, and when in a textbook on mental diseases you could hardly find the body mentioned. As a contrast the so-called somatic school was formed by physicians, and it lived in the form of materialism through the greater part of this century. We know now that we must attack the problem from the biological side, from the point of view of *mental* pathology and of *physiological* pathology; further, that we must not attack the two at points which are farthest apart but where they touch each other most closely.

The most common mental disorders are those of intoxication and fever delirium. In these we see plainly that the mental disease is purely symptomatic, so much so that fever delirium and acute intoxication, with alcohol or other poisons, are not usually looked upon as mental diseases. We look quite correctly on the cause of the fever and on the process of poisoning as the principal pathological feature. The same probably holds for a great number of mental diseases.

Alcohol or the typhoid toxins show us how widely the symptoms of the mental disorder may vary with the same pathological process. An acute alcoholic intoxication acts quite differently on different men. The one becomes vivid, boisterous, jolly, exalted, with a feeling of huge mental and physical strength, even when the motor paralysis has set in; with this more or less irritability of character may crop out. Another person becomes rapidly stupid, dull, or depressed and emotional.

If the alcoholic intoxication is associated with gastritis and a changed metabolism acts on the weakened brain, besides the alcohol itself, we meet with a different picture—delirium tremens—usually with fear, excitement, and a great number of hallucinations; the feeling of being persecuted and in danger gradually vanishes with the attack. In a third form the change comes more slowly; during the slow deterioration of the brain, and under the demoralizing influence of the drinker's surroundings, a deep change of character takes place; the slow vitiation of the views of the drinker leads to a more orderly and better assimilated system of delusions of persecution (usually with hallucinations), and to a change of the personality. Even when the mind seems well rested and sober, the delusions of jealousy and persecution persist. They are not a simple toxic delirium, but a slowly acquired conviction.

Another instance of how the mental symptoms are largely symptomatic, and not the principal factor to go by in the consideration of insanity, is general paralysis. The etiology is so clearly worked out that it is difficult today to believe that it occurs on any other but a syphilitic basis. The work of Hirschl, Fournier, and others justifies us in defining it as a deterioration of the brain and mind under the influence of the change of metabolism, brought about by a syphilitic infection associated with excesses of any kind. The common features are the progressive dementia, occurrence of motor symptoms, and the almost inevitably fatal termination. The ordinary mental symptoms, such as delusions of wealth, exaltation, are by no means essential, because they may be absent; hallucinations, which undoubtedly may occur, are certainly rare; sometimes the picture may be that of melancholia, sometimes of the old "mania of persecution," but whatever the special mental form be, on superficial inspection, the disease and its termination remain typical.

Considerations of this character show us that not so much a depression, or an exaltation, or delusion, or hallucination, make up the disease as a clinical entity, but that the whole course and the fundamental disorder underlying the mental manifestations decide the diagnosis, and with it the prognosis.

The mental symptom complex which we call hallucinatory confusion may occur in a fever delirium, in delirium tremens, and in almost any form of the so-called acute insanities. In itself it does not constitute a diagnosis; also what we call "mania" makes no diagnosis; it occurs in alcohol intoxication, in general paralysis, in the so-called simple psychoses. These symptomatic diagnoses are worth as much as a diagnosis of brain fever or lung fever, or cough, or albuminuria. If a diagnosis shall be more than a name, shall give us an idea of the real condition and its probable course, we must resort to the general pathology of the organs affected, including symptomatology, but building it on rational principles.

In many cases a number of data, which we call collectively "hereditary predisposition," are to be held responsible for the readiness with which abnormalities are acquired. That certain forms of disease practically occur only on such a basis is a fairly well-established fact. We must say, though, that a statement that heredity is present is by no means a pathological explanation. If we want to make any progress we must try to find out why heredity shows itself in some and not in other cases, and whether it is really necessary to consider heredity with the customary fatalism. There is another factor besides "heredity" which may modify the *Anlage* [predisposition] so as to change the general constitution. This is the influence and residuals of previous diseases during fetal life, or childhood, or later. On careful study, many of the cases of "heredity" will perhaps be shown to have been under the influence of one or more pathological factors during the years of growth.

You are familiar with the saying that whoever has been insane is liable to become insane again. A careful study of a great number of patients who had been discharged, and kept under observation for years after discharge, convinced Kraepelin that the majority of the cases of mania and melancholia of the older writers, which did not belong to psychoses classified as depending on exhaustion or intoxication, or essential dementia, had such a tendency to recur without any apparent cause, and sometimes with great regularity, that they could well be compared with epilepsy. What we know as mania or depression would, therefore, not be a disease in itself, just as little as the attack of epilepsy is the disease itself; but the disorder would be a constitutional defect characterized by periodic conditions of disturbed metabolism, the chief symptom of which is the occasional epileptic attack, or the mania, or the depression. This is not without practical importance, both for the prognosis and for the problems of pathological study. Simple mania, eminently curable, is not such a harmless incident, but is the manifestation of a constitutional condition.

Paranoia is a mental perversion of slow and gradual development, a chronic constitutional transformation of the personality. The disease has more than once not been recognized as a mental disease by the courts of this country; for instance, in the Guiteau and Prendergast trials, probably because the legal views of insanity have lost touch with the rapidly progressing psychiatry. Who could nowadays say with good conscience that the recognition of right and wrong excluded a diagnosis of insanity, and say that insanity was identical with absolute irresponsibility?

If I have succeeded in showing you that psychiatry *has* problems essentially medical, that we cannot afford to disregard any side of the biological unit in the patient, but must use psychological as well as physiological and anatomical methods under the guidance of general pathology, and that on this basis progress has been made and will continue, I have solved the task I put before myself. You will understand what I mean by saying in conclusion that the customary pathological laboratory is not sufficient to meet the needs of the study of so-called mental diseases. The first and fundamental prerequisite is careful and broad clinical observation. This will necessarily lead to careful collection of histories, physical and psychical examinations with exact methods; for this purpose the means for clinical chemistry and clinical microscopy must be procured, and finally the laboratories will also be fitted so that post-mortem pathology can be carried on. Wherever they began at the wrong end, at post-morten pathology, the results have been so meager that we have a right to urge strongly the need of clinical facilities.

I conclude with the following statement:

The biological view of man offers a fruitful working hypothesis in medicine, especially for psychiatry.

A mental disease is a disorder of the person following the laws of general pathology like any other disease.

Mental symptoms do not constitute the disease exclusively, and are not safe guides for diagnosis without general pathological views taking into consideration all the aspects of a man.

The clinical study of psychiatry is the natural basis for the study of mental pathology.

5

Action in New York

Events in life proceeded by "orderly chance," Adolf Meyer said. In 1901 the prospect of coordinating the pathological work of the thirteen mental hospitals of New York State was laid before him by a delegation of superintendents sent by Dr. Frederick Peterson, newly appointed president of the State Commission in Lunacy. Ira Van Gieson was to retire as director of the Pathological Institute, which would be reorganized along its originally intended lines. As usual, Meyer could see larger opportunities for work beyond the surface implications of a title, but he had to be persuaded that the shift from Worcester would not lead him up a blind alley. The Institute was situated in New York City in the Metropolitan Life Insurance Building at 1 Madison Avenue, where the correlated scientists pursued neuron energy in happy isolation from clinical experience.

Meyer and Peterson had met at various medical-society sessions, and Peterson was familiar with his writings. Meyer knew that the New Yorker's hope in joining the Commission was to bring about a psychopathic hospital for receiving early-stage cases without legal commitment, possibly as an extension of the Institute. This was good. It would widen the field of study.

The first goal of the Institute, Meyer believed, should be to establish a basic standard of work in the thirteen hospitals. In a Worcester report he had expressed dissatisfaction with a science department "grafted somewhere in the traditional asylum" and sought "the growth of the whole hospital idea in conformity with the principles of modern medicine." The pathologist's department could be a valuable branch only if the general efficiency of hospital work furnished "the soil and atmosphere and needs."

The time had come to give up laboratory side shows maintained "chiefly to ward off invidious comparisons with general hospitals and the reproach of unprogressiveness." It was time to train staffs for their responsibilities, to develop cooperation among the hospitals, pool accumulated experience for progress with patients, collaborate in the study of conditions under which abnormal constitutions developed, and use the facts as indications for work and for prevention.

"Pathological," in the current use of American medical jargon, was something of a misnomer. Meyer had already discarded faith in the old role of the pathologist and now treated as superstitious the belief that pathological anatomy was of more than possible help. To uproot the idea would be "one of the first tasks of this century." Autopsies failed to sustain the theory of lesions of the nervous system except in cases of profound idiocy, general paralysis, senile and organic dementias, and the like. Bodies could not give the answers.

But there was such a thing as a pathology of insanity. Mind was a function of the brain, mind disorders were functional disorders; hence a pathology of function. "The problems must come from the study of the living and not from the dead." Taking mental phenomena as its main field, the new school of thought led by Meyer sought to understand patients by their behavior, although identification of causal chains was not yet clear. But material was available, and psychiatrists could turn to it instead of resting satisfied with "what the judge needs for the commitment." They would pass up such Lombrosian fancies as morbid taints and stigmata of degeneracy—"a verdict as gloomy as the dogma of infant damnation"—and look into influences during growth, education, and other determinants of individual life.

Meyer's distrust of symptoms as a mark of a specific disease, and of a disease as an indisputable entity, brought radical results. Disease types were a snare unless resolved to events. But did not a logical inference from the facts point to reaction-types?

He laid out his lines of thinking in *A Reference Handbook of the Medical Sciences* (edited by A. H. Buck, 1902):

Every good history of a case of mental disorder should give us accurate information concerning the make-up of the person before the complex constituting the disease was complete. . . . We do well to look into the nature and extent of the development, the habits, and the efficiency as the chief features of the constitution of an organ or an entire person.

These features should be chosen for comparison among items which could be brought in line with other biological facts. "Thus the pathologist will arrange people from points of view different from those of the moralist or the artist or ordinary statistician."

Although little had been done in differentiating psychiatric types, practical orientation could be gained by using such characteristics as

. . . sociability or seclusiveness, efficient and systematic or desultory nature, determination or oscillation, social or antisocial instincts, normal or abnormal sexual life, the existence of definite psychic peculiarities and defects, etc. For practical purposes and for possible avenues of research all these features offer problems nearer those of fundamental individual pathology than the theories of heredity can offer, because they are present in the available subject of our study, the patient.

Turning to symptoms of abnormality, Meyer wrote that their sum total and evolution provided an abstract principle of the disease process.

To this is referred the whole string of events which we have reasons to designate as abnormal. . . . The analysis of a large number of faithful records of cases of insanity furnishes certain natural groups of almost identical conditions. The similarity may lie in the etiological constellation, or in the temporary symptom complexes, or with reference to the outcome of the whole process, or the events in the subsequent life of the patient. Where there is a coincidence of the main points in all four directions we have every reason to surmise a definite law of development, especially if the type occurs often enough to free one of the impression of chance. Where three or only two of the directions coincide, we have at least reason to search for the value of the points of coincidence as compared to those of difference. . . .

Even short experience shows that apparently identical symptom complexes occur under so variable conditions that conclusions drawn from a temporary picture as to etiology and outcome and the general nature of the conditions are apt to be guesswork. The most valuable determining feature is, as a rule, the *form of evolution* of the complex, the time and duration and circumstances of its development, and the character of the possible transformations of the picture. . . . In the evaluation of the symptomatic phenomena the *form of the outcome* is probably next in importance to the etiology . . . as it furnishes an index to the amount and nature of the damage done.

In time, large types or nosological entities would be recognized, leading to detail investigations of the temporary symptom complexes, these leading in turn to readjustment in the concept of the large type; and as superficially similar complexes were differentiated in their settings of separate kinds of evolution, it would be possible to discern distinguishing features as a basis for diagnosis, prognosis, and treatment.

To classify types for simplicity's sake, without real advantage, was anathema to Meyer. He preferred to start with many groups, take generalizations as "purely hypothetical temporary helps," and grope one's way through careful observation toward common denominators—mental, functional, morphological—all of which were to be studied from the viewpoint of "types of reaction of the whole individual."

Here was the Meyer method:

We put down the established facts in a loose chain only as far as our actual knowledge goes, and we frame our provisional disease picture with due reference to all the features: etiological constellation, evolution of the symptom complexes, course, and outcome. Experience shows that this method furnishes general concepts of great use in formulating diagnoses which mean something for prognostic and therapeutic purposes, and that it puts workable problems for investigation into our hands.

Immediately after arriving in New York in 1902, Meyer moved the Institute to Manhattan State Hospital on Ward's Island for proximity to clinical material. It did not matter that the only quarters available there were an abandoned bakeshop (and there was no objection to the saving of rent). The change was meant as a makeshift until a reception hospital could be built. Meanwhile the Institute's clinical staff could study patients in two wards set aside for them at Manhattan State.

In December the thirteen superintendents came to hear his plans, and he considered it wise to allay whatever antagonism change was apt to arouse. For Meyer intended to break the "narrowing charm" of self-sufficient tradition and instill a spirit of inquiry; to change the deadening feeling of routine into eager appreciation of "ever-new experience." So he showed the superintendents how the Institute was offering opportunities; how the hospitals would win appreciation for improvement of medical work and not on a basis of unreliable recovery statistics.

Without directing criticism at the New York institutions, but generalizing on his knowledge of American asylums, Meyer declared that records were a slapdash affair, often regarded mainly as a means of self-defense in case of accident or complaint, not as tools of scientific value. Their greatest defect was a failure to follow the course of a disorder's development; while changes from previous observations might be noted, explanations usually were omitted. The only truly satisfactory way to work was to obtain all the information available on a patient, from pre-hospital history and from repeated thorough examinations; then arrange the facts, scrutinize them, and draw conclusions conscientiously.

Meyer proposed to give short courses to assistant physicians and interns attending the Institute from the various hospitals. Besides lectures he would provide instruction in research, give clinical contact with Manhattan State, teach orderly or telling methods of record keeping, and furnish typewritten outlines to serve as guides for following up patients' histories, idiosyncrasies, needs, or prospects. "It is habits and methods of work that are wanted and that cannot be got in didactic courses." He would arrange a program of staff activity in each hospital, including case discussions in place of the reticent etiquette which shut out questioning. It was bad enough that hospital walls protected medical men from exposure to criticism, from the healthy competition which general practitioners had with consultants.

The improvement in the medical work must be seen in the run-of-the-mill case: medical accuracy throughout. "Our ordinary work must be the plan of attack." He told the superintendents not to expect any revolutionary novelties. "We work mostly for system and for a love of conscience concerning facts. It is not enough to know all these old facts merely when they are mentioned, but we must see that they are used." [2]

In his first course on Ward's Island, during the winter of 1903, Meyer sketched the principles of pathology as applied to psychiatry and reviewed the works of the German leaders—Wernicke, Ziehen and Kraepelin. He discussed the place of mind in biology and pathology; showed the best ways of viewing and using mental symptom complexes; examined case records which his pupils had brought from their hospitals, and worked with them on cases studied on the Island.

To some of the young doctors the two-hour lectures in the small ex-bakery seemed overlong, and the heat of exposed steam-pipes along the wall made them drowsy. To keep from falling asleep they huddled their chairs in a semicircle—if one student dozed off his neighbors could jar him. The instructor would be disappointed when no questions were asked at the end. Yet they agreed that they learned much from his demonstrations and from the training they received; and socially, after classes, they found Meyer lively and charming.

The Institute director's first visits to the out-of-town hospitals were not universally hailed. Intruding on a comfortable rut was bound to stir up resentment. The new procedures Meyer offered for staff work and record keeping were somewhat less attractive than tennis and certainly more laborious than the indulgence in drink that some of the men favored. He spent a week at each hospital and held conferences, clinics, ward rounds, and consultations, revealing to the physicians what was under their noses. Despite some initial resistance, the impact of the new program upon the state-hospital system soon brought pleasing results. Once the discouraged feeling about medical achievement was relieved, the vision Meyer gave the doctors carried them into doing twice and three times more work. They discovered their patients. They woke up to an interest in their jobs, in their patients' problems.

One instance was the effect of his visit to Willard State Hospital, which was under the direction of Dr. William L. Russell. Russell had been at Willard since 1893 and had seen Meyer at work in Worcester. The reception was warm, the response electric. The men had not known how to go about their work scientifically before Meyer taught them. They were now enthusiastic with purposeful activity, Russell told him: "You have done more with the staff in one week than I have been able to do in ten years. Now they talk about their cases while eating lunch!"

With each staff Meyer reviewed fifty cases: fifteen were consecutive cases admitted since the Ward's Island course, fifteen consecutive discharges in the past month, fifteen special-interest cases, and the rest with autopsy. This scheme was followed to counteract the notion that there were never more than a few worth-while cases to study and also to keep an eye on performance. The results of discussions shaped themselves in the form of directions for work.

"My chief effort went in the direction of eradicating the old illusion that classification could ever precede an accurate knowledge of the facts. It was a sad day that brought psychiatry to a craving for premature classification." The usual practice was to let dogma and definitions serve in place of individual case-studies, and at the year's end to distribute the legalized disease types freely for statistical purposes. "My first advice was to let classification rest or give it a secondary place." Facts, collected for their usefulness, could be grouped according to their merit but not according to "antique and venerable, but alas! almost meaningless names." [9]

By dint of discipline Meyer in time earned the reputation of having transformed the state's insane asylums into mental hospitals. His clinical guides made possible the assembling of clinical data for practical study. Though he presented the teachings of the established leaders of psychiatric thought, he opened the physicians' minds much in the manner of Forel before him; and they came to realize that Meyer had broken with descriptive psychiatry to enter upon the more promising valley of dynamic psychiatry.

Out among the members of the American Medico-Psychological Association, meeting in Washington in 1903, he pleaded for "a conscientious study of the mental life of patients" as a parallel to the physician's knowledge of the body and its functions and the examination of them for physical symptoms. There was a medical truism that a patient's mental attitude was important in physical disorders. Then surely in mental cases a careful appraisal of the psychical side would do justice to the patient and to the psychiatrist's scientific needs. By making it a practice to examine from both mental and physical points of view "we shall get those means into our hands to enable us to employ psychotherapeutic helps without exposing ourselves to the objection that we are dealing with something approaching humbug." Meyer's main thesis was: "A knowledge of the abnormal workings of the nature of the patient's mind is the foundation of a knowledge of the nature of the disease—*i.e.*, pathology—and of therapeutics." [10]

The same year he made what he called his "pivotal commitment." This was his first formulation of personality types, in an article entitled, "An Attempt at Analysis of the Neurotic Constitution." It paved the way to his concept of habit-disorganizations as a topic of concern in psychiatry.

AN ATTEMPT AT ANALYSIS OF
THE NEUROTIC CONSTITUTION

Paper by Dr. Meyer in American Journal of Psychology, 14:90 (*Commemorative Number, July-Sept.,* 1903).

When considering the etiology of mental disorders we should distinguish the cases in which a person in the height of health and development is taken by a more or less definite illness with mental disturbances from the cases in which a lingering condition of constitutional or secondary weakness is aggravated by a certain disease.

It is consequently desirable to start with a few statements concerning the constitutional defects and chronic subacute and acute states of debility, such as may usher in one of the more definite disease forms.

Here we meet at once the favorite term "run-down condition," unfortunately as vague as its therapeutic counterpart, the "tonic," and, let us hope, not an insurmountable difficulty but chiefly a cover for defective determination to make accurate examinations, and a consequence of the exclusive and perhaps wholesome interest of modern pathology in specialties which yield more glory with easier and more conclusive work.

A step toward discrimination has long been made by the creation of the concept of *diathesis* and its broader foundation, the "constitution." Discarded for a long time, these matters are being brought back to the notice of the physician by the introduction of more trustworthy methods of study. During a fairly broad course of medicine I never had heard the topic spoken of in the later eighties of the last century, except in allusions to the *habitus phthisicus* [consumptive type] and the like, and was really surprised to hear it made the subject of a series of lectures in the course on the practice of medicine by Sir Grainger Stewart in Edinburgh, 1890. He enumerated the classical constitutions and diatheses as follows:

1. The nervous constitution: generally with fair complexion, bright eyes, frequent change of color and facial expression, the bones and muscles not vigorous; the heart, like the nerves, excitable.

2. The lymphatic constitution: with great head, irregular fleshy face, slow weak pulse, large hands and feet, etc.

3. The sanguineous constitution (Scandinavian race): fair hair, blue or gray eyes, easily flushing face, strong and excitable heart, but no nervousness.

4. The bilious constitution: with a tendency to obesity, dyspepsia, diarrhea, etc., and melancholia.

Further, the gouty, rheumatic, strumous, and syphilitic constitution, etc.

A certain practical justification of such a classification is quite undeniable, and attempts are slowly coming up again in the form especially of two types of study:

1. Individual psychology.

2. The types of functional efficiency, or insufficiency, such as are being established by Krauss and Martius for the heart and stomach.

The problem of immunity, too, gives a few valuable allusions to the question of temporary or fundamental constitution.

In psychiatry and neurology there is especially one type of interest, the psychopathic-neurotic type. It lacks as yet sufficient definition, and to analyze it will be one of the first tasks of a conscientious etiology of mental and nervous diseases. Since many individuals of this type belong to families in which a family tendency is present, it is usually dealt with peremptorily under the heading of *heredity*, and hereditary statistics seem to dull the interest in a collection of accurate facts, although numerous cases occur in which no heredity is demonstrable. The confusion has even been increased by the popularization of the term "degeneracy," which is used promiscuously with heredity and individual deterioration. The principle of heredity and degeneracy had, however, better not occupy us before we have made a good investigation of what abnormal constitutions we can recognize in the individuals called nervous or exposed to nervous and mental disorders.

Types of persons are difficult to define. Once for all, we should give up the idea of classifying them as we classify plants. We deal with a sum of items of which each can vary; whereas botanical classification only mentions the differential traits which would make sure that a seed of the plant would again grow into the species of plant which is thus distinguished. The issue of species is settled by the laws of heredity, while the varieties of people must be classed according to different principles. *The best medical standard is that of adequate or efficient function.* Martius has pointed out that concerning the function of the stomach we can recognize types with permanent constitutional deficiencies; Krauss has made the functional efficiency of the heart a standard for types of circulatory constitution. And in a similar way we classify people for their efficiency in those mental adaptations which we know to become actually deranged, the emotional sphere, the equilibrium of reason, or for their susceptibility to febrile delirium, alcoholic intoxication, effects of sexual excesses, etc. Further, we put forth as types of "constitutional inferiority" in the psychiatric sense certain forms of special nosological or symptomatic traits.

In the process of emancipation from traditional and untenable views of man, an iconoclastic attitude toward all attempts at practical characterology and theories of constitution was probably the only safe procedure. The existence of special types is nevertheless obvious to commonsense, and when we feel the need for a practical utilization of such data, it would be wrong to deny oneself the privilege of taking them for what they are worth. The call of warning, "back to morphology," or "back to what can be studied with mathematical, physical, and chemical accuracy," has its good sense and value; but since in practical life we know and speak of types, there is no harm in attempting to come to an agreement as to just what is to be understood by them. Physiology and psychology and anthropology have attempted it with their own specific problems; we physicians have our own, and while we deplore the lack of medically helpful material in the existing literature of individual psychology, we need not be discouraged and shall do well to use our own methods and needs as our guides.

The purpose of characterology is to give a forecast of what a person would do in a considerable variety of emergencies. As alienists we shall especially have to try and find out whether persons show any combinations of reactions which would make them in our eyes candidates for mental derangement, or which would modify the form of mental derangement which they might happen to get.

Of late years the herculean task of defining characters has been taken up from several sides. Frederic Paulhan necessarily makes his classes from several points of view, just as we are forced to do for the questions of heredity. I mention his divisions because they will be of some help as an explanation of why we consider the task far from hopeless. He recognizes the plurality of lines of efficiency or defect in the same individual, because various functions are to be considered and many types of combinations are possible. We can only mention the large headings of his book, *Les Caractères*.

Paulhan starts with the types produced by the predominance of one special form of activity. He analyzes them according to various types of association, *i.e.*, various ways in which the streams of interest and activity shape themselves. He starts from the well-balanced and the harmoniously purposive; passes to the types in which inhibition and reflection predominate (those who are "masters of themselves"); then to a type of great interest to us, that in which associations by contrast abound, persons who inevitably think of that which is not, that which is different, that which might be, instead of acting in the healthy commonsense way on that which is before them and leaving the contrasts as a matter understood or of value when there is a special cause for considering them. He calls these types "the uneasy," "the nervous," "the contrary."

Another type, also of importance for us, is that characterized by predominance of association by contact and resemblance, that is, persons in whom the inner interests are not the chief guides of their activity. What they meet accidentally while they are doing other things becomes permanently fixed in their memory, such as conditions under which they read a book or hear some music; while they pursue something they notice other matters and divide their attention and may even drift completely from their topic. Where this trait is predominant the feature of distractibility is apt to influence the course of life considerably and there results the last type from the point of view of association and characterized by an independent activity of mental elements, the impulsive, the variable and compound, the incoherent (of, as it were, crumbly interests); finally, the suggestible, the weak, the distracted. We might take a scale in which the individual with relatively steady plans stands at the top and is followed by those less dependent on themselves and more and more easily influenced, until we reach those types in which the cohesion of personality is very slight and the person is a prey to circumstances.

Another division is that according to the definite qualities of tendencies and mind, considering the breadth of personality—the broad and the narrow; or considering the purity of the tendency —the calm and troubled; considering the strength—the passionate and the enterprising and the hesitant; considering the persistence— the energetic, obstinate, and constant; and on the other hand—the weak and changeable; from the point of view of adaptability—the pliable, the inconsiderate, and the unadaptable; and from the point of view of sensitiveness—the wide-awake and impressionable, and the cold and phlegmatic.

In the second part of the book Paulhan distinguishes the types determined by the predominance or absence of some tendencies: in the first place, those tendencies which refer to an organic appetite, the types of the high liver and the sober; those sexually excitable or cold. Then from the point of view of mental functions: those principally visual or auditory or gustatory, or principally motor; further, the intellectual, the emotional. Then he passes to the types determined by social tendencies: the egotists and altruists; and types in whom love or friendship or family affection is predominant. Then those types whose interests go mostly in the direction of communities, or of the national feelings. Then he puts together types with predominance of impersonal tendencies, the worldly, the professional; then with regard to property—the miser, economizer, the generous, and prodigal. Then the vain, the proud; those eager for fame. Then the domineering, the ambitious, the submissive, and other types; and finally, as compounds of these special types—the happy and those enjoying themselves; and, on the other hand, the pessimistic and those denying themselves. Moreover, he speaks of tendencies which stand above the social relations, the general idea of duty; types of political passion and of religious interest, mysticism, etc.

In the third part he shows how these various elements cooperate in the constitution of the individual.

This brief summary may induce the reader to study Paulhan's work as an attempt to bring some order into complex facts. It is obviously our duty to develop along similar lines some definite descriptive entities for the characterization of those features which lead over to the directly odd or abnormal character.

We start from the truism that *a large number of those who become insane are individuals in whom a turn to the worse could be anticipated.* Are the indications open to any sort of analysis? The retrospective method of analysis is the only one available now in the majority of cases. Perhaps, among intelligent and observing families, it can be pushed much further than is actually done. Moreover, when we know better what to look out for we may undertake studies of *developing* abnormalities which are not insanity yet and follow them out so as to accumulate material of *actual observation* on which to build a solid theory of constitution.

Kraepelin in his *Psychologische Arbeiten* (1:78) mentions that it is probable that the mental constitution of the neurasthenic, the hysterical, the paranoic, and the manic-depressive is different from the very start; but he does not tell us of the actual distinctions. He expects them from his method of biological tests. We certainly must do something to outgrow the stage at which "de-

generacy" is considered a sufficient verdict instead of being shown
up as a block in the way of much-needed knowledge.

The development of man is not a simultaneous evolution of
all the traits of the complete adult, but one function after another
comes to maturity, and as a rule there is an uneven development.
Nobody is perfect in every respect. The special organs which
make up the human cell colony and the uniting links of all these
organs, the circulatory apparatus and the nervous system, may
all demand special tests of efficiency, as has been shown by
Krauss for the heart. Each apparatus may have its ups and downs,
or actual defects, and even show a more or less final tendency
to deterioration, either from defective endowment or through
defective chances in life. The biotrophic energy or vitality of
each organ should be determined in order to arrive at a summing
up of the constitution of the entire person.

It is obvious that there is no limit of time for the development of traits which would have to be laid to the individual
endowment. A child who appeared normal may show failure in
coping with puberty, and a perfectly well-balanced and healthy
person may show premature senile reduction, and we *may* find
this to be a peculiarity of the family. In some children we may
be able to trace the abnormal development in harmful surroundings, such as acquisition of abnormal habits, to defective nutrition
in periods of growth, to a disease or traumatism; in the arterio-
sclerotic senile we may be able to point to alcoholism, nicotinism,
physical overwork, etc., in the absence of all family tendency.
Hence the rule that we shall first outline the facts in the case and
analyze the positive causal factors *before* we assent to a negative
conclusion, such as the admission of an unknown and undemon-
strable agent, as heredity, is all-important.

It is obvious that a really satisfactory analysis is achieved only
where we can point to specific factors which caused the deviation
from the normal, with something like experimental necessity.
Although a large number of cases will not be open to explanation, we speak provisionally of heredity when we see a disorder
occur several times in a family. But this provisional statement is
all we should imply by heredity in medical language. Moreover,

where we find peculiarities of make-up we must remember that many of them must be ranked as normal and do not lead to further trouble, except perhaps indirectly through the clashing with the environment; while other peculiarities are beginnings or agents of the undermining of the make-up and would interest us more.

In our analysis we shall now try to establish some differentiation in order to get over the extremely unsatisfactory haziness of terms like degenerate, neurotic, etc. We shall try to distinguish certain groups; but we must submit all these cases to the question: "Do we deal with persons in whom some incidental affection of the brain or malnutrition during development or constitutional disturbances like rickets or poor educational conditions have produced that state of affairs which has left scars or residuals and stamps the person as one maimed in various directions by more or less different causes, and for such reasons left with an inadequate material and the strain of life? Or do we deal with persons in whom, with or without such residuals from early development, there are present and still in operation various vitiating influences, such as disease, anomalies of constitutional metabolism, abnormal toxic or sexual habits, an inadequate and unsatisfying life, etc.?"

With this in view we have to review first the various stages of development.

Constitutional defects from infancy are very frequent and manifold. Those defects which lead ultimately to dependence are naturally most important and best known. They are classed as idiocy and imbecility (feeblemindedness). The best available statistics (in Switzerland) show that 1.53 per cent of all the children between seven and fourteen belong in this category. The marked forms need not occupy us. They present a tremendous field, since imbecility includes the results of everything that can possibly leave traces in the pathology of the nervous system and mind during infancy. In all these disorders we must, of course, be prepared to see beside the functions demonstrably impaired from childhood, defective evolution of functions which should have matured later and may have been affected in the bud, and it is quite conceivable that certain peculiarities of development in later life might be due to alterations brought about in undeveloped stages, where the existing functions appeared to recover completely. This might hold for the effects of asphyxia, infantile convulsions, disorders of teething and early nutrition, and traumatisms. The number in whom actual facts are demonstrable is small and apt to discourage one; but what is obtained is all the more valuable in the struggle against fatalism.

The constitutional development of the *child* is of greater importance for us. Many cases of imbecility begin to show here, but moreover a large group of poorly known and poorly differentiated types of peculiarities which, without doubt, play an important part in the abnormal constitutions of later years. Poor habits of sleep with fearful dreams, somnambulism, emotionalism, idiosyncrasies, irritability, being startled and unbalanced easily, and distractibility are often complained of. The nervous child may show from the start or gradually the more specific traits of the epileptic constitution, of the hysterical, the neurasthenic, etc., which we pass over because they are more apt to appear later.

Puberty and adolescence are the decisive period for the formation of the make-up and for the cropping out of many defects (see Marro, *La Pubertà*, and Clouston, *Neuroses of Development*). Here we should deal with many types usually left to the pedagogue, but I refer only to the following traits: The normal youth develops an individuality with personal aims. A large number of young people remain children of the moment, distractible, swayed by desires and casual opportunities, showing flashes of enthusiasm and emotional display but without cohesion or sound plan and consistency.

Another extreme is the prematurely and one-sidedly conscientious. In this type there is frequently a furor for abstract matters, exalted religious and moral standards in marked contrast with the actual immaturity of the conduct in the frequently precocious sexual development; periods of fantastic daydreams and perhaps lying; an increasing isolation and aloofness from chances of wholesome correction by intercourse with the average companions of their age, combined with a keen eye for the faults of others; a clinging to older persons and isolation in matters in which the youthful instincts are deficient or abnormal, such as interest in games and sociability. The intercourse with older people and the great interest in words and books rather than actual experience often give these young people an apparent start as compared with the average of their age, and many parents have been children so little themselves that they overlook the danger.

It is among these persons that the lack of normal balance is especially apt to lead to the appearance of overburdening, of overwork, and all those traits which mark the legion of nervous people of today. Irritability, outbreaks of temper, erratic and unaccountable actions break through, or the young persons become too good for the world, seclusive, faultfinding with themselves and with their brothers and sisters. They become as egotistical in actions as they may be altruistic in words or in public. Interests in perfectly remote religious and philosophical matters do not make up for the defect in that which is most important, the adaptability to life as it is, with a healthy independence. Very often a decided change along these lines shows itself with or shortly after puberty. The connection with often quite precocious abnormal sexual practices is exceedingly frequent. They are a very aggravating factor, as they increase secretiveness, morbidly imaginative cravings, and many signs of nervous exhaustibility.

The danger awaiting the inconsistent easygoing is more often that toward social dissipations in alcohol and venery and their consequences; and that awaiting the exalted seclusive, the development into neurasthenic, hypochondriacal, and dementia praecox types; while hysteria, psychasthenia, and epilepsy appear on somewhat more independent ground. Various peculiarities not necessarily combined with nervousness appear, but more usually later in life.

From the general picture of nervousness we now should attempt to select and discriminate certain types and especially to define certain names and distinctions:

1. The psychasthenic. This is a term applied by Janet to a group of psychopathic and neurotic conditions which comprehends obsessions, impulsions, manias, phobias, scruples, tics, states

of anxiety, etc. These states also figure under the term of constitutional neurasthenia, but are not necessarily connected with the
truly neurasthenic complex. The ground of these disorders is a
special type of character; these persons are abulic, undecided,
hesitating, timid, not combative, not able to take the world as it
is, idealistic, longing for love and kindness, and, correspondingly,
they have ways that solicit a kindly and just attitude; they are
misunderstood and meek; easily led or misled; they need stimulation and are apt to yield without decision, notwithstanding their
usually superior intelligence and vivid imagination. This leads to
a life given to avoiding troubles, decision, and action. The child
avoids active play and is perhaps encouraged by solicitous parents; the choice of occupation is away from the trying struggle.
The young man or woman shirks responsibilities, is passive in
questions of marriage and choice of work. New situations, a
threat, or a joke, examinations, new religious duties, or some emotional shock prove too much and bring forth the symptom complexes so well described by Janet.

   2. The neurasthenic, closely allied to the above. The term
should be reserved for the cases combining the symptoms of great
exhaustibility and irritability, depending largely on the mental
attitude of lack of repose and of ready recoverability, frequent
head pressure, palpitation and uneasiness of the heart, gastric disorders, phosphaturia and oxaluria and, in men especially, often
abnormality of sexual responsiveness. It is necessary to distinguish
acute forms following exhaustion or infectious diseases in persons
without hereditary or constitutional defect, the subacute and
chronic forms or habit-neurasthenias frequently without heredity,
and the chronic constitutional type, said to be to a large extent
familial. It is frequently associated with the psychasthenic type.
It may be well to specify cerebrasthenia, myelasthenia, gastro-
intestinal neurasthenia, vasomotor and sexual neurasthenia.

   3. Frequently associated with other traits of nervousness, we
meet with hypochondriasis, usually built on a feeling of ill-health
which leads to self-observation and explanations. These are apt
to become the center of thought and interest, are elaborated, or
the person merely is troubled with vain fears over trifles, consults

quack literature, etc. On the whole, the impressions are apt to become dominating.

4. The hysterical constitution. Dana gives a picture of the simple hysterical constitution as consisting of crises of an emotional character and an interparoxysmal condition of emotional weakness, nervousness, hyperesthesia and pains in the head or back, poor sleep, disagreeable dreams, globus, and vasomotor instability. These patients are mostly girls or young women, unduly sensitive, depressed, easily alarmed; they feel nervous, lack emotional control. It is rather difficult to say whether these forms are necessarily hysterical and not better classed vaguely as nervous instability until some characteristically hysterical symptoms occur.

Ziehen limits the hysterical constitution to emotional instability, egocentricity, craving for attention, peculiar predilections, disorders of imagination and attention (fantastic instability). He refers to sensory symptoms, regional, or referring to special objects; and to peculiar illusions and hallucinations of vision (hypnagogic or with open eyes) following emotional episodes or accompanying headache; usually with insight and without loss of memory.

To start with, we must discard the popular use of the term hysterical as not sufficiently coincident with the nosological term. It is to be replaced by statements of the actual symptoms, such as emotionalism, or stimulation, or exaggeration, or craving of attention, which may or may not be hysterical and had best be called by their plain name. I am inclined to refer to hysteria all the mental and physical disorders which are produced by the effects of an emotion or idea which may work unconsciously to the patient, so that the situation claimed by others is usually beyond the control of the patient and the whole explanation best accessible in hypnosis. On close investigation it usually is possible to see the foundation of the varied disorders in a peculiar limitation of the field of consciousness and range of thought, frequently with additional exhaustibility, and the existence of emotional trauma or instability.

These disorders appear either on a broad constitutional basis —perpetuation and one-sided elaboration of traits inherited or acquired during the years of development—or they come with some other disease—hemiplegia, tabes, etc., or after some sudden shock. Many of the same symptoms may also occur in other grave constitutional or other disorders, without being plainly on hysterical ground (as it were, symptomatic hysteria).

5. The epileptic constitution manifests itself largely before or after the convulsions in signs which might be called part of the fit; Ziehen mentions, as a form of aura, hallucinations such as a threat or stab, or the vision of a large figure, or anxiety with pre-cardial sensations, or the recurrence without motive of some vivid memory. In the intervals there is a certain *irritability* with occasional violent outbreaks regardless of consequences, or peculiar unwarranted sulkiness or periodic dipsomania. Later there is an increasing defect in mental capacity.

6. Of much more importance to alienists are certain types already akin to definite mental derangements. I refer to:

a. The unresistive (responding easily to fever, to intoxication).

b. The manic-depressive type, described by Hecker, and the constitutionally depressed—to be distinguished from the neurasthenic by the more direct feeling of insufficiency, not secondary to exhaustibility, and more likely to lead to suicide, and by the occurrence of periods of exaltation.

c. The paranoic type, continually ready to see a meaning in things, suspicious and at the same time with growing inclination to isolation. These persons are continually concerned with what other people may think; they further attribute intentions to indifferent actions of others, more and more without judgment or attempt at verification of their suspicions.

d. The deterioration type. In cases of dementia praecox we find over and over an account of frequently perfectly exemplary childhood, but a gradual change in the period of emancipation. Close investigation shows, however, often that the exemplary child was exemplary under a rather inadequate ideal, an example of goodness and meekness rather than of strength and determination, with a tendency to keep to the good in order to avoid fights and struggles. Later, religious interest may become very vivid, but also largely in form; a certain disconnection of thought, unaccountable whims make their appearance, and deficient control in matters of ethics and judgment; at home irritability shows itself, often wrapped up in moralizing about the easygoing life of brothers and sisters; sensitiveness to allusions to pleasures, health, etc., drives the patient into seclusion. Headaches, freaky appetite, general malaise, hypochondriacal complaints about the heart, etc., unsteadiness of occupation and inefficiency, daydreaming, and utterly immature philosophizing, and, above all, loss of directive energy and initiative without obvious cause, such as well-founded preoccupations, except the inefficient application to actuality. All these traits may be transient, but are usually not mere "neurasthenia" but the beginning of a deterioration, more and more marked by indifference in the emotional life and ambitions, and a peculiar fragmentary type of attention, with all the transitions to the apathetic state of terminal dementia.

Just as the traditional theories of temperaments or constitutions have served in a system of pathology of the past, such an attempt as the one offered here must rise and fall with its empirical usefulness. It seems to me to have several points in its favor. It aims at definitions of a nosological character, etiological as far as is warranted by the facts and stimulating in the direction of more precision in etiological investigation; yet at the same time careful to remain on the safe ground of clinical description. It is open to many supplements, and it will be an especially grateful task to push the inquiry of individual make-up along the lines of changes of constitutional make-up due to traumatism, to toxic influences, to sexual insufficiency, to the prevalence of certain thought habits (especially estrangement from actuality in the form of occultism), and under the influence of the period of involution and senescence.

It must, of course, be our ambition gradually to reduce the types of constitution to entities produced by definite conditions instead of simply classing them in a descriptive way. There will, however, always remain a residuum which resists etiological classification. Yet even there we must not be too easily tempted to turn to the problems of heredity and generation before we have made a thorough search of the patient's own life.

ARREST OF DEVELOPMENT

IN ADOLESCENCE

From remarks by Dr. Meyer following an address on this topic by
G. Stanley Hall before the National Education Association, Boston,
July 9, 1903; Proceedings, N.E.A., at p. 813 (1903).

As an alienist I divide the arrest of development during adolescence into forms of imbecility and constitutional inferiority, and into actual disorders of adolescence. Constitutional inferiority represents the persistence or cropping-out of signs of defect in one of the many directions of human development, as evidence of poor endowment or of scars produced by disease or mismanagement in early childhood. In a large number we are unable as yet to describe the conditions which might figure as real causes; at the same time we know the difficulty in influencing these defects.

What concerns us more is the second group, which seems to develop from adolescence itself, from conditions which are still open to influence. Even here part of the trouble is, as it were, a simple perversion or stunting of growth of essential components of our personality. But quite a few causes seem to be avoidable, which we can do something to forestall.

Above all, you must free yourselves of the idea that insanity is something utterly different from simple nervousness, lack of balance, and so-called nervous breakdown. Some forms of insanity may appear as if a poison, such as alcohol, or other direct

117

damages of the brain, brought in foreign elements; but the types of adolescent deterioration can very largely be traced to disharmonies of thought, of habits, and of interests which bring about a stunting in one direction or another. It is true that, during the disease, peculiar physical changes take place in the circulation, and in striking variations of weight, which has called for the theory of Kraepelin that we deal with a disease of metabolism. Unfortunately, physicians are rarely in a position to study the candidates of deterioration during their relatively healthy days. We see them when the foundation of the peculiar, fantastically religious, mystical, or hypochondriacal or fretful interpretations or imaginations is already in the foreground and has roused the fears of the family.

I read out of the accounts of the friends many of the traits which have been insisted upon as marking the final outcome of the deterioration—a dilapidation of interests, erratic attention, social indifference. Above all, I miss a sense for actuality, a living with life as it is and an enjoying the opportunities that are within reach. Where flights of thought rise above indifference in such individuals they naturally suffer from not being adapted to actuality. In the ambitious we see the features of daydream rather than of strength. Virtue and social emotions remain abstract and in exalted words. Many of these weaklings become conscious of the contrast between their words and their nature. They become self-conscious, suspicious of being discovered, and drift into solitude. Abnormal hankerings fail to be corrected there by a healthy spirit of social and other activity; the touch with actuality is lost more and more, and over a shock or some disappointment, or a setback in general health, the poor frame of judgment gives way and the person loses balance. The eagerness with which hypnotism, mesmerism, mystic powers, and the unreal are elaborated into delusions and depended upon for explanation of the peculiar sensations connected with disordered circulation, nervous heart, the nervous excitability shown by increased reflexes, feelings of uneasiness and anxiety, and unusual intestinal and sexual sensations, seems to me to show the great danger of all half-understood things which are not brought to the test of actuality. An aversion to actuality seems to lie in the trend of much modern teaching.

The emphasis of nature study does perhaps much to bring a healthy turn into education. But we need more: we need greater wholesomeness in the training for human relations and aspirations; a better knowledge of what is likely to rouse a sound interest even in those who are naturally careless and indifferent, and otherwise tickled merely by the sensational or by what gratifies crude emotions; we need a preparation for actual life, not for dream existence. What is called "New Thought," though to a large extent a mere revival of the food for the eternally gullible, may do much good where it incidentally encourages healthy instinct; but it is like strong wine—a questionable article of food, sometimes a useful drug, but really unfitting one for a good digestion and assimilation of what makes man the master of nature. Too many suffer from the effects of intoxication or the untimely use of these mental stimulants.

The greatest stumbling block is undoubtedly that which stands in the way of the development of sexual maturity in that broad and lofty sense of becoming the originators of a better race. That which in actuality is the center of the highest altruistic possibilities of mankind is allowed to be a social playground of chance, fed by dime novels and literature of doubtful adventures; fashions in dress and in social customs usher the young precociously into a world in which even too many adults fail. Abnormal responses lead to abnormal seclusiveness, and quack literature nurtures a fear and hopelessness and frequently wrecks the chances of timely reconstruction.

Don't let us say that this is merely one of nature's methods of weeding out the unfit. Among the 25,000 persons who are today in the public and private institutions of New York State alone, there are many brilliant hopes buried, largely owing to a lack of knowledge of what some people need in the way of social and personal hygiene. Remember that some of the most illustrious members of the race have been dangerously near the borderland of insanity, and although they seem to have been great they showed obvious traces of the same misled instincts that have completely wrecked others. Are such people not worth our help? Should not the home, the press, and the school know these dangers and shape their ethics and methods accordingly?

This is the practical lesson to be drawn from the theory of degeneracy which is spread into immature minds as a doctrine of fatalism, so that even high-school pupils excuse themselves in some such way as, "I can't help this. It's heredity in the family." Part of this may be sadly true. But it is the duty of pedagogy and of psychiatry to distinguish what is to be accepted as inevitable from what is open to correction. We have faith in gymnastics for the correction of physical defects. Let us devise more efficient gymnastics which lead us heartily to enjoy actuality, instinctively to shrink from antisocial ideals and aimless fictions, and to get time for an unsophisticated growth. For this I believe with Dr. Hall that we need special provisions, and perhaps even special institutions. It will be necessary to select teachers with especial care, to frame the course as a training in life habits rather than in schooling as ordinarily understood. We must keep these classes as free from stigma as possible.

EMOTION AND INTELLECT

IN PARANOIA

From "The Relation of Emotional and Intellectual Functions in Paranoia and Obsessions," by Dr. Meyer, in Psychological Bulletin, 3:255 (Aug. 15, 1906).

Any unsophisticated student and observer who has followed the literature on paranoia during the last ten years has had some reason to wonder why such emphasis was put on the question whether paranoia was fundamentally an intellectual or an emotional disorder. I never could see much use in the discussion except in so far as it illustrated the doubtful definition of the distinction of emotional and intellectual function as soon as one left the most striking examples of the one type and the other and got into a zone of mixed and doubtful conditions. It is easy to see that it is wise and inevitable to emphasize the emotional nature of a fright and the merely intellectual nature of my present use of the word "fright," or the intellectual nature of the sensation of a red line and the emotional feature of the reaction to a flash of lightning. But in many mental happenings the two belong together in a way that makes a ripping apart, or even emphasis of the one or the other, unprofitable and dogmatic.

Broadly speaking, almost every mental activity allows us to recognize relations to two fundamental systems, that of the shaping of the personal physiopsychological ("emotional") attitudes of our circulatory, respiratory, and vegetative side, and that of the more fleeting and more impersonal neuromuscular ("intellectual") relations, based on the sense organs *per se* and the muscular apparatus carrying and directing them. Or, to speak in other terms, almost every mental activity implies an adjustment of the emotional attitude (that balance which is attended to largely by the sympathetic nervous mechanisms and their central connections), and an adjustment within the intellectual system (the apparatus of sensations and ideational relations). The moving entities or *"idées-forces"* are, however, compounds which we must have the courage to use as units for what they are worth without allowing ourselves to be distracted by endless quibbling over the nature of components and their real functional relations. We must learn to work again with complexes and provisional biological entities instead of assuming merely arithmetical relations between postulated fragments of the situations. There are some important relations about which we cannot afford to have finally settled ideas, and among these stands foremost the relation of the emotional and the intellectual aspects of mental activities. By dealing modestly with *situations* as they present themselves and for what they are worth, we can use them in our work and draw just as valid inferences and we may hope to keep nearer the fundamental science, biology, and its utilization.

We frequently hear of patients awakening with a feeling of indefinite anxiety or sadness or nervousness which we cannot class otherwise than as emotional states, while at other times these same patients attach their emotional attitudes to special events, or to anticipations of definite events: the thought of the death of a friend, or the thought of ill will or persecution from another person, or the memory of a perfectly irrelevant fact of absolutely insufficient bearing, as in the case of a woman who fretted over having disgraced herself and her family by exposing a slightly soiled petticoat in getting into a buggy, or some other plainly incidental food for her fundamental uneasiness and agitated despair.

Or we have a patient complain of the annoyance of hearing an imaginary orchestra play and occupy his attention so as to drive him to distraction. Here the fundamental fact is his uncontrollable musical imagination with the vividness and independence of a hypnagogic hallucination, and the distress is largely present owing to collision of the musical drift with the ordinary and more important and pressing interests of the person. But there are many instances where the predominance of the emotional trend or of the intellectual side is far less conspicuous and more variable and the whole event none the less plainly a vital factor in the determination of the patient's conduct and trend of mentation. In practice we weigh the emotional factor and the purely intellectual one of such constellations as jealousy, or anxiety, or uneasiness, without, however, assuming that there would be any advantage in pushing the analysis so far as to have one mass of pure emotion and one mass of pure intellectual processes.

Emotional and intellectual determinants are frequently worth weighing independently for their different bearing as well as for the fact that different parts of our organism are involved. Yet empirically we deal with the situation as with a compound which loses its essential traits by decomposition, and we must be ready to deal with such compounds for what they are worth and likely to mean in the stream of events without distracting ourselves over temporarily irrelevant questions. When we have to study the physical relations and properties of certain substances and bodies, to load ourselves down with chemical discriminations would be a useless accumulation of ballast. In empirical psychology we stand, as it were, on grounds of the more relational science of physics. Even within their proper domain of analytical psychology we have good reasons to doubt that an analytic knowledge of elements can have any such claim to justification by results as the elements in chemistry deserve. The psychic "elements" are the most detailed and refined products of differentiation and so numerous that work with these "elements" is quite a different proposition. It is quite possible that the psychological elements had better be dropped as essentials of a *dynamic* psychology and that the maintenance of the sharp division of sensation, idea, emotion, and will is not worth the effort, except in their proper place and sphere, especially when we inquire into the specific participation of definite sense organs and nervous mechanisms for our neurological diagnoses. A paranoia would no doubt be the same process in a blind deaf-mute and in a person with lesion of both pyramidal tracts. Its interest lies much less in the elements "sensation" and "volition" than in the existence of peculiar complexes and arrangements of *"idées-forces."*

Since the days of Westphal, distinctions have been canonized between disorders primarily of the emotional field of mental activity and disorders primarily of the intellectual field. In the somewhat bewildering domain of psychology a clean-cut and apparently simple contrast is a veritable godsend, and once established in a mind it becomes a path of least resistance, just as some contrasts enslave the mind of the struggling tyro in composition who falls back on the "internal" and the "external" reasons of things and similar trite formulas of roads to thought. The formula lingers apparently as a stimulus to thought. In reality it leads to usually gratuitous discussions, and stands in the way of broader perspectives, until independent instincts crowd out the obstacle.

There is no doubt that the contrast of emotional and intellectual features of mental activities has a certain practical foundation. But the dogmatic division of emotion and intellect leads to unintelligible conflicts. An excellent illustration of this calamity in psychopathology is given by Ziehen, who, after opposing psychoses "without intellectual defect" to those "with defect," contrasts among the simple psychoses the *affective* psychoses (mania and melancholia) with the *intellectual* psychoses (stupidity, paranoia, dreamy states, symptomatic deliria, and obsessions and impulsions and psychopathic constitutions). The unsophisticated reader will, no doubt, suspect behind it all some reason, in Ziehen's system of psychology. We might understand the tendency to oppose the more localizable side of mental facts (the sensations with their physical stimuli and accepted cortical substrata) to the nonlocalizable general emotional reactions, or something like this. As a matter of fact, the above division is largely empirical. Ziehen (*Psychiatrie*, p. 5) admits "but two psychological elements, sensation and concept. The only process which works with both is the association of ideas. Its product is action." There are no special "mental powers," no need of a special "will," nor a special apperceptive power, nor special emotional powers. Emotions are never isolated but always attached to sensations and concepts, as parts of the same. (With most of this we would agree if he would also surrender sensations and concepts to their modest position of abstracts.) Yet few alienists perpetuate Westphal's distinction of primary and secondary emotions more than Ziehen. This inconsistency in recognizing *primary* emotional disturbances does not seem to even disturb such a forbidding intellectualistic system as that of Ziehen.

The whole embarrassment comes from the lingering dogmas concerning the relation of intellectual and emotional data and is a veritable spook which haunts the thoughts and writings of some of the most productive and independent writers, and it will do so until it is thoroughly exposed to daylight. It is a question of the doctor taking his own medicine if we recommend the modern psychoanalytic method as a therapeutic measure in this difficulty. Some clearness on this issue is one of the first steps toward making dynamic conceptions possible in psychopathology.

A review of this issue is by no means merely a work of destruction of idols and criticism. We are in a period of reconstruction, or rather of construction, and the psychopathologists' problem in this field may possibly be of some interest in connection with the discussion on the topic of "feeling" brought out at the last meeting of the American Psychological Association. We deal with a very concrete field, and any way of establishing closer contact with events as they present themselves in life and the theoretical considerations is bound to bring the reader into touch with actual experiences and to relax temporarily the systematic interests which become so prominent if the discussion is largely one of nomenclature.

In his discussion of the relative independence of affectivity, Bleuler furnishes rich material offsetting the unconvincing dogmatic presentation of those who speak of "feeling tone" merely and leave the factors of the drift of association not further analyzed or accounted for. In this he seems to me to be in line with a tendency inevitable with those who wish psychology to be a study of the determining factors of the stream of mental life, and not merely an analysis of abstract and forceless epithets and epiphenomena. It is a movement intimated in many places and already clearly provided with the designation "dynamic psychology" in Thorndike's *Elements of Psychology*. Bleuler's plea for that which we would call the dynamic role of "affectivity" is a wholesome call for a recasting of values and an emancipation from the set conceptions which have so far repressed the dynamic viewpoint.

Bleuler himself considers the dynamic conception premature. He disputes Fechner's claim of having measured the strength of psychic processes; "affectivity alone and its manifestations appear to us as intensive or quantitative magnitudes; we size up its strength but cannot measure it as yet and have no knowledge of what determines it." Yet he adds: "We therefore have no possibility as yet to found dynamic theories and even little cause to search for them. It is, however, true that a better knowledge of the physiological basis of our psychic life will some day bring the dynamic factor into the discussion." These efforts, Bleuler justly remarks, will, however, have little in common with the pseudo-dynamics of the questionable theories which claim that sensation is "the same thing as idea," but "of greater intensity," and *therefore* hallucinations of more powerful influence than ideas. Bleuler mentions this claim as an illustration of the precocity of dynamic conceptions. It would seem better to say that these dynamic differentiations are largely speculative and that true dynamic psychology will have to start with the "force" of actual events, without much concern for the traditional definitions of sensations, ideas, feelings, etc., but with due respect for what would appear as moving factors. Mere comparisons of the "strength" of sensations, idea, and hallucinations are based on considerations of abstract entities and appear altogether speculative and not the proper material for investigation to start on.

Whether Bleuler has made it altogether clear what affectivity is, in his sense, is not certain, and it may be just as well that we have no final formula for it. This is certain, that Bleuler consciously or unconsciously encourages an emancipated study of a number of mental reactions slighted by intellectualism; but he maintains his very emphatic differentiation of intellectual feelings and affectivity, while the general broad meaning of his use of "affectivity" suggests even an emancipation of the concept from the pleasure and pain paradigms. "The feelings of pleasure and pain, to which we must add the affects, the affectivity," makes his attitude less plain than when he says, in his interesting discussion of association: "Attention is therefore nothing but a special instance of results of affect." Or still better, when he contrasts intellectual and affective processes in their ontogenesis: Intelligence, as a mere form of combining memory images, is, no doubt, developed at birth; the child merely lacks the contents of experience. Affectivity also exists; it, however, demands no content, no material from the outside; experience furnishes merely the occasion to the production of the affect. "It, therefore, can express itself from the very start in all its complications and finesse (naturally with the exception of the sexual sphere, although perhaps even there to some extent, as Freud shows)."

It is easy to see that his interesting samples of largely "affective" reactions in children are a striking mixture of experience and readiness for distinct responses. If he emphasizes the affective nature of these responses, he approaches them to the instinctive reactions and thereby comes near to identifying "affectivity" with the mainspring of all responsiveness and activity which is not purely mechanical or reflex.

Bleuler claims a pure intellectual process when he sees a suspicious individual with a revolver who makes him get ready for an assault, and when he adduces as proof of the absence of affect in the suspicion that he can describe the situation without speaking of an affect, in purely intellectual expressions, and that the amount of the affect may vary without a change in the fact of suspicion. In this he discusses the *word* suspicion rather than the situation, and then concludes that paranoia cannot be allied to the affect psychoses but must be something wholly different.

When I review my observations of paranoia I find that there are a greater number than Bleuler seems to admit in which the fundamental attitude was for a fairly long time an *uneasiness* with *vague* suspicions and a *vague* readiness to see in a rather great variety of things material for the suspicions, until gradually the dominant direction asserted itself. In many cases the lasting delusional complex governs the situation from the start, but only intellectually, if we may say so; affectively, there is as a rule the same *vague* unsettled and uneasy feeling, with a decided deviation of the broad field of affectivity from the normal consistency and harmony of trend and instinct (the functional sum of *idées-forces*). There remains the fact that there are cases in which without sufficient cause states of mind arise which are to all intents and purposes the affective attitudes of the paranoic, but without any definite content, an attitude of vague uneasiness, of a feeling of loss of true adjustment with environment, that *"meine Ruhe ist hin"* [my peace is gone], in all its versions, from self-reproach to suspicion, anticipation, etc. What stamps them as paranoic is the inaccessibility to the usual relief of unbalanced states, the fact that they do not produce deep disorders of the stream of thought, apart from the general, perhaps specific, diversion of attention and constructive imagination; *i.e.*, their definition lies in the entire complex situation. In one phase it may be the general affective state, in another a situation better described in terms of a delusional complex (but not the less affective), and under no circumstances can we dispute the weight of a fundamental disruption of the affective apparatus, a disruption of the normal instincts.

May we assume for a moment the *possibility* of paranoia being a circumscribed affect psychosis? In most cases of paranoia we meet with a complex in which it is difficult to determine a purely intellectual defect. The mere "facts" of the delusions are more or less correct; but the inferences? Even they appear logical but rouse wrong valuations. But what are valuations if not essentially tied to affectivity, *i.e.*, to the instinctive reaction of certainty or doubt? What determines the *idée-force* of doubt if not the presence or absence of a certain uneasiness and hunger for adjustment? Why should we all of a sudden draw the line of affectivity when we approach the intellectual feelings?

The whole discussion has a value if it leads to heuristic results. If Bleuler's working hypothesis leads to facts which prove the existence of corrigible or fatal flaws in the reasoning, without disorder of the affective side, but nevertheless paranoia, the finding is an addition to our knowledge. At present we should designate such cases as freaks of make-up, if they are conceivable at all. If the appreciation of the affective difficulty draws attention to avenues for the saving of the fallible intellectual frame from miscarriage, the study of the *affective* side will deserve emphasis. Considering that affectivity is the moving and determining principle, and intellect the static apparatus, we had reasons to *welcome* the emphasis on the affectivity even in paranoia, and may be able to make the facts useful in dealing with the beginnings of the condition in paying more attention to the affects than to reasoning.

If, further, in the differential analysis of the factor determining the fixation of the disturbance, special perspectives of affectivity, intelligence, and volition prove of value in addition to the search for physiological and general biological components of the constellation, we can use them systematically for what they are worth without any barriers. From the point of view of *nosological* differentiation we may trust that we have safely passed the period when anything short of a comprehensive biological sizing-up could be considered safe ground for conclusions; but even there we have reasons to expect special help from an empirical sizing-up of the *idées-forces*, in their preeminently affective or intellectual or motor bearing.

In other words, dynamic psychology will use the analytical data for what they are worth and beware of a priori limitation of affective principles and exclusion of the "intellectual" feelings in psychopathology after they prove so satisfactory in broad and liberal use in the analysis of child life. Rather take the broadest list of kinds of affective type (such as Baldwin's) than an artificially narrowed one. The affective trend of paranoia is worth much more study than the adverse discriminations by Bleuler would admit. The chief cause of the artificial self-restriction would seem to lie with a priori views of what should be admitted as affect, and with a priori views of what should be admitted as paranoia. Neither for the one problem nor for the other is the necessary work *done*. The emphasis on positive and negative affects, to the exclusion of qualitative types, is natural enough in psychophysics and in the study of the physiological accompaniments, which do indeed point to a mere + and − of the blood-wave, and not in favor of Wundt's triple system. But there is no end of possibilities of well-founded qualitative differentiations, and Bleuler's own remark about the affective *types*—that unfortunately they have not been studied yet—should have precluded an emphatic and final judgment and exclusion of the "intellectual" feelings as affective agencies. And the assumption that Kraepelin's paranoia is more than a practical group, and that it should be considered alone in the attempt to determine the final explicability of paranoic developments, is another unfortunate effect of definition at the wrong end.

According to Bumke, the term *Zwangsvorstellung* [obsession] was introduced into German literature by von Krafft-Ebing, 1867, in connection with the fact that in depressions the stream of ideation becomes painfully limited to what harmonizes with the depression. This constraint in ideation, volition and action exists even where there is no actual confusion of thought and is sometimes felt keenly by the patient.

Griesinger next used the word for conditions in which, contrary to the best intention and conviction of the patient, thoughts recur in the form of questions or otherwise, wholly beyond the control of and against the better knowledge and realization of the senselessness by the patient. This type was fully discussed in a masterly paper by Westphal (1878), who made the following definition:

Imperative concepts are those which, with otherwise intact intelligence and without being determined by an emotional or affective state, assume prominence against the will of the patient, cannot be thrown off, impede and cross the normal course of ideation, and are always recognized as abnormal and strange by the patient, who realizes them with his healthy consciousness.

This definition and the cases on which it is based point plainly to the identity of the phenomena with what the French have very properly grouped together under the term "obsessions." But while Westphal insisted on the negation of their dependence on emotional or affective conditions, probably in order to offset Krafft-Ebing's limited application of the term to the self-evident dominating influence of *depressions* on the stream of mental activity, the

French never lost sight of the emotional foundation of obsessions insisted upon by Morel, although they distinguish phobias—that is, obsessions consisting of fears—and the ideational obsessions in which the anxiety and uneasiness manifests itself with an idea. In either case the process is felt as involuntary, automatic, and irresistible.

These French studies were unfortunately ignored by the earlier German writers, and, owing to Westphal's characteristic tendency to separate emotional and intellectual disorders and the provocation furnished by Krafft-Ebing's application of the word, there developed a tendency to make a clear-cut division of all the cases that showed uncontrollable ideas with the subjective feeling of obsession, with absence of an emotional or affective state, and recognized as morbid. More extensive clinical experience naturally brought forth the question whether it was admissible to speak of imperative sensations, imperative hallucinations and imperative acts; imperative affects or moods being excluded at the very outset. Since sensations never give the feeling of freedom or option, they would seem to be something by themselves. In the same way affects are not under voluntary control so as to allow a contrast of voluntary and involuntary forms; but ideas and possibly actions, when they arise directly from imperative ideas, can figure as obsessions. In this compact the phobias are put apart unless their nucleus is an idea (such as the idea of dirt in mysophobia, whereas agoraphobia, the fear of open spaces, is not included because the primary feature is anxiety).

We find here largely on grounds of psychological or logical reasoning a disruption of what clearly belongs together as shown by their appearance on the same etiological foundation, and the frequent transition-types. Practically it is of course of some importance to distinguish whether the obsessions depend on or are accompanied by marked states of anxiety and uneasiness. But to make of the differences a fundamental issue and to cultivate the inquiry habitual to a certain type of German psychiatry, whether in any given case the emotional disturbance is primary or secondary, and whether therefore we have an emotional or intellectual disease, is bowing to a mere system of thought and belittling the rules of empiricism.

The Anglo-Saxon literature has steered remarkably free of such dogmatic outgrowths. When associationism became very pronounced it was neutralized by an instinctive indifference by the physicians working with the conditions in question. The whole discussion of Bumke gives one the idea that besides the quibbling and the desire to live up to psychological definitions he becomes wholly incapable of a broad grasp on the recent discussions on this topic by Janet, Friedmann, Loewenfeld, and others.

These highly systematic conceptions may give a feeling of perfection and superiority over empiricism. But here, as in the paranoia problem, they lead their devotees away from the affection for the plain facts, the cases become degraded to imperfect illustrations, and that which should above all things be the starting point of new trends, *a new response to concrete events,* is surrendered for a plan of doubtful fertility. We may be able to learn a great deal from an analysis of our thought and deductions about things, but as soon as such analysis distracts from what I just called the instinctive affection for the concrete events, we cannot help but suspect an estrangement from the best roads of natural science.

If we obey our soundest instincts, we study events far less for their absolute nature than in order to learn the conditions under which they arise and under which they can be modified. Apart from this, there may be a justified craving for systematic knowledge, but that should be considered as something of a private hobby, or possibly a yielding to scholastic traditions owing to its didactic advantages. It should be judged by its fruitfulness in the creation of heuristic hypotheses and only secondarily by the pleasure and satisfaction it gives to the author and to lovers of word-architecture.

In all of these systematic attempts we meet a very fundamental issue with regard to the shaping of psychopathological methods. Definitions and lawmaking instincts are a problematic aid in this field, and apt to do as much harm as good. When they attend to the *accessible* issues, the determination and differentiation of concrete components of events, and leave the grouping of the necessarily complex events subject to practical differentiation, they have a healthy role; but how can we expect to make useful definitions of that which naturally ramifies and is divergent owing to the introduction of factors which cannot be included in definitions, and where every special instance demands a specific inquiry? Scholasticism has produced a hypertrophy in the faith in definitions, and an irradiation of their application to domains in which they have merely verbal value and become an obstacle to sound empiricism.

Definitions of words are always welcome; but they should not claim to be definitions of facts unless they can be proved to deserve it. Psychopathology is full of such blunders. Definitions of insanity and of various forms of insanity are almost all in this boat; they usually stultify inquiry because they clip the individual case of many of its facts and overstate what little is known of some rule-of-thumb deduction. The desire for definitions in domains which *must* be left to empirical rules is a caricature of the sense of accuracy, very much as labor in statistics when the number of cases is thought to make up for inaccuracy in the majority of single cases.

Psychopathology needs perspectives rather than definitions, lines of inquiry rather than a priori clipping of the object of investigation, and a veritable feeling of sanctity of the individual case in all its manifestations. To group what has proved sensible and helpful in the sizing-up of a hundred kindred cases, a process of natural summation of experience, is quite a different method from doctrinal splitting of emotion and intellect, and from starting with a definition, be it that of Kraepelin or Westphal.

THE "HOPELESSNESS" OF

PSYCHOLOGY

From "*Misconceptions at the Bottom of 'Hopelessness of All Psychology,'*" *by* Dr. *Meyer, in* Psychological Bulletin, 4:170 (*May* 15, 1907), *a review of Möbius.*

The latest publication of Möbius [*Die Hoffnungslosikeit aller Psychologie*, P. J. Möbius, 1907] gives in his usual clear and smoothly readable style an excellent sketch of that dogmatic dualistic schism between psychology and natural science which is the bulwark of those who have to make a fundamental contrast between biology as physiology or physicochemical investigation of living organisms, and a psychology serving as the grammar of *Geisteswissenschaften* [science of the mind]. "As far as man can be perceived, he belongs to nature; as he thinks and feels he is something different from nature." Since science has only a physical basis, it cannot be applied to mental life. Such a statement would almost sound archaic if we were not aware of the fact that, after all, it voices the opinion of many of the foremost—not to say the best—thinkers of the day.

Möbius shows up mercilessly the barrenness of our formal psychology and the bulk of laboratory work, and sees in "metaphysics" the only salvation, the only spice, that will make psychology acceptable. After having shaken one sham support of traditional psychology after another, and after having given the reader a better taste of the meat of psychology than I have ever

134

seen offered in so small a scope, he leads him into—idealistic monism.

Möbius, like so many others, starts out with assumptions concerning nature and mind which we do not need, which merely embarrass, and at once give one cold shivers; which remain to be proven, unless we already become convinced on the way of their uselessness and futility. He is not satisfied with a biological viewpoint, and swells the problem of the essence of mind to a complexity out of touch with all experience and therefore wishes it kept out in a special sphere. We need not wonder at his final resignation to the *saltum mortale* [fatal leap] into panpsychism: the invention of souls for every cell, for every atom, in order to make intelligible the existence of what he claims to *know* as a soul in himself and in himself exclusively! Such psychology is hopeless and, fortunately for us, can be spared readily. It cannot be a topic of science in the sense of systematized experience.

With many physicians I have long revolted against many of the assumptions which seemed to be forced upon one in studying mental life. Many of these are the same as those which Möbius discusses. But my result has been different from his.

The psychopathologist is very directly confronted with mental activities, since their miscarriage is often enough the center of the disorder for which the patient seeks his help. Certain unusual mental events appear and others fail to take place, and the result is inability to meet the demands which would be met by normal mental reaction. Like all other *biological* provisions or developments, the mental mechanisms meet, or fail to meet, definite kinds of biological demands, and the legitimate question is: "What is the type of demand and what is the mechanism or type of reaction that meets it? Further, since there are evidently degrees of efficiency in this function as in all others, we legitimately ask: "Which are the conditions for the proper working of this function and what are the ways of influencing it if it threatens to miscarry?"

In our daily life we use this attitude as a matter of course; and as soon as we enter psychology, whose business it should be to deal with these questions, and to guide us, should we surrender it? As soon as we do, psychology becomes powerless, merely because it pays more attention to extraneous contemplation than to its direct issues.

The effect of this is disconcerting to physicians and to others who should have some training in the accurate, and above all things, purposeful, use of psychology. Instinct usually shrinks from panpsychism as a working hypothesis. The result is that with all the advances in laboratory psychology, it is still impossible to convince physicians of the necessity of introducing psychology into a medical curriculum. They are confused and bewildered by the authority of those who want to make psychology hopeless and prejudice its role by claiming that psychology occupies itself merely with the abstract "subjective" something which cannot be called activity or function or anything belonging to the domain of biology, and that it is a sphinx in matters of practical issues; they find singled out a certain aspect of the possible problems and are asked to turn over the rest to physiology, without being allowed to realize that to do this demand justice, physiology must extend into psychology at its best, not merely laboratory psychology, but an extension and deepening of the way in which we use our *own* mental activity *and* that of others in practical life.

As soon as the physician sees a mental condition pass from the normal and justified reaction into one demanding his attention, he is apt to surrender his commonsense attitude, considers it unscientific to view the abnormal mental trend as a genuine but faulty attempt to meet situations, an attempt worthy of being analyzed as we would analyze the blundering of a distracted pupil, or the panic of a frightened person, or the bungling of one who reacts poorly in trying to meet an unusual situation. Instead of analyzing the facts in an unbiased way and using the great extension of our experience with mental efforts to get square with things and with oneself in states of dream or under dominant preoccupations, in states akin to hypnotic dissociations or a faulty development of interests and inadequacy of habits, they pass at once to a one-sided consideration of the extrapsychological components of the situation, abandon the ground of controllable observation, translate what they see into a jargon of wholly uncontrollable brain mythology, and all that with the conviction that this is the only admissible and scientific way.

If there were more of the unprejudiced attitude such as that shown in the course of psychology outlined by Professor E. C. Sanford, more training to *observe ordinary events correctly*, and a demonstration that observation must be accurate according to demands, and that accuracy is not primarily a question of instruments, physicians might feel less hopeless and less inclined to use that delightfully impersonal and noncommittal emphasis of the physical disorders and of heredity, where a sizing-up of the whole situation (for instance, the problem of the whole family), the mental working of the patient, and his way of meeting the situation *as well as* the regulation of his physiological mechanisms, should receive an unbiased and unexpurgated consideration. To divest psychology of its dynamic interest is making it hopeless.

A fundamental dogma concerning science leads Möbius at once to divide man into what belongs to nature and that which transgresses it. Such a division brings serious embarrassments and is contrary to the trend which sees the domain of *science* in the task of *unbiased systematization of experience*.

According to Möbius, natural science conceives everything from a physical viewpoint and it knows only of physical explanations. "Physics may give up the attempt at explanation, but it cannot replace a physical by a psychological explanation." On this ground he even wants physiology to eliminate the concept of activity. He accepts such a definition of reflex as "all reactions or answers of a living being to a stimulus," but then at once proceeds to expurgate these reactions of an essential part, the "inner experience" which "does not really concern natural science." "All that which goes beyond experience is metaphysics, and this holds for all psychology as soon as it claims general validity, and especially for animal psychology."

This assumes an absolute division of experience into physical and mental, such as seemed justified as long as biology formed a sort of uncertain go-between or *cela va sans dire* [a matter of course], and as long as one was not willing to give the benefit of the doubt of possible artificiality to some of the embarrassing constructions and cul-de-sacs to be discussed point for point.

1. From the practical viewpoint we must eliminate as fruitless the term "metaphysics" as an obviously arbitrary weapon of argument.

2. We must surrender sham unity in science and replace it by pluralistic consistency.

3. This consistency can be attained in a nondogmatic hierarchy of systematizations which allows us to maintain a sincere respect for the world, unsystematic as it may appear, and for the order of the things and events as they actually occur. The world is too pluralistic to be grasped by but one simple formula without doing serious harm to our capacity of scent for error and our appreciation of the actual combination of the things in the real experience which science must not try to ignore, but in which it singles out principles of regularity.

4. The fundamental change in the modern attitude is the elimination of unprofitable pondering about the final and absolute nature of "things" and the turning to *inquiry into events* and their actuality. The theory of atoms is to us the theory of actual and possible relations of qualitatively different materials, and not a means of an unnecessary revisualization in a garb of exclusively quantitative features. The theory of molecules and the various forms of physics, the theory of organization and of inner activities or adjustments (of physiology) of the biological objects of experience, are all dealt with with less imaginative substitutions for what we at last enjoy seeing and accepting again in exactly the form which they have in our experience.

Our concern is with the events or "doings," not with the being or final essence, and therein lies the great difference between the old frame of thought and the modern one. We study the relation of occurrences and experiences, and among them we find, on exactly the same ground as the rest of experience, the occurrence of events and activities which we call mental and which we specify on account of certain specific features of working and the specific role in the economy of the individual and the world generally.

The result is "science" if it is consistent with the systematized experience of physics, chemistry, and biology, and especially if it is consistent with the syllogism of the modern mind: the laws of experimental test. In this physics is most fundamental, but not all-embracing. It deals excellently with a certain range or aspect of facts and has within itself a certain hierarchy of "physical sciences." Its laws are further in harmony with those of chemistry, but they do not express all the facts of chemistry, inasmuch as they eliminate the factor of kind of substance, so essential to chemistry. Physics and chemistry furnish a scientific basis of biology, but at their present stage they do not exhaust the problems of organization, and the adaptation of the organization in strata of biological function of widely different complexity; and finally, the strata of ultrabiological relations such as are thought of in the terms of soul and God, in logic, etc.

We need not wonder that the relations of the mental domain were long singled out and presented in a terminology of their own. Working hypotheses had to be made long before adequate facts were available. We need not be surprised either over the difficulty of harmonizing all the old and new data into one whole and the transformation of the various schemes of simplification: the dualism, and the trinitarianism of many physicians who think of body and mind as subserving the higher ultraphenomenal part, the soul; and the gradual evolution of the thought that the body is deciduous as compared to the soul, to a growing realization that the same holds for mind, and that mind as we know it should not be identified with the essence of soul, since it is changeable with the body, nor with the essence of things as in panpsychism.

5. The next problem is the relation between mental events and the other biological types of function, *i.e.*, circulation, respiration, metabolism, digestion and elimination, regeneration, and the neuro-muscular regulations.

The range of mental functions is approached in complexity only by that of the chemical metabolism, but for the sake of simplicity we take as a paradigm of comparison the function of respiration. The essence of respiration, as far as we know it today, is the unitary principle of aeration of the blood. Nobody would, however, think to eliminate from the practical study of respiration the consideration of architecture of the lung and respiratory tract and of the neuromuscular mechanisms on which the function rests. Among the mental functions we find a wide range of types, determined by the extent of participation of various parts of the organism, as in sensation, in activity, or in the more intrinsically cerebral and "subjective" processes. The complex coordination of the mental reaction-types at any given moment is one of the striking features which has led to the concept of the stream of consciousness, with which, for all practical purposes, we would, as in the process of respiration, include the whole range of pertinent collaboration of the sense organs, nervous system, skeletal and vascular muscles, glandular activity, etc. It is *a specific mode of collaboration*, the final essence of which is as yet as unknown as the essence of all things, but concerning the working of which, and the conditions for its work, and the effects, we have a fair stock of working knowledge, which we use adequately in everyday life, and increasingly so under unusual or "abnormal" conditions without changing our attitude, or attempting to establish a parallelism of a physical and a mental "side."

6. At this point the plain man is easily disconcerted by a number of products of insufficiently checked reasoning, either residuals of pre-biological, or legitimate topics of ultrabiological considerations. The first is the question of the essence of mind. Instead of a functional qualification distinctions have been made by emphasis of what is called the *subjective nature of mental activities*. In logic we have a right to make an absolute contrast between subject and object. In the interpretation of events we can, however, only give a relative application of the logical principle according to the extent to which the subjective or objective aspects balance one another. If Möbius tries to remove from biology generally the principle of activity, he deprives us of a very useful conception, merely for fear that it might be taken not in the sense of the logic of facts, but in an absolute sense which only holds within abstract logic.

The concept of activity is one of the most useful and harmless formulas of expressions of events, emphasizing the importance of the role played by the "subject." Where this role is slight, we usually speak merely of objects. Where it is more important, the "subject" is singled out for the role it plays in the event and in the grammatical construction. The central position of the mental functions within an individual is apt to give a special prominence especially to the volitional processes; and since in pre-biological days the contrast of volitional elements and physical "execution" was unhesitatingly taken as one of causative principle and effect, and mind was made the prototype of subjectivity, the connotation of an absolutely subjective agency became a natural corollary. To this is added the fact that among mental activities some can become the knowers of others, which approaches the simplicity of the absolute subject and object of logic.

In this respect we keep clear of misunderstandings if we stand by the above definition of "activity," that it expresses the preponderant role of the subject in any event. A stone plays its role in the stream of the world according to its qualities and make-up, essentially as an object and according to its capacity of resistance. It resists, falls, hits, and "acts" for what it is worth. The seed of a plant plays its role with a greater range of possibilities depending on its organization. It is to a less extent a mere object of the forces of the surrounding world. In the animal series the inner working of the individual reaches an increasing development to which we give expression in the term of function in the sense of activity. Among these functions the mental activities have the leadership of conduct and, on account of their importance in the religious and ethical evolution, this kind of inner working became characterized as "absolutely subjective," as we have seen, with only relative justification. Since the logic of facts knows of no absolute activity, there is no need of being disturbed by the term.

Another specter or product of unchecked logical consistency is that of solipsism: "You can know and feel only yourself." "The mind is beyond human ken," etc. The whole conception is one of those conclusions which are very perplexing but which at once lose their alarming trait if we consider practically the extent to which we can act on the knowledge of the mental states of others, and all that without an attempt to translate the facts into a terminology different from that used in mental reactions generally, including our own. We know mental events best in terms of mental events, and use them in our experience according to the effects they produce. That presupposes, of course, that we do not make artificial and unessential subdivisions between a subjective something and its physical manifestations.

Hand in hand with this goes the puzzling thought: "How can mind be evolved from matter?" The puerility of this question is obvious. We admit that we do not know why certain combinations of molecules of definite kind form a constellation which implies with necessity the phenomena of electricity. It is a fact which we accept as a fact of experience. Those who are trained to make the dualistic division between mental experiences or occurrences and physical ones, merely assume that they can understand why such constellations of certain metallic stuffs as the above-mentioned go with the phenomena of magnetism, others with the phenomena of electricity, etc.; and they refuse to see that the biological events of the order of mentation are no doubt in a similar way dependent on sufficient organization and constellation of an organism, and that the coexistence of these constellations with their manifestations is a fact which we have to accept as merely one instance of the general problem of qualitative differentiation of the universe.

The question why is mind mind, and just what it is, can be as little answered as what gold is and why it is and why it should be so. Consequently, the impossibility of getting an answer to the puzzle—what makes mind mind, and what the relation is between the underlying physical constellations and the "result"—is only part of the problem of why the world is organized as it is. Our inability to answer that does not imply that we are any worse off in regard to mind than with other facts of quality that we accept without puzzle, satisfied if we can determine the *conditions* of their occurrence; and it does not follow that for this reason, mind must be something quite different from the rest of experience, provided that we realize that it presupposes sufficient organization and opportunities of work.

There is of course a certain justified longing for a working hypothesis concerning the role and position of mental activities, since without one few people can keep from drifting into misleading ruts of thought. A working hypothesis can, of course, not be expected to be more than an abbreviation of the things as they are, especially in a complex field; we therefore try to say very simply what we know needs more amplification, and we inevitably must use terms which cover but relatively the general principle, especially if we are with necessity limited to expressing the whole range of mental functions with one mental reaction or thought or expression.

The question has so far come up chiefly in connection with the problem of animal psychology. Is there now, or will there ever be, any advantage in distinguishing mental and nonmental biological reactions? As soon as constellations arise such as we cannot express fully in any other but mental terms with our present knowledge— in other words, wherever we see steps of "mental causation," in the sense of assertion of biological energy with a conscious link— we have evidence of a special reaction-type. The easiest criterion of mental reaction is what we have in ourselves. We merely ask: ·"Has anyone ever experienced a given event as a mental one, and can it not also be conceived without the principles of mental activity?"

The question of such criteria is a very young one. Loeb has used that of association memory. He would take a certain activity or function to imply a mental character or to work with mental principles, if it implied evidence of associative memory. For a number of years I have used as a formula, under the heading of biological adjustments and elaborations, the concept of "symbolization." Mental reactions constitute a type of biological reactions which act as part of a system of symbolization, working through their meaning as well as through the *direct* change they involve, a conjoint elaboration of needs of intercommunication between individuals, and, within the same individual, a complex interaction of various simultaneously occurring components, and the possibility of using the same symbols or reactions in the elaborations of constructive imagination, in the chronological memory scheme, in the utilization of what is beyond immediate experience, etc. Through the unequaled role played by quality, as opposed to mere quantitative propositions, it is a marvelous saver of energy and the field of highest evolution. The reactions are essentially of one kind, as far as they make up consciousness or are parts of it; but, according to the special laws of their occurrence, they appear as "sensations" or "ideas" or "memories," etc., as adaptive reactions to stimulations, as "volitions"; as dreams and wake-states; as part of direct effective activity or of thought.

The theories concerning their organic foundation or the histological conditions for their occurrence are wholly inadequate; but we have no reason to think that the reaction, if it does occur, occurs otherwise than full-fledged, and that a division into a physiological part and a mental concomitant would be a complication which should not be accepted without better proof than can be given today.

It may be that the term "symbol" suggests too strongly the addition of a "meaning." The main point of the hypothesis is that it does away with parallelism, and forms a contrast between mental and nonmental biological functions without ripping apart the principle and the somatic reaction. The stream of mentation and the entire somatic activity as far as the stream of mentation forms its essential link form the mental activity of the moment, and the only difference between the two extremes is the extent of collaboration of extracerebral mechanisms.

Such a hypothesis is perhaps unessential if we adhere to the principle that for the study of psychology we must adhere to the events as they occur; we study these for what they do, for the conditions under which they arise and for the ways in which we can modify them.

The writings of Professor James, Professor Woodbridge, and Professor Stratton and others mark a striking change in the consideration of the problem of conscious life. I should hardly have brought forth the above views but for the hope that some further helps may be elicited by them in the adjustment of a great difficulty —the attitude of hopelessness about psychology and the even greater calamity of indifference and inaccessibility produced by dogmatic notions about science in physicians and others who should help us in building further in the evolution of practical experience.

6

More Action in New York

Psychiatric ambition in the past century had tended to culminate in the classification of patients—an excellent thing for statistical purposes, but statistics had sham value. Statistics garbled facts to preserve form. They made for a dictatorial instead of a medical psychiatry, and the preparation of reports impeded the progress that could come only with free inquiry. When Adolf Meyer dared to stress research he upset the statistics and was damned for his tinkering.

Closer attention given to the patients themselves in the flux of the early nineteen hundreds discerned deviations from accepted patterns and a need to change one's concepts of disorders. But panic clutched the traditionalists and threw them into self-commiserating confusion. "Is there no more paranoia?" The cry came up after Kraepelin had established the dementia praecox group, including paranoia, which had stood on its own feet for nineteen years as "something stable" in psychiatry.

In 1904 Dr. Alexander E. Macdonald (one of the experts at the Guiteau trial) made the presidential address before the American Medico-Psychological Association in St. Louis and denounced the abandonment in New York State hospitals of "a simple and concise" classification that had been good enough in the years of his state service. Not ideal, it had nevertheless made possible uniform tabulations and comparisons. Macdonald deplored the latitude which Meyer encouraged, and he called upon his colleagues to resist now and prevent for a good long time any recasting and innovating that would render the existing system useless.

The German writers usually went to extremes in their nosology. Meyer attributed this to "the indomitable longing for logical consistency and the feeling of moral obligation to take a stand with one of the divergent schools of psychological thought." [11] In the English-speaking countries, psychiatry had developed a business-like aspect—huge hospitals to care for hordes of incompetents, no time in the medical curriculum to teach psychiatry in practice, and statistical tables to take the place of recorded facts—with the result that a scheme of nomenclature as a handy tool had become the ideal achievement. Yet in these cherished tables Meyer found manic-depressive cases figuring under arbitrary headings because physicians unfamiliar with manic-depressive psychosis had been obliged to fit them into hand-me-down compartments.

He induced the New York hospitals to make such clinical distinctions as would be valuable to them; to ascertain all the facts and put the decisive ones to the fore rather than the less important traits that happened to conform to an old classification. The criticism that this took up too much time betrayed a lack of insight into the real purpose of the revolt against slavish adherence to ill-defined terms: the purpose of inducing physicians to study their cases. Even if they failed to agree on a formula for the differentiations, this very failure would be worth while, as healthy evidence of the seriousness of their opinions. Meyer said:

Unless one has a chance to use with ease, and with a feeling of justification, a free pluralistic method of dealing with things, dogmatic restrictions kill off many a possibility of seeing things for what they are worth. The greatest need we alienists have is a general recognition of sound pluralistic principles of experimentation, and in this direction the Anglo-Saxon mind, with its empiricism, seems to have a strong interest.

The logic of a sound empiricism has no set form of classification, and is free to recognize the unfinished character of many of our stipulations. The value of things is determined by their working value rather than by the logical harmony of the picture, within certain limits at least. The emphasis of one point or another appears as the personal contribution of the temperament of individual observers. And while everyone is given full chance to carry into the field the best array of facts, nobody is expected to make a finally exhaustive and still less an exclusive system.[11]

Even as Meyer discouraged any hope for a strict classification, he cautioned against headlong revision. Diagnoses had to be summaries of the available facts, arranged according to their pathological or nosological bearing, and where the record was hazy or the nomenclature vague, "nothing short of a concise rendering of the findings in plain language should be considered good enough, instead of a term which has too many connotations and may be used differently by writers and readers." [12]

He saved American institutions from indulging in "the wild boom which for a time led the Heidelberg Clinic to diagnose fifty-one per cent of its admissions as dementia praecox." (The figure declined to eighteen per cent after Kraepelin changed his definition.) Meyer provided a new device for transition cases, marking them as conditions "allied to" standard entities where there were surface similarities, gaps in the record, or complicating admixtures.

One term he favored eliminating was "melancholia," which Kraepelin was keeping for the menopause depression. It implied specific knowledge of a disease process—something the profession really did not possess. "Depressions" would be a better designation for the large group of types, each of which would be distinguished according to etiology, symptom complex, course of illness, and results; according to acute and chronic forms; according to the intrinsic nature of the depression. There were pronounced types, such as manic-depressive depressions, anxiety psychoses, depressive deliriums, depressive hallucinosis, depressive episodes of dementia praecox, and symptomatic depressions, as well as nondifferentiated types. Showing the hazards of separating "melancholia" and "mania," Meyer singled out the nonagitated type which, marked by much inhibition and subjective inadequacy, was the form that developed mania.

The pitfalls of classification played a part in the execution of President William McKinley's assassin, Leon F. Czolgosz, in

1901. Alienists assigned to the defense made a week-end examination of the killer and pronounced him medically and legally sane; they could not classify him as a case of melancholia, or dementia, or paranoia, or mania, or degeneracy; his skull was symmetrical, his ears did not protrude, his palate was not highly arched. He could distinguish between right and wrong. (And to clinch the case posthumously, there was no brain lesion.)

The doctors' explanation for Czolgosz' heinous act was anarchism. It may be recalled that Guiteau, twenty years before, had not been called an anarchist, and at this date psychiatrists generally thought of President Garfield as the victim of a victim of paranoia. But not even now did the examiners trouble to trace the prisoner's history beyond directly questioning him. The jurors tarried a half-hour in the juryroom for appearance's sake, and Czolgosz was rushed to doom in the horror of his crime.

Not until a year after the electrocution did a private investigation into his background, made by independent psychiatrists, bring to light that Czolgosz, three years before his crime, had suffered a breakdown, undergone a complete change of character, refused to let anyone prepare his food for fear of poisoning, and developed a dominating delusion of a duty to be performed for "the working people"; also that he turned to an anarchist group for support, and they rejected him on suspicion of being a socialist. Poor Czolgosz, he never could be classified.

All in all, a diagnosis was only a label, and no one-word diagnosis was able to do the job of presenting a patient's status for working purposes. Such a term was dementia praecox. Its flexible use in changing meanings had created much uncertainty as to its proper application, although to Meyer it did not matter whether a condition was called dementia praecox or something else so long as the physician made use of the psychological events and the mechanism leading up to the deteriorations in cases in this group. Thereby you put the individual, not the label, in focus and displaced fatalistic outcome as the central theme.

What we need is to turn from generalizing attitudes to the conscientious observation and careful evaluation of the actual facts, to definite chains of causation.[13]

Pursuing this exacting quest for facts, he found among dementia praecox patients a galaxy of constellations which became visible to the naked eye as reaction-types of habit-disorganization and deterioration. Here was something more than a name. It showed a principle in action. It was material for therapeutic work and early detection and prophylaxis. On January 3, 1905, at a small gathering of a group of men who called themselves the New York Psychiatrical Society and met in a member's home, Meyer presented his new formulation of dementia praecox. In 1906 he publicly offered this dynamic conception—that mind can undermine itself and its organ—at the British Medical Society's meeting in Toronto. His paper, he said later, was "the first full blast at tradition." The profession received it with skepticism, at first.

He was working to break down an artificial picture of psychiatry based on data derived mainly from artificial conditions in large, isolated hospitals. There you had patients committed by law after losing their grip or becoming unmanageable. You did not see them in earlier, developmental stages. What you had were merely statistical units.

Experience in Meyer's family and his concept of the dynamic nature of normal mental functioning, and of most mental disorders, pointed to the necessity of reaching beyond the hospital to the family setting and the community for sources of illness; if possible, back to the place where a person began his social existence, the school as well as the home. He had long wanted a broad social understanding.

This ambition he was able to translate into action after his marriage in 1902 to Mary Potter Brooks, of Newburgh, N. Y., whom he had first met as a high-school girl visiting her married sister's home in Worcester. After studying at Radcliffe she returned to Worcester to teach. Meyer was now thirty-six. They were married on the way to his post at the Pathological Institute, and the bride's interest blossomed into volunteer service. In 1904 Mrs. Meyer began to visit patients on Ward's Island, and inevitably she and her husband discussed cases. Often he was obliged to give her a helpless answer: "Well, I don't know any more than you do concerning the nature of this malady or its development. I would like to know more."

By and by he added: "And the only way to learn more is to go out and get the information." Mrs. Meyer went out. She made trips to patients' homes on the East Side and spoke to their relatives—the first psychiatric social worker. She brought back to the doctor a clearer view of events in the patients' lives and thus gave him contact with forces at work during the growth of their abnormalities.

"I was greatly assisted by the wholesome human understanding of my helpmate," Meyer said. She gave him, in addition, an awareness of the situation to which a patient would return upon discharge. "In a short time her work became absolutely indispensable."

The task of after-care might have taken on the tinge of paternalism but for Meyer's alertness. He nipped a proposal of the State Charities Aid Association (a very worthy organization) to give discharged patients financial aid. "An antiquated, patronizing scheme," he called it. It would have turned Mrs. Meyer's social work in the wrong direction. More important than concentrating on the few people who were likely to be friendless and penurious on their parole to society was the education of afflicted families beforehand. The person's mental climate and diet needed to be regulated, since the brain was "man's social organ, dependent on mental environment for its functional life."

Speaking of pauperism, those who are poor in mind and experience are the poorest of all, and they can be found on Fifth Avenue as well as in the ghetto, in the crowded slum districts or in the country, or anywhere else.[14]

He realized the expediency of hospitals beginning their extramural work with after-care cases; this would provide solid experience with known quantities in place of effort stemming from "mere good will and generalities." When an after-care system was approved at a conference of the State Commission in Lunacy in 1906, the charity aspect gave way to the need of guiding families in their relations with home-coming members to prevent relapses and to maintain continued contact with the hospital as a friend. The next year the first paid psychiatric social worker was engaged at Manhattan State Hospital, and soon the new profession grew into full-fledged hygiene work as Meyer had outlined it. (At about the same time Dr. Richard C. Cabot of Massachusetts General Hospital also advocated drawing the social worker into psychiatry. He was one of the few physicians who paid attention to patients psychiatrically in an organized way.)

Mrs. Meyer now channeled her sympathetic intelligence into occupational therapy. There had been shopwork and menial work but little that entered the patients' lives to give them the pleasure of achievement and appreciation of time. She introduced work into the wards as a systematic activity of hands and muscles. Instead of exhortation to behave and cheer up, she gave them incentives of interest and satisfaction, being careful not to overstimulate elated patients with tasks requiring large movements. Mrs. Meyer also organized recreation and lured the wallflowers into folk dancing as a form of group therapy, having in this the assistance of Betty Burchnall.

The New York period was rich in enterprise. Cornell University Medical College appointed Meyer professor of clinical medicine (psychopathology) in 1904 on Dr. William L. Russell's recommendation to President Jacob Gould Schurman, and at Cornell Meyer set up the first mental clinic in the city. It was an outpatient service. Assisting him were his Institute associates, Dr. George H. Kirby, who had worked with him at Worcester, and Dr. C. Macfie Campbell, his clinical assistant in psychiatry. At the Cornell dispensary they treated patients paroled from the Institute service on Ward's Island and others who had not been hospitalized. Later they were joined by Dr. August Hoch, coming from McLean Hospital to the Bloomingdale Hospital and an instructorship at Cornell, eventually to take charge of the clinic under Meyer's direction. Hoch, like himself the son of a Swiss minister, became a vigorous exponent of his chief's thesis that human traits must be made the basis of psychiatry.

Besides his Cornell work, Meyer gave a seminar in biology at Columbia University in 1904. In this seminar he presented a view of psychology as "a study of the determining factors of the stream of mental life, and not merely an analysis of abstract and forceless epithets and epiphenomena." Here he formulated his concept of consciousness. He described consciousness as a specific integrate of a functional kind, but he had difficulty in putting across his idea of integrates, although reflexes were beginning to be understood as an integrated function of the nervous system. Meyer defined integrates as "sets of facts forming a unit that cannot be completely expressed in terms of other sets of units—a term used for specifically characteristic products of integration." Consciousness, then, was "an integrate of the person and not only of the brain," the brain acting as a carrier.

While giving the seminar at Columbia, Meyer renewed contact with John Dewey. Sunday nights the Meyers would dine with the Deweys or the James Harvey Robinsons, or the Deweys and the Robinsons dined with the Meyers—maids' night out.

Meyer had not forgotten Dr. Frederick Peterson's dream of a psychopathic reception hospital. It was not dismissed as a mirage on the Manhattan horizon. But when Governor Benjamin B. Odell, Jr., took up the advocacy of such a hospital in 1903, Meyer distrusted the Governor's motives. Odell thought of it as a budgetary way of disposing of the needs of the thirteen asylums for custodial accommodation of committed cases and thereby cutting down their allotments for better equipment. Meyer felt it was better to postpone the project to a riper time than push it under such circumstances. Later, Peterson, with the powerful backing of the State Charities Aid Association, won legislative sanction for the city to acquire a site and lease it to the state. Again Meyer objected: the site selected was next to a huge powerhouse along the East River and decidedly unsuitable.

At Meyer's insistence the name of the Pathological Institute was changed in 1908 to Psychiatric Institute. Not until he had left New York did plans culminate in the construction of the Psychiatric Institute and Hospital as part of a great medical center on land deeded to the state by Columbia University.

PRINCIPLES IN GROUPING

FACTS IN PSYCHIATRY

From Report of the Pathological Institute, 1904-1905, *by Dr. Meyer, at p. 8, State of New York* (1906).

Unfortunately the intemperate craving for logical unity which our education teaches us to strive for as the only worthy resting place, and the habit of sacrifice of the concrete reality to the moloch of simplicity at any price, are apt to seriously vitiate our standards of moral responsibility in the presentation of facts. Psychiatric experience has sadly suffered from veritable debauches in unwarranted systematization. To this are added the effects of a common self-deception about the meaning and purpose of diagnoses.

An orderly presentation of the facts alone is a real diagnosis. Wherever facts or groups of facts occur often enough they naturally lead to the formulation of a terminology. With the public and often enough in the physician's mind the diagnostic terms tend, however, to assume an importance out of proportion with the actually correlated facts, and to represent a lofty vantage ground from which the facts are viewed condescendingly as a necessarily inadequate illustration. In this way the actual and real foundation is surrendered in favor of frequently unsafe generalities. Thus it came to pass that in psychiatry diagnostic terms obtained the undue tenacity which goes with all dogma, while we can hardly understand today how the terms could figure so long as "diagnoses."

Nothing but the inevitable complexity of the facts of psychiatry explains why there has not been a revolt against the obsolete residuals of more than 2,000 years' tradition, presenting the shallowest kind of compromise between scholastic terminology and all the experience of actual life. This can be explained only as the result of a diversion of the healthiest interests in a totally different direction. It was a more than excusable effect of the status of psychiatry, that the usually unreasonably overburdened and not infrequently poorly directed hospital physician learned to follow the line of least resistance, to divert his attention from the concrete case to the general management and to subordinate the concrete facts to some trite traditions and definitions.

After all, it inspires confidence in human nature to see how efficiently human instinct has, even under these unfavorable conditions, matured remarkably efficient principles of management of the concrete facts of general administration and nursing; and it is also a pleasure to see how of late years sound instincts begin in turn to take to a more responsible attitude toward the concrete facts which we use in the individual case and want to use for a system of data of reference. Yet the old habits are bound to linger. For a long period the sham diagnoses of mania and melancholia have been tolerated with indifference, as sufficient to fulfill the requirements of official statistics, teaching, and conversation. Now we find here and there a heralding of "new classifications," as a substitute for the old gods, the manias and melancholias, the confusions and dementias and paranoias of our immediate past, but also a tendency to consider an actual study of the patient's condition sufficient if it yields a few shabby facts thought to be needed for a lofty diagnosis of "manic-depressive insanity" or of "dementia praecox."

The superstition about the value of a diagnosis of a disease prompts many to believe that a diagnosis once made puts them into a position to solve the queries about the case not with the facts presented by it and naturally considered in the light of principles based on experiment and on clinical experiences with concrete series of cases, but by a system of rules and deductions from the meaning of the newly defined disease entities, with their prognosis and autotoxic or other origin held out to the believer as sufficiently settled for practical purposes. The routinist has no use for actual study of the cases beyond the hunting up of a few diagnostic signs, and asks, "What is the use of any special study of a case of general paralysis or senile dementia, or manic-depressive psychosis, or dementia praecox, if the diagnosis is made?" And by this he really means but the bare diagnosis with as little detail of fact as possible. He feels satisfied with the conviction of quiz-medicine, that the presence of three or four symptoms "spells the diagnosis." And the one who has a sound instinct of pathology, the study of the real nature of the disease, is discouraged by scholastic warnings even by the guides who have shaped the new views of diagnosis.

When we come to the individual case and ask how we explain the working together of the demonstrable facts toward the result proclaimed by the generalization of the system, we get the same windy comfort which scholasticism has always offered the inquirer: warnings against using the facts as they are, because they would mislead the believer, and a reference to some authority who plainly says that such and such a symptom complex means a definite something to be accepted in the doctrine.

In the Kraepelin school, mental symptoms are dethroned unless they are characteristic of etiology, course, and outcome. The reasons for this are fairly convincing and yet it would seem natural that many a reader interested in psychiatry would carry away the feeling that there was a dangerous distance between the few etiological facts and the elaborate entities of "uniform" outcome, and a dependence on symptoms very little understood and correlated; and that we ought not to surrender so readily the common-sense conviction that what determines the importance of a symptom is not so much its formal relation to etiology, course, and outcome, but the question how near it comes to designating a determining factor in the disease process. If we admit this, we may expect, after all, a future for the real study of the symptomatic factors, which in the minds and practice of many are now sized up lightly with stereotypies and mannerisms and silly smiles as supposedly easy marks making thorough study unnecessary.

It may be that even Kraepelin exposes himself to misinterpretations of his rather peremptory propositions, notwithstanding his occasional confession of the provisional nature of his groupings, because he speaks so often of disease process in the sense of disease unit, and of the necessity of arriving at some sort of diagnosis at as early a date as possible. But with all this it would probably be a misinterpretation of his inspiring help in shaking up effete conceptions, should it be turned into a revival of scholasticism and of the diagnosis notions cultivated by the ordinary medical tradition. Can we not use general principles and valuable deductions without pulling them into the service of a vicious attitude of mind, the attitude of that medical conceit which delights in surrounding the diagnosing and prescribing with a mystic halo so much adored by the patients trained to see wonders in the wise terms? Why not regard the "diagnosis" as merely a convenient term for the actually ascertained facts which do or do not tell a clear and plain story, and, accordingly, are or are not especially gratifying data of medical insight?

In proposing a plan of grouping the facts of any series of cases of mental disease, we recognize, to begin with, the indisputable fact of complexity and therefore high degree of permutability of the data to be grouped. An absolutely clean-cut classification is not to be expected unless the number of groups be made unwieldy and therefore an obstacle to the purpose of furnishing the facts for which we can vouch, which we propose to go by as results of experience, and which we consider worth bearing in mind. The failure of many an apparently logical system of the past encourages us to follow the trend of our period of emancipation from scholasticism and to embrace an empirical eclecticism which would have to look to practical results and efficiency as its sanction.

Here the question arises, "Practical results and efficiency for whom and for what?" For the physicians who work with the patients and whom the community entrusts with the task of the care of the insane. A great share of medical work is done on conviction, with the help of science, but not really as part of a strict and sufficiently founded scientific system. It may be well to have part of the convictions canonized just as is done in all "tradition," to serve as an easy tool of instinct and as a short cut. But the really worthy part of our activity, the part which does the growing and budding, is the individual action, not merely following a rut, but clearly based on definite experiences, and these should be kept in evidence, even where our mental habits prefer to admire the mere formula.

The number of inductive principles which we *can* all accept and work with as we all work with the same principles of mathematics, or of the experimental sciences, is gradually increasing, and if we do not disturb its order by premature systematization it serves as a valuable common ground. But especially where we move beyond it, into the sphere of merely suggestive diagnoses, we should encourage every effort which would tend to keep the *facts* in evidence and the tentative acquisition of principles from becoming an obstruction to the free development of others.

The soundest instinct in medicine is grouped around the interest in causes and effects. The principle is represented in its simplest and safest form by what we might call the fundamental syllogism of the modern mind, the formula of an experiment: given a definite constellation of factors, what will be the result? And given a modification of the definitely tried and established constellation, what will be the modification of the results? We have indeed the rudiments of a general pathology which puts together the best tried constellations and their results as standard guides in line with this simple rule of thought. In our clinical work the equation is naturally turned around. The question is: "Given the abnormal condition, what is the constellation leading to it, and how can it be modified?"

In many domains of medicine the conditions are so simple that the two aspects of pathology, the experimental and the clinical, coincide very readily. Traumatisms and infections are such clean-cut experiments of nature, of great simplicity, and more and more devoid of diagnostic halo. In mental disease the manifestations are extremely complex and apt to distract one from direct and simple reasoning into the cul-de-sac of unprofitable speculation passing beyond the bearing of the available facts in the case. Our understanding of the relation of special factors to a situation under investigation revolves on our knowledge of the weight of modification of that factor for the course of developments. As a rule, a disorder has its cardinal facts beside more casual ones; and our aim is to find out the determining factors, to subject them to a study of the ways in which they can be influenced. In the fact of symbiosis, the effects of what we call infection, the effect of the struggle between the tissues of our body and the self-assertive invaders, we have an ideally clear field of medical inquiry. Once the central fact is recognized, the invader is studied, subjected to experimental influences, and, similarly, the organism is tried as to modifications of its power of resistance.

In psychopathology the kinds of possibly active principles involved are usually much more complex, and according to the principles of permutation the number and qualitative difference of the factors involved greatly complicate the conditions of experiments. Yet the principle remains the same. We must try to get methods with which to determine the essential factors and by observation and experiment determine the weight of each factor and of any modification of its working.

In the first place, we are confronted with the make-up of the person—which is an extremely problematic entity and oftener sized up from the result of damage in the conflict than by any previous estimate. The only really safe measure of vulnerability to poisons, to infections, to trauma, to disorders of metabolism, is the test of endurance, and the same holds for the effects of habits, of strains on the regulative balancing functions of the organism; and owing to the multiplicity of the foundation for mental activity, there are many types and directions of biological issues to be attacked: In the first place, the division of labor shown in the data of localization of the nervous system; in the second place, the division of labor shown in the nutrition of the brain (circulation and metabolism); in the third place, differences in the functional disposition of the curve of activity of the components, the question whether a dovetailing with new requirements is easy or difficult, and what is the ease with which the individual passes from one state into another, from one interest, from one emotion to another, and especially to the ones most likely called for by the actual situation demanding adaptation.

Where so many factors are to be heeded, it is natural that one combination of facts may be appropriately viewed in more than one way, and that the mere accentuation of one element or introduction of a simple new factor is apt to invite the use of a correspondingly different viewpoint. We may, for instance, use the principle of etiology and name the situation according to the essentially etiological factor. There is no doubt about the existence of alcoholic insanity. There are many forms, dependent partly on the mode of action of the cause, partly on the original make-up of the individual, partly on incidental factors. We may meet with derangements of which we can claim that they would not have occurred without alcohol, or without some similar toxic substance; while other derangements may be precipitated by alcohol but another cause might have done the same, the main factor being the constitutional make-up. Alcoholic intoxication, delirium tremens, alcoholic hallucinosis, alcoholic constitution, and perhaps alcoholic paranoia may be viewed largely from the point of view of alcohol as the chief factor; manic states, depressive states, epilepsy may occur at first merely in response to alcoholic excesses, but often enough in the course of prolonged exposure independently as well, so that the etiological role of alcohol sinks. This is why the etiological principle could, as little as any other, claim the advantage of doing for us what can be done in a collection of stamps or books. But why should it? We are not collectors. We only want order in our thought about facts, and for that we need not garble the facts and force them into artificial lines.

The secret of any real progress in psychiatry will be an increase of clearly definable facts; and wherever we invite differentiations we must feel sure that they point to the mainspring of action and interests in the physician and not merely to superficial traits, or to the other extreme, dogmatic and doctrinal subdivisions, and therefore tend to become dogmatic encumbrances rather than helps in clearness and accuracy.

In order to make the directly practical interests of the physician in the patient coincide as much as possible with the more remote interest in a more or less statistical presentation of the experience acquired in a period covered by a report, theoretical aims have been subordinated altogether in the following suggestions. What is offered is obviously very fragmentary, but it is an individual effort to use our material so as to get clearness as to what we want to pay attention to in the future.

Certainly, in the broadest outline, the arrangement proposed would seem acceptable as a common working basis and as a help in clearness and directness of conception; in the detail a great deal of personal liberty can find its place, so that every opportunity will be given to individuality in experience and interpretation without any serious sacrifice in the comparability of the material. Absolute comparability is not to be expected, nor should it be shammed by suppression of the individual tendencies of the various hospitals. On the contrary, the best thing that can arise among us is a spirit of courage of one's convictions on condition that evidence for one's views is furnished.

It seems advisable to start from *three large groups:*

A. The diseases which depend on a fairly tangible interference with the brain or its nutrition, in the form of some definite brain disease, or some intoxication, or some autotoxic or infective or exhaustive disorder.

B. Disorders which provisionally and owing to their more or less striking symptomatology are most interesting from the point of view of *symptomatic equivalents, and their course and outcome;* simple excitements and depressions, dementia praecox, paranoic developments, and manic-depressive states.

C. Disorders in which we see the marks of some of the recognized neuroses, hysteria, epilepsy, neurasthenia, psychasthenia, and peculiar make-up; and imbecility and idiocy.

Each of these groups is to be subdivided as far as possible according to such principles as would be conducive to clearness of conception of nature's experiment, and to stimulation of sound medical interests.

We begin with the subdivision of the first large group *A,* into definite brain diseases, intoxications, and autotoxic infective-exhaustive disorders.

The first subgroup might be called "psychoses which are part of an organic or at least definite disease or disturbance of the brain and nervous system generally," and consists largely of disorders which are usually thrown together as "organic dementias" but should not be passed over with this indiscriminate term, all the more since some forms need not figure as "dementias." In the cases classed here the *neurological diagnosis* clinches the vital issues. In many of these disorders we are apt to know more about the localization of the lesion and of its general nature than of the complete causal chain of its production (as in brain tumor, or in focal disease of vascular origin), and the recoverability and prognosis depends largely on the nature and the extent of the *lesion*, and we have reasons to think of the extent of the disorder in neurological terms.

On account of their very specific nature and the prominence of the estimate of the mental function in our estimate of the disorder, we give a special position to the truly senile psychoses (without or with focal symptoms) and to general paralysis (cerebral type, simple or with focal symptoms, tabetic type, or mixed), and to cases suspected of general paralysis.

Epilepsy and imbecility perhaps ought properly to be ranged with this group if a unitary system were the chief issue. It would, however, seem more essential to think of them in terms of make-up, and to deal with them in connection with the constitutional defects, because we cannot as yet size up the amount of idiocy and epilepsy in terms of nerve lesions, and because the psychotic symptoms lead us much more naturally to a comparison with constitutional mental defects and their reactions, in their kinship to constitutional inferiority and hysteria.

Thus, our first subgroup appears as follows:

I. Psychoses with a nervous disease or nervous complex or tangible brain disease in the center of attention:

a. Brain tumor with mental symptoms.

b. Traumatic psychoses.

c. Distinct focal cerebral disease.

d. Diffuse vascular brain lesions.

e. Brain syphilis.

f. Diffuse processes: multiple sclerosis, chorea, central neuritis, polyneuritis (if not specified under "intoxications").

2. The truly senile psychoses, without or with focal symptoms.

3. General paralysis, cerebral (diffuse or focal), tabetic or mixed.

3a. Cases suspicious of general paralysis.

The second subgroup of tangible derangements of the nervous system is that of the *intoxications*. According to their sociological importance we specify the alcoholic psychoses, morphinism or cocainism, and other drug habits, excesses in consumption of tea or coffee, and the trade and food toxicoses. Here a cross reference must be made to the polyneuritic forms mentioned above.

Pellagra and ergotism are practically unknown with us, but would find a place here.

Thus, we find the second subgroup to contain:

II. Psychoses of intoxications:

1. Alcoholic psychoses:

Pathological intoxications; delirium tremens, acute and subacute hallucinosis; Korsakoff complex; alcoholic constitution; alcoholic paranoias; alcoholic disorders of more independent symptomatic type.

2. Drug psychoses:

Habits; acute or subacute poisoning; trade toxicoses; food toxicoses (pellagra, ergotism; tea and coffee).

The third subgroup is that of autotoxic or infective or exhaustive psychoses not already included in *Sub. I.* We give it a few special headings: in the first place, we mention true and demonstrable autointoxication of the type of thyroidism (myxedema, cretinism, and Graves' disease), or uremia, diabetes, and whatever "auto-intoxications" could be sufficiently specified and verified to deserve a place in nosology. A practically larger group allows of no such specification, and is best defined with emphasis on the symptomatic type, the delirious nature (with Head's reactions to referred pains, and truly delirious states, as prototypes), as infective-exhaustive psychoses, delirious or paranoid, discriminating, however, as in the alcoholic group, the cases in which the infection or exhaustion merely brought out a much more fundamental constitutional defect (such as a deterioration psychosis).

Hence we have:

III. Autotoxic, infective or exhaustive disorders.

a. The thyrogenous disorders (cretinism, myxedema, and Graves' disease).

b. Uremic, eclamptic, diabetic, and demonstrated gastrointestinal disorders.

c. Febrile and postfebrile deliriums.

d. Exhaustive deliriums and kindred psychoses ("confusional states," "amentia").

We now pass to the second large group, which has so far made the bulk of the statistics under the terms mania, melancholia, paranoia, and primary and secondary dementia. For didactic and practical reasons I accept Kraepelin's subdivisions, but not as they are often used, as if they were easy substitutes for the old terms and merely denoted whether the case was recoverable or not.

Kraepelin's manic-depressive insanity and dementia praecox are very important groups of cases, which do not, however, exhaust the material that presents itself to us. His types had best be used as paradigms. We should discriminate what can be definitely identified as manic-depressive insanity, or as dementia praecox, but not extend the scope of these terms to merely set up a new kind of arbitrary confusion. There are, for instance, many *depressions* which command our attention as alienists without their belonging to the above groups, through the mere fact that depression, of whatever origin, is apt to be dangerous as a foundation for suicide and tends to shut *in* the patient in self-absorption so as to exclude the corrective influences of the environment and so as to allow a cropping-out of uncorrected ideas and developments which may take a progressive character, of the nature of a vicious circle, especially where for some reason constitutional safeguards are lacking. This seems to be a necessary conclusion from the fact that so many depressions have neither the characteristics of manic-depressive depression nor those of a definite type of agitated anxiety psychosis belonging more especially to the period of involution.

There also remain certain cases which resemble to all intents and purposes the infective-exhaustive psychoses without our being able to demonstrate such an etiology. We, therefore, are obliged to provide for them in order not to adulterate the facts which we can safely class as autotoxic or infective or exhaustive.

In taking over Kraepelin's dementia praecox in the more restricted sense of an essential deterioration, we class only those cases as such which have demonstrable defect symptoms. As a rule we find here a complex etiology with habit-deterioration in the foreground, either on ground of constitutional defect or on ground of merely acquired habit-disorganization. This had best be taken as the central point in sizing up the cases and the outlook. There are, however, many cases in which there is evidence of habit-deterioration without sufficient evidence of formation of permanent defect, or other cases in which habit-deterioration is not very prominent, or not demonstrable, but which show mental disorders of those striking types which occur in the undoubted cases of dementia praecox, such as many catatonic states, or peculiar delusional episodes, cases which are apt to be kept apart as allied to essential deterioration, until more definite discriminations become desirable and possible. The paranoic conditions form another striking symptomatic group and deserve to be kept apart. It will, however, be well to discriminate between the pure types of delusional development and those with evidence of deterioration or admixtures.

In the manic-depressive group we include only those types which have the classical symptoms; in the depressive forms, subjective feeling of difficulty of thinking and acting, with or without obvious retardation, and with sadness or downheartedness; or in the manic forms, flight of ideas, flight of activity, and either exhilaration or irritability; or in the mixed forms, combinations of these fundamental symptoms. Any cases which do not show these symptoms or show additional symptoms not belonging to this set should, however, be classed as allied to manic-depressive psychoses only. We thus single out the cases in which the manic-depressive traits are less decisive, and naturally all the cases in which they are merely subordinate features of a general paralysis, or a dementia praecox, or other disorders. It will then be seen that the manic-depressive group proper includes the cases with recurrence in the same form or with alteration of equivalents, whereas the disorders allied to manic-depressive insanity have a much less sharp symptom-picture, general setting, and outlook.

We thus subdivide our second large group as follows:

B. Symptomatic prognostic groups with complex etiology:

1. Conditions akin to the exhaustive-infectious types (nondifferentiated deliriums and confusional states).

2. Depressions:

a. Essential depressions not sufficiently differentiated.

b. Symptomatic depressions.

c. Depressive hallucinosis.

d. Agitated depression or anxiety psychosis.

e. Depressions with additional symptoms (paranoic traits or other complications).

3. Essential deterioriation or dementia praecox; simple, hebephrenic, catatonic, and paranoid types.

3a. Conditions akin to the deterioration types, symptomatically or etiologically or both.

4. Paranoic conditions.

5. Manic-depressive depressions, excitements, and mixed states.

5a. Conditions akin to the manic-depressive psychoses.

In our third large group *C* we deal with psychoses that really form part of the so-called general neuroses or of simple constitutional inferiority or involve fundamental defects of make-up and development. Thus we would speak of neurasthenic, psychasthenic, epileptic, hysterical mental disorders, if they are merely an emphasis of the fundamental trouble of these diseases extended into the mental mechanism of conduct. Since many of these disorders are compounds difficult to disentangle, and quite a few obviously belonging to this group do not show the characteristics of any of the recognized "neuroses," we provide for a group of psychoses of constitutional inferiority arising from peculiar make-up but not already provided for in the large groups *A* and *B.* Idiocy and imbecility are added here, for while as such they are not cases to be admitted to hospitals for the insane, they are apt to have more or less characteristic outbreaks, not infrequently characteristic enough to be considered allied to dementia praecox or even to manic-depressive insanity.

Hence we have:

C. Psychoses belonging to definite neuroses or make-up.

1. Neurasthenic.

2. Psychasthenic.

3. Epileptic.

4. Hysterical.

5. Constitutional inferiority and abnormal make-up with or without outbreaks.

6. Idiocy and imbecility.

The last group is formed by the cases not classified, whereas the cases not insane really form a group of merely administrative importance.

In making such a table, I am fully aware of a number of compromises. In the first place, a number of cases represent *combinations* of fundamental disorders, such as combination of senile, alcoholic, epileptic disorders with other conditions. If we wish to keep our classification of medically important facts for statistical purposes without entering one person twice, we must either make subgroups for these combinations or class the case as allied to the disorder which seems to us fundamental and decisive of the patient's fate and control.

There is no doubt that criticism will come concerning the justification of the "allied groups." We shall hear it said that a case of continued fever either is or is not typhoid fever, and that the statement that a patient came near having typhoid fever is so thoroughly objectionable that nobody would use the designation of a case being "allied to typhoid fever." Yet we have to meet the situation as it is. Even in general paralysis the best of us will find it necessary to class five to ten per cent of the cases as suspects only, just as to this day quite a few cases of continued fever resist an absolutely certain diagnosis. Our statistics cannot neglect the mental status of the ones who make them, and the clearer the differentiation between facts offered as safe and facts offered tentatively, the greater the chance of honesty of the tables. The cases classed as allied to a special group are not meant to denote necessarily a haziness or confusion of nature, but rather an uncertainty in the mind of the physician, and these groups will forever be centers of "more work" and of need of further discriminations, plainly before the eye of the worker, and therefore stimulating and a means of profitable order.

Another objection will necessarily arise—that of complexity of such a system. To this I have but one reply: the results of the grouping suggested can easily be contracted into fewer groups by whoever wishes to make relatively simple tables the issue. But if the groupings serve the purpose of stimulating the medical interests of the staff in the direction of practical efficiency, the tables will, at least for some time to come, be an adequate expression of the diagnostic problems and, I hope, invite a great deal of healthy tinkering against which there ought not to be any objection in this country of free developments.

Psychiatry, more than any other branch of medicine, is confronted with a necessary reform in the practice of medical thought. Over and over again I hear certain individuals say that when they started to record a case or to examine a case they had made up their minds that it must be a dementia praecox or manic-depressive insanity, or what not. This is an inevitable effect of the faulty teaching that the first aim of the physician is to make a diagnosis instead of saying that the first aim is to get at the facts. Unfortunately, too many physicians interpret this in such a way that they consider it their duty when they see a patient to start out with a notion that they have to get some label for the case with one of the names on the schedule. This is a most vicious habit inculcated by our quiz methods of cut-and-dried schemes.

Above all things we have to determine the facts in the case and see whether they fit together in a natural way so that we can make allowances where discrepancies show weak points of our data. We then proceed to ask ourselves whether the facts established point to any principle which we have acquired by experience and which might help us to formulate our deductions from the facts—our prognosis, our therapeutic indications, and the general and nosological sizing-up of the case. However scanty the facts may be for such a responsible sizing-up, we always find some facts which we have to meet and can meet with therapeutic measures. In a fair number of cases we find that the disorder coincides with a definite nosological entity which means something worthy of the term diagnosis. In a rather large percentage of cases we will have to limit ourselves to the determination of the immediate therapeutic indications and to a consideration of the issues of differentiations to be considered; and we shall then have to resume the examination of the patient with a view to finding the decisive facts. At this point the physician assured of his facts will distinguish himself from the careless diagnosis maker by being able to state frankly whether a diagnosis is warranted at all in the case or not.

What we act on should be facts. If the facts do not constitute a diagnosis we nevertheless must act on the facts. To jump from the facts at an arbitrary diagnosis and then to act on that abstract diagnosis is a procedure hardly ever needed in psychiatry, and bound to lead to self-deceit and confusion of the minds of all concerned. The claim that the practitioner and the family want a diagnosis is a matter not of medicine but of professional habits.

MENTAL FACTORS IN

PSYCHIATRY

From "The Role of the Mental Factors in Psychiatry," read by
Dr. Meyer at the annual meeting of the American Medico-
Psychological Association, Cincinnati, May, 1908; American Jour-
nal of Insanity, 65:39 (July, 1908).

Take the case of a woman of somewhat restricted capacity who
was forced by circumstances to move on two occasions and each
time, and on no other occasion, worked herself into a depression;
she did not see how she could do the work and, instead of doing
the best she could, she dropped into a state of evil anticipation,
lamentation, perplexity—a typical depression of several months'
duration. Her sister too had a depression of a rather different
character, but also on provocation.

We do well to point to the constitutional peculiarity—a lack
of immunity. Since there *are* cases in which we cannot find any
precipitating factors we are apt to spread ourselves on a statement
of heredity and possibly degeneracy of make-up, of possible
lesions, etc., and to overemphasize these issues. What we actually
know is that this patient is apt to react with a peculiar depressive
reaction where others get along with fair balance. The etiology
thus involves (1) constitutional make-up and (2) a precipitating
factor; and in our eagerness we cut out the latter and only speak
of the heredity or constitutional make-up. It is my contention
that we must use *both* facts and that of the two, for *prevention*

and for the special characterization of the make-up, the precipitating factor is of the greater importance because it alone gives us an idea of the actual defect and a suggestion as to how to strengthen the person that he may become resistive. It is a problem of index of resistance with regard to *certain difficulties of mental adjustment.*

Take another case: a girl taken advantage of by a neighbor's boy at six. She did not dare tell anyone for shame; and without knowing what it all meant she imagined things about it, that she had become different from others. It is difficult to know how much children can elaborate such feelings and how much they can become entangled and twisted by amplifying dreams and talk of others and what not, if once started on a track without the normal corrections. At eleven, the patient had a slight accident and limped for six months. A plain ovarialgia with typical hysterical convulsions and paraplegia followed her nursing her sister through an illness at eighteen; recovery in one year. Then, at twenty-one, after nursing and losing her grandmother, she experienced a new collapse, again with recovery. At twenty-five, there came a hysterical psychosis which was mismanaged and drifted into stupor, then excitement and then a classical catatonic dementia.

For every step there are adequate causes; usually causes which would not have upset you or me but which upset the patient. Now what makes the difference between her and you and me? A different make-up, yes; but what kind? Can we expect a full answer in some general term? Do we not, to explain it usefully and practically, have to express it in the very facts of the history? Every step is like an experiment telling us the story and giving us the concrete facts to be minded; while to speak merely of "hysteria" or later of "dementia praecox" gives us no good clue as to what to prevent and what sore spots to protect and what weak sides to strengthen, but only a general characterization of the possible mischief and the probable *absence* of a palpable lesion, and the fact that the disorder consists of a faulty hanging-together of the mental reactions or adjustments, shown by and promoted by previous maladjustments.

Some of you are probably familiar with my explanation of many of the conditions now lumped together as dementia praecox. I started from the realization that in some diseases we are continually promising ourselves lesions, and besides that we neglect facts which are even now at hand and ready to be sized up and the very things we must learn to handle. Some persons are immune and readily balanced; others get wrecked. The main question is, "What makes the difference?" Some talk of degeneracy, others of autointoxications, and still others of glia-overgrowth—but these statements are often enough mere conjectures or refer to merely incidental facts and do not give us much to go by.

Take a case of catatonic stupor. There are evidently many factors involved. All I want to know is whether I can best clinch the facts actually known about the patient by using what is accessible (usually a characteristic string of habit developments and experiences and maladjustments), or by *inventing* some poisons or what not.

It has been my experience to find in many a case of dementia praecox far more forerunners of actual mischief than the average alienist gets at by his examination when he avoids these facts or does not know how to use them. And it has become my conviction that the developments in some mental cases are rather the results of peculiar mental tangles than the result of any coarsely appreciable and demonstrable brain lesion or poisoning—the natural further development of inefficient reaction-types; and that I would rather look at the bird in the hand and act on the available facts, while I can still live in hope that some day I might find an organ or poison which is more involved than another, and which might be given a prop.

I should consider it preposterously absurd to try to explain an alcoholic delirium merely on fears and psychogenetic factors, leaving out of sight the stomach condition and lack of food and sleep; and I consider it equally absurd to disregard the experience with the moving and all it implied, the twist of the hysterical woman along the line of a supposed internal injury, and its being used in the development of a catatonia, or the weight of habitual indecision and lack of completion in psychasthenia, the habit conflicts and deterioration of sound instincts in dementia praecox, etc. Where these facts *exist* we should use *them* rather than wholly hypothetical poisons. Where we *do* find somatic disorders we use them; where we should have to invent them first in order to get anything to work with we had better use the facts at hand for what they are worth to reconstruct the disorder in terms of an experiment of nature.

Why the dissatisfaction with explanations of a psychogenetic character?

1. Because the facts are difficult to get at, and difficult to control critically, and often used for stupid inferences; for instance, a notion that a psychogenetic origin, *i.e.*, a development out of natural mental activities which need not harm you or me, could not explain occasional lasting and frequently progressive disorders (in the face of the fact that nothing is more difficult to change than a political or religious or other deeply rooted conviction or tendency and nothing more difficult to stem than an unbalanced tendency to mysticism, lying, etc.).

2. Because there are prevailing misleading dogmatic ideas about mind. It is unfortunate that science still adheres to an effete and impossible contrast between mental and physical. More and more we realize that what figures to our mind as *matter* is much better expressed in terms of combinations of electrons, if not simply of energies, which throw off many of the forbidding and restrictive features of those masses which form the starting point of our concept of inert matter, which is practically sufficient for most demands of ordinary physics but a hindrance to a better conception of the more complex happenings of biochemistry. Mind, on the other hand, is a *sufficiently organized living being in action;* and not a peculiar form of mind stuff. A sufficiently organized brain is the main central link, but mental activity is really best understood in its full meaning as the adaptation and adjustment of the individual as a whole, in contrast to the simple activity of single organs such as those of circulation, respiration, digestion, elimination, or simple reflex activity.

We know, of course, that in these reactions which we know as mental, the brain forms the central link at work, although we know but little of the detailed working. Sensorimotor adjustments form an essential part, and as soon as we pass from the simple representative reactions such as sensations and thoughts, to the affective reactions, emotions, and actions, we get a distinct participation of the work of glands, of circulation, of respiration and muscular adjustments, so that organs serving *as such* more limited "infra-psychic" purposes enter as intrinsic parts into emotions, appetites, instincts, and actions, so as to form the concrete *conduct and behavior*, which is the main thing deranged in our patients.

Thus we do not contrast mental activity with physical activity, which can be shown to be an artificial contrast with untenable and not truly scientific foundation, but mental activity and nonmental activity, contrasted with the activity of the individual organs when working without mental links (as the heart does when removed from the body, or the various organs in the mere vegetative regulations and functions).

We do not know all the details of the modes of collaboration but the main lines. We study their differences of various reaction-types and of modifiability in various individuals and determine their chances of adjustment and their ability to work themselves through the conflicts, tangles, and temptations of usual and unusual demands. The extent to which the individual is capable of elaborating an efficient reaction determines the person's level. Our comparative measure of the various disabilities (of a patient getting through the difficulty of moving, the difficulty of getting square with an infantile trauma and its imaginary elaborations, the difficulty and twist resulting from psychasthenic habitual indecision and substitution of ruminations and panics and all that) is the normal complete reaction or adjustment to and of the situation. Why the tantrum? How can it be forestalled? Such would be the questions and problems uppermost in my mind.

The common reasoning is that if the patient gets through one tangle or one delusion the disease still remains and other delusions will form. This I think is very often not correct, unless we bow dogmatically to an unwarrantedly broad notion of "disease." Mere disposition is not the disease. In practice that assumption is certainly very often *proved* to be false if we handle the conditions correctly.

Very often the supposed disease back of it all is a myth and merely a self-protective term for an insufficient knowledge of the conditions of reaction and inadequacy of our present remedial skill.

Unfortunately, our habits of diction lead us to call mental only the most specialized central reaction, the "thought," or at least the more essentially subjective part of the reaction. Yet as practical persons you do not take the word of an unknown person but the act as the real event. If you do that in psychopathology, and not before that, you also deal with conclusive factors. The act, not merely the possible step to it, counts; the *reaction* of the person as a whole, not merely one "thought" or part-step. We can under no circumstances afford to ignore the mental facts in the development of a large group of mental disorders. They *can* be the only expression of the facts to be heeded and to be worked with. But the mental facts we speak of are not mere thoughts but actual attitudes, affects, volitions, and activities and possibly disorders of discrimination (which are oftener due to infra-psychic disturbances, as is shown by the psychosensory deliriums).

Every mental adjustment must be in keeping with the laws of anabolism and catabolism; it has its somatic components. It is, therefore, intelligible that it *may* be easier to precipitate harm than to correct it, and that some disorders or conflicts may permanently damage the processes of anabolism.

The *test* of the whole proposition is: the existence or non-existence of psychotherapeutic helps. If mental factors meant nothing, psychotherapy would be a snare and a delusion. Is it so? What is psychotherapy? Lately I heard two papers on this question—one an excellent sketch of the history and not without an occasional emphasis on the queer and on the yellow streak in what is commonly known as psychotherapy and suggestion. The other was a simple discussion of the treatment of constipation by establishing an unshakable habit. It was psychologically interesting to watch the distinguished audience. The first paper expressed what in the main has been the general practice and the foundations of some of the more recent developments, with many sidelights but no urgent appeal to any special reform in the attitude of the physician. It elicited full appreciation as a fair and conservative general statement.

The report of the cures of even the most obstinate constipation with the simple method of Dubois and good sense and establishment of a habit met with smiles. Why? Because many men believe they *have* tried that method and have failed; and they do not realize that usually it is because they did not insist on the chief principle of psychotherapy, *viz.*, that it is not talk or "thought" alone but *the doing of things* that is wanted. A physician will ask a patient whether he took his pill; but when he gives a sometimes somewhat elaborate régime of how to do things—*i.e.*, the best psychotherapy by help and education—he often does not take correspondingly elaborate pains to control the carrying out of the plan to the dot— and he fails.

Psychotherapy is regulation of action and only complete when action is reached. This is why we all use it in the form of occupation or rest, where it is an efficient and controllable form of regulation. This is why we teach patients to actually take different attitudes to things. Habit training is the backbone of psychotherapy; suggestion merely a step to the end and of use only to the one who knows that the end can and *must* be *attained*. Action with flesh and bone is the only safe criterion of efficient mental activity; and actions and attitudes and their adaptation are the issue in psychotherapy.

To sum up: There are conditions in which disorders of function (possibly with definite lesions) of special organs are the essential explanation of a mental disorder—a perversion of metabolism by poison, a digestive upset, a syphilitic reaction, or an antisyphilitic reaction of the nervous system, an arteriosclerosis, and in *these*, the *mental* facts are the *incidental* facts of the experimental chain.

But there *are* cases in which the apparent disorder of individual organs is merely an incident in a development which we could not understand correctly except by comparing it with the normal and efficient reaction of the individual as a whole, and for that we must use terms of psychology—not of mysterious events, but *actions* and *reactions* of which we know that they *do* things, a truly dynamic psychology. There we find the irrepressible instincts and habits

at work, and finally the characteristic mental reaction-type constituting the obviously pathological aberrations, and while it may
be too late in many cases to stem the stream of destructive action
—action beyond correction and in conflict with the laws of balance
of anabolism and catabolism—seeing the facts in the right way will
help us to set aright what *can* be set aright, prevent what *can* be
prevented and do what *can* be done to secure gymnastics and
orthopedics of mind—*i.e.*, of the conduct and efficiency of the
person as a whole.

Modern pathology sees in most "diseases" nature's way of
righting inadequate balance. They are crude ways of *repair*, not
the enemy itself; reactions to be guided, not to be suppressed; and
to understand the whole process you can no longer get along by
dreaming of lesions when your facts are too meager; but you see
the facts as they are, the reaction of the patient; and he is a psychopathologist who can help nature strike the balance with the least
expense to the patient. Much psychopathology and psychotherapy
will depend on the bracing of weak organs; but its work is not
concluded before the patient is shown the level of his mental
metabolism, the level of efficient anabolism and catabolism in terms
of conduct and behavior and efficient meeting of the difficulties
worth meeting, and avoidance of what otherwise would be a
foolish attempt.

The old problem of "causes" will remain a bugbear as long as
we insist on merely looking backward at the events and on picking
out a few salient facts which seem safe and sufficient to account
for the whole result. As soon as we make it a rule to reconstruct
the facts in each case also from the point of view of prophylaxis in
future similar conditions, we are bound to balance our estimate of
the facts. We get along without the dogmatic concept "the
disease" and without gratuitous assumptions that the *possibility* of
some other experience as inadequate could minimize the weight of
the actual experience which brought the level of a man to a crucial
test. Anyone who studies depressions and their prevention sees that
we must concern ourselves with the capacity of individuals to

meet situations, their "mental" as well as other physical preparedness, and that this is an issue of mental hygiene.

The whole problem has its counterpart in the plainest and
simplest and most experimental of all diseases, the infections. There
was a time when a cold was an indiscriminately used "cause" of
pneumonias. Then came a time when the notion was laughed at,
because the infection was the link of the chain chiefly in evidence.
Today we know that in a certain percentage of cases the person
carries the infectious material with impunity, and without the
"disease"; and that the combination of circumstances which we
call "catching cold" can indeed play a role in lowering the de-
fenses. Why do we pay attention to adjusting our dress to sudden
change of temperature? Practically we acknowledge the causal
value of the situation, until we shall have more accurate ways of
specifying the facts. So it is with emotional causes of disease. The
fact that a "causal factor" does not inevitably lead to the same
results in all persons and in the same person at all times does not
eliminate it as a "factor."

The greatest master of Anglo-Saxon thought has given us in
Lady Macbeth's dream states a marvelous picture of a psychosis
of the type which is just beginning to play a more prominent part
in psychopathology—the psychogenetic disorders—in this case the
living over of troubling episodes in hysterical dream states. And he
has depicted the physician in his dilemma when he lives under a
dogma. He makes the doctor say: "This disease is beyond my
practice; yet I have known those which have walked in their sleep
who have died holily in their beds." Again: "Infected minds to
their deaf pillows will discharge their secrets; more needs she the
divine than the physician." And monologizing over what he has
seen, he remarks: "I think but dare not speak." He sees the plain
facts and he thinks but dares not speak, and would like to pass the
case to the minister of the soul. We begin to reach the stage when
we allow ourselves to think, yea, teach that it is our duty to think,
and to act—and to handle the facts as we understand them.

THE ROLE OF

HABIT-DISORGANIZATIONS

From a paper read by Dr. Meyer before the New York Psychiatrical Society, Jan. 3, 1905; Nervous and Mental Disease Monograph Series No. 9, Studies in Psychiatry, 1:95 (1912).

For years I have been struck with the frequency, not to say
uniformity, with which a number of peculiarities of make-up
present themselves in the history of the cases which form the
nucleus of the disease group which deserves the name "essential
deterioration process," or dementia praecox, in the sense now
generally accepted by most alienists and perfectly intelligible to
those who prefer not to commit themselves to any special nosology.

I refer to those cases of deterioration in whom we cannot point
to any satisfactorily determined or experimentally or clinically
demonstrable constellation of outside factors, as we do in alcoholic
insanity or in general paralysis. The prototype of the disorder
would be those patients who, without any special positive manifestations, undergo an apathetic deterioration. Many cases have
some positive symptoms in the form of hypochondriacal additions,
or paranoic developments with more or less deficient systemization,
or some acute mental disturbance of a more or less characteristic
type. The term *primary dementia* is avoided and replaced by
essential dementia, because it has been used in a very promiscuous
way so as to include also stuporous disorders, whether they belong
to this dementia group at all or not.

The mainspring of investigation is the question of establishing the definite constellations which lead to any deviation under consideration, so that it may be better understood and avoided or corrected. The present formulas are heredity and stress, or heredity and autointoxication, both pointing to matters which can be reached but indirectly and which do not seem to me to touch the working principles of the disease which we want to understand and modify.

Heredity is an extremely important statistical fact, and it embraces very largely the excuses alienists have to offer for their inability to cope with certain things. In the field of action we are forced to decide what we can do in the face of heredity. Stress undoubtedly involves more of what is directly at issue, but it also is an expression of excuse concerning a feature of modern civilization which cannot be changed by the physician. Autointoxication is the happy word which has all the advantages of humoral pathology and expresses the principle of many methods of patching up the disordered mechanism. It sounds like an expression of accuracy, but there are no direct methods of demonstrating anything specific. It is always but part of the disorder, and the setting of this disorder is what is to be established. Everything points to evidently rather complex constellations, and our aim must be to pick out those factors which actually do the work.

During the past years more and more dissatisfaction has developed with Kraepelin's notion of disease process. Already, in my review of his fifth edition in 1896, I criticized the arbitrariness of calling dementia praecox a disorder of metabolism. Instead of suggesting a disease process which would be apt to befall any individual patient without special predisposition, and without necessarily any heredity, I should propose for discussion the concept of habit-disorders as suggestive of investigation of fact and of modifiable and accessible factors, also not necessarily dependent on heredity.

Instead of merely appealing to cortex changes of obscure correlation, or to equally obscure autointoxications, or to arrest of development, I refer to the disharmony of habits, disharmony of those regulations which shape a well-balanced economy: the intestinal and circulatory functions, the sexual life, and above all the trend of interests depending for its integrity and efficiency on a certain equilibration. I have been led in my thought by the analogy of the development of morphological phenomena. Roux has shown by his experiments on the mechanics of development how each part of the organism has a certain dynamic and morphogenic possibility, but that in many points the shaping to a final perfection depends on regulation of the balance of the simultaneously growing other organisms and their functions. Deficient growth or precocious growth of an organism disturbs these regulations, and the necessary result is a disharmony, and every plus is apt to be held up by some minus in another direction.

This same principle is eminently valid in functional life, and especially valuable in the most complex of biological regulations—those of mentation. Here a veritably practical and critical presentation of the early work of James has very justly pointed to habits as a unit of observation and biological interest. And it will be our duty to define in actual cases what sets of habits we find interwoven and with what effect. This directs the attention to the investigation of matters which are open to influence in education, and to a more rational management of dementia praecox, as well as many other mental disorders; and habit-disorder is to be treated by habit training, not by vague encouragement and excessive protection and mere fighting of incidental disorders.

To be sure, all incidental disorders, such as the phenomena usually lumped together as autointoxication, must be corrected as far as possible, and their correction gives a vantage ground on which to begin and promote the more fundamental principle—that of habit training. And in cases where we see disorders developing, whether on the ground of heredity or not, it is this issue which guides us in the concrete plan of teaching and prevention. And since the other elements which are apt to figure in our presentations of etiology, nosology, and pathology are much more hazy, it is much more satisfactory to come out frankly with a statement that we wish to make distinctions of various types of habit-disorganization, to study the working of the various sets of activities and habits in the patient, determine their relative values by accurate observation coming up to the mark of the experiment, and shaping our therapeutic measures in accord with these principles. This naturally does not exclude in any possible way the consideration of the factor of heredity, and the disorders of this or that organ, but, on the contrary, gives every manageable part its working chance.

In viewing the cases of insanity which are not plainly of exogenous origin, we find certain types of combinations of a more or less distinct symptom-picture, course, and outcome. [See paper, page 103.] I am inclined to put the emphasis on a deficiency of critical and consecutive thought habits, with a prevalence of interest in the fantastic, mystic, religious, and unreal, owing to deficiency in working interests which would dovetail with the progressive active course of the world.

Clinically it is rather remarkable that the types keep fairly distinct. We find in many presentations of neurasthenia, hysteria, etc., the comfortable and probably usually true statement that simple habit-disorganization of most of these types has nothing to do with insanity, and there need be little fear of its coming on. Experience justifies this comforting remark to a large extent. There is also a certain justification in the strong efforts of many writers to discourage the uncritical intermingling of these types, in terms of hystero-epilepsy, hystero-melancholia. And Kraepelin's effort of taking most of the endogenous deterioration forms into his group of dementia praecox is in part a similar attempt at being systematic. If we take dementia praecox to be a disease by itself which might befall anyone, it is not very intelligible; we emphasize in dementia praecox the fact of looseness of judgment and consequential thought with preponderance of habits of the unreal, with either a gradual deterioration of interests, or more acute collapses over difficulties to which the individual is not equal.

We might say that the psychasthenic, as a rule, is not of this type, the hysterical is more organized, the true neurasthenic the same, also the manic-depressive type, and in part the paranoic. In the epileptic, deterioration may occur in the form of epileptic deterioration or as a typical dementia praecox superseding epilepsy. Psychasthenics are not apt to deteriorate to the level of lack of initiative of the dementia praecox class. That plainly or simply hysterical individuals are apt to develop the characteristics of the dementia praecox complex is denied by some, while Janet claims that a few of their cases of hysteria have to be transferred to the service of mental disease on account of deterioration. Many cases of dementia praecox begin with hysterical symptoms. The whole symptomatology of catatonia shows so many traits in common with the phenomena of hysteria and of hypnotism that certain French authors look upon it as a hysteriform psychosis.

Looking over the whole field we see in dementia praecox above all the psychic deficiency to meet actuality, a tendency to unreality, to the mystic, common enough outside of dementia praecox but here combined with deficiency of judgment and habit due to the undermining effects of other disorganizations of mental and organic habits. The prevalence of defect in the habits of the reproductive zone is most striking, especially in walks of life where the difficulties are less likely to be swallowed up by the muddy stream of open immorality, where conventional morality and frequently excessive observation of superficial morality create remarkable pictures which figure very well as classical representatives of these disorders.

Looking back over the merits of the point of view taken, I should like to say in its favor that it tends toward putting into the center of nosological and pathological attention the only factors which can be of practical importance in the management of these disorders.

In the general discussion on the paragraphs of etiology, these points of disharmonious development are put down as the product of mere fatal constitutional defect, the result of mere statistical fate, reminding one of the dogma of infant damnation, training in the students a habit of moving in generalities and fostering a disinclination to go into the study of the actual case; the age at which the disease occurs, the sex, the climate, the stress, and a lot of other things which no individual can escape are rehearsed, and with a sort of disdain for the actual pathological and morphological value of the directly important things, which are relegated to casual remarks under therapeutics, where we find warnings against masturbation, against overactivity of the artistic imagination, etc.

Didactically, and from the point of view of keeping oneself in the frame of soundest activity, it seems to me very desirable that these factors, the working factors of the disease, should be utilized to the utmost; and, in the face of the inevitable criticism that these are old matters which everybody knows and that what is wanted is some absolutely new discoveries, we need no longer be afraid of conjuring up a moralizing psychiatry if we hold each other down to speaking of the facts as they occur in actual cases, and as they are not only conceivable but actually at work. There is hardly anything of which it is not possible to say that the ancient Hindus, the Greeks, and our forefathers thought exactly the same way or that we do these things in everyday life. Unfortunately, speculation too easily solves many puzzles which it takes many years of experimental and clinical work to put on a safe working basis. It is, nevertheless, concrete work that has to be done and that will prove the soundest ground for stimulating the interest of the physician in his work of understanding and modifying cases, and in forming sufficiently definite problems in what otherwise would be a mass of arbitrary creations of nosology.

FUNDAMENTAL CONCEPTIONS

OF DEMENTIA PRAECOX

Read by Dr. Meyer before the British Medical Association, Toronto, Aug., 1906; British Medical Journal, 2:757 *(Sept.* 29, 1906).

Notwithstanding the appearance of much divergence of opinion among those who speak and write, there are very few workers in clinical psychiatry who do not consider Kraepelin's creation of dementia praecox the greatest advance in psychiatry of recent times. The number of those who object on principle has, of course, been rather great; and the great bulk of objections really goes rather against the actual or dreaded misuse of the new concept and some of its misinterpretations than against the principle itself.

Briefly stated, the principle is an assertion that it is time to think of creating disease entities in psychiatry, with due utilization of our knowledge of the combination of cause, course, and outcome. In the older textbooks and many of the recent ones we look in vain for a truly helpful and convincing description of the factors which determine an unfavorable course of mental disorders. Instead of the usually hazy statements, Kraepelin has pointed out features which are common to a great number of the so-called terminal dements, and he has found them to exist from the very beginning in a very large number of all cases that ultimately deteriorate. The emphasis of these features, somewhat at the expense of the temporary pictures which have so far received the main attention, was a real stroke of genius.

The older symptomatic considerations have very largely failed to bring out the most vital factors. The tendency was to adapt the description of the symptom complexes to a conventional presentation of a transformation from the normal to the diseased condition. On such a ground we can understand some melancholias and some manias, and even some states of bewilderment, as exaggeration of conditions belonging to our normal experiences. But as soon as we enter on things in which we can no longer appeal to the conventional experiences of the normal forming the scheme of traditional psychology, the description ceases to be as minute and faithful, and such terms as heredity and degeneracy, defective endowment, autointoxication, etc., are resorted to to replace what from the descriptive point of view appears as a disjointed mass. In this respect we are, I believe, ready for a decided progress. We can follow the normal instinct of description, that of showing the transformation from the normal, and, I believe, greatly to the advantage of a sensible comprehension of the situation.

Kraepelin's bold picture allows of a correct estimate of a very large number of cases which formerly partly resisted description and partly figured as doubtful with regard to their outcome and nosological position. Every alienist knows that he does meet cases in which from the very beginning the prognosis is poor, and to a very large extent these cases are the ones stamped by the signs of Kraepelin's deteriorative process. Briefly stated, these signs, according to Kraepelin's differential diagnoses, were the appearance of negativism, of mannerisms and stereotypies, and especially of *Willensstörung* [disturbance of the faculty of volition].

From our present viewpoint—and we must say that Kraepelin's last description has turned more emphasis on several of these points —we would ascribe as the essential features disruption of judgment only insufficiently accounted for by any special mental or physical upset (*i.e.*, without any evidence of intoxication or other delirium, or without the manic-depressive thinking disorder, or the foundation of the hysterical or epileptic disorder), discrepancies between the mood and the general reaction, peculiar attention disorders, and feeling of interference with thinking and deterioration in matters which are largely dependent on sound instinct, such as differentiation of the real and unreal, and the critique of imaginative material—all this in the face of relative clearness, so that we are forced to think of a fundamental deterioration or defect as the only means to account for so much perversion of instinct and reasoning. In connection with this there appear a number of symptom-pictures, also met with occasionally as more or less adequate reactions, such as states of puzzle, of religious and mystic fascination, of automatic and stuporous states, such as can be in part obtained by hypnotic suggestion, or such as arise as psychasthenic and hysterical reactions, as we call them when they appear on sufficient and characteristic foundation. The insufficiency of the provoking factor, and the oddity and incongruity rather than the mere excess of what might be the result of a sufficient cause in an average person, constitutes one of the most important criteria for the estimation of the seriousness of the process.

Every individual is capable of reacting to a very great variety of situations by a limited number of reaction-types, which we want to characterize briefly, without distracting ourselves by exhausting our natural interest over the classifications and traditions of logical and analytical psychology with its sensations, feelings, and will.

We approach the facts directly from a simple empirical standpoint for what they are worth, for the conditions under which they arise, for what they can do, and for ways of modifying them for the better or worse. The full, wholesome, and complete reaction in any emergency or problem of activity is the final adjustment, complete or incomplete, but at any rate clearly planned so as to give a feeling of satisfaction and completion. At other times there results merely an act of perplexity or an evasive substitution. Some of the reactions to emergencies or difficult situations are mere temporizing, attempts to tide over the difficulty, based on the hope that new interests will crowd out what would be fruitless worry or disappointment; complete or incomplete forgetting is the most usual remedy of the results of failures, and just as inattention and distraction correct a tendency to overwork, so faultfinding with others, or imaginative thoughts, or praying, or other expedients are relied upon to help over a disappointment, and, as a rule, successfully. Other responses are apt to become harmful, dangerous, uncontrollable—a rattled fumbling, or a tantrum, or a hysterical fit, or a merely partial suppression, an undercurrent, an uncorrected false lingering attitude, or whatever the reaction-type of the individual may be. What is first a remedy of difficult situations can become a miscarriage of the remedial work of life, just as fever, from being an agent of self-defense, may become a danger and more destructive than its source.

In the cases that tend to go to deterioration certain types of reactions occur in such frequency as to constitute almost pathognomonic empirical units. I would mention hypochondriacal trends, ideas of reference, faultfinding or suspicions, or attempts to get over things with empty harping, unaccountable dreamlike, frequently nocturnal, episodes, often with fear and hallucinations, and leading to strange conduct, such as the running out into the street in nightdress, etc., or ideas of strange possessions with hallucinatory dissociations, or the occurrence of fantastic notions. All these appear either on the ground of a neurasthenoid development, or at times suddenly, on more or less insufficient provocation, with insufficient excuse, but often enough with evidence that the patient was habitually dreamy, dependent in his adjustment to the situations of the world rather on shirking than on active aggressive management, scattered and distracted either in all the spheres of habits or at least in some of the essential domains of adjustment which must depend more or less on instinct or habit.

On this ground reaction-types which also occur in milder forms of inadequacy, in psychasthenia and hysteria or in religious ecstasy, etc., turn up on more inadequate foundation and with destructive rather than helpful results. We thus obtain the negativism no longer as healthy indifference and more or less self-sparing dodging, but distinctly as an uncontrollable, unreasoning blocking factor. We obtain stereotypies not merely as substitutive reactions and automatisms on sufficient cause such as everybody will have, but, as it were, as a reaction of dead principle in a rut of least resistance. We see paranoic developments with the same inadequacy of starting point and failure in systematization and in holding together the shattered personality, etc.

This presentation differs from Kraepelin's by working from the premises to the results. Kraepelin seems to despair of the possibility of a causal analysis, and merely puts down the formal results as the simplest guide which would most likely keep within the realm of natural-history observation, and less likely seduce the alienist to relapse into the habit of making a plausible explanation for a result even if it should have to be at the expense of the facts of the case. Throughout his description of dementia praecox we meet with the emphasis of that relative clearness of the mental activities, as far as they go. His mode of presentation has, however, the disadvantage of failing especially in those cases in which this contrast is not as plain. There are undoubtedly cases which temporarily present the symptomatic earmarks of Kraepelin's dementia praecox that certainly do not belong to the group and should be classed with true hysteria, true manic-depressive insanity, etc. The question then arises in the individual case whether the standard symptoms are fundamental or incidental, and the diagnosis finally turns on the balancing of cause and effect, and an estimate of the patient's elasticity, matters which, as far as I can see, have not been sufficiently emphasized by Kraepelin.

There is no doubt that many diagnoses of dementia praecox are made on ground of rule-of-thumb principles. This danger can be obviated by our taking a definite view of what diagnosis in mental disease means. Somehow physicians have always been more or less superstitious with regard to what they imply by diagnosis. Where they are on safe and easily controlled ground the diagnosis is plainly a brief term for the statement of fact. As one gets into ill-defined facts, the diagnosis becomes a name for what one would like to do, what one would like to know, etc., that is to say, an expression for a substitutive attitude rather than for the actually demonstrated facts.

A diagnosis usually does justice only to one part of the facts and is merely a convenience of nomenclature. In psychiatry the facts occur in very complex combinations, and therefore a one-word diagnosis is almost sure to fall short of what it ought to do, namely, short of presenting the actual facts in the case sufficiently to designate the etiological, symptomatic, prognostic, and therapeutic status. Psychiatry has not reached, and probably never will reach, the stage where a small number of one-word diagnoses would be more than a formal index. It is, of course, convenient to have them, and there is a temptation to discuss the names and write papers about them; but as a rule that does not add much to our knowledge in psychiatry and only helps to undermine our standing beside other branches of medicine through the appearance of continual vacillation of mere opinions, of aberration from real investigation of the nature of facts and from the normal instincts of the physician, and of something really being devoid of sufficient practical importance.

All the desires to pigeonhole various forms of dementia praecox represent a sport which really distracts from the fundamental labor of psychiatry. G. Stanley Hall has very pertinently criticized the tendency and the absurdity of giving the group a name such as dementia praecox. It would be much more satisfactory to keep the issue of deterioration as a principal perspective and to work for greater precision in sizing up the factors which in one combination leads to one result and in another combination to another. It is probably not wise to take the muddle of nomenclature in psychology very seriously; but its realization ought to be a sign to begin work at the other end. In trying to do this we abandon, of course, the easy road of making chains of plausible definite terms, which, as one of the most commendable features, has the soothing effect of making us believe that after all the principles are simpler than the facts themselves. Simpler they may be, but if made too simple they are not much of an achievement, and, alas! in their application they cease to be more than of casual interest, especially to those who actually do work with the insane. Nobody looks with more suspicion at these inventions of terminology than the active alienist himself, and we can safely say that for a while to come the best criterion of a profitable attitude of mind is whether we can hold the attention of the average working force of our hospitals and stimulate to activity and interest in the actual cases.

We should bear in mind that the concept of dementia praecox had better be looked upon as designating a perspective of deterioration and, thereby, the most important feature in many cases.

In many cases the deterioration is, however, not imminent, nor the most interesting feature; it is a result to be borne in mind and to be dreaded, but not as directly interesting as the process which threatens miscarriage. In a fairly large number of cases we should therefore designate the process not with the term of a possible or even probable outcome but with one designating the principle at work—the hysteroid reaction, the abnormal habit-reaction, the type of attention defect and of judgment defect.

As soon as we shall learn more about these specific factors of individual cases, the term which designates the perspective of the broad group will be replaced by terms designating the principles at work; but they will be quite different from the "confusion" and *Wahnsinn* [nonsystematized delusion], etc., of the present day— terms which must be sacrificed and will not be wanted again. We shall thus relegate the term "dementia praecox" to those cases which have in the very center the stamp of deterioration; while cases in many ways akin to these, but with a less certain deterioration, will pass as allied to dementia praecox, as I have called them in order not to multiply nomenclature prematurely. The subforms such as the hebephrenic and the catatonic and the paranoid will in the main preserve a standing but they will appear less important as we learn to single out the determining factors. As our knowledge increases, combination terms designating etiology and reaction-type, and possibly a measure of the balance, will take the place of the as yet rather schematic types; but for the time being the small number of types taken over by Kraepelin from Kahlbaum and Hecker will be used without much hairsplitting.

Etiologically, the constitutional make-up counts for a great deal, but not in the vague sense of heredity and degeneracy merely. There is much more to be had in the study of deterioration of the habits and undermining of instincts and their somatic components.

Therapeutically, this way of going at the cases will furnish the best possible perspectives for action. We stand here at the beginning of a change which will make psychiatry interesting to the family physician and practitioner. As long as consumption was the leading concept of the dreaded condition of tuberculosis, its recognition very often came too late to make therapeutics tell. If dementia is the leading concept of a disorder, its recognition is the declaration of bankruptcy. Today the physician thinks in terms of tuberculosis infection, in terms of what favors its development or suppression; and long before "consumption" comes to one's mind, the right principle of action is at hand—the change of habits of breathing poor air, of physical and mental ventilation, etc.

In the same way a knowledge of the working factors in dementia praecox will put us into a position of action, of habit training, and of regulation of mental and physical hygiene, as long as the possible "mental consumption" is merely a perspective and not an accomplished fact. To be sure, the conditions are not as simple as with an infectious process. The balancing of mental metabolism and its influence on the vegetative mechanisms can miscarry in many ways. The general principle is that many individuals cannot afford to count on unlimited elasticity in the habitual use of certain habits of adjustment, that instincts will be undermined by persistent misapplication, and that the delicate balance of mental adjustment and of its material substratum must largely depend on a maintenance of sound instinct and reaction-type.

There is not much definition yet about the histological process which is the structural expression of the deterioration. Its slightness suggests a mere bankruptcy under anomalous or even ordinary demands with insufficient funds of adjustment. Many forms are so acute that they suggest a histologically well-defined crisis; but the data are still too slender—the neuroglia increase of the deeper cortical layers and various other findings.

For any settlement of the histological problem we need more data which would form a chain of events instead of mere fragments; and when we can say that we have the histological changes in the controllable intoxication well in hand, we may also be able to attack those much more subtle variations which go with the ordinary functional states. As long as we have not even solid ground with regard to such contrasts as sleep and wake states, or an alcoholic intoxication and the normal state, we must not try to stretch the histological facts of the dementia praecox types, not even with a compliment to the favorite notion of autointoxication —that simplifying formula which merely exalts the art of purging, and is meant to spare the physician the trouble of studying the more complex facts about the patient. Encourage the laboratory man to search every gland of the body, from the liver to the parathyroid, but do not spoil his pleasure in possible discoveries by saturating the atmosphere with stale autointoxication guesses.

In his eagerness to get rid of pre-biological conceptions of mind, the disciple of Aesculapius believes he has to overcorrect commonsense, rule out mental reactions from the domain of legitimate study, and reduce all mental diseases to the paradigm of general paralysis. If he continues to believe that the only condition of mental health lies with the proper amount of indican and the ideal status of the parathyroid, and a few other glands which lack of knowledge makes a home for a wealth of theories, he misses his chance with the great percentage of simple dementias. Mind, like every other function, can demoralize and undermine itself and its organ, and the entire biological economy, and to study the laws of the miscarriage of its function and life is one of the conditions for any true advancement in psychopathology.

SUBSTITUTIVE ACTIVITY AND

REACTION-TYPES

From "The Problems of Mental Reaction-Types, Mental Causes and Diseases," by Dr. Meyer, in Psychological Bulletin, 5:245 (Aug. 15, 1908); and "The Relationship of Hysteria, Psychasthenia and Dementia Praecox," read by Dr. Meyer before the New York Psychiatrical Society, March 4, 1908, Nervous and Mental Disease Monograph Series No. 9, Studies in Psychiatry, 1:155 (1912).

Odd as it may seem, psychopathology has produced most fruitless debates over two of its favorite issues: the desire to understand the peculiar reaction of mind as signs of irritation or other lesions of its organ, and the effort to use in a dogmatic way the medical formula of specific diseases.

Both of these tendencies are legitimate and fruitful enough in their sphere, but outside of it they become a distracting and misleading rut, away from the line of sanest development.

To counteract this I have made use of the term "substitutive activity" for a group which it is unprofitable to discuss from a neurological viewpoint, and I have tried to divest the notion of diagnosis and disease of its dogmatic noumenal characteristics.

First, the foundation for the term "substitutive activity."

Psychopathology has been somewhat misled by traditional psychology to a premature stabilization concerning an issue which is relatively unessential except for systematic analysis: the problem of elements of mental life with its inherent hankering for the

Ding an sich [thing-in-itself, noumenon]. Most psychiatries make us believe that morbid mental activity is morbid owing to the introduction of absolutely abnormal additional elements, and they enumerate them as hallucinations, delusions, melancholia and mania, obsessions, etc. With these supposedly specific products of "disease" the psychopathologist proceeded to apply the venerable formula ubi est morbus [where the disease is], and it utilized the systematized inferences of neurology, until finally the dogma arose that what we call mental in daily life could not be scientific unless it was translated into a form of metaneurology—a systematization of neurological inferences, usually least supported by those who have a firsthand knowledge of the brain and its lesions.

The result was that psychopathological inquiry rested its case on an archaic method which clings to it even where the modern developmental and relational formula of knowledge and inquiry with its three dimensions and obligatory time-component, viz., the formula of experiment, has superseded the static, geometrical schemes which telescoped the natural events if possible into one plane devoid of time-component, thus playing with dynamic principles to the extent of making even biologically thinking men content with the parallelistic theory.

The consequence of the noumenal attitude—the attitude that hunted for the Ding an sich, the element and if possible its "lesions," instead of the events in terms of experiment—is that the events which should occupy us are not studied as experiments of nature, on the ground on which they are accessible, but on the ground of a system of assumptions which forms a pseudoscientific tautology, just as the morality of the past had to rest on a religious-moral construction rather than on the plain sociological and individual needs. Most of what is offered as neurological explanations of mental processes and especially abnormal mental processes is a tendential precipitation of a mixture of truisms and assumptions into a terminology of a field in which there is today no possibility of bringing the conclusions to a test. It is neurologizing tautology of what had better be expressed as we experience it: biological reactions of the mental type.

Neurology certainly has its field, and is one of our most valuable controls, but why should we surrender to it the wholesome pluralism of practical life when we work in psychopathology?

To reduce the facts and events of this world to a system in which they can stand word by word as peacefully coexistent, as in an encyclopedia, with elimination of the time-component and with a towering logic of noumena, was the luring dream of an earlier stage of knowledge. To see things as participants of *events*, to reduce the complex *events* to simpler *events*, but still events with a time-component, is the modern logic of science and also the leading feature of biological psychiatry, and we favor it especially because its schemes give us space to note essential factors and components of our observation and logic of events which were too hastily crushed out in the telescoping process copied from the logic of words.

To describe events, biological or nonbiological, we record the starting points or conditions of the outset, then the developments, and the final result and resting point. We are satisfied with the correctness of the picture and the implied interpretation, if the various steps are in harmony with fundamental experiments or thoroughly tested and standardized events, and if we find that the experience with principles of modifications of the experiment allows us to correctly foretell the modification of the results.

This practical attitude allows us to take account of all the corollaries concerning the material which enter into the events. The psychological observations must tally with the laws of neurology, or if they do not there is cause for a danger signal. Since, however, not every psychologist is a neurohistologist, we should encourage all methods which keep the observer on the ground on which he has a fund of experience—the observer of mental life, behavior, and conduct on the ground of mental life (in the sense of biological adaptation of the type of behavior and conduct) and the neurologist on the ground of neurological experiments; but last of all things should we encourage the hasty translation of events into inferential schemes of structure, the psychological histology and the histopathological psychopathology. I have too much respect for the spheres of histology and study of behavior, with their respective laws of propriety and rules of test and control, to encourage the hybridization which does not usually favor high standards in the outcome.

We therefore see in psychopathology the study of abnormal behavior and of the modifiability of its determining factors. To use a slang phrase: we study what is doing, and the safest final test we can introduce, better than that of any ready-made and plausible nerve-cell scheme, is the question: "How does the result of an analysis influence the observer's *action* in the shaping of events or in formulating the experiment of nature?" The most essential achievement is not the erection of a word palace of logic or of description, but the enlargement of our command of action, however modest.

Creation of comparative standards with the same denominators, and measurement of the achievements by their influence on our action in further analysis or in fruitful modification of the experiment, is the ideal which I should like to make for.

For a long time physicians had to discourage attempts to explain abnormal conduct along the lines of what we experience with the supposedly normal. In the first place, this averse attitude was most urgently demanded by medicine as long as human conduct was too exclusively sized up according to moral schemes to be looked at in a fair, matter-of-fact manner. Abnormal mental reactions were met with the schemes of moral training and punishment on a doctrine of sin, even when rating the situation as sinfulness was glaringly a grave transgression of justice. The physician further saw that under the guidance of ordinary, untrained, everyday, practical psychology, abnormal conditions were often not satisfactorily influenced, and he settled into the noncommittal regime of procuring rest and protection and physical improvement; and since there was no inducement to look for the possibly helpful, though less obvious, psychological determining factors, he satisfied the instinctive impulse for explanations in a chase for the histological noumenon, that is, the "real" morbid cause, encouraged by the dogma that mind is anyhow either an epiphenomenon or an independent essence, outside of the sphere of the physician.

As we study anomalies of mental activity and conduct we find some plainly due to extrapsychological events, for instance, happenings in the brain, such as vascular occlusions with consequent softenings, or inflammatory processes, or simple senile atrophy, or intoxications; that is, conditions which in their etiology, evolution, and outcome are clinched in terms of physiology and pathology of the nutrition and vascular apparatus of the brain. There are, however, other disorders in which the circulatory and nutritional facts are merely incidental, and which we find best expressed in terms of mental events or reactions and their consequences. As such I should mention the results of emotional shock or of emotional fretting, or of continued uncorrected and unchecked false reasoning. Since in these conditions certain infra-psychic biological reactions are frequently found to be at fault as well, through incidental loss of sleep, and malnutrition, etc., the physician is inclined to overrate them in his psychophobia and, finally, to *assume* these subcerebral conditions as the noumenal or "real" cause, even where he does not *find* them or has nothing whatever to work on.

In the face of these tendencies and especially in connection with the study of hysteria and psychasthenia, it has become possible to demonstrate chains of mental happenings which tend to fulfill all the conditions of an experiment, *i.e.*, to single out the initial factors, to show their natural elaboration and the development of the inevitable result; moreover, it has become possible to show how successful treatment depends on definite laws of modifiability of these factors.

One of the first things that has proved of value in this direction has been the abandonment of fussing over the supposed *elements* of psychology and the attempts to explain the chains of events out of such elements. It proved to be much more satisfactory to speak in terms of situation, reaction, and final adjustment and to describe all the facts of interaction according to their weight without excessive scruples over the systematization of what will be the last thing to reach a stage of more than logical certainty. It is better to use the broad concepts of instincts, habits, interests, and specific experiences and capacities, than the concepts of structural analysis at the present stage of our biological knowledge.

Some of the reactions are so closely akin to what we experience in normal life that they do not create any difficulty. An excessive depression, leading to a suicidal attempt and a profound alteration of the whole biological attitude, presents a plausible chain of evolution, and is apt to tell us all that we can act upon in the case. But how about the hysterical developments, or psychasthenia with its strange ruminations and tantrums, or the odd reactions in delusional states where the patient becomes apparently incomprehensible? In all these conditions somatic explanations have been tried; hallucinations have been described and explained as the outcome of peripheral irritation with resulting secondary sensations, or hallucinations and delusions have been described as sejunction of nerve mechanisms. Visceral anesthesias and paresthesias have been appealed to without in the main achieving more than paraphrasing the conditions or broadening the field from which valuable explanations can be taken, which helped in relaxing the one-sided dogma of exclusive salvation in anatomy sufficiently so that some investigators again see practical advantages in working along functional and experimental lines.

As soon as we make the reactions appear as part of an adjustment, a response to a demand, the issue of our investigation becomes infinitely more practical and nearer to what we really can handle. Steering clear of useless puzzles liberates a mass of new energy. When we come to such waves of events as sleep, or many of the more strictly mental reactions such as emotions, and still more, the complex, compound reactions such as a day's work, we cannot get along with a bulky inventory of a body of a definite number and arrangement of cells and interaction without outside stimuli grouped according to these cell-units of our scheme and the elements of structural psychology, but must accept higher units, reaction-curves, reaction-types, and without dropping back into a faculty psychology we are forced to admit as practical the characterization of reactions as part of *an adjustment, a response to a demand.*

What recommends this concept as a preliminary summary formula is its close adaptation to the fundamental formula of systematized experience, the experiment. The reactions are put down as experiments, as adjustments of a situation. This puts us on the track of facts without our altering them to nonrecognition and putting them into a narrowing strait jacket of traditional assumptions. The excessive fear of the personal equation is ridiculous. The first step has always been keen observation of some real events or real possibilities, and the analysis of the means is a secondary process. Newton's apple story and the steaming pot of Watts are anecdotes in point, perhaps not historically true but illustrative of what happened. In the concrete things we surrender more quickly our defects of observation and judgment than in the routine of traditional systems which create anomalous settings not easily checked. The theorizing is an inevitable evidence of the type of mind that can discover things, but the discoveries lie in a keen grasp on actual events and sensitiveness to new facts.

Within this study of adjustments, the concept of substitutive reactions is meant to keep us from wandering from the ground of the experimental formula of investigation. To try and explain a hysterical fit or a delusion system out of hypothetical cell alterations which we cannot reach or prove is at the present stage of histophysiology a gratuitous performance. To realize that such a reaction is *a faulty response or substitution of an insufficient or protective or evasive or mutilated attempt at adjustment* opens ways of inquiry in the direction of modifiable determining factors and all of a sudden we find ourselves in a live field, in harmony with our instincts of action, of prevention, of modification, and of an understanding, doing justice to a desire for directness instead of neurologizing tautology.

The conditions which we meet in psychopathology are more or less abnormal reaction-types which we want to learn to distinguish from one another, trace to the situation or conditions under which they arise, and study for their modifiability. For this reason I teach the students to start essentially from six types of disorders or reaction-types:

1. The reactions of organic disorders:

a. Types which can be reduced to the symptom complexes of asymbolia (mind-blindness and mind-deafness), apraxia and aphasia, and the symptoms of callosal lesions.

b. Reactions, on ground of focal or diffuse affections, in the form of epileptoid responses, actual motor fits, or psychic epilepsy, or less defined states of bewilderment or dazed activity, wandering, or acts of violence, usually with subsequent amnesia; or states of diffuse memory defects and defective judgment—(a) Korsakoff's complex: very deficient retention, relatively clear grasp of what is in sight, but hopeless time disorientation and fabrications; (b) general paralysis: especially marked discrepancies in dates and calculations, change of sensitiveness and judgment, and extravagant notions; and (c) senile reaction: defective memory, retention, and orientation; tendency to live in reminiscences, often with occupation-delirium.

2. Delirious states with dreamlike imaginative experiences, hallucinations, especially of sight, or especially of hearing, fleeting or more systematized under a leading effect (fear, suspicion), with deficient grasp and orientation; reaction in direct intoxication (hashish, belladonna), or fever or exhaustion, or prolonged exhaustive, toxic, or infective influences. The exogenous (toxic-exhaustive) and organically determined forms usually show certain *physical* marks of their own; the endogenous or psychogenic types (hysterical or epileptic delirium or other psychogenic tantrums) are usually marked by stigmata of their own (hysterical or epileptoid marks and setting), and traceable to substitutive reaction-types.

3. The essentially affective reactions: the manic-depressive reaction-types are marked by oscillations in the direction of feeling of well-being and exaltation and tendency to flight of ideas and activity, or in the direction of feeling of difficulty, retardation, or real inhibition, and sadness, downheartedness, or mixtures of these elements; the anxiety type follows rather the series nervousness—uneasiness—anxiety; the simple depressions are, more or less, excesses of normal depression.

4. Paranoic developments—with formally correct conduct and grasp but inability to adapt the personal trend of thought and elaborations and attitude to the facts. We thus see the following grades of developments:

a. Feeling of uneasiness, tendency to brooding, rumination and sensitiveness, with inability to correct the notions and to make concessions—paranoic constitution and paranoic moods.

b. Appearance of dominant notions, suspicions, or ill-balanced aims.

c. False interpretations with self-reference and tendency to systematization, with or without—

d. Retrospective hallucinatory falsifications, etc.

e. Megalomanic developments, or deterioration, or intercurrence of acute episodes.

f. At any period antisocial and dangerous reactions may result from the lack of adaptability and excessive assertion of the side-tracked personality. Paranoic developments occur wherever assertion of the personality on logical grounds and reasoning occurs on false premises with inadequate realization of need of correction —hence the occurrence of incidental paranoid episodes and the paranoid character of "recovery without insight."

5. Substitutive disorders of the type of hysteria (submersion of the disturbing experience or issue, and conversion of the reaction into the hysterical manifestations, as a rule with amnesic mechanism), and psychasthenia (ruminations leading to states of tension and panic, and substitution of phobias, of obsessions, and incomplete reactions generally).

6. Types of defect and deterioration: existence or development of fundamental discrepancies between thought and reaction, defect of interest and affectivity with odd reactions; dreamy fantastic (crazy) or hysteroid or psychasthenoid reaction, with a feeling of being forced, of peculiar unnatural interference with thought, etc., frequently with paranoid, catatonic, or scattered tantrums.

These conditions are not to be taken as "diagnoses" but as reaction-types: The first two with prominence of somatic conditions; the third and in part the fourth anomalous developments of individual reactions, partly dependent chiefly on the make-up (the genuine manic-depressive and paranoic reactions), and partly dependent more especially on general situations (such as many anxiety states and simple depressions). The fifth and the sixth groups are less overt and direct excesses of response than direct faulty substitutions of variously conditioned modes of evasion, untimely evolution of instincts, etc. In every anomalous mental constellation we ascertain: (1) The infra-psychic components (general somatic disorders or effects of disorders of special organs, including the nutritional and coarsely histological disturbances of the nervous system); (2) the components which are fully sized up only with psychological conceptions, either overt and direct miscarriage, or substitution.

With such a subdivision the student is at once put on a practical basis which is suggestive of the main directions of discrimination and action in terms of the accessible facts. He is expected to describe the case with a view to the situation and personal factors and to discriminate between anomalous reactions which point essentially to infra-psychic disorders and others, chiefly *excessive* responses of individual reaction, and still others which are provisionally best described as substitutive reactions, *usurping* the place of what is wanted to really meet the constellation and suggesting an inquiry into what determines the substitution (the hysterical or psychasthenic or other reactive habits with or without circumscribed "complexes").

It is obvious that with such an arrangement of our data we break with the sham problems of psychophysical parallelism and much of what constitutes traditional psychology. Structural psychology has its place in psychopathology as a help in the discriminative and analytical problem of identification of events; but dynamic conceptions must constitute the problem proper. In order to be dynamic the "mental reactions" are taken as complete phases of adaptation, or conduct and behavior, including both the "physical" and the "mental" aspects, as reactions of adjustment of the person as a whole in contrast to the nonmental reactions or activities of the special somatic organs.

The mental reactions are necessarily physical, but contrasted with the nonmental reactions, and distinguished by the qualitative feature of consciousness in the modes of their hanging-together. They are the *attitudes and reactions of the person as a whole.* They have their anabolic and catabolic aspects. Their temporary constellation determines the start and execution of any new reactions; they may make for smoothness in the reactions *or* interfere both in the proper hanging-together and flow of adjustments *and* in the anabolic and catabolic balance. Disorders may prevail in either direction, in the adaptation of the stream of activity to mental or functional balance, and in that of the nutritional issue, according to definite laws of incompatibility. But the function and its disorder *may* be the only accessible material to work with. Jung speaks of the effects of complexes and claims the production of toxins, while I insist more on the interference with smooth and adequate habit-reactions and responses with possibilities of anabolic and catabolic disturbances. Why then should we have to insist so on the "physical disease," if it is a mere formula of some vague obstacles, while the functional difficulties give a plain and controllable set of facts to work with?

It is deplorable that what can at the best be only a temporary help and scheme to give the facts of a complex disorder like dementia praecox a suggestive and helpful order, should be given as rigid and dogmatic a position by physicians as that which figures definitely as a disease. The "disease" is a formula which becomes vague and distracting unless it sums up some essential facts or embodies some workable heuristic principles. The notion of disease or disease entities is hardly ever conspicuous where it is easy to maintain the entity. Fractures and contusions are so plain that we need no noumena back of them; in infectious diseases the formula is equally plain: an organism with a certain susceptibility to a definite form of infection reacts in a definite manner. A large complex of "diseases" consists of insufficiency or poor adaptation of function to demand, in other words, disorders of regulation. As soon as these disorders entail deficient repair of progressive structural alterations in any given part of the mechanism, that feature is apt to be singled out as the "disease" or, as medical slang has it, "the pathology."

The "disease" is the noumenon for certain expectations about combinations of manifestations. If the term is to have any value it turns on some facts which may be superficial or recondite but which must mark points of central interest. In their contrast between hysteria and dementia praecox, Bleuler and Jung appeal to the difference of the "disease." What constitutes a disease unit is either merely a reaction-type or it is a reaction-type under special etiology and special evolution and outcome, or it is possible to single out a definite item of events (infection or intoxication or even a simple rough injury or a lesion). But in these days in which the experimental interpretation has become so much superior to the old-fashioned way of telescoping events into the concept of a "lesion," we cannot afford any longer to ignore the chains of conduct and behavior or mental reactions, as they may give the safest and most sufficient presentation of the facts in a disorder.

The maintenance of the disease concept has a great advantage for orderly thinking, but like the neovitalistic modes of presentation of biological facts, it would be most detrimental if it should be considered as more than a formula of available facts or a starting point of more fundamental work. Under all circumstances we must beware, however, of any a priori definitions which might rule out strings of facts because they are "mental."

We have strong reasons to consider the foundation of these reaction-types to be the result of conflicts and deviations of instincts, and in cases of deteriorations we find invariably that the complex-phenomena occur in an especially vulnerable field, or denote from the start the deficiency of balancing instincts.

Why should a patient drift so strongly into more or less absurd imaginations preeminently in the sexual domain, in religious elaborations, and in fantastic spheres? Why should there be such a striking tendency to ideas of reference which denote so strongly a feeling of inferiority of action? What determines the striking tendency to feelings of passivity, of being influenced, etc., in the automatisms, which the more hysterical takes in a self-possessed, not in a passive, attitude?

A careful study of the cases shows the ravages of habitually incomplete or directly inadequate and ill-adapted and ill-controlled reactions, a tendency away from contact with reality and self-correction, a scattering of the personality, with or without the sham consistency which we see in the paranoic forms, and through it all a stultifying of the instincts which are essential for balancing in the complex demands of life. We therefore attribute a pernicious effect to a trauma in the sense of Freud or Jung, even when, instead of its merely leading to the hysterical reaction-type, it plays a role in an actual interference of development of instincts. In this respect it takes little skill to realize how different the sexual evolution of the hysterical is from that of the dementia praecox case; there is much more inferiority or miscarriage of function in the future dementia praecox case, to suggest voices or electric currents in the womb, or the imaginations of love answered by a stranger through passive movements of the tongue. In all this we invariably see additional interweaving of habit-deteriorations, ruminations instead of youthful pranks and of a rash trial-and-rejection method of the more wholesome development, with its instinct for touch with reality. And beside these defects we see precocious one-sided moralizing, top-heaviness, leading the patient further and further away from the life with concrete corrections.

The effect of spreading into ill-protected domains and the determination of the seriousness of such combinations are easy to demonstrate in the question of masturbation, which to this day is dealt with in the most dogmatic and absurd fashion by a large number of physicians who think they can settle the issue by the negation of all importance, and the mere assumption of fundamental defect where it happens to lead to disaster. Masturbation, like the use of alcohol, must be judged specially in every case.

It will be the task of a publication of a sufficient number of thoroughly studied cases to show the lines of cleavage between deviations of instincts which do and which do not become progressively destructive. Thinking of these matters in terms of auto-intoxication is not ruled out if such a relation is demonstrated, nor should we of course be satisfied with an abstract statement that we deal with conflicts and deterioration of instincts; but at the present juncture it is best to recognize the probability that in many cases a number of factors combine and that among these, many can only be expressed in activities, habits, and instincts

206 The Commonsense Psychiatry of Dr. Adolf Meyer

and that a sweeping oversimplifying terminology obscures the clearness of observation and reasoning.

Neurology has led us too much out of a functional appreciation of developments. It reasons largely with stationary and progressive focal conditions and their occasional repair, rather than with balancing mechanisms, such as we must work with in psychopathology.

The concept of substitutive reactions brings us back to a normal foundation of direct activity again. It frees us from excessive definitions at loose ends, furthers definition of the actual situation and of the means of adaptation available in the patient. Instead of a plan of identification with names of arbitrary patterns, we get attention to the facts at hand without arbitrary expurgations. We can see and teach what we have in the pure cultures of hysteria, psychasthenia, and dementia praecox, and if we find collaboration of special factors, we have a place for them according to the facts, be they of the type of regulation of conduct and behavior, *i.e.*, mental, or infra-psychic, toxic, or what not.

This mode of presentation can be made just as simple as that which works with the disease entities and much more just and especially much more valuable in plans of handling the case and in shaping facts for prophylaxis.

PLAN OF EXAMINATION

From Notes of Clinics in Psychopathology *by Adolf Meyer and G. H. Kirby, at p. 99, privately printed* (1908).

The examination consists of a series of tests of efficiency of the various organs and functions, and the coordination of the results for the determination of the types and nature of disorders. The record consists of the family history, the description of type of make-up before the onset, the components of the etiological constellation, and the course of the disease up to the examination. The direct findings must be given in exact terms of test and reaction and, in the mental examination, to quite an extent, with the verbatim account of question (or prompting) and answer. A stenographic record is frequently essential.

For a complete review of a case for diagnostic purposes we need:

1. A sizing-up of the situation, *i.e.,* the situation and circumstances to which the patient is expected to adapt himself or which he fails to meet. In this respect we find that in some disorders the situation matters little (especially in toxic-infectious disorders, direct affection of the brain) except inasmuch as it brings with it the toxic or infectious or other factors. In the psychogenic disorders, however, the situation is apt to be the very cause of the finally unbalanced state of reaction and requires a careful study.

2. The somatic material of adaptation—as shown by a "physical examination."

3. The mental status.

THE MENTAL CONDITION

1. The general demeanor and adaptation to the environment without the patient realizing the observation or examination, but including helps from the nurses and friends: the appearance and trend of mood and activity (commonsense picture with due reference to the points of special diagnostic importance). ·

2. The patient's own spontaneous or half-spontaneous picture of the condition and the spontaneous drift of mental activity and utterances, to be recorded with discretion, so as at least to give a clear point of departure for further investigation, and a picture of the spontaneous productivity and the nature of the stream of thought and activity. It is especially necessary to give a verbatim sample where the stream of mental activity and reactions shows peculiarities of diagnostic importance, and these are to be analyzed and tested in the subsequent inquiry.

These two headings cover in a preliminary way the questions: "What does the patient do? And what does the patient say?"

3. The systematic investigation of special features of the patient's general mental trend: the existence of special moods and emotional traits (sadness, anxiety, fear, uneasiness, puzzlement, bewilderment, apathy or abnormal ease, elation, irritability, etc.), and of imaginative and foreign reactions (delusional and hallucinatory states,* and their foundation and importance in the entire picture), and topics of rumination, and evidence of substitutions (obsessions, etc.).

In the three topics given, special attention is to be paid to the reactions which are of diagnostic importance: the existence of the manic-depressive, catatonic, and other reactions, with careful attention to the description of what the patient actually does and says, and the situation to which he reacts.

---

* Delusions are false notions or beliefs; an "insane" delusion is a false notion or belief by nature or origin of such character as to demand legal protection of the patient or of society (any other than a definition of practice to be avoided); hallucinations are false impressions of things present when there is no outside cause for a sensation; illusions, merely false interpretations of actual sensations.

4. The special inquiry into the condition of the sensorium (the appreciation of sensory stimuli and the responsiveness to impressions), as shown in the grasp on the past and present, and including: tests for orientation as to place, time, and persons, memory of recent and remote events, retention, fund of information, counting and calculating, reading, enunciation, writing.

5. The patient's judgment covering himself and the situation and his disease (insight).

6. The evolution of the symptoms in several days or weeks of observation, and the correlation with existing physical disorders.

This plan is to be adapted as seems most profitable. Not infrequently topics under *4* are to be taken before those of *3;* but under all circumstances all the topics must be covered as far as possible, in order to exclude serious surprises, oversights of general paralysis, etc.

The mental reaction-types present too many combinations to allow of easy tabulation, but the types [outlined in preceding chapter] are to be borne in mind.

Since the conditions are complex and the factors involve great variability, one-word diagnoses are not desirable; but an estimate of the facts presupposes a designation of nature and type of developments in the light of the symptomatic evolution, the etiological factors, conclusions with regard to forecast, and the possibility of therapeutic modification.

The following questions must therefore be answered: "What is the faulty reaction? What are the conditions that led to it? How does it react to special tests and attempts at modification? What can we expect to achieve, and what are the steps to be taken?"

We thus stand largely on the ground of dynamic pathology, since the traditional question of an anatomical pathology—"Where and what is the lesion?"—is as a rule not answerable, or at least not a matter of direct demonstration but largely of inference, and in many cases observable and manageable only through the functions of the supposedly deranged mechanism. The proper use of the outline presupposes a good grasp on the organic and functional disorders with which general medicine and neurology deal. Moreover, it demands a working knowledge of dynamic psychology.

As standard material for our conclusions we use:

1. Cases which were well observed in their entire evolution to recovery or autopsy, showing the principles to be used in other cases.

2. The constructive principles of general pathology, *i.e.*, our knowledge of fatigue, intoxication, various brain disorders, autochthonous or as a result of disorders of remote organs, and our knowledge of mental conflicts and types of inadequate reactions.

Since neither the clinical psychopathology nor the constructive psychopathology is in any way complete, we must make it a rule to apply both methods for what they are worth and never exclusively.

THE CRIMINAL INSANE AND

MEDICO-LEGAL PROBLEMS

From "The Problems of the Physician Concerning the Criminal Insane and Borderland Cases," by Dr. Meyer, in Journal of the American Medical Association, 54:1,930 (June 11, 1910).

The layman and, I am afraid, most lawyers consider insanity as a condition characterizing a more or less final subdivision of humanity which is, or should be, fenced in by asylum walls.

Insanity is not a "disease" in the sense in which tuberculosis or leprosy is a disease, but it is a condition to which a number of totally different diseases may lead; some of them clearly mental disturbances from the outset, mental defects, or poorly balanced mental habits miscarried to a point where the individual is no longer able to extricate himself, where he cannot be considered competent to manage his own affairs and to look out for his personal interests, not to speak of the altruistic demands. Some of these other diseases which may lead to insanity are more or less clearly the effect of poisons or of the undermining of the metabolism of the nervous system. Still others are diseases directly affecting the structure of the brain, through tumors, or injuries, or vascular disease, or the like.

The nervous system is in one way a very enduring and hardy tissue; it loses least in states of emaciation, but it has little power of reconstruction if once organically damaged. This is the cause of the existence of the irrecoverable wrecks who no doubt form a class requiring for life special care and protection against themselves and the encroachment of others.

But on the other hand, functional disorders of a character most alarming to the uninformed are absolutely curable: the patients pass through periods in which they are not themselves, and then again reach a comparatively normal state in which they can hardly understand the abnormal actions ascribed to them. The fact that twenty to twenty-five per cent of those who come to our state hospitals can be discharged recovered, and nearly as many fit for a protected home existence, shows that we are dealing not with a permanent class of individuals but with a group of diseases apt to present a common feature of more or less deep and more or less permanent disorder of conduct and behavior. The number of those who pass merely as nervous, but who have really the same disorders with less marked affection of conduct, is difficult to guess. From a medical point of view it is well to remember that the common saying that neurasthenics and hysterics and psychasthenics do not become insane is a comforting tradition, but one not well borne out by experience, when those terms are used in a broad sense.

If we do not deal with a definite unit but with widely differing disorders, what is the common link that makes us speak not of "insanities," as we should, but of "insanity"?

They tend to make it necessary to interfere with the patient's own control and legal responsibility. They affect the patient's ability to regulate his conduct and behavior, and expose him and others to risks, perhaps only through his unwillingness to accept ordinary rules of hygiene and medical direction, refusal to rest, refusal of food, tendency toward self-mutilation or suicide, or aggressiveness and liability to disturbance of the peace, or actual violent assault.

Or the patient may betray an unwarranted yielding to impulses, such as unchecked sexual yearnings, from merely platonic pursuit and insistence by letter to startling expressions of affection, proposals and attack, or a mere surrender to the opportunities of immoral houses; or the impulse leads to drink and its dangers; or to a wild and reckless spirit of expenditure, shown, for instance, by buying a dozen pairs of shoes, ordering a champagne bath in the Waldorf-Astoria, or ordering a piano each to a whole string of female friends; or inner emptiness and unrest combine to prompt kleptomania, or incendiarism. Or a husband says that his wife has either become a tantalizing faultfinding devil, making his life miserable by insinuations and scenes and complaints and inconsistent behavior, or she must be sick; it is a question which he cannot settle or put up with any longer; something must be done to control the aberration. Or the wife of a well-known ghost hunter begins to take the spirit warnings too seriously, beyond all reason, and creates embarrassing situations. Or note the attacks ranging from terror in epilepsy, to the fright and suspicion in alcoholic delirium and states of persecution, and to all the strange and startling outbreaks of the fantastic dementia praecox.

These are some of the innumerable difficulties the patients, or their friends, get into and the point is reached at which the former have to be checked. When the danger is acute and great, as in fever delirium, matters are not minced; the patient is unquestioningly left under the direction of the physician, taken to a hospital, kept there and if necessary held in bed and subjected to the treatment and hospital rules without any discussion about the legal rights of the citizen. The citizen's first duty there is to submit to lawful order and best regime.

In many other "insanities" the patients are just as unable to control themselves and to look out for themselves; they also remonstrate and resist, but in such a way as to appeal more connectedly to the fellow citizen and to demand legal consideration. To take such patients to general hospitals is unsuitable because they often do not do well there, are disturbing, often do not feel sick, and feel out of place. They need physicians and nurses trained to meet the peculiar demands, and perhaps merely a routine of orderly, quiet life with occupation, and sufficient rest and protection against irritating influences.

The only available places are the private sanitariums and our state hospitals which serve as homes for the incurable and for the acutely disturbed and also for those in the protracted states of mental unbalance. To judge from contact with many trustees and visitors, these institutions are places really little known to the public, little known even by the authorities controlling these hospitals, and by the judges and the average physician and other persons likely to be appealed to for advice when the conduct of a patient becomes difficult to control. Outsiders repeat antiquated tales not much better than the gossip palmed off by "antivivisectionists."

The consequence has been a barbarous, inconceivably stupid fence of laws around the institutions which alone are adequately equipped to bring timely or lasting help to the affected patients. The whole conspiracy of facts and imaginations and traditions has created a class of humanity under a special legal ban called forth for the protection of a few cantankerous individuals, where all that is necessary is the application of the quarantine principles, and provisions for legal reinforcement of medical persuasion and advice, or provisions for legal relief from unwarranted interference.

Nobody has a right to go where he pleases with diphtheria or smallpox. Nobody has a right to display himself in the street in a delirium. Nobody has a right to attempt or to commit suicide. The more we look on the matters as issues of health, the more do we accept even the impending danger as reason for action. We do not want to wait until a person exposed to smallpox breaks out all over, because he is a danger to the community before that. Even if a diphtheria carrier has not diphtheria sores, he must be quarantined if he is the carrier of a virulent strain. In a mental case much stronger evidence is asked for as a rule by those who do not know the seriousness of the conditions. Danger and threat of suicide can be foreseen by any experienced physician; but a judge may want evidence of unmistakable threats or attempts made. It actually looks more as if the field were ruled by the principles of criminal law with its provisions that nobody can be punished for a thing that has not been done.

We see then even in the case of noncriminals that the term "insane" is a high-water mark justifying the application of *some process of quarantine* or commitment. It applies to a stage or conditions of many kinds of disorders which can exist without being destructive of safety or self-control, but are apt to involve the behavior so as to make protective measures necessary. Quarantine principles would be the ideal thing. Since the restriction applies to individuals who often do not submit to persuasion (as do most reasonable subjects of quarantine) but who object and fail to understand the situation, the right of legal appeal must, of course, be freely granted. It is decidedly an anomaly that has made legal decision obligatory for all admissions to a hospital even if there is not the slightest objection on the part of the patient or friends, or on the part of anyone except the patient deprived of his own judgment—merely to do justice to all the railroading yarns of the dime-novel type or to relieve the superintendent of responsibility.

By another anomaly the committing judge asks the testifying physician whether the patient is insane. To my mind it is the physician's business to state what the patient says and does and shows in the way of disease, and that the disorders thus reported prove him incompetent to direct his own case. It is the judge's privilege to declare that the patient's condition is that of insanity, while the physician uses whatever medical terminology he may favor, terms which hold good whether the case has reached the high-water mark of insanity or not, and which do not put a painful stamp on the patient and family.

Whenever we say that a patient is insane, we say no more than that he is sick, and that the disorder is one of the kinds of disorder of conduct and behavior demanding certain special precautions of management and especially protection against his or her own warped judgment and impulses. The nature and condition of the disorder which is the physician's chief concern is immaterial to the judge, who cannot know it without study and thus has to keep alive a phantom unit, "insanity," and the notion of an insane class, instead of a problem of quarantine.

We hear sometimes of a contrast of medical and legal definitions of insanity. This is an absurdity. "Insanity" is a term that I, as a physician, hardly ever use spontaneously. It is a practical designation for a practical situation and through our laws it has become a legally sanctioned term, while in psychopathology it has become a secondary issue. In some textbooks there are peculiar strings of words called definitions of insanity. One of the simplest definitions demands that there should be protracted morbid deviation of the condition and conduct of the patient, such as incapacitates him to think, feel, and act in relation to his environment in harmony with the standards of his bringing-up, and such as would entail a danger to himself and others. (This is a good formulation for matters of commitment but too lax for those who assume that insanity should spell irresponsibility. The following definition of the issue in criminal cases was offered by Judge Barnes: "If at the time the crime was committed the defendant knew it was wrong to commit such a crime and had the power of mind to choose either to do or not to do the act and of controlling his conduct in accordance with such choice, then he ought to be held responsible, although he was not entirely or perfectly sane." This definition does not use the term insanity, which really becomes an undesirable complication.)

Law wisely abstains from any attempt at a definition of "insanity." As a matter of fact, it has several widely distinct standards and always according to the specific issue, namely: (1) commitments, (2) legal and testamentary competency, (3) criminal responsibility. The common link is the question of the existence of a mental disorder. The declaration of the legal status of insanity depends on special conditions for each of the three issues mentioned. The commitment, of course, is the most widely and fortunately the most liberally applied category. As such it means nothing but "fit to be taken to a hospital against his consent." For certain contracts and even as a witness such a patient can still be competent, at least as much as a child between twelve and the age of majority, and in many points more. To take away the right of management of the property requires an additional legal procedure.

With regard to testamentary capacity, the law has definite standards of a peculiarly broad character: the testator may be as insane as can be in any other sense as long as he knows the nature of the bounty and his natural responsibilities to his family, and the property relations. Any delusions or disorders not involving these do not make the person incompetent.

With regard to crime the matter is not simple. Many physicians think that a declaration of insanity is equivalent to a declaration of irresponsibility. The consequence of this assumption is an endless quibbling and begging the question. If one feels that one should say "irresponsible," one says "insane"; if responsible, not insane. And yet afterward the excuse is urged that the person was irresponsible because of insanity; or the public may demand the execution of a Prendergast or a Guiteau, in the face of undeniable mental abnormality, so that evidently the issue must be different from that of mere mental disorder. In this matter the written law is somewhat misleading.

Another complication comes through the relation of the corollaries of a state of "insanity" to the punishment. When punishment is measured by responsibility, and mental disorders reduce the responsibility, we come to the further inference that the perpetrator of an insane act shall go free. We shall discuss this monstrosity later.

Let us turn first to the criminal acts themselves. Crime is any act that subjects the doer to legal punishment. Without a specific law no act can be called a crime. Which of these acts occur among the insane?

The bulk of morbidly determined crimes is attributable to states of defective or uneven abnormal development, *i.e.*, the various grades of imbecility, probably about twenty-two per cent. Certain types of imbecility and defective balance are directly called moral insanity. Here we find thefts, forgery, swindling, sexual assaults and exhibitionism and other perversions, sexual murder, acts of revenge and spite, or mere impulse such as incendiarism. About twelve per cent of the cases in Köppen's statistics belong to the paranoic group, much more likely to present distinctly aggressive impulses: murder and assault, disturbance of the peace in church or homes, insults, libel, threats, and forgery or acts of revenge and sham defense. The simply paranoid forms of the deterioration processes lumped together as dementia praecox shine with tramp life, prostitution, exhibitionism, forgery, thefts, and occasionally acts of revenge or sham defense. The paralytic and senile become collectors, thieves, sexually aggressive, perjurers. Their occasionally impulsive acts ally them with the epileptics, who present the most dangerous and brutal assaults, murder, rape, theft, and calumny; hysterics follow similar paths, alcoholics perform acts of revenge and supposed self-defense and at time epileptoid murders. Depression has led to family murder, a sort of vicarious suicide; or even murder committed for the sake of passive suicide by execution, and other abnormal ways of breaking through the morbid feeling of tension and restraint. Manic excitements prompt to transgressions and excesses, especially in sexual matters, or vituperation, or violence.

The question arises, "Are there any crimes which are clearly the act of an insane person?" Concerning this point I should be cautious. Some of the crimes are so blind and violent that they exclude all cool consideration. But this may hold for any acts of passion. If a murder is well planned and well covered up, or if the delinquent acts normally and with perfect coolness, the act may still be the clear result of an abnormal mental state. It is by far the best rule to claim that no crime or act as such can be estimated properly without a study in the light of other acts and tendencies and the general reaction and complete record of the person.

The practical side of the question of the criminal insane is to determine not so much what crimes occur among the insane as what shall be done about certain crimes in which the issue of insanity is raised, and what the aims are of the criminologists and the judges in their decisions. I assume that the aims are: (1) to ascertain the facts, (2) to determine the guilt, (3) to assign the punishment or judicial remedy, (4) to bring about the effects expected from punishment.

As to the determination of guilt, we seem to have a three-cornered interdependence between responsibility, guilt, and punishment. The only safe statement is, I suppose, that responsibility is liability to punishment. We might make that mean that every defendant exercised a certain amount of choice to do better or worse. The lesson which the punishment should teach him and others is that he should have chosen the better course and that, not having chosen it, he has made himself liable to that punishment. It is further supposed that it is his duty as a citizen to know that lesson and that he cannot be excused for not knowing it. Irresponsibility through insanity would, I suppose, only apply if on account of mental defect he never could have learned this, or even with this helpful experience or knowledge he would not have been able, not only to choose the better, but really to know his moral lesson. The whole question of guilt is forced to operate with a hypothetical argument because it presumes an answer to the question whether his condition did allow or might have allowed him to know certain things and to make the proper use of what he did not use or choose. It is the theory of the intent that looms up. However that be, it certainly is best to leave out of discussion the question of free will and determinism which divided the camps in Germany. Practical will and practical determinability is all that concerns us. We need not prejudge the universe by a doctrine.

But now how about punishment? It is, after all, more than retaliation and correction. Our aim is also prevention and protection of society. In this respect jurisprudence cannot remain behind medicine very long. Its rule is, of course, that the individual shall not be punished for acts not committed. We cannot well speak of punishment for mere intentions. Yet we must correct intention. And those intentions which lie, as it were, in the flesh and blood of a constitution long before they are conscious, call for some measures if protection of society demands it.

Social quarantine is the only hope for the future. Actual detention of antisocial elements and the prevention of their propagation are as much or much more our duty than is the quarantine of the leper and of Typhoid Mary and the temporary quarantine of the carrier of smallpox. Punishment which does not prevent is insult added to injury. The question thus should arise in every case and it should be addressed to the competent expert or a commission of experts: "Should the mental disorder or condition found modify the punishment or, to speak more exactly, the disposal of the case? Is the person fit to undergo the ordinary course of justice? Will he be improved by it? Will he need other measures for prevention than the punishment which the law considers a good enough method for the average?"

On this score I should like to say most emphatically that medical jurisprudence has made egregious blunders. It has been sentimentality-mad or the victim of verbal logic. Infinitely less harm would come from making the sick man take the consequences of his liability to such sickness, just as we put a man liable to smallpox under quarantine, instead of letting free a lot of unworthies and raising an appetite for the plea of insanity to a point with exhibits which nauseate every sober-minded citizen. Physicians do not care to be the vaulting pole for escape from natural and proper consequences of a person's nature. It is true we want decent places for the persons detained, chances for a decent and profitable life. Men like Forel have long written and spoken for special colonies for special types of cases. My own feeling is that if we get decent prisons run as they ought to be run, many persons now sent to asylums for criminals or let loose had better be sent to prison, unless it can be shown that actual harm to their mental health would come from it.

Punishment was and is a means of correction in normal education. This has changed much during the past two generations. There has probably been too much of a reaction from the life of Puritan duty. Laws would mean more if we could keep them stern and firm. Among the insane we have abolished the word and thought of punishment. But we have the responsibilities for discipline. We want to make our patients as responsible as possible, and it is mainly our task to protect them from spheres in which they would flounder hopelessly. If you abhor the conception of relative or partial responsibility, I should stand up for the principle that there is no absolute irresponsibility even among the insane and that it is much better to deal with them from case to case for what there is sane in them, not with the principle of retaliation but by placing them with a clear understanding just where they belong, according to their make-up and temporary condition. Where mental disorder is demonstrated, none but the principles of equity will wear well. Can they ever be looked forward to here? They will be as little cherished by the real criminal as the indeterminate sentence is liked by the professional; but every fair-minded victim would fare better than with our present way of using legal rules.

A commonsense consideration of the facts of conduct and behavior is in order, if possible to avoid having the victim really become dangerous and be allowed to perpetuate the poor stock of our race. What a preposterous condition when juries have merely the alternative between the electric chair and acquittal! This is where help is needed and an introduction of equity principles might justify preventive considerations.

We may be a long way from special colonies. Certain individuals can be employed *near* institutions if they are too well to be kept there and too dangerous to go wholly free. And others should at least be asexualized—a point on which I hope more of our citizens will in time agree with us when enough evidence is at hand to convince open-minded opponents.

To look back one moment: The law must give us more clearness as to what it wants. It must be ready to deal with disease according to the principles of disease, and therefore realize the necessity of equity principles (rather than the "rules of the game" of evidence in a fight about liberty) and the necessity of consulting the expert, not only concerning the indefinable term "responsibility" but also the effect of the special condition on the preventive steps required.

How, now, about the physician in a concrete case? In a genuine and unmistakable case of mental disorder in which an accident otherwise amounting to a crime failed to be prevented, the perpetrator will, according to our present practice, be taken to a jail but probably be seen by a physician, if not taken immediately to the proper reception hospital, if one exists.

In almost all the *questionable* cases no move was made to get a competent and trained physician until the question of a "plea of insanity" arose. It should always be a suspicious sign if no move is made equivalent to the examination of the patient for a commitment as soon as possible after the act. Where the defense of the criminal is the main thing and insanity the only means of saving him from the consequence of his act, the procedure is usually from the start a perversion of psychiatry. Physicians are called as partisans; examinations must be made under the most unpropitious circumstances. There is no official impartial record kept such as we demand in a well-conducted hospital today; there are no trained attendants employed.

As soon as the authorities have reason to suspect a mere suspicion of insanity, or of a plea of insanity, the immediate attention of a trained physician should be called; and to be on the safe side every prison physician should have training and experience in psychiatry. He should make a full examination with a satisfactory record and should have the proper type of attendants for the examined prisoner. During the whole stay of the prisoner or suspect the written record of the physician should be kept up, consisting of statements of what the prisoner said, did, and showed on medical examination. Where the condition is doubtful, some states can send the prisoner to a hospital for observation for a maximum period of six weeks. In making an examination for one side or the other, the only way to proceed is to come as near as possible to the plan mentioned. Under well-regulated conditions the competent hospital men of the district should do the work for the state as state officials and they should have the right to apply for a period of hospital observation of the patient and always the duty to furnish a written report. The alienists of the defendant would naturally and automatically be guided by the standards of the official physicians.

Now the physician's share in the determination of guilt! The physician's duty above all things is to determine and report the existence of any mental defect or disorder at the time of examination and in the record of the past. This should consist in the simplest possible terms of what the patient did and said and showed medically, rather than a mere learned treatise on the diagnosis and symptoms which should be reserved for the summing-up of the written record, if one can be demanded.

If there are no plain facts sufficiently convincing to form a demonstration of an abnormal trend, learned terms will only confuse. The aim should be to show that, in other situations and actions, an abnormality was present and that it played a definite role in the determination of the act under legal consideration. To avoid ambiguity, the terms "insane" and "insanity" should be replaced by "mental disorder," specified by its effects in various actions, including or not the act *sub judice* [before the court]. In this, Mercier insists on a psychologic examination of the acts. I agree to this only as long as we move on objective ground. The main question is that of intent. Therefore the relation of the existing disorder to the intent must be defined, and here comes the chief point at issue.

Unfortunately, the role of the physician is at this point involved in an issue which I think should not be looked on as a medical question. If the physician has to say "yes" or "no" to the questions: "Do you consider the patient 'responsible'?" and "Do you consider the patient 'insane'?" he becomes part of the jury or in the absence of a jury expresses himself in a judiciary capacity. Neither responsibility nor insanity is a medically useful or even an admissible term. The physician must make it clear that there is a mental disorder that had or had not a bearing on the act and offer, as far as possible, the evidence by which he can prove it. But the rest is a judicial interpretation gratuitously offered by a physician at the risk of being turned down by a jury or a judge who knows more of the law than the doctor and, at the same time, appears to decide a medical question for him.

I do not want to jeopardize the rest of my propositions by insisting on this subordinate point, however. I favor it because physicians are too well trained in their business and science to believe themselves able to give always an out-and-out positive or negative reply to a question to which they know science and plain fact can give only a conditional reply. Legal practice opposes the concepts of the relative or diminished responsibility, and for this the plain man or layman is available more readily than a man who must aim to keep toward the scientific attitude.

In each case in which a mental disorder is demonstrated, no matter whether it figures as insanity or not, the alternatives of allotment of punishment should be put before the expert for a statement as to the probable effect on the success of the aim of punishment or the effect on the disorder and the needs of protection of society.

Much has been said, and with sad justification, of corrupt medical testimony. It is one of the most disheartening displays of the low standards of our general and business morality. When nobody steps forward to slap the one who can say with impunity, "Every man has his price," we have to hear it until it becomes an accepted standard. And if the professional expert works for his client, what does he do? Ninety times out of a hundred his worst crime is that he assumes what he calls the lawyer's attitude. Where are the legal standards of the great masters? Why do we not ostracize the man who sacrifices the facts and his better knowledge to the undeserved success of his client? This is a matter of public standards of business morality and of morality within the professions. The scandal, I am afraid, is a symptom of our kind of general ethics. I do not know how the legal profession will check the doings of some of its most successful agents of perversion of fact. We physicians are trying to make some of the men accountable for their standards. But they invariably put the blame on the legal methods, the questions asked, and the like.

For this reason I urge a wider use of the *written reports* of the observations and conclusions made by the medical expert which exclude the gambling of the questionnaire without in any way excluding the most searching cross-examination. Most cases are simple and cause little trouble. But the cases which give trouble are just the ones in which a man who poses as expert should make a statement for which he makes himself wholly and unmistakably responsible, without any excuse or subterfuge. German expert testimony has its high standards through no other tangible thing but this accessibility of written and responsible documents.

In trying to prepare this paper I deplored the absence of digests of the practice of our courts. When will the judiciary and the legal world introduce research as an obligatory condition of a career of a teacher and put the young elements to work to keep up a system of monographs and digests and to make inquiries into groups of concrete cases and their specific difficulties and demands, rather than dialectic dissertations? The consideration of concrete cases as practical experiments alone will bring order into the bewildering chaos.

My theses are:

1. The solution of the medico-legal problem of mental disorders generally lies in a further development of the quarantine principle, medically and legally.

2. In handling the criminals presenting mental disorder, jurisprudence will have to develop rules of preventive care besides the rules concerning acts already committed.

3. To avoid begging the question, and confusion of definitions, the question of the bearing of mental disorder should not be settled under the heading of guilt only. Insanity and irresponsibility are not coextensive and should not be made so and are not safe terms medically and legally. Therefore, the procedure should cover

a. The fact of commitment of the act.

b. The existence of mental disorder at the time and its bearing on the act.

c. The bearing of any existing mental disorder or tendency on the legal consequences of the act, the punishment, the prevention of similar acts, etc. In every case with mental disorder it should be obligatory to ask: "What is the relation of the mental disorder to the act? And what does the mental disorder demand to make the punishment and correction and further prevention efficient?"

4. In order to meet the problem of partial responsibility and crimes of passion, the law should create better alternatives than the unwritten law, and in cases of mental disorder the equity procedure should be substituted for an unconditional declaration of not guilty.

5. I strongly suggest the requirement of written statements of facts and opinions by the experts employed as the only means of establishing standards.

7

Dynamic Psychology Established

Psychopathology, the study of unhealthy mental life, received vigorous impetus from the literary output of European researchers working with the principles of dynamic psychology. In America the subject was snatched up as a lively new theme for exploitation in the popular book and magazine market, and the simplification was as misleading as it was entertaining. Conservative physicians, shocked to their moralistic marrow, clung tighter to the old teaching that mental findings must be accepted in terms of physical disorders. The notion of disease died hard—if at all.

Orthodox psychology also refused to be dynamic, and a leading exponent, Professor Edward B. Titchener of Cornell, washed his hands of evaluations, meanings, and associations as matters belonging to "the set of the brain." Meyer pointed out that psychiatry in practice, irrespective of varying theories, had long taken the commonsense route of treatment via occupation and profitable regulation of conduct and interests, and had found it sound. He reiterated his thesis that mind could undermine both itself and the brain through maladjustments, habit-disorders, and their progressively harmful failures. This was true not only of dementia praecox but even more plainly of hysteria, psychasthenia, and many of the depressions. On the other hand, Dr. Eugen Bleuler, Forel's successor at the Burghölzli Clinic, concluded that dementia praecox was an organic disease whose secondary (mental) symptoms were explained by the mechanisms of Freud and Jung.

From Vienna, by way of Zürich and highly articulate adherents, came the psychoanalytic theory of Dr. Sigmund Freud, undertaking to study mental events from the standpoint of repression and the unconscious. It was an unconscious of revengeful determinism. The process of repression led, in hysteria, to conversion into body innervation; in psychasthenia, to substitutions; in paranoia, to projections. These manifestations were interpreted as a defense against painful open expression of desires lodged in the unconscious. Freud first sought to trace undercurrents through hypnosis and later developed a method of analysis which found clues in dreams, forgetfulness, slips of speech, and free ventilation of thoughts. Inevitably the psychosexual life came to the fore—as an emancipated topic of conversation for laymen but a still-forbidden door for many doctors.

"Freud," Meyer wrote in 1906, "has opened the eyes of the physician to an extension of human biology which differs very favorably from the sensational curiosity shop of the literature on perversions." Freud's study of the infantile period was "pedagogically important," an absolutely essential supplement to Stanley Hall's work on adolescence (and Hall himself introduced psychoanalysis in his classes at Clark). Pointing out that Freud was as important to the psychopathologist as the study of dietetics was to the general practitioner, Meyer warned "in fairness to Freud" against an early judgment which might close avenues of exploration, for here was a hypothesis which dealt with life experience—although built on conflicts rather than on a general conception of life.[15] Freud's method of analysis, he added, required "the instinct of the prosecuting attorney and the talent of constructive imagination."

Meyer's own bent was away from "the mystical hankerings which mislead such a large portion of the miracle seekers in our public." When he came to this country he had material on the unconscious that he might have published but did not. Temperamentally he agreed with Dr. James J. Putnam, of Massachusetts General Hospital, who was one of the first American physicians to take up the Freudian theory but who regarded the unconscious as a constant flux, not as an entity. Meyer rejected the imputations of Freud's theory of the unconscious and its mysticism. Psychoanalysis was an "esoteric system" that engendered a spirit of psychiatric denominationalism, a breeder of controversy.

Meyer did not believe in participating in controversies. He ignored the storms and kept steadfast to his principles. It seemed to him that the unconscious would in time cease to be treated as a topic separate from consciousness.

It would be better to realize that there are in the stream of mental activities leading activities and less prominent ones; some closely connected with the leading trend, others more independent or perhaps truly dissociated; some more likely to weigh in the determination of the general trend than others, etc. This would seem to be the very field in which dynamic conceptions will have to find their way into psychology; and as soon as dynamic issues are in the lead, the "conscious" or "subconscious" nature of the event under study will be of interest according to the clearness of the conditions and mechanism of submersion and dissociation.[16]

Freud, Dr. Carl G. Jung (Bleuler's assistant), and Meyer all stood on the ground of dynamic psychopathology, but Meyer did not look for "complexes." He asked: "What is the faulty reaction? What are the conditions that led to it? How does it respond to special tests and attempts at modification? What can we expect to achieve and what are the steps to be taken?" Putting the issue thus, he declared that the Freud-Jung concepts were "too largely emphasis of a portion of the situation," and he expressed his personal preference for "a broad formulation of the problems in terms of substitutive activity." All biological function was adaptation. The pathological person was one who used poorly planned, ill-adapted makeshifts and thereby undermined the development and maintenance of healthy instincts. Meyer's broader base opened the way to prophylactic opportunities, "helping the mental activities themselves to become adjusted to a hygienic balance."

In his work at the Institute he used with success some of Jung's word-association tests for a glimpse into undercurrents. They showed peculiarities of interest and emotional trends. He acknowledged this technique as a great step toward achieving systematic objectivity in the quest for determining factors of psychic life.

Assuming that symptoms were, as a rule, faulty ways of trying to overcome certain difficulties, Meyer strove to uncover these problems and recognize them before the patient drew attention to them by abnormal reactions; and to manage them. Therapy in the past was "like moralizing, trying to induce the individual to live up to abstract ways without any special regard for his difficulties. Now we have learned to shape our work, not according to what the individual ought to be in an abstract way, and according to a definite scheme of making him reach his salvation, but we are ready to deal with the kind of quandaries the patient presents." Understanding how the patient came by his notions helped to show him how to get better results along different lines of thought and application, or along the same line with better judgment. "It is the activities of the person, the whole attitude toward things and his conduct, that we have to regulate." [17]

Much reluctance to size up the data of psychology in terms of behavior had yet to be overcome, although the anatomical evidence for the positions held by Wernicke and Kraepelin was "very largely spurious" and Kraepelin, indeed, suppressed highly valuable facts in adhering to disease processes and specific lesions. Plowing the ground, the New Yorker paved the way for a Viennese; for Freud's visit to Clark University in 1909 served to advertise the dynamic conception in psychiatry and helped to win American acceptance.

Freud had "front-page glamour," in Meyer's phrase. Stanley Hall and Dr. Putnam invited him to take part, with other scientific workers, in the second decennial celebration at Clark—an experience which "encouraged my self-respect in every way," Freud wrote.

In Europe I felt as though I were despised, but in America I found myself received by the foremost men as an equal. As I stepped on the platform at Worcester to deliver my Five Lectures upon Psychoanalysis, it seemed like the realization of some incredible daydream;

psychoanalysis was no longer a product of delusion; it had become a valuable part of reality.[17a]

Along with Freud and Jung, Meyer received a doctor-of-laws degree and also lectured. He elaborated on his dementia praecox concept and indicated his divergence from these distinguished visitors. He had a chance to chat with Freud for a half-hour and received from him a brochure on the Id.

After the celebration, at an interhospital conference for New York State physicians, Meyer discussed psychoanalysis as propounded by Freud (he maintained that Freud had appropriated the term for his own special meaning), and gave it due credit for opening up "many unsuspected paths." When the New York Psychoanalytic Society was formed in 1911, with A. A. Brill as president, Meyer was elected an honorary member. (Dr. Brill had been in his first class at the Pathological Institute.) And when the American Psychoanalytic Association was organized soon after, Meyer was again a charter member. It was obvious that his dynamic psychiatry had prepared America for Freud.

While looking upon the new doctrine as "unfortunately too denominational" and upon some of his fellow psychiatrists as being attracted by "sin and vanilla," he kept his mind open to developments and welcomed emphasis on the living patient. Nevertheless, it struck Meyer that psychoanalysis was an ingenious way to practice medicine, by which he meant both the fee system and the mystical atmosphere created by the patient's facing away from the doctor.

Advocacy of the extremely time-consuming and taxing process of psychoanalysis would not be fair outside of exceptional cases and under sufficiently promising conditions. It is a disgrace to see extravagant sums squandered at the time of acute flurry during which no collaboration with the patient is possible and then be forced to relegate the patient to the other extreme of *low* standards of care when the storm has blown over and chances for reconstruction might normally be expected to become better again.[18]

The work of psychopathology was to learn to use the concrete facts of habits, habit conflicts, psychogenic disturbances, "and the

problem of getting square with the demands of mental balance."
In short,

The real value of a psychopathology will ultimately be determined
not at the autopsy table but in the true and efficient methods of
psychotherapy in the sense of mental orthopedics.[17]

CASE HISTORIES REFLECTING

SCHOOL YEARS

From "What Do Histories of Cases of Insanity Teach Us Concerning Preventive Mental Hygiene During the Years of School Life?" read by Dr. Meyer before the American School Hygiene Association, Atlantic City, N. J., April, 1908; Psychological Clinic, 2:89 (*June* 15, 1908).

Mental hygiene has made decided strides in our schools during the last decade. To be sure, the work thus far accomplished has had little bearing on the psychological problem of adult mental efficiency. It has very properly occupied itself first with those impediments which must be removed to make teaching itself possible, *i.e.*, the correction of disorders of vision and hearing, the avoidance of overfatigue and other causes of wear and distraction, the regulation of sedentary work and play, the maintenance of general health and nutrition, not to mention the problem of faulty ventilation which so often spoils the clearheadedness of a pupil. In the main, chief attention has been paid to the physical machine, while no adequate provision has been made for its proper direction and control. As a result many will stumble and perhaps fall at the critical period of individual development, when most of the concrete difficulties of mental life arise, such as the direction and balancing of instincts, the shaping of convictions, and the adaptation of one's capacity to the many possibilities and impossibilities presenting themselves in real life.

Here is evidently another problem of which we are forced to take cognizance, the attainment of *mental balance*. The study of those pronounced mental disorders of adolescence and adult life, which appear to be the magnified results of fate and poor hygiene, should teach us much that will incidentally add to the efficiency and happiness of those who are not so seriously involved or threatened. What does at times *fatal* harm is often enough a mere hindrance in a life; it may make just the difference between wholesome success and getting along with discomfort, a difference which may grow to be serious and is bound in any event to cause the failure of many a good effort.

To what extent these more remote issues of mental hygiene become a matter of concern in the school years is a question worth consideration. It seems to me that a knowledge of modes of miscarriage is best fitted to show us the *weak spots* of our mental mechanisms. None of our organs are perfect. We can only ask that they be fairly efficient. And in this respect our mental organ is no exception. It is the finest product and the very climax of our evolution, but much attention and patient culture are needed to enable it to cope with the difficulties of ordinary existence, not to mention those realms in which originality, aggressive and productive activity, or conflicting passions and instincts are wont to play an important role. It behooves every workman to discover the weaknesses and limitations of the tools on which he must rely, and the first step toward a mental hygiene is an adequate knowledge of the weaknesses and limitations of the individual mind, and of the places at which we do well to provide for braces and balancing material. This knowledge of the limitations of mental capacity and adaptability brings with it not only a direct practical gain, it furnishes also a glimpse into the psychology of modern psychopathology that is itself of no small value.

Our experience with the phenomena of mental life must be extended. We need adequate forms of expression in which to incorporate the results of a widened experience, as well as properly arranged and classified facts to make clear the significance of our conclusions. That the Herbartian psychology, for instance, with its way of seeing some facts, furnished valuable principles to the pedagogue, nobody but a partisan would dispute. That the principles, and still more the plain *facts* of modern psychopathology, furnish us with some practical and helpful standpoints, I hope to be able to show. What principles to guide our action and to shape our teaching are we taught under the merciless whip of disease, and through the encouraging experiences of therapeutics?

To understand the significance of my appeal for mental hygiene from the psychological side, it must be borne in mind that psychopathology is beginning to assign a definite role not only to the growth, nutrition, and possibly extraneous diseases of the brain, but also to the brain conditions which we know and use only as mental states and mental activities in the sense of a dynamic psychology. We are beginning to consider as legitimate material of science what commonsense has taught us and the teacher has long used in practice. We want to know the effect of certain activities and reactions on subsequent life, and also whether by modifying mental attitudes and habits we may not be able to avert trouble in the future.

Of special interest to us in this paper are disorders of those *adjustments* of the organism which consist in the proper mental reactions. Among these we may perhaps distinguish the logical, the emotional, and the volitional reactions or modes of adaptation, to use terms which do not deviate too far into medical psychobiology. I refer to those depressions which are a mere exaggeration of an otherwise normal reaction, to hysterical disorders, and especially to those peculiar stupors and delusional and other developments which depend partly on inherited or acquired types of mental endowment, but more especially on factors which by themselves are mentally upsetting, although at times helped along by incidental physical disorders.

The most serious affections which fill our hospitals for the insane are due to those difficulties of *instinctive and emotional* adaptation, which form both theoretically and numerically the most important types of psychobiological problems. We may admit that approximately ten per cent of the admissions to hospitals for the insane suffer from general paralysis or paresis, and about twenty per cent from alcoholic psychoses, that is to say, from disorders with a plainly bacterial or toxic nonmental factor as the exciting link—to be sure, also based primarily upon a deviation of instincts, but rather upon an excess of what is considered sane enough to be tolerated as a mere social evil, namely, alcoholism and irresponsible sexual relations entailing risk of venereal infection. But at least thirty per cent of the admissions seem to make up a group of disorders of the more personal, instinctive adjustments involving a miscarriage of instincts through lack of balance —dementia praecox. This type of mental disorder is peculiarly liable to lead to permanent collapse, and is one in which the so-called psychogenic factors are especially prominent. To be sure, even this group of psychoses is referred by many to autointoxications, and to other hypothetical assumptions, while the simple laws of disturbance of the proper activity and anabolism and catabolism of the nervous system would give us adequate explanation.* Certainly the number of those is increasing who agree with me that the bulk of the manifestations subsumed under the caption of dementia praecox may be most practically expressed as the inevitable and natural development from a deterioration of habits, partly due to developmental defects of the mental endowment, but in part at least to the clashing of instincts and to progressively faulty modes of meeting difficulties, and the disability of a proper balance of anabolism and catabolism which they entail.

Looking over the records of sufficiently studied cases, I find that the children who later developed abnormal reactions of the type of dementia praecox were peculiar, rather than defective in the sense which we have in mind when speaking of those who are backward or retarded. Furthermore, I find that as a rule we are concerned less with aggressive mischief (which is more apt to lead to the truant school and to social delinquency) than with *repression*, and with what is at times characterized as "depth of thought." The children affected are the very ones whom a former generation might have looked upon as model children. Allow me to present a

* Anabolism and catabolism imply the constructive and destructive changes during nutrition and growth on the one hand and function on the other; metabolism includes both the integrative and the disintegrative processes of a chemical nature.

few brief histories of patients, in which I shall refer more particularly to facts observed in the years of school life. I purposely abstract the statements of the cases in the language of the original histories.

The first case is a school girl of sixteen, coming from a family of ignorant Russian Jews, without any history of insanity in the family. The parents considered her a bright child, but of an unusually *quiet* disposition. Beginning about four years ago, a gradual change manifested itself in the patient; she became abnormally quiet, grew dull and apathetic in her behavior. She seemed in poor physical health, was easily irritated, occasionally had crying spells, sometimes laughed without apparent reason—she lived with her mind turned inward. She exhibited lazy traits, slept a great deal and refused to do errands for her mother, giving as an excuse that she was not dressed well enough to go out. The patient had been in the public schools for nearly two years. A note from her teacher states that while the patient was well behaved, she was very *dull*, noticeably *peculiar* in her manner, and of an *unsocial* disposition. Four months before admission she was examined by a school physician and ordered to report to the officer of the Board of Health. This appeared to frighten her; she feared deportation, remained home from school, and it was difficult to get her out of the house at all. She would stand for hours at a time gazing out of the window, occasionally she talked excitedly, or repeated one word over and over again.

Two months before admission to the hospital she ceased to talk. She remained in bed and slept most of the time. She finally became excited, threw herself about, struck and kicked anyone who approached her, yet remained mute. With us she showed a simple stupor, at times with drooling, but of late she has begun to take up a little work when requested, but remains mute.

While this child attracted the attention of the school physician, it was evidently only when too late, and with results that merely aggravated the difficulty.

On looking over a number of records I find the following remarks about several other patients during their years at school:

L. M. was giddy and backward in school, excessively timid and bashful; masturbated from ten years.

N. B. was very quiet, sleepy; of inefficient mentality; *seclusive*, shy, retiring.

M. O'N. was bright; later was *discontented* and shiftless; masturbation.

L. L. said, "I seemed awfully stupid and dreamy." Although diligent, she failed of promotion.

R. S. learned slowly and was *seclusive*.

Another very frequent type is the one furnished by the following case, who is said to have developed normally during childhood, though she was looked upon as a "nervous child," easily startled and subject to bad dreams. She began school at seven years, was smart, and applied herself well, but at the age of eleven she seemed to be *failing* and was thought to be studying too hard. She grew thin, seemed nervous, and complained of headaches. At twelve she was in poor health. After she began to menstruate at fourteen, she brightened up, had fewer headaches, and seemed to be in better health. Her sister never suspected any disordered sexual habits, but the patient says that she began to masturbate when nine years old; and she probably has continued this up to the present time (masturbation observed in the hospital). Its effects and whether or not it had anything to do with the failure at school, the headaches, and the later difficulty over work, cannot be definitely determined retrospectively. The patient says, "It spoiled all my youth, and my life. I wasn't like other girls. I didn't want to go out anywhere,"—and therewith she probably hit the truth. She was disappointed at home, for some time dreamt of becoming a teacher, but soon sank into hypochondriacal ruminations and finally, at twenty-one, after useless operations, passed into a confused religious excitement followed by stupor, in which she sits inactive and irresponsive, with the top-heavy and yet empty notion of being good, of saving the world, etc.

I have used purposely the expressions which the histories contain, that is, the terms in which the facts were submitted and thought of by the friends or teachers. What is mentioned would probably appear to the routinist as quite unimportant and trifling, and it is only through an examination of these expressions in the light of later events of a plain and serious mental disorder that they gain their proper value.

I wish to be clearly understood here. A very sane human instinct forbids borrowing trouble. We realize that there are many children who show the traits mentioned, and possibly we know that some of our friends manifested traits like seclusiveness, occasional day-dreaming, and discrepancies between thought and action. It must be admitted that these traits alone are not sufficient indications of inevitable failure. On the other hand, we insist that those who can take and heed a warning will be saved from danger by a timely recognition of what risks there are. A knowledge of the mode of development of some of the graver mental disorders must help us to discriminate those traits of character that should serve as warnings to be heeded.

A good instance of this is furnished by an analysis of the cases of dementia praecox. The lesson which these cases teach us will be lost only upon those who close the road to investigation, with the prevalent idea that these cases develop through some fatal necessity, as the result of what some choose to call the laws of degeneracy. These supposed laws, however, are conclusions drawn from statistics that have been collected without reference to whether anything was done for the patient or not. Admitting the importance of the mental traits, it may be contended that the small accomplishment of traditional pedagogy in its efforts at prevention argues for the belief that these cases would have failed in any event. But let me ask, Are not these traits usually slighted, and are they not most difficult to treat, and is not a better knowledge of the facts necessary to their satisfactory treatment?

The laws of degeneracy are based, in part at least, upon cases and facts concerning which the last word of a practical psycho-biology has not yet been spoken. There is no reason to assume that the mental reactions of cases presenting "symptoms of degeneracy" are essentially different from the mental reactions of normal persons. We need not assume any special or unusual toxic agency in order to account for the tenacity of these symptoms. Consider in this connection how difficult to eradicate from even the normal mind are superstitions and queer ideas, not to speak of peculiar religious or political conceptions. These ideas are only less harmful than the reactions we have been considering, because they happen to occur in domains of thought and action wherein the patient is less likely to be involved in practical tangles, for the very good reason that society ordinarily avoids encouraging them, whereas the more harmful directions are those in which few or no corrective helps are offered. We can, therefore, understand that a pedagogy with knowledge of the principles may achieve what the ordinary pedagogy has failed to accomplish as yet. This achievement will come less as the result of attempts at eradication than through the more rational method of furnishing such timely protection and balancing material as will make dangerous tendencies harmless.

A consideration of carefully studied cases of dementia praecox convinces me that in reality we have to do with a perfectly natural, though perhaps unusually persistent, development of tendencies difficult to balance. Evolution's method of trial and rejection will lead some children into a reading craze, others into mere daydreaming of an apparently indifferent, though often fantastic kind, and still others into sexual imagination, which in passing, it may be well to remark, is often as serious if not actually more serious than the often harmless abnormal sexual practices by themselves. All these tendencies are common traits of adolescence, usually offset in one way or another by the more natural and sociable children. The correction comes from more powerful attractions exercised in an opposing direction by better instincts; or the consequences of the failure to meet the requirements of actual life may call for a halt. Here the very habits of the patient, the loss of sense for the real and the abnormal satisfaction in mere dreaming and good resolutions encourage a mere dodging of the consequences rather than the giving up of the harmful instincts.

To those who meet with failure, there come as further burdens the comparisons of themselves with others and the resultant feeling of being at a disadvantage. These feelings are especially strong in those who have ventured or have been hoisted above their level, and they are augmented by a natural irritation at being reminded of the disadvantage under which they labor—an irritation which is added to that which is the natural outcome of brooding over disappointments and incapacities. In the real failures we then find a covering up, rather than a correction of the harmful yearnings.

There develops an insidious tendency to substitute for an efficient way of meeting the difficulties a superficial moralizing and self-deception, and an uncanny tendency to drift into so many varieties of shallow mysticism and metaphysical ponderings, or into fantastic ideas which cannot possibly be put to the test of action. All this is at the expense of really fruitful activity, which tends to appear as insignificant to the patient in comparison with what he regards as far loftier achievements.

Thus there is developed an ever-widening cleavage between mere thought life and the life of actual application such as would bring with it the corrections found in concrete experience. Then, under some strain which a normal person would be prepared for, a sufficiently weakened and sensitive individual will react with manifestations which constitute the mental disorders constituting the "deterioration process" or dementia praecox. Unfinished or chronically subefficient action, a life lived apart from the wholesome influence of companionship and concrete test, and finally a, progressive incongruity in meeting the inevitably complex demands of the higher instincts—this is practically the formula of the deterioration process.

It is interesting to watch nature's way of coping with these incongruities of development. Very often the traits which we are analyzing appear in pupils of relatively good endowment. The result is then, often enough, merely a so-called nervous prostration, a temporary breakdown, or a mere slump in which the patient goes through a period of relative inactivity during which he gets a chance to find himself, his friends, and his teachers. These cases show us nature's plan: she uses a period of invalidism which furnishes temporary protection against the harsher demands that would have to be met in an environment of normally healthy persons, and affords opportunities for a gentle acquisition of balancing material. It is our duty toward those of less fortunate assets to provide a more timely and more rational reduction of the demands made upon them and to supply them with the balancing material which will rescue at least a certain number of them who would otherwise completely fail.

To those who think that it is scarcely worth while to trouble ourselves over the few who would fall by the wayside anyhow, I can address no stronger plea than to urge that what often leads to complete breakdown in some will partly spoil the life of others, or at least seriously interfere with their success. What appears as though seen through a magnifying glass in the serious deteriorations is met with on a smaller scale as frequent impediments. Consequently, any increase in our knowledge is bound to help us to formulate the best possible hygiene of conduct even for the normal. It will make us realize that the ordinary principles of work and rest, of exercise and its influence upon our readiness to meet the ordinary demands of life, must also be applied to the more personal issues of our life, where we are concerned with the training of character, and with the storing up of energy with which to meet the inevitable conflicts of both the individual and the social instincts of a more complex nature. It is in this sense that I have lately spoken of the solidarity of mental hygiene and ethical conceptions.

I cannot expect to do more than indicate very briefly some of the methods of training the type of conditions herein referred to. The psychologists have scarcely touched as yet the most interesting chapters of psychology, those that deal with the evolution of instincts in the individual and the methods of controlling and guiding them through their inevitable conflicts. The problem is first presented in tangible form where we follow the development of habits, the mutual reinforcing of inhibitory influences upon one another, and their compatibility and incompatibility. We there feel the need of principles which would guide us in measuring the capacity of a child to acquire and balance new habits. The study of defectives and failures brings home to us most forcibly a fundamental fact of economics—that certain persons are adequately endowed for small demands, but are bound to fail under an excessive demand. There would be far more happiness and real success in mental hygiene if more people would realize that at every step, every person can do *something* well and take a satisfaction in doing it, and that this satisfaction in something *done* is to be valued as ten times greater than the satisfaction taken in mere thought or imagination, however lofty.

Most failures in life are persons who withdraw from straightforward and wholesome activity into seclusion, into flights of imagination, or so-called "deep thought," all of which tends to make ordinary concrete activity appear as shabby and inferior. To find pleasure in mere activity, however humble, is a safer ideal and constitutes to my mind the basis of what is sometimes called the Anglo-Saxon superiority. It must be remembered that thought at its very best is only a link in a chain of events leading up to some achievement. Its real and lasting fulfilment is found only in action.

Janet has constructed an interesting hierarchy of mental functions. His study of psychasthenia brings him to the conviction that *complete action* is the most difficult and highest function. I am tempted to add that completed action is the first essential for rest and for beginning something new. I thus come to describe the development of dementia praecox as being essentially a deterioration of the instincts of action. It consists in a substitution of inefficient and faulty attempts to avoid difficulties rather than meet them by decisive action. The seclusiveness is usually a poor method of seeking protection which might be obtained in other ways less likely to lead to cumulative trouble. If opportunities for doing and accomplishing simple and enjoyable things could be furnished, mere *dreams* of doing and accomplishing things would be less tempting. Otherwise for lack of the steadying control exerted by real activity there results a scattering of thought and with it the odd dissociations constituting dementia praecox: a splitting not into the picturesque multiple personalities that tempt the novelist, but into mere grotesque fragments of mentality, which become well-nigh unintelligible to one who is unfamiliar with psychopathological analysis. The wildest and most incongruous products of constructive imagination parade in the patient's mind, and the symptoms of dementia praecox stand before us as the natural evolution of miscarried mental development.

The study of imbecility teaches us that if the defective only finds his level, there is no danger of further complication, but where nature is not kind enough to take away the temptations and ambitions, as well as the capability for a successful adjustment, we find often enough that imbecility is superseded by dementia praecox. Here we must apply nature's principle of protection. We must find the proper level for the child, and for a time at least withdraw it from unhappy and untimely comparison, from the strain of disappointment, from inactivity, and from poorly balanced flights of imagination.

One of my most urgent suggestions would be to take seriously every falling off in efficiency of the pupil, and to consider not only the nutrition, and the condition of the eyes and the possible existence of adenoids, but also the more intimate needs of self-direction. It would be well to submit to the school physicians many of the requests that are made for relief from studies. Headaches are an excellent barometer of practical mental hygiene; even where physical causes are found and removed, headaches in children are almost always an evidence of blundering by the child, by the parents, or by the school.

I should like to insert here, as further illustrations of what is needed, a number of cases kindly communicated to me by Dr. August Hoch:

1. At school, in the rather problematic setting of a church home, the patient had no ambition, no stability of purpose, is said to have *disliked* work, and always laid this to headaches and the like. Besides, she was untruthful. All these are statements of a teacher who added that nothing seemed to take a deep hold of her. When twenty she became silent, sat about apparently dreaming, and did nothing; then developed the catatonic stupor, which soon terminated in dementia. (This is the result with a child evidently placed in a wholly unsuitable, probably excessively repressive environment and kept in a mood of discord for years.)

2. The patient is said to have been retiring, modest, shy; had to be driven to play. The parents say that the other child they have is aggressive, while the patient was not; that the other looked out for herself, while the patient relied on others. She was always afraid she had not done things right, and told other children that they must obey their parents. She was ashamed of her menstruation, and studied too hard. When thirteen she became inactive, lost interest, also was dissatisfied with things, got rattled at school and could not do her work. Then followed occupation with and vague talk about deep subjects, such as "why does the universe exist?" and so on. By fifteen she was gravely deteriorated—(plainly the victim of forced competition with a sister of wholly different endowment).

3. It is claimed that especially since the age of eight, after measles, she did not grasp things so readily as before; she was self-conscious, felt awkward, especially socially, and was very sensitive about it; but said little in regard to it, and in general talked very little. The mother says that in this respect she was like her father, from whom you never could get anything, or, as she put it, *"Man hat nie etwas aus ihm herausbringen können."* Besides that, she often sat brooding, was uncommonly systematic and "finicky." At about the age of fifteen a seclusiveness became more marked. At seventeen she went to a fortune-teller, who told her she would go insane, which prediction preoccupied her much. At eighteen she fell in love, and her love was not reciprocated, and then she became careless, apathetic, and deteriorated rapidly, presenting a great many phenomena of blocking delusions, catatonic states and the like.

[handwritten margin note: One has never been able to get something out of himself. trans.]

To sum up, I should urge that we spread among teachers and pupils a realization of the fact that knowledge must be a knowledge of doing things, and next a knowledge *ready for doing* things. Even in cultivating the instincts of play and pleasure we must aim to make as attractive as possible those games and diversions which require decision and action, and carry with them a prompt demand for correction of mistakes and reward for achievement: actual play with others and for others, and not the play of mere rumination. We further must aim to find levels of activity with moderate demands and well within the limitations of even the less brilliant or less vigorous children and yet giving full enough satisfaction to remain attractive and truly stimulating.

It is lamentable to hear youngsters, encouraged by their elders, refuse to do certain things because they already know how to do them. When doing things becomes less attractive than knowing things, an avenue for disappointment if not for failure has been opened before the pupil. It is evidently the plain duty of those who have to map out curriculums and those who have to advise as to the life of children who are in danger to see that the doing of things is made infinitely more attractive than is usually the case. I do not see why the success of efforts directed toward this object should not appear more glorious than, or at least as glorious as, the devising of some new plan of cramming the pupil with the subjects of a conventional curriculum. Thus it is that through training in wholesome action as well as in physical culture a real hygiene is making its way into the schools.

It would probably be wrong, and certainly utopian, to expect that schools should create special classes for every special emergency. I rather look forward to the establishment of school hospitals, or hospital schools, which will undertake at the proper time the investigation of special difficulties presented by certain cases, and provide for the training of the child and the parents. At the same time, a more careful study of levels of capacity and of ways of making the easier levels sufficiently attractive and full of meaning may well become a matter of serious cooperation between the pedagogue and the psychopathologist.

THE DYNAMIC INTERPRETATION

OF DEMENTIA PRAECOX

From a lecture delivered by Dr. Meyer at the celebration of the twentieth anniversary of Clark University, Worcester, Mass., Sept., 1909; American Journal of Psychology, 21:385 (*July,* 1910).

Up to recent years the ambition of scientific medicine was to trace all morbid conditions to some kind of anatomical lesion. This inevitably left a large field in which there was "no pathology as yet," and therefore a suspicion of inevitable chaos. The trend of the last decade and the experience with biological serum reactions and especially also the progress of psychiatry has, however, greatly strengthened a functional and biological view of the events in living beings, so that the work of *pathology* appears to us primarily as the *determination of causal chains or conditions with the accuracy of an experiment*, and the lesions then take their place among the simple facts or symptoms, according to the extent to which they can be understood in terms of dynamic developments, *i.e.*, of cause (or conditions) and effect.

This functional way of seeing things has the great advantage of allowing us to arrange the facts as we see them.

Most attempts at translation of the functional facts into neurological homologies leave out the actual amount and duration of the function, and the all-important laws of compatibility and incompatibility of sequences, and the discrimination between what are *moving factors* or more decorative staging or incidents. Turning to the functional and dynamic conceptions allows us to remain true to neurological conceptions where we are entitled to any and yet to take in the entire psychological setting without which the events would be difficult to grasp, artificial and devoid of the spark of life and interest to most physicians.

The dynamic conception which I shall present in this lecture is not new in one sense, but in another it reconquers and makes safe the ground of commonsense psychology abandoned by medicine during the struggle against superstitions and also under the influence of philosophical speculations, now become indispensable again if we wish to bring differentiation into our field and account for, and explain, the events constituting mental disorders. I have been said to resurrect the layman's opinion of the causes and nature of mental disease. I grant that to some extent; but we are also adding the *conditions* and critical safeguards under which we are justified in accepting and pursuing our normal instinctive interpretations.

Among mental diseases certain chains of events recur with such regularity that they become valuable clinical units or reaction-types. When the development appears natural and plausible we consider the disorder accounted for and, under certain conditions, explained. In this respect we find, for instance, that the so-called organic dementias are accounted for and to some extent explained by the extent and kind of brain disease, determination of which tells us what the symptoms and the development must have been or would probably be. In a more functional field we find the deliriums of intoxication, perhaps not explained but empirically accounted for by a sufficient amount of intoxicant material *and* personal disposition.

In a second place we may rank certain depressions and excitements and paranoic developments of which we may say that they come nearer and nearer being both explained and accounted for psychobiologically; when we have all the facts they are apt to rank fairly plainly as exaggerations of relatively normal reactions, as is the case with many depressions and delusional states.

In a third place there are, however, disorders which seem to defy both explanation and accounting for; among these figure, according to the claims of many physicians, certain disorders prominent in the dementia praecox group. But, in fact, they deal with developments far from being inconceivable as chains of faulty mental adjustment and far from demanding artificial explanations by specially invented poisons and a clamoring for invented "things back of it all," if at least we acknowledge the long time and mass of doings and their kind.

These conditions have been grouped together by Kraepelin under the term "dementia praecox," embracing derangements which very often tend to end in peculiar defect conditions, ranging from the not-infrequent cases of simple disappointment of parental hopes by apparently promising individuals who fail to make their mark, to cases with rather characteristic mental upsets and characteristic, usually progressive, apathetic dementia.

These cases do indeed make a group worth distinguishing as a nosological entity and they offer certain common and characteristic traits always carrying a warning that the tendency is toward deterioration. The unfortunate feature of Kraepelin's view is that this possibility or great probability is made to appear as a great dogmatic certainty, dictated by merely suggestive but not causally correlated signs which are seen in the end stages and appear also in the very beginnings as mere empirical earmarks, merely classified as disorders of emotion or volition, hypothetically due to toxins and brain lesions but not reduced to any chain of cause and effect.

The picture as a *whole* makes the *diagnosis*. There are no decisively pathognomonic facts. The deterioration gives the disorder its name; but it need not always be realized; the essence of the process is a hypothetical toxic influence or disorder of metabolism—entirely hypothetical—with definite brain lesions—also vague and not explained. What he deems essential comes out most clearly in his differential diagnoses, where we find the enumeration: emotional apathy, and specific disorders of will: negativism (mutism, refusal of food, etc.), automatism (catalepsy, echopraxia and echolalia) and mannerisms (grimaces, oddity, stereotypy, verbigeration), silliness, unaccountable and odd acts, etc.

This description, to a great extent taken over from Hecker and Kahlbaum, figured originally under the "degenerative" disorders. There it would be a mere dispute about words in debate whether or not the early symptoms were evidence of the disease or not. The fact that these early signs *need* not lead to more trouble might still be compatible with calling them degenerative, and the mental factors *might* be admitted to play a more or less active role in the development of those cases which progressed further. But in 1896 Kraepelin, taking general paralysis as the paradigm of psychiatry—each disease having a definite etiology, definite course, and outcome—included a much wider range of cases in the original group, *viz.*, practically all cases of the simple psychoses which tend not to recover or are apt to deteriorate in the end; and he explained them all as disorders of autointoxication with a special assumed brain disorder. Then the question might have arisen: "If we deal with a toxic state, where does it become established and when; and what would we have to modify to prevent it? What role do the biological reactions play which represent the early symptoms?"

Kraepelin purposely declines any idea that special antecedents in the life of the patient are worth considering as causal or even as aggravating dynamic factors. About twenty per cent would, according to him, show some early premonitory signs like seclusiveness, oddity, excessive religious devotion, moral instability, but trusting his *deus ex machina* [stage-god] he sees in this mere evidence of a very early setting-in of the so-called "disease itself." As a matter of fact, the cases in which early symptoms *are* found are much more numerous than twenty per cent; as I claimed in 1903, a very large number of these cases show what Hoch has lately called a shut-in personality, specially exposed to inner friction—a percentage of actual demonstration about as great as that of actual demonstration of evidence or suspicion of syphilis in general paresis. Kraepelin, however, underrated these facts and by absorbing many doubtful and poorly analyzed cases in his group came to suggest that this disease might befall anyone and that it was an autonomous brain disease.

Even in the hands of the originators of this new large entity embracing all the cases passing into apathetic deterioration and many others that at least tended to deteriorate, the definition of the term is evidently much more fluctuating than the uncompromising theory would suggest. In Heidelberg it has fluctuated from eight per cent to fifty-two per cent, and now back to eighteen per cent of all the admissions. In the Munich clinic the optimistic tendency is still more on the increase and fewer cases are dubbed dementia praecox on the female side than on the male side. The inevitable conclusion is that between dementia praecox and manic-depressive insanity and simple psychopathy there is an uncertain territory which refuses a categorical arrangement in the easy and simple dogmatic terms that "some disorders *must* be a deteriorative brain disease because they early present certain signs also seen in actually accomplished deteriorations" and the claim that it would be futile to make an effort to analyze the data as a whole in terms of cause and effect.

To this empirical and formal conception I have opposed for a number of years a conception which aimed to be less dogmatic and more likely to be conducive to the determination of the facts actually present in the cases in terms of an experiment of nature, in terms of determinable initial constellations, reactions with probabilities rather than fixed laws of termination; in terms of natural nondogmatic developments, to quite an extent measurable in advance by the facts at hand in the case and not merely by the intermediary of a dogmatic fatelike noumenon or largely hypothetical construction.

As dynamic factors in these developments there stand out certain activities and states of disturbed balance and regulations which have far-reaching effects upon the mental adjustments themselves, and *incidentally* upon the organic understructure of the personality.

We have so far failed to find any tangible poisons and infections as in any way essential in the process. The extent to which regulative substances akin to hormones may play a role and figure as nonmental short cuts of reaction is a problem for the future to decide. Berkley's claim of hyperthyroidism is not very convincing to one familiar with a goiter district and large numbers of thyroid affections. Kraepelin's suggestion that the poison may have some relation to the sexual functions merely flirts with the truth and is so vague as to demand consideration only if actual facts can be adduced and other facts should fail.

On the other hand, we find in evidence factors which are apt to shape or undo a life—specific defects or disorders of balance, with special tendencies and *habitual* ways of bungling and sub- stitutions and a special make-up which is liable to breakdown in specific manners.

In my first formulation of the situation in Toronto ["Funda- mental Conceptions of Dementia Praecox," p. 184] I started from the paradigm of *complete action* as the function which gets more and more disorganized by first trivial and harmless *subterfuges* or *substitutions* which, in some individuals, lead further, become harmful and uncontrollable, tend to assume types of definite anomalous mechanisms, unintelligible and crazy if viewed apart, but more or less intelligible as a string of actions substituting for, and often missing, an efficient adjustment to concrete and actual difficulties.

These substitutions constitute the symptomatology and chains of events which we have found and which I need not rehearse and analyze before you because the facts are more trustworthy than verbal formulas. Suffice it to say that we meet neurasthenia, hysteria or psychasthenia-like substitutions, or mere dilapidations of interests or states of conflict or depressions of a morose, *topical* character— usually with one or more initial tantrums—and delusional develop- ments either with episodes of ruminations and giggling and the like, which may absorb more and more of the patient's actual life, or catatonic developments, or paranoia-like delusional states, all with a number of earmarks; in the main, freedom from hysterical haziness and tendency to systematic amnesia, but evidence of con- flicts of reaction, of blocking, of peculiar automatic interferences, *i.e.*, evident disorders of the highest integrations, and fantastic ruts especially in the sexual or religious spheres and their symbolic elaborations, with very frequent dissociation of the personality and pseudospontaneous experiences; further, a growing divorce from concrete environment, a deterioration of interests, and perversion of impulses and actions.

The catatonic reactions are often mentioned not only as being oftenest connected with certain brain lesions but as being un- explainable from the psychological side. The catatonic reaction is by no means so far from yielding to a psychobiological interpretation. It is a breaking-down of normal conduct and adaptation too closely related to what is seen in hypnotic states and in mystic fancies; too directly like stages in religious symbolism and feelings of submission to influences by mystic powers to be compared with what happens in organic psychoses. In general paralysis and arteriosclerosis and senile deterioration it is not the *synthesis* into a personal integration that is *most* lacking, but the *material* used in the synthesis is decreasing, through lack of memory, judgment, and the range of capacity, without any distinct following of the lines of functional cleavage in the process of disorganization. In dementia praecox the dissociations follow the lines of functional and topical complexes.

The very frequency with which especially catatonic reactions appear outside of the actual deteriorations, though preferably in dementia praecox, would corroborate their interpretation as a specific functional reaction-type possibly founded on a phylogenetically very old reaction, partly of protection and partly of mystic surrender. If they are apt to appear occasionally in organic psychoses, the same holds for manic-depressive and other more essentially psychogenetic reactions. It is, however, certainly significant that catatonic disorders are *most* apt to accompany the *traumatic* forms of organic disorders such as also produce hysterias and other aftereffects most likely connected with a functional shock. In the simple *dilapidation* and the paranoic developments, the psychological staging is too much in keeping with the situation and the harmonious evolution on prevailing premises to create serious doubt against an essentially functional interpretation of the evolution and, also, of the lesions which may be found.

Sizing up the disorder in terms of a break in the working of conflicts, of balance rather than in terms of an autonomous disease of the brain, will stand and fall with the extent to which the initial data allow us to predict the course of nature's experiment, a point concerning which only the publication of casuistic material will give sufficient proof. Our work with these principles warrants the conclusion that while general paralysis is *relatively* incalculable in the *details* of its course, and certainly remarkably independent of mental determinants, the fluctuations observable in dementia praecox are decidedly too often accounted for by renewed upsets and tangles and irritation of idiosyncrasies, and that the prognosis of the ultimate tendency is remarkably often foretold, so that of the cases interpreted as actual deteriorations but few surprise us with a recovery, and those that do recover are as a rule specified at the outset as cases merely akin to this group worth naming by the end stage, but with varying amounts of balancing material. Such a disorder is, to be sure, as little open to *absolute* prediction as life's vicissitudes, and a continued test of estimates of events in the light of ultimate results gives one a certain reserve and modesty; but with it all, the conviction grows that the factors depended on in the estimate of the make-up and in the ratio of the reaction and balancing material are really *factors at work*, and leave less and less space to a craving for what is "back of it," instead of attention to what is the "go."

Where a break or morbid reaction has once set in, it is very difficult to bring relief directly. The fundamental shutting-in and the whole mechanism enable the preoccupations to live themselves out and to exclude interference. Automatic resistance against the most natural impulses frustrates even the occasional pathetic spontaneous appeals of the patient for help. The best procedure is to tide over the acute tangle with as much tact and ease as possible, to promote relaxation, and to relieve the situation wherever that can be done, bearing in mind the facts obtained referring to the upsetting factors, the probable complex-constellations and prevailing physical disorders. As soon as the patients feel that they meet with help instead of an argumentative and corrective attitude, they can be led considerably when the time comes or where the difficulty has not led to complete blocking. Then a positive reeducation in the form of habit training and of readjustment has to set in. It is obvious that experience brings a certain divination and that individual capacity plays a decided role in the straightening-out of the difficulties, both during the tangles and in ultimately marshaling the forces to a more practical unity and level again; it is also obvious that we cannot be very optimistic in most cases, as little as when we try to win over our less unbalanced neighbors to a better mode of thought, belief, and conduct and behavior.

We owe to our European guests, Professor Freud and Dr. Jung, the demonstration that what is at work in the center of the stage is a complex or group of complexes consisting of insufficiently balanced experiences in various ways modified by symbolism. Their ingenious interpretations have made possible a remarkable clearing-up of many otherwise perplexing products of morbid fancy, in ways the discussion of which, no doubt, I had better leave to their lectures.

Yet, if I interpret their accounts correctly, the reason why only few persons create these complexes and fewer yet develop them to a disastrous form and often to a deterioration, is mainly left to heredity or finally to toxins, whereas I would prefer to adhere to my attempt to define the responsible factors as far as possible in terms of prophylactic suggestiveness, in terms of untimely evocation of instincts and longings (actually as fatal as premature destruction of naïveté), and ensuing *habit conflicts* with their effects on the balance of the person, and on the sum total of mental metabolism and actual doings and on the capacity for regulation in emergencies. In some cases the *habit-disorders* preponderate in the sidetracking and the curbing of leading interests and creation of disastrous substitutions; in others, definite complexes play a special role and as a rule the sizing-up of the disposition must consider both factors. In practically all cases the scope and funds of mental deviation form a consistent evolution and offer the safest material for prognosis and practical handling.

For all I can see, the main obstacle to a wider acceptance of a functional theory in terms of habit and complex conflicts and definite responses thereto is on the one hand the habitual or intentional lack of the necessary penetration into the life of the patient and family, and on the other hand the readiness of the physician to turn to set interpretations and to reiterate authoritative statements with a certain pedagogical self-sufficiency. I refer especially to the traditional rut shown by physicians when they have to meet the question of habit-disorders, such as masturbation, which invariably leads to reasoning in a circle by calling the disorder a symptom of a disease and evading the possible role in additional abnormal developments instead of to a frank inquiry into the facts and difficulties in the case. Further, there is perhaps also a more or less legitimate aversion to any extreme dogma, using too exclusively the sexual origin or the weight of complexes, and special displacement mechanisms, and an aversion to certain other "atomistic" types of psychopathology, and especially also the fact that so many spontaneous recoveries occur and also many failures under almost any procedure.

The most serious cause for relapses into opposition to psychogenetic interpretations is the blind acceptance of any anatomical findings as definite evidence of an autonomous disease, after the paradigm of general paralysis. And to this point I wish to give a brief discussion.

The lesions found by Sioli and others are very different from those of general paralysis in their nature *and* as to autonomy of origin. They are most akin to fatty involution of the brain tissues, probably as incidental to the disorder of function as is the brown atrophy of the heart, the fatty degeneration of muscles or of the liver. The one disease in which disorders similar to those in dementia praecox, and even more marked, have been seen is Huntington's chorea, which is a striking instance of familial insufficiency of the nervous system and hardly a product of a toxic disorder. The occasional late recoveries of apparently demented patients and the peculiar clearing-up of some cases during intercurrent diseases—in which the most vital instincts of self-preservation and of complex-free family interest are brought out again—would certainly make one doubtful about the "profound deteriorations of the cortex" being on an autonomous basis as in general paralysis.

Until we know much more about the ameboid neuroglia and the protagon degeneration seen in dementia praecox *and* in Huntington's chorea and probably elsewhere, we certainly do well to leave open the question whether a disorder of anabolism and catabolism incidental to the prolonged and often profoundly vitiated attitudes and defects of balance is not sufficient to explain the findings (which are possibly as incidental to special chronic disorders of function as the finding that Dr. Hodge has established in acute fatigue states), or to what extent they are perhaps short circuits; that they are incidental to a broad frame seems unshakable, and the more we teach the physician to think in terms of what is demonstrable in the case, the better for him and for the patient and for prophylaxis and for the formulation of further problems of investigation.

The lesion in general paralysis is of a totally different kind, depending on a previous infection with syphilis and forming a peculiar infiltration of the brain vessels, similar to what happens in the African sleeping sickness, but accompanied by additional degenerative processes in the brain tissue. This exogenous disturbance leads to death within a limited number of years and accounts for certain fundamental symptoms of dementia of a kind quite different from that in dementia praecox. In addition to that, there are, however, symptoms not common to all cases, such as the development of exaltations or depressions or delusional states, sometimes following certain traits of dementia praecox. These superadded psychotic symptoms have been attributed to different localizations or distribution of the characteristic lesions. A careful inquiry into this question on the material in the literature and our own observations of focal general paralysis shows, however, that the focal lesions may give aphasic attacks or neurological disturbances, and occasionally precipitate epileptiform reactions with amnesic phases, fugues, and states of bewilderment; but the psychotic symptom complexes occur without any regularity.

The comfort of working under the cover of fatalistic and analyzed conceptions of heredity, degeneracy, and mysterious brain diseases—and the relief from responsibility concerning a real understanding of the conditions at hand, and concerning the avoidance of preventable developments—is a powerful and unconsciously cherished protection, very rudely disturbed by these conceptions which make the physician partly responsible for the plain and manageable facts. I deny that fatalism is inevitable, without admitting that my conception should imply unwarranted optimism. It is merely a return to the facts at hand which will prepare us all the better for the actual work and pave the way toward prophylaxis, where something can be done.

The position is, however, equally important in the utilization in psychological teaching. There probably is a certain comfort in arranging the courses within a narrow range of laboratory problems. Unfortunately, that does not always train the student's sense in using the foot rule of ordinary life with any degree of accuracy or conscience, when he passes to more complex domains. Scientific accuracy in one field does not guarantee a critical attitude in the field of nature's experiments, which are complex and cover larger spans. If we make the student wade through a mass of rather artificial psychological laboratory work and, on the other hand, equally artificial philosophical puzzles, we will leave him in the end without help and training to meet some essentials in life. Even a nontechnical knowledge of the facts in some mental patients is bound to widen the horizon and would to my mind be an intrinsic part of any course or program of psychology (as good as, or better than, an abstract course on mind and body).

I have on purpose avoided entering upon the details of many excellent modern trends of psychological investigation in our field. I wanted to make a plea for the broader frame of things. This frame must be grasped with an understanding of the broader elements in the disorders with which we deal. Within this frame the details get their perspectives. In the theory-ridden physician and in the ultra-exact psychological laboratory worker, I should like to awaken the natural instinct of curiosity concerning the keenly interesting broader biological settings brought out by the mental disorders and destinies discussed. I should like to make all feel the sanctity and paramount interest of the concrete cases.

I cannot resist recalling what is so well expressed in the recent presidential address of the great physicist, J. J. Thomson, in his appeal to the mathematician to avail himself of the power of the concrete. He says: "Most of us need to tackle some definite difficulty before our minds develop whatever power they may possess"; and we cannot deny that the field of habit conflicts and of far-reaching and complex emotions and longings gets its most wonderful representatives in disease. Ribot opens his last study with the remark: "*Le meilleur procédé d'expérimentation en psychologie, à mon avis, est la maladie avec ses désordres.*" Diseases are the most crucial experiments in man. Here the momentous things occur in a way which might well supplement the man-made experiments of our laboratories and suggest problems in a way which really goes at the causal relationships vital to the student, vital to any layman who wants to know what psychology is and does, and vital to the physician who wants to help also where help would rarely come without him, and may even be too late with him, as long as we fail to make sure of prophylaxis.

We are, I believe, justified in directing our attention to the factors which we *see* at *work* in the life history of the cases of so-called dementia praecox. We are justified in emphasizing the process of a crowding-out of normal reactions, of a substitution of inferior reactions, some of which determine a cleavage along distinctly psychobiological lines incompatible with reintegration. Psychobiological analysis and reconstruction furnish us the essential material, and progress is to be expected from a frank and unprejudiced weighing and use of this material, including its non-mental components, rather than from the stereotyped lesion-pathology and the dogmatic nosological principles when they become intolerant.

I could not have had a more delightful opportunity to present a discussion of the essential facts in favor of a dynamic conception of dementia praecox than this occasion, as I realize that my development has to no small extent been influenced by the spirit at Clark University, its genetic attitude, and the liberality in admitting the facts for investigation whether they seemed to fit preconceived plans or not, and its strong faith in the selective capacity of interest and in an unprejudiced inquiry with or without laboratory methods, but also with an interest in the conditions under which reactions develop.

SOME FUNDAMENTAL ISSUES

IN FREUD'S PSYCHOANALYSIS

From "A Discussion of Some Fundamental Issues in Freud's Psychoanalysis," read by Dr. Meyer at Manhattan State Hospital, Oct. 28, 1909; State Hospitals Bulletin, 2:827 (March, 1910).

It is by no means easy to reduce a complex and still growing direction of investigation with its more or less theoretical and jargonlike rules and formulas to a simple account in commonsense pictures and commonsense principles.

One of the most startling generalizations of Freud is the great role ascribed to the *wish*, and the second to the *symbolization*, and in both, the accentuation of sexual life. Let us first see how far we have gone without these apparently overspecific tendencies, and what ground we have to build on.

In my sketch of the reaction-types [see page 193] I have summed up very briefly my generalizations concerning *substitutive activity*. In my explanation of the events in dementia praecox I had spoken chiefly of the habit-deteriorations and the gradual substitution of more and more inferior and distorted material, taking the place of the real squaring with the actual problems of life. The developments thus are presented as entanglements in a poor adjustment. Among the end stages we thus have either a relative readjustment to normal life, or the production of a sham adjustment, possibly in the form of a wish fulfillment, to use Freud's term. Many cases, especially of the paranoid types, seem to become provisionally clear in this light. The determining factors are either deterioration of habits, especially the miscarriage of the sexual habits and ideals, or specially powerful longings and cravings, which, Dr. Hoch says, break through and assert themselves. In this respect several of our cases are perfectly simple and plain illustrations.

When you go more carefully over the details of cases and take those recently published by the Zürich school, you find, however, a much greater entering upon details and, with the help of the association experiment, an explanation of many points which would have remained odd and like products of chance but for the demonstration of peculiar laws of transformations for the understanding of which it becomes necessary to master Freud's methods of analysis of dreams.

No method makes more necessary than Freud's the principle that every fact to be discussed or explained must be first described and fixed as it presents itself (*i.e.*, as an event in a situation, or as a function of the situation), then analyzed for determining factors of the development in the light of what would have been the fulfillment of the adaptive reaction, and finally reconstructed as if we tried to make the test of our calculation in the form of a repetition or experiment. But in order to do this we must have a good knowledge of the working of the factors involved and we really should begin there with a review of the sexual theories of Freud, and then pass to the conception of the paradigm of dreams, before we can review the principles of psychoanalysis.

No experience or part of our life is as much disfigured by convention as the sex feelings and ambitions. Not to speak of them at all or only under cover of symbol is the pedagogical and social ideal of our civilization, but evidently also the source of survival of much superstition and ignorance of how to meet the situations.

Schiller says very cleverly:

> *So lange nicht den Bau der Welt*
> *Philosophie zusammenhält.*
> *Erhält sich das Getriebe*
> *Durch Hunger und durch Liebe.*

[While no philosophy may keep together the structure of this world, its "go" is taken care of by hunger and by love.]

Hunger represents the need of individual self-preservation. *Liebe* or love attends to the altruistic features of life and racial preservation. Both conceptions must be viewed in their broad ramifications if we wish to see in them the two mainsprings of life's push and yearnings; at the same time each has its center or chief representative in a type of mental experience (or "sensations") of a relatively simple character, the feeling of hunger for food and the sexual longings and sensations.

Freud's merit lies in his demonstration of the existence of early stages of more or less vaguely sexual interests and needs in the earliest childhood and not merely at puberty. In this matter we must trust the guidance of those who have really studied the matter, and if our own tendency to repress the sexual aspect of life wants to be considered, we may do best to put the matter aside for a later reading, but we should beware of condemning it on account of any personal obstacles in the assimilation of the facts.

Freud evidently starts from infantile sources of satisfaction generally, and partly for lack of a better word and partly because the activities discussed furnish the stuff for a great deal of the setting of the more specifically sexual realm of later years, he uses the term "sexual" for a broad field of undifferentiated material, embracing the satisfaction from certain feelings used later also in the altruistic life in the broad sense of love and ambition.

Freud begins with the discussion of the sexual aberrations, and after getting a concrete field there, he traces the data into infantile life. It seems very probable that primarily the sexual longings are independent of a definite sexual object. This lack of a direct and plain aim or material facilitates that sexual hunger which is more readily miscarried than food hunger. The correction by immediate aftereffects is less direct, and the dependence on imitation is apt to bring in the influence of nurses, teachers, and companions, with a very wide range of possibilities.

Freud first discusses the finding of the sexual object and the frequency of "inversion" or "homosexuality." It evidently is wrong to class it merely as degeneracy. It occurs in normal individuals, even with specially high intellectual and ethical standards. Freud feels justified in assuming directly a bisexual start in every individual, and chance and other factors determine the ultimate evolution: the normal, the homosexuality or inversion, and the perversion. As a rule the inverted man is manly and calls for an object approaching the feminine; the inverted woman is more apt to be masculine.

Apart from the perversion in the choice of the object, Freud points to further perversions in the manifestation of sexual activity itself: (*a*) in the transgression upon unusual parts of the body, or (*b*) in the arrest within intermediary relations to the object. The whole process tends to be all-absorbing, to carry away the whole individual, and to create a reduction of critical judgment; indeed, belief in authority gets a most important foundation or at least example here.

The trangressions of sexual activity upon nonsexual parts of the body are partly "stimulators" due to a need of variety (fulfilling the role of animators, just as many so-called automatisms, odd movements, etc., help along the more directly essential functions); partly they are a real miscarriage into abnormal fields (lip-tongue, anal region, and fetishisms). In many ways these anomalies throw an interesting light on the first infantile impressions to be mentioned, which may play a decided role in the foundation of later tendencies.

The lingering in intermediary sexually tinged relations naturally also has many forms of overemphasis: vision and contact, sadism (active) and masochism (passive), etc. *Ekel* (disgust) and *Scham* (shame), in turn, are the contrast reactions and "censors," the early development of which may be of great importance to the guardianship and checking of the functions.

To put the matter freely in our own terms, we may put down to sexual life all that which converges into the instinct of propagation and altruism. More specifically you find in the normal individual the normal sexual activity, with its general curve of evolution and the minor or incidental rises and drops. Within it Freud would probably claim that there is an aggressive element and receptive element; he calls the former male and the latter female. The infant has both tendencies prepared; the one or the other gets the lead, but we must not be surprised to see them side by side even in the normal.

Perversion is evidently apt to consist of a number of components which Freud analyzes briefly, with the help of the findings in neurotics. The sexual instinct of the neurotic is most clearly uncovered in psychoanalysis, which treats the symptoms as a substitute or transcription of a series of affect-charged processes, longings and connotations which are shut out from full-fledged and conscious reaction through a special agency (the censor with its *Verdrängung* or displacement or suppression), because they are incompatible with the personality. They find their discharge (*Abfuhr*) in a conversion into somatic phenomena and, we may add, symptomatic acts. The analysis aims to bring into consciousness the original affect-charged ideas and to estimate the underground effects of the uncontrolled and unanalyzed material. In hysteria an excess of shame and *Ekel* is apt to suppress the sexual problem or to cause an instinctive flight from even an intellectual occupation with it. At the same time it is excessive sexual needs or yearnings that may precipitate the very contradictoriness of the hysterical, and, in turn, serious demands by real sexual situations are apt to precipitate the conflicts and conversions. The neurosis (as also the paranoic development) is the product at the expense of an abnormal sexuality; it is really the negative of perversions, an arrest of sexuality in the infantile standpoint. Inversions play a role (without exceptions!); the extension of ramifications of residuals of the sexual tendencies to the oral and anal and other regions are the rule and show themselves in the symptoms of globules, etc.; abnormal curiosity, exhibitionism, and active and passive cruelty play a role, and also transformation of love into hatred, so characteristic of paranoia. Subconscious perversions are usually present in active and passive pairs (exhibitionist–voyeur; sadist–masochist); but usually all forms are more or less presented and intermingled. Beside the motor *Trieb* (drive), we can point to more or less definite sensory erogenous zones (oral or anal, apt to be specifically sensitive in the hysterical). In obsessive states and paranoia the developments are more intellectualized; but the contrectation (*Moll*), *i.e.*, the working up to the realization and gratification, is especially elaborated. It is a question whether the various perversions have not all their specific symptomatic consequences.

If neuroses are a kind of sexual infantilism, it is of importance to study the infantile sexuality. The study of the infant's life may indeed throw an important light upon peculiarities of make-up much more satisfactory and direct than the vague appeals to explanation by degeneracy. To demonstrate peculiar conditions in the child is certainly more likely to throw an explanatory light on the personal constitution than a simple assertion of trouble in the progenitors.

In the discussion of infantile sexuality Freud cannot resist seeing a relation between a common feature which infancy shares with certain phases in the life of the neurotic. It is odd that the most important period of receptivity of our life is veiled by oblivion. This amnesia may account for the fact that one does not analyze the sexual elements in that period; another reason is, of course, the fact that its manifestations present no obvious extraindividual effects or at least rather a passivity if not latency.

Education especially helps along the natural balancing of inhibitory factors: shame, disgust, esthetic and moral concepts with their inevitable "sublimation," or transformation into extrasexual efficiency. It is interesting that pedagogy chiefly struggles against the "vices" of premature real manifestations perhaps much more as a pedagogical reaction to the pedagogical enemy, the overpowering strength of these factors as tempters and seducers and sources of undesirable passions and longings, than out of the worthier feeling of regret over the loss of so much material withdrawn from sublimation (utilization and elaboration in higher aims and pursuits).

Freud draws in a number of apparently indifferent doings as manifestations of infantile sexuality. Sucking fingers, a toe, the lip or the tongue, at times with rhythmic pulling of the ear or rhythmic frictions, and at times leading to a kind of orgasm and climax in sleep, is (at least in some children) a kind of autoerotism (Havelock Ellis), apt to be developed further later on, and rarely missed in the history of excessive tendency to kissing, or tendency to drink or smoke, various disorders of eating, globus, pharyngeal constrictions and vomiting. The main point is the autoerotism and dominance of an erogenous zone upon which the child happens or tends to hit. The repetition and creation of a habit is ushered in by a state of tension and of centrally conditioned but projected feelings of tickle (which, for instance, brings the finger back to the mouth). I might in this connection draw your attention to the close association of nail biting to longings for satisfaction in autoerotism. It may be a link between the cases of sucking which seem wholly innocent and those passing to more dangerous cravings.

The anal zone gets into evidence through intestinal catarrhs, constipation, which can pass over into actual retention to produce special sensations and at times becomes first manifest and clear as psychogenic with a refusal to act when the discharge is wanted (the "holding back" of naughty children) and may even become a voluntary retention and reserve for moments when the child can give himself undisturbed function. This is the source or beginning of many a neurotic constipation and other scatological mannerisms and even anal masturbation. Jung gave a good example in his Amsterdam report.

The genital zone is provided with all kinds of helps by which its sensations are bound to be brought out into the form of onanism of infants, which, after a period of latency, is later revived again, as tickle or pollution, without or with active helps, before or at puberty, in a way largely determining the character of the developing individual. Enuresis takes the place of pollution at the infantile stage. Freud claims that the child (like most uncultivated women) can be led into any type of perversion until shame, disgust, and ethics stand up in defense. A polymorphous disposition creates the prostitute.

As detached *Partialtriebe* [part-drives] we find exhibitionisms, first in a general naïve satisfaction, later showing again in the voyeurs, the individuals craving to see (we might say "starers"); its suppression is apt to show up again in a morbid obsession.

Masochism may originate independently or is connected with infantile punishment (Rousseau). Cutaneous impressions (warm baths), rhythms, shocks, swings, rocking, shocks in driving (connected by Freud with the craze to become a driver or conductor), railroad travel, all may elicit reactions—and in repression become the source of train-phobias. Traumatic neuroses must have their source here (a combination of fright and mechanical shock attaching itself to infantile repression). Passive motions create kindred feelings. Many get their first orgastic sensations in wrestling. Affects play a role (the strain of examinations) or peculiar shivers over positions long maintained; also impressions gruesome as such may provoke the same thrill. The phenomena of "overwork" also belong here, and give kindred but repressed (because objectionable) sensations.

It is evident that many constitutional types can evolve not only from the differences in the erogenous zones but also from the balancing of associated and corroborative functions which should furnish the ground for sublimation (leading over the trends to nonsexual satisfaction).

The transformation of puberty is full of problems. In the transition from the autoerotic phase to that with distinctly altruistic sexual objects, the various partial trends converge upon a type of person or sexual aim, and the extragenital erogenous zones become subordinated to the genital zone. In man, the seminal discharge becomes a center for adjustments. In women Freud claims rather a tendency to involution.

Feelings of pleasure (vision of beauty, contact) call for a longing for more pleasure until the climax is reached. The *Vorlust* [preliminary pleasure] with its tension and pressure is long prepared; the *Endlust* [terminal pleasure] belongs to puberty. The role of the sex glands is not uniform and probably was overrated. Chemical theories might, nevertheless, be suggested considering the great similarity of the sexual neuroses to states of intoxication and abstinence from exhilarating alkaloids (a claim which might as well be turned around—that the reactions in states of intoxication and phenomena of abstinence can only be explained with an adequate knowledge of psychobiological adjustments generally;

for medical interests the investigation for chemical short cuts is of course of the greatest importance).

Freud is inclined to minimize the sex differentiation in childhood. He admits the greater susceptibility of girls to shame, disgust, sympathy, and a passive attitude. But the autoerotic and masturbatory manifestations have always a "male" character and in general he pushes this conception to the contention that *libido* is always a "male" characteristic—whether in man or in woman and irrespective of the male or female sex of the object. Freud sees additional evidence in the fact that the female child in its autoerotism mainly shows excitability of the clitoris, represses it at puberty and after a while transfers the excitability altogether to the entrance of the vagina. This transition offers many opportunities for abnormalities and a special tendency of women to neurosis, especially to hysteria.

According to Freud, the normal evolution is this: First there is satisfaction of both hunger and sexual *Trieb* at the breast; then the child learns to see the mother as a distinct and independent individual and enters the autoerotic phase of infancy and early childhood; then after a latent period comes the *Wiederfindung* or rediscovery. The mother thus plays an important role. She teaches the child to love (in Freud's broad sense of the term); she lays the foundation for the instinct which has the strongest effect on all ethical and psychic efficiency—and she must, therefore, keep aloof from overindulgence of affection as well as from indifference.

Anxiety of children is originally an expression of missing the loved person (much more than of fear roused by stories) and is a tendency only of children with excessive or prematurely developed or overstimulated need of love or sexual *Trieb*. And the adult whose unsatisfied *libido* turns into anxiety acts again in many ways like a child when seeking protection ("infantile reaction").

The direction of the instinct to its proper object is of the greatest importance. Education raises specially powerful barriers against incest. But even then parental affection remains important and disorders of the same are of great influence on the later finding of the object (see Jung's study on the influence of the father on children).

Inversion is most frequent when homosexual help predominates (slaves and servants). Abnormal constitution is often due to the prevalence of certain sources of excitement (apart from other factors, for instance the peculiar observation that in over fifty per cent of the severe hysterias and psychasthenias studied by Freud the father had had syphilis or tabes or general paralysis). The further evolution may either lead to "premature fixation" (arrest at normal or abnormal stages), as in many typical perverts; or to "displacements," which are usually an abnormal making-up for excesses, and by no means a real suppression; or then "sublimation," which may lead to virtues which may really have their source in actual infantile perversions or peculiarities of sex development.

Constitutional responsiveness, precocity, persistence (or fixation), and accidental excitement of the sexual *Trieb* by extraneous influences play a fundamental role in the neuroses.

In later studies Freud gives us further discussions of how the sexual evolution in its organic and in its more lofty manifestations is affected by the secrecy with which it is surrounded; he describes how children work themselves through the difficulties partly misdirected, partly misled by fancy. In a discussion about educational methods and in another on the influence of our present ethical standards on adult existence, he gives remarkably powerful sketches of material for a sane treatment of the whole problem.

The chief interest of these studies to the physician comes out in the study of the neuroses. In these the role of the sexual life has long been suspected. My own attention was first drawn to it by a study of Peyer's book on the effect of *coitus interruptus* in 1892. My analysis of the histories of cases of dementia praecox confronted me over and over again with the role and type of masturbation in these cases and later to a broader formulation of the concept and general theory of "habit-disorders." In the work reviewed here, Freud has given a much more searching presentation of the sexual facts, and that probably owing especially to his discovery of the frequency of symbolization, which would naturally lead us to a description of both his analyses of hysterias and obsessions and of dreams.

The first steps in Freud's development of psychopathology lie in the joint publication on hysteria with Breuer and in his interpretation of *Angst* or anxiety as due to suppression of libido; this was followed by his book on the interpretation of dreams, of various disorders in daily life and in humor and finally the longer accounts of analyses of cases. Stekel and especially the Zürich school, the latter with Jung's applications of the association experiment, have brought excellent material so that we already have a rich literature.

Freud's psychoanalysis works on the theory that there are conflicts and disorders of emotional or affective balance at the bottom of the neurotic symptoms and that the latter are transformed realizations of suppressed "wishes" or, in the case of anxiety states, of suppressed libido.

This is no doubt an assumption very difficult to swallow unless we become familiar with a rather wider range of usually neglected facts and then learn to give a sane and sensible interpretation to the startling words. How can we harmonize the sickness with a "wish"? We know, to be sure, certain patients who bask themselves in the reiteration of worries, fears, invalidism and its consequences, and who prefer being sick to a life with responsibilities. Another large number are undoubtedly real sufferers, very much to their own distress and discomfort, and to speak of a wish there looks like an injustice and like nonsense. There need not, however, be much doubt of the possibility that in the face of their better self certain parts of their nature are really at work causing mischief, parts which long for gratification, yearnings only partly mastered, ill-digested and perhaps distorted, in the face of and perhaps directly owing to the importunity of the supposedly best intentions. Where is the person who would claim to be quite clear on all his motives and to have analyzed them in a way that could not be improved on? And if in some cases there is evidence that suppressed affects or pushing agencies, springs of action, or whatever you want to call them, are discernible where the patient himself had covered the field with a kind of self-deception, why should we not admit that it might be worth while probing the matter, if only for the sake of a better understanding of the facts?

To grasp the situation clearly we have to assume a standpoint not generally accepted and really bitterly opposed by some—that of introducing into our scientific and medical thought not merely a system of reactions and elements, but conceptions of "things to be attained" and estimates of the actual result in the light of the attainment desirable or necessary for balance.

This is a practical and sensible postulate of work in the more complex parts of biology, and to establish its rights among the means of scientific work and reasoning is a most urgent task. Most naturalists of today taboo the method as too dangerously like the old teleological "explanations"; you will see that in reality it only puts the *problem* differently; and even if it does involve the principles of teleology or explanation in the light of purposes, it is bound to become a necessary condition for advance.

We hear it often said that teleological conceptions have never advanced science. But explanation in the light of purposes is different from explanation by purposes. I truly believe that we cannot afford to exclude this principle in psychology and in those other branches of biology in which the concept of "balance achieved" or "balance disturbed" is the only safe starting point and material guide of inquiry.

Put yourselves before the task of straightening out any one of the tangles in which our patients are apt to come to grief; for instance, any maladjustment of a longing or craving.

That which we might have to count on at any given moment is to such an extent merely *potential* material, and the end is attainable in so many ways that it would be difficult to foretell what of the available material will become *active* first and next. To try and speak of "elements" at work would force us into overpositive imaginative constructions. As a rule, however, we can make an estimate concerning the situation to be met. But, as I said, there are usually many ways to meet it, and while we can figure most safely with the habits and the customary ways of an individual, we would be less safe in defining the coming reaction if we tried at once to express the forecast in terms of detail of specific fundamental experiences and their effects, with sufficient allowance for recondite determining material. We may define more safely the usual reactions and the likely material in the light of the purpose or of the attainment to be reached. The very way the patient sees his aim tells us to some extent what stuff he has to meet the situation. But the problem is more likely to be on a safe basis if we include the consideration of the whole situation.

With the courage of conviction in the use of situations to be met and quasi-purposive, or if you wish teleological, estimates, it has become possible to speak of *substitutive activities* and of faulty substitutions, which characterize actions in the light of a functional equation. From the point of view of determining the relation of the *actual* reaction to that which would be *efficient normally*, we find it natural enough that the shifting of a fundamental longing or craving or push or affect, or whatever we may find to be singled out as an active component in the functional equation, may come out in many ways and with varying success, or may be transformed to nonrecognition. Freud uses the expression "wish" for the pushing factor or mischief-maker. In this he no doubt uses the word in about as broad and uncommon a sense as he does the term "sexual"; which must, according to him, be understood in the broadest sense of such a broad word as *Liebe* or love, which really includes the whole range of altruistic instincts. Freud evidently leans toward the specific and concrete, and therefore he preferably uses words which often seem too specific for what he aims to express, especially to those who are rather generalizers and feel, like myself, that only a vague term such as *Trieb* or "affect" or "go" would be fair enough to all the needs of the meaning implied.

Let us now return to the situations with which Freud has taught us to deal. Take first the lapses and slips of everyday life, our ways of forgetting things, the inability to recall certain names, or slips of the tongue. The study of slips shows, to be sure, that other factors play a role, such as fatigue, anticipations of sounds, perseverations, and condensations; but there is no doubt that with some persons these slips, like the uncritical mentation of dreams, allow us to get valuable glimpses into the unguarded tendencies of a person, and the same with the casual forgetting of words. Freud says it is because one really *wishes* to forget a word for some recondite reason and quotes a case of Jung's in which a businessman had to ask very often for the name of a frequent correspondent whom he knew very well, but who had happened to marry a young woman with whom he was in love, which gave him an unpleasant feeling of defeat. This principle will hold true in quite a number of cases, and Freud seems to me merely to emphasize the *frequency* when he says that there is always such a reason, instead of saying with somewhat more moderation, There is always *a* reason and usually one very different from mere chance. The same holds for mannerisms, tics, and other apparently meaningless doings.

To consider every not sufficiently intelligible or trivial act or thought under the heading of substitution before it is dismissed is, of course, a serious request on our time and patience and justified only if the returns warrant it. This, I believe, Freud has proved to a remarkable extent. He goes very far and says there are no meaningless doings. And he certainly also does it in quite a different way from the patient with dementia praecox with his obsession for meanings. It may be that some of the labor in finding meanings is practically superfluous and furnishes merely amplifications of what the practical mind sees at the first glance from the general impression; the results may at times look like but a meager reward for a scientist's obsession. But this is a question to be answered by trial and results, and if we do not succeed at once we do well to remember that seeing meanings may well become a matter of training and critical cultivation. Freud has shown his claim on the apparently most refractory and hopeless material, on dreams, to which we now turn to illustrate in what sense Freud uses meanings and interpretations.

Traditional science sees in a dream *merely* the symptoms of some physical events. As a rule, the emphasis of the "merely" points to a weak spot or an arbitrary narrowing of the horizon. To show that mental life generally is "merely" a feature of physical events has long enough been an ideal when the physician cherishes his neurologizing tautology and thinks that loose psychological terms become more respectable when they are first translated into the jargon of imaginary brain physiology and brain pathology. Unfortunately, the neurological data are "merely" part of the evidence. What counts is also the situation in which the body with its nervous system works, and it is just this wider setting which demands a function of broader integration than simple neurology—those "neural" functions which are bound to be mental. In psychiatry we have finally developed the courage of simple psychological expressions and even of purposive conceptions beside those of simple synthesis and we have taken up what commonsense works with, with welcome results. It is this same method that Freud tries on dreams—a study of the events in their settings.

According to Freud, every dream presents a piece of mental work open to analysis. The organic sensations play a limited role only. The dream is like a story of a writer, a complex product of motives and tendencies given a setting that may disguise them if one only views the story but which might furnish material for a psychological analysis of the author. To use the dreams for the purpose of getting an idea of the mental working of a person, Freud distinguishes the *dream story* and the *latent material*, and by following the principle that even in dreams we have no right to accept *mere* chance, he has certainly demonstrated that many dreams lead us more closely to the fundamental individual motives and mental constellations of man than many of the more impersonal and calculating wake-deeds and words.

For our social life we have learned to suppress many important factors of strong affective and even emotional value; but in dreams they assert themselves directly or through various effects in a way less strenuously guarded, very much as the apparently harmless and meaningless replies in an association experiment. Our motives (or, as we may say more psychologically, our affects) can be expressed in terms of either wishes or resistances, and our mental work tends toward the realization of the wish-element. Dreams, according to Freud, must be analyzed until the wish-element appears clearly before us and the dreams as the fulfillment of the wish, however disguised. Our wake-existence is made up of conations and wishes which command our consciousness. Other tendencies are repressed and it is especially these repressed undercurrentlike tendencies that are lived to completion in dreams only.

The repression hits those topics which are disagreeable and painful. Freud speaks of the repressive factors as the "censor," a sort of personification of the resistances which oppose a simple and frank deliberation and ventilation of matters which nevertheless determine our attitude even if we do not think of them and which pop up in a veiled form if we repress them otherwise. The dreamer does not see the affective factors back of his dreams because it is he who cultivates the censor and the repression for his comfort and self-defense. But if we cannot get at the facts directly there are indirect ways which Freud has shown us.

Instead of going for the sense of the dream as a whole, Freud takes up the harmless items one after another and collects the collateral thoughts suggested by them. Wherever there is a tendency to vary the account or to insist on a lack of motives, Freud with his detective spirit assumes and usually finds a real resistance, very much as the blocking of thought in the association experiment; and the very lack of a reply stamps the question or situation as one specially guarded by the censor, especially important and to be got at in other ways.

Like the association methods, the analysis of the dream and the following-up of experiences brings out concrete material which one would hardly get otherwise. There is no doubt that dreams express much more directly and uncritically the trend and bend of our imagination than anything we expose in our more circumspect wake-thought. But the remarkable thing is the peculiar process of distortion and condensation or transposition or symbolization of the material, and it is chiefly the unraveling of the connections in these states that has furnished Freud and his pupils the practice with which they become able to unravel other strings of events, the symptoms of the neuroses, the inner connection of which escapes the ordinary mortal, patient and physician alike.

That the studies of Freud and Jung have uncovered a rather surprising prevalence of trends more or less closely connected with the sexual life is probably most annoying and objectionable to many persons who have been brought up under the principle of secrecy and dissimulation not only of exaggerated prudery but also of the standards and taste of most social units of modern civilization. But thus are the facts and thus is our nature, at least in states of disease, and if it is so, the best we can do is to learn to size it up correctly and to face what there is without unnecessary ceremonies, just as we do not expect physicians and nurses to flinch from the disregard of social etiquette by untidy patients or those that force us to study fetid expectorations or discharges. Whether it is wise to comment on this undesirable task as "rehashing all this sexual filth" (W. D. Scott, *Journal of Abnormal Psychology*, 3:376) or wallowing in the dirt and smut, as others have called it, is ultimately a question depending on what it is done for and how it is done.

It is quite obvious that the whole method can easily be attacked and also discredited by the uncritical use by imaginative and self-sufficient workers. As a mere gratification of curiosity or hasty exploitation of theoretical claims, this work will have its undesirable representations. Many physicians will find it too difficult to decide to their own satisfaction what is the legitimate use of the principle of substitution and symbolization and appeal to the usually ignored realms of experience in the sexual and other instinctive life. Not everybody is a born detective. Not everybody can venture upon the ground of rather delicate constructions and interpretations. We can only say today that many unsuspected paths of indisputable importance have been opened up; that familiarity increases the certainty of a large number of the claims even when stripped of their personal way of putting things; that knowledge acquired would hardly be missed and forgotten and discarded again in any given case, and that the whole tendency is at least a most valuable balance of exclusive nonmental types of investigations of mental disorders.

8

Reaching to the Public

Do they ever get well?"

The layman's pessimism about patients in state hospitals—the feeling of horror—echoed the ignorance of many a medical man whom Adolf Meyer heard say that a person once insane had best be exterminated as a hopeless wreck.

In the center of the twofold task of educating the public and the practitioner stood the hospital, "much too walled off from the community." Meyer told a conference of superintendents with the New York State Commission in Lunacy in 1908 that the hospitals should push out their barriers and adopt a wider horizon; cooperate with community committees in an organization for the prophylaxis of mental disorders, starting with the concrete problems of after-care and prevention of relapses. He called for contact with "leaders among the healthy"—public-spirited persons, physicians and their wives, clergymen, heads of settlement houses, educators, groups fighting alcoholism, civic clubs interested in public hygiene. Find them, organize them! Make them familiar with the hospitals' work.

But at the same time the institutions themselves must not be crippled by the relegation of only so-called hopeless cases to so-called asylums; for this was just what would happen if special hospitals for acute cases were set up as a separate, unrelated system. The medical workers in the state hospitals would lose interest. New graduates would not care to take posts there. All because of a state monopoly of insanity, created by the legal issue of commitment.

277

The feasibility of reception hospitals, psychopathic wards, and medical-school hospitals was discussed at the 1907 Washington meeting of the American Medico-Psychological Association. Meyer said they should be constructed close to the centers of eruption. Private physicians should get better chances for psychotherapeutic work and should not be forced to surrender a patient to the "stigma" of a commitment.

So far the state has not concerned itself with any cases which were not either adjudged insane or committed or provided with papers which merely required formal sanction and already contained all the material and evidence calling for commitment. If the state opens its hospitals more liberally to voluntary and emergency commitments, it may have to assume responsibility for the expenses. Where special provisions are to be created it would seem to belong to a system of municipal education and avoidance of paternalism to demand that the locality provide for the outgrowth of its own kind of social hygiene or lack of it, with the condition that the protection come up to the required standard.

The whole matter of prophylaxis ultimately depends on local initiative, and since as a rule poverty and destitution run parallel with sufficient wealth, local improvements can be expected to get sufficient support for provisions in emergencies and patients who still are able to assert their own needs.[19]

Access to the community's sore spots was essential. "Nothing but work with the real difficulties will rouse our public to mind the dangers of alcohol, of syphilis, of insufficient hygiene of work and recreation. In these matters the state is too remote." But the public must be made to feel, in cases of mental upset, that desirable places were available for temporary quarantine—not strong-rooms in general hospitals or lockups. Voluntary admission must be encouraged.

Meyer looked to state-hospital psychiatrists to make the start because they had the obligation and knew the needs.

The human race of today is so opportunistic and ready to gamble with its chances that we cannot expect much of spontaneous realization of the seriousness of the whole problem, especially if it is veiled to the disadvantage of the people under the soothing and impersonal terms of heredity, degeneracy, and strain. It will take persons with much actual knowledge and with very strong conviction and determination to shape the conditions for prophylaxis and organization of early remedial work. The mere psychopathic hospitals will therefore not be a panacea unless they have the inspiration and well-balanced judgment of convinced and trained workers and leaders. It is personality rather than system, or perhaps better, the necessary combination of personality and system, that will make for success in such movements, as a history of their development would readily show.[19]

He was as hopeful as he was persistent. Let the profession see what was done in the state hospitals. Demonstrate what the actual cases and the localities needed. Then, with better training of medical students and a growing interest in psychopathology, Meyer could venture a prophecy: "Ten years will bring psychiatric hospitals to many of the medical schools and occasionally small state hospitals to meet special needs." [19]

A beginning had been made by the University of Michigan in 1906 with its Psychopathic Hospital at Ann Arbor. "As neither August Hoch nor I was any longer available to take its direction as originally planned, the choice fell naturally to Albert M. Barrett."

Meyer felt that hospital physicians should acknowledge their responsibility in the field of public education with a view to guiding "the struggle against morbid tendencies." He delivered a public lecture in 1907 in a series at the New York Academy of Medicine, arranged by the little group called the New York Psychiatrical Society. He was obliged to report that the plan did not work out as well as expected; more progress would have to be made in arousing public interest by using object lessons, such as court proceedings (an easy point of contact), and by encouraging visits to mental hospitals.

Public instruction had to be stripped of mumbo jumbo and whittled down to what was actually known about psychiatry; what could be expressed in plain language. Speakers must "stick to the plain facts, abstain from the oracular parading of mysterious names," and the public must be warned against the validity of such "high-sounding terms." The message to be brought home was simple enough: "the miscarriage of the mental adaptations or functions."

The big job of initiating the work of prevention, and of stirring the hospitals to perform the full scope of their mission, languished. Officialdom could never be expected to tackle it alone. Fiscal authorities shrank from it. The hospitals, it must be said, were closed corporations. With the charities, mental illness was "a mere foster child" simply because the task seemed too difficult. The press was injudicious in its crusades, nor did individual reformers show more good judgment than opportunism. The whole trouble was a lack of information put in communicable form, and the remedy Meyer proposed was an organized body of capable persons who could waken public conscience and supplant makeshifts with a permanent program.

In September, 1907, a salesman for a bank-construction company, Clifford W. Beers, called on Meyer with a book in page proofs. He had passed through a cycle of manic-depressive psychosis, was burning to tell the world the story of his horrifying years in institutions, and was determined to sell reform in every state. Ex-patients had often agitated for unwise legislation and sensational investigation, missing the point that they should get at the roots instead of the consequences of trouble. Beers came with a recommendation from William James, who had read his first draft and advised against any rewriting: "Don't you do it. You can hardly improve your book." The visitor also bore a letter of introduction from Dr. Stewart Paton, of The Johns Hopkins University, as a person with a cause that needed Meyer's support in order to make any headway in winning national approval. The cause was to found a society to be endowed for the improvement of conditions among the insane; to rob insanity of its terrors and induce the rich to supply funds for the erection of model institutions for incipient cases.

Meyer sized up Beers as a serious, zealous man who was seeking advice with an open mind—that is, he could accept a broader vision than the one he came with. When Meyer suggested that he turn his energy into a hygiene movement with a sociological tie-up, Beers caught the ball. With enthusiasm, he was willing also to subordinate his activity to a directing board of medically and socially well-trained workers instead of surrounding himself with apostles of legislative agitation. Here was a layman with unique equipment for a constructive task that would be insurmountable without "the personal experience and instinctive foundation for what must equal a religious vow of devotion of his life." Meyer wished him godspeed. A few days later he gave Beers a name for the movement.

"It was Dr. Meyer who suggested 'mental hygiene' as the words to use in naming the National Committee and the movement," Beers noted.

In October he armed Beers with an open letter to psychiatrists, hospital officials, and social workers. "It looks as if we had at last what we need: a man for the cause," Meyer wrote. Beers was worthy of their help in enlisting the best minds of the nation to further "work which will be one of the greatest achievements of this country and of this century—less sensational than the breaking of chains but more far-reaching and also more exacting in labor."

Beers delayed publication of his book to revise part of it on Meyer's advice and correct some of the errors Meyer found. He assembled thirty supporters to serve as an honorary committee and then launched *A Mind That Found Itself* in March, 1908, and the Connecticut Society for Mental Hygiene the following May. The book was an immediate success and stimulant, all the better for being unlike the usual true-confession type of diatribe of a recovered patient.

In the preliminaries of organizing a national group there were a number of conferences in Meyer's home in Harlem—and occasional clashes when hurried zeal ran into thoughtful analysis. Mrs. Meyer sat by, as Beers remembered those busy evenings, "ready to pour oil." The differences lay usually in contrasting concepts of the movement. On February 19, 1909, the National Committee for Mental Hygiene was born in a New York hotel with a program calling for better work in the asylums and in special hospitals, the education of physicians in psychiatric clinics, the organization of local efforts to assist returning patients and those needing early treatment, and gradually a campaign of efficient prophylaxis. For the progress of psychiatry the mental-hygiene movement would have a leavening effect. In time it actually served to liberalize "a no longer wholly hidebound science" and linked psychiatry, Meyer said, "with intelligently guided humanitarianism."

Psychiatry was already on the modern ground of scientific and critical empiricism—"the ground on which experience and experiment, not metaphysics, are the supreme judges; and activity, not contemplation, the goal." Apology was no longer fitting for the work being done in the state hospitals. Meyer was proud to report that the growing efficiency of their case-studies put the medical world under increasing obligation. But the most significant step in the first decade of the twentieth century was, to his mind, the beginnings of the expansion of state-hospital influence "to the sphere in which mental disorders may relapse and do originate."

These hospitals offered splendid training opportunities for graduates, despite the assumption of many medical leaders that institutional work disqualified a man for effective outside practice. But it was still difficult to attract the right type. Most of the men in charge of institutions had drifted into the work more or less by accident. Meyer's hope was to make the Institute in New York a recruiting place for young physicians thinking of taking up psychiatry, but the absence of funds and the overworked small staffs both in the hospitals and at the Institute inspired no feeling of a worth-while career; consequently few candidates applied for the positions.

Since 1902 the work of the hospitals had increased under the demands of the newer methods. In this period Meyer had been making urgent, unheeded calls for "a businesslike adjustment of working forces and amount of work to be done." For the Institute he wanted adequate quarters in order to bring the laboratories and clinical divisions under one roof; a larger staff to do the research that really would be the chief stimulus beside the greatest one of doing the best for one's patients. Any attempt to improve the quality of the work would be "purely academic" without greater financial support, he declared again and again.

It was an era of arctic exploration. But there were other things to explore. Advocating research fellowships in psychiatry, Meyer told his colleagues patiently: "Perhaps when the North Pole and the South Pole shall at last be properly discovered, man will bestow more attention upon the most wonderful creation of nature, the organ of plasticity of behavior." [20]

PROMOTING A

PRACTICAL INTEREST AMONG

PRACTITIONERS

From a paper read by Dr. Meyer at the Conference of Superintendents with the New York State Commission in Lunacy, Albany, Jan. 28, 1908; State Hospitals Bulletin, 1:5 (May, 1908).

There prevails a widely spread idea that it is no easy matter to interest physicians and medical students in mental disease. In the first place, medical training is usually directly opposed in its whole tendency to a consideration of mental conditions. In the little instruction the student gets he is apt to be made to understand that it is unscientific to think of mental disorders in any other terms than disorders of the brain itself or cerebral disorders induced by disease of various internal organs. Thus it comes that the physician complicates the inevitable difficulties by making himself believe that there must be an absolute distinction between mental disorders, to be dealt with by the teacher and moralist, and the disorders which must be left to the physician.

If we ourselves had to be tied to this theory and had to consider our sphere limited to what can be expressed in terms of disease of the brain and treated in such terms, as for instance, malnutrition, anemia, hyperemia, inflammation, atrophy, etc., we could not bring any clearness into some of the most practical distinctions and topics of work which we are cultivating today. Where could we find our principal diagnostic distinctions and especially the newer efforts to explain some diseases as the product of the clashing or lack of balance of mental experience, habits, and instincts? Can we blame the physician for being at sea with the older teachings of essentially anatomical pathology in such a field as ours?

There are other reasons why the practitioner might tend to shrink: the great demands on his time, and the frequently embarrassing responsibilities and complications into which he is led as soon as he takes an interest in the *mental* experience of a patient, and the conditions of his life and that of the family, or the situation on which they depend. Further, very often mental disorders cannot be satisfactorily dealt with at home, and therefore the patient is apt to pass out of the hands of one physician into those of another or into institutions. Thus the physician loses the natural stimulus which goes with the desire to see the patient through the trouble. Hence the first thought in the presence of a mental disorder is that of getting rid of a task so little gratifying.

To this we must add that many physicians, in and outside the hospitals and through them the public, believe that psychiatry deals with a hopeless task, with the statistically established law of inevitable degeneracy—very much as there used to be absolute fatalism concerning measles and tuberculosis; that psychiatry has completely exhausted the means open today, and that wholly different methods would have to be invented to make it worth while to class psychiatry with truly medical work, as the average physician would want to define it. The practitioner does not realize that less rut and more commonsense has done a great deal and will do more.

What can we expect if in our own ranks it has been said that no more recoveries are obtained today than a hundred years ago? It is true that the wave of promise about treating mental diseases as physical diseases are treated in general hospitals has hardly made good its extreme claims. We know too well that mere rest cure is far from being a specific even with all the theories of autointoxication worked into the scheme. We must meet as well the practical demands of mental adjustment. In the meantime the attitude of fatalistic indifference of a large majority of physicians is euphemistically and systematically justified with the often repeated statement: "There is no pathology of insanity as yet," or "Mind is beyond human ken," or other dogmatic excuses for inactivity if not for ignorance.

Among these considerations there are some absolutely inherent in the nature of the material and they cannot be changed. Others at least leave open possibilities. The physician probably does show good sense if he keeps his hands off where he can do nothing, or not enough to justify his interference. With his instinctive philosophy of pragmatism he has a right to be guided by faith in commonsense and the bald dictations of its wisdom. Our task will, therefore, be in the first place to show that in psychiatry the physician *has* some opportunities for action, that they are profitable, and that even where his activity is restricted it will tell in a system of work in which most physicians can take an intelligent interest.

The incentive must come from those who know, and the task is ours. We must show that some of the difficulties are not insurmountable, and we must reduce the inevitable feeling of indifference which comes from the passing of the patient out of the physician's hands. Let us work on the hypothesis that it is our task to win the attention of the medical profession, to guide their opinions and, through theirs, public opinion; and that we cannot achieve this by sermonizing, but by showing that we have some helps worth the attention of others.

The first condition on our part is that we shall have really something to offer that will help in the situation in which the physician has to work. It is not enough to show a physician the arrangement of the hospital, and the formal machinery of organization: such as wards for special cases, prolonged baths, rooms for examination and treatment, and laboratories, which may change his notions about the actual working of the hospital but not necessarily give him an idea of what he could do to get the patient there in the best possible way, and what he could do long before commitment. Nor should we lead the physician into abstract and more or less artificial stunts of classification and nominal diagnosis, but rather into an appreciation of definite conditions under which special helps can achieve something toward understanding the situation and the case, the prospects, and the best way to proceed.

All this must be shown on concrete cases, and none serve the purpose better than those which the physician has had under his care, and which may have been committed by him.

To be helpful to the practitioner we must have a good *history with special attention to the early developments and to the possibilities of early management*, showing that even before getting rid of the patient there are some things possible, if not absolutely needed, as well as very gratifying and worthy of the attention of the physician: means of preventing unnecessary complications and of forming a forecast so important in the choice of the institution, and other practical steps.

Let us remember that psychiatry consists in what we have learned to *do* with the patient, and only in a secondary way with theoretical issues. The fewer the dissertations about abstract disease entities, and the more telling the descriptions of what has been done with an actual case, the more we shall gain the attention of the rational practitioner.

Efficient consultations on the concrete cases are thus the most useful means of contact with the practitioner. Our first task is to keep alive an interest in the cases sent to the hospital. As far as possible the relatives and the patient are to be asked who is their physician outside, and advised to keep him in touch with the case while the patient is with us. This will, of course, lead to a profitable reply in only a limited number of our cases, but sufficient for a beginning in our purpose. The point is that the relatives and the physicians shall feel that we recognize the professional relations which existed and that we encourage them to continue during the patient's stay at the hospital and after his return home. A week before the staff meeting at which the patient is to be presented the second time, a carbon copy of the summary should be sent to the family physician, with questions and such suggestions as might elicit questions on his part. In some cases it would be the most satisfactory and mutually profitable thing if the physician could be invited to the staff meeting at which the case is brought up for consideration of all the facts available. It might perhaps be possible to assemble some cases from a district for a meeting of a district society at the hospital, such as has been arranged at times in various hospitals but usually with more didactic purposes than this definite issue of taking up cases which are known to one or more of the physicians.

My claim is that it is possible in this way to enter upon the difficulties of action and interpretation in the cases which actually troubled the physician, while didactic cases may seem so plain that they do not suggest anything special, *i.e.*, they neither are properly assimilated nor do they bring out matters on which there ought to be a mutual discussion. The success of such a step would absolutely depend on the extent to which the work on the cases is to the point and convincing and rising above the usual grind of a history. Put the essential facts into the line of attack, and the negative incidental facts where they are needed and do no harm, and it will be possible to make of practically every case a narrative and statement of facts which would excite the interest of the most indifferent.

The place to cultivate the practical sense of valuation and presentation of the facts is at the staff meetings, which would thus incidentally receive a most practical stimulus. Staff meetings should of course take up matters of fact and action and also of presentation, rather than quibble over terms; and to have these matters brought under the critical judgment of levelheaded outside physicians would certainly tend to further their value and usefulness. I can easily see that I might not be able to reach an ideal presentation with every case; but to have to make it worth the presence of the family physician would certainly increase the feeling of responsibility and further a possibility of bringing out actually useful facts rather than the discussion which so often mars staff meetings.

Where the distances are too great, a physician from the hospital might occasionally meet the physicians from a district at their medical meetings, and give a report of the cases from the district, as was lately done by Dr. Robert C. Woodman, of Middletown, but with a fairly full account of some of the more instructive cases and a discussion of local issues: the methods of care pending commitment in that county, matters of prophylaxis and after-care, etc. Such a visit might profitably include a visit to the district general hospital to render some help where desired, with regard to arrangement for patients pending commitment, care of delirious cases, etc.

The aversion of the practitioner to a valuation of the mental issues will be overcome by contact with those who know how to handle what cannot today be better expressed than in terms of mental activity, *i.e.*, of activity of conduct—certainly much better than in terms of hypothetical anemias and hyperemias of the brain and the like. Another point along a similar line would be to encourage physicians to send or bring patients to the hospitals for a provisional examination or advice, after the type of an outpatient department, a matter advocated some years ago by Dr. William Mahon.

The second recommendation I should like to make concerns the matter of publication of leaflets of information to be sent to committing physicians, and to any other physician who would wish to have his name on the mailing list, similar to the practice of some city health boards. The leaflets should present a record of the most important facts with special attention to the local cumulative occurrence of any special etiological factors, evidence of better care pending commitment and better after-care work, and a report of special achievements in any of these lines, with communication and discussion of specially instructive emergencies concerning commitments. I strongly feel that in all these matters each hospital should become the leader in its district. It was a sad policy which made it necessary for neurologists to find fault and for only partly informed humanitarians to take the initiative in a number of movements in which after all the physicians in the hospitals should be nearest to the core of information and in possession of a knowledge of the actual occurrences and demands for action.

A third proposition would be that the State Lunacy Commission should cause to be published annually a sufficient statement of all the habeas corpus cases with their subsequent history, including that of further developments in cases of earlier reports. We are committing no breach of confidence in this because the cases are all voluntarily brought to public notice in court, and their publicity, even with names such as would be omitted in the printed report, is therefore inevitable. At the present time, owing to the predominance of the legal element in the court action, no notice is taken of the fact that the method of getting at the facts through testimony given on the witness stand is apt to favor inaccuracy. Nothing would bring before ourselves, the profession, and the legal and general public a more valuable set of facts than such a publication. All the cases are interesting, and if everything is well weighed and the facts are well presented, nothing could be more instructive or a better stimulus toward improvement. Today we cannot seriously blame the legal profession. How many members of it have ever seen a well-digested record of a case? And we cannot seriously blame the average physician, who becomes a hasty witness because he has no standards as to how much information a physician should have to be justified in going on the witness stand.

A final suggestion: Not infrequently it is possible to rouse the attention of physicians through the interest taken by a wider public. An effect similar to that attained by the migratory exhibit of tuberculosis might be achieved by a migratory lecture with good illustrations, not merely of the pretty things, but also of the difficulties; a picture of the life and work in a modern hospital, touching also on such matters as the management of excited cases at their worst, the conditions leading to accidents and injuries (which means not only the record that the patient was noisy and violent, but what made him so, and what measures might serve to prevent turbulence), the requirements in cases of suicidal attempts, the comparative value of police and nurses, the provisions for transportation. The nature and frequent difficulties of delirium, of general paralysis, of senility and of psychogenic processes could also be brought before audiences of physicians and the educated public. But care should be taken not to make the matter a cheap medical course with sham information on matters which would only lead to misconstruction, as I am told is the result of not a few public lectures given, for instance, at some of our medical schools.

I want to draw your attention to but one more point. I believe the medical profession in this country is unwise in the matter of demanding absolute passivity with regard to the press and in encouraging the pernicious insinuations of self-advertisement wherever any person gets into a position which demands some notice. The medical profession must have been in a state of hysterics when it tried to meet the advertising skill of quacks with a code of ethics which is absolutely at variance with the principles of the press today, and when it invites any comparison between quack advertisements and legitimate assertion of individuals for a civic or public cause. I can, I believe, vouch for a keen conscience on matters of publicity; but I consider as most pernicious and a reflection of a bad spirit the frequent and stereotyped remark which stamps as self-advertisement many a meritorious effort to get out of a rut.

My recommendation of several years ago that every hospital give the friends of patients and the physicians of the district a printed pamphlet giving an account of the hospital and some helps with regard to commitments, visits, correspondence, etc., has been carried out in but one place, and there with the name of the physician who wrote it attached to the pamphlet. Whether this was the reason why the printing had to be done privately and was not officially sanctioned I do not know. Personally, I feel that work of this sort cannot and should not be absolutely impersonal, and that the credit of work done should come to the worker.

It is, I think, inevitable to realize that today the press occupies a position which cannot be ignored but which demands cooperation. There is no corporation or club of any importance that does not meet the situation by a press agent whose business it is to forestall misstatements by offering that which the public has grown to demand. An infinite amount of good can be attained by attention to this matter, not only in the public press but also in the medical press, which I think could only profit through authentic information from a known and responsible source.

MODERN PSYCHIATRY:

ITS POSSIBILITIES AND

RESPONSIBILITIES

From a public lecture by Dr. Meyer at the New York Academy of Medicine, 1907; State Hospitals Bulletin, 2:323 (Sept., 1909).

The last few years have brought us a most interesting development in the awakening of our people to an appreciation of the possibilities and responsibilities in social hygiene. For centuries the oughts and should-be's ruled the world with scant accounting for the reasons of these oughts. Authority rested on tradition and the chance evolution of general thought, but it took the form of dogma and was helpless and irresponsive.

The last century has yielded so many discoveries within the reach of all, that facts (or more correctly speaking, experience) have assumed their true importance and, throughout our people, there is a sound yearning for data rather than dogma to set aright the many miseries of this world.

Public hygiene is at last receiving practical attention. The rousing of public responsibilities about water and milk supplies as related to epidemics, sanitation as related to malaria, and the as yet somewhat halfhearted restriction of the dangerous spitting nuisance has initiated a new era of social morality. The civic duties of medicine appear in the progress of school physicians and of school hygiene. The sexual morality of the community is being put on a basis of better knowledge of the facts, as in too many cases merely abstract or ethical teachings do not affect conduct. The defects of our communities are more and more looked upon as the product of a *general* morality as well as the good will of the individual, as social problems demanding the help of social organization and of social science. The fight with tuberculosis, the "white plague," has become a matter of social as well as of personal hygiene. The effort to bring about a systematized prophylaxis of the disorders of that even more eminently social function, the human mind, thus receives no small amount of help through the fact that the community is already organized in many ways and that in many of our own efforts we can go hand in hand with those who are already at work without having mental disorders in mind.

One of the most important lessons of modern psychiatry is the absolute necessity of going beyond the asylum walls and of working where things have their beginnings; and experience shows that there only organized cooperation will achieve success. It might be thought that psychiatry is as yet in rather too primitive and turbulent a condition to rival in interest those domains of hygiene which have become so lucid and inviting through the wonderful discoveries of the last twenty-five years. We have now definitely settled more facts and methods than our community is willing to deal with unless it is properly guided. Our first aim is to make accessible the main facts with which we work.

We no longer mystify ourselves and our hearers by such queer statements as that there cannot be any diseases or disorders of the mind, but only diseases of the brain. The mental activities, whether normal or abnormal, with which the physician deals cannot be thought of without activity of the brain. But the dogma of *perfect* mental activity and diseases *merely* of the brain has led to a multitude of assumptions of brain anatomy and brain physiology which cannot stand the test of critical experimentation. We have learned to see that if a patient has a definite type of delirium, or obsession, or depression, or nervousness, we can draw practical inferences and plan measures of treatment without trying to translate these plain and useful facts into terms of obscure brain speculations which nobody can control, and most of which are either erroneous or as yet so imperfectly proven that they had best be expressed more modestly. We are much more willing today to say that we do not know some things, because we know better what to do with those which we do know. By sparing ourselves the trouble of discussing plain facts in terms of brain cells and hypothetical brain centers unless we can prove them or really further our activity by the hypothesis, we save ourselves time for a better functional analysis of the facts, and the hearer unnecessary and harmful mystification.

The courage of using the facts as we find them and in terms of plain experience is largely the achievement of the last decades. It has required experience with mental suggestion and also the bold work of mental healers to convince some physicians of the absurdity of pseudoscientific antics in presence of the plain facts, and of the fact that the proper direction of mental life is and always has been the keynote of management of quite a number of diseases and an important help even in disorders of organs other than the brain. If we know now that mental life presupposes a sufficiently organized and normally acting brain, we also know that abnormalities of mental activity interfere much more deeply with the life of the brain and the organism than was believed in the days when mind was thought to be wholly independent and wholly supreme, especially since the unprejudiced study of mental life has disclosed a whole range of mental activities which were ignored as long as the facts were divided merely between the extreme headings "the moral" and "the physical."

Freed of hampering dogma, psychopathology—as we now call the whole range of theory and practice of mental disorders—proceeds exactly as do all other branches of medicine and practical life. In surgery things are relatively simple; you study what you want to remove and how you can get at it, and bring the parts together so that they will grow again into the best state of efficiency. In general medicine we help a diseased heart to do its work so that whatever disorders there are may adjust themselves. Or we relieve the work of a kidney or stimulate it, or we facilitate the task of digestion or assimilation, or put the whole economy under a regime of general adjustment. And in mental diseases we do exactly the same thing. We spare and help mental activities and regulate the conditions on which they depend.

Modern psychiatry talks much less of the mysterious changes in the brain, even when it knows them to exist, unless there is something to be done about them. Through the emphasis on what there is to be done we have found safe ground. We do not worry about an all-embracing system, such as might force out of consideration the hygiene and the disturbances of mental activities themselves as we see them; but instead, we set to work at what is at hand, and shape our working hypotheses as we need them in our activity. We can speak of the medical or psychopathological issues, of the medico-legal side, of the administrative issues; we can speak of the problems of the state and of local problems, all on their own merits, and without having to shift our theoretical foundation.

This assertion of the natural instincts of experience has led to a recasting of many of the traditional notions of psychiatry. We first touch upon the question of *forms of mental disorders*. In this respect our conceptions have undergone a most fundamental change in the last ten years.

Overawed by the difficulty of doing better, and in deference to the Graeco-Roman traditions revived in the days of the French school by Pinel and his Continental and English followers, psychiatry had long adhered to a very simple division of mental disorders into *mania, melancholia* and *dementia*, from which general paralysis was soon split off as a sort of concession and deviation from the traditional psychologizing scheme. Unfortunately, all but the last are very vague terms and are very differently used by different physicians. The division is hardly decisive enough to command much medical attention, while it is apt to sidetrack the attention from matters which are better worth knowing and working with than is the question of whether or not a patient is maniacal, melancholy, or delusional, and whether he has suffered more than one year.

The truth is that while in a general way patients *can* be classed as excited or depressed, a clear distinction does not *exist* and cannot be *created* along such lines. We know that excitement is almost directly in the ratio of the degree of tactless management, police interference, and the like. If you should go through the Manhattan State Hospital on Ward's Island today you might well be amazed by the absence of practically everything the public expects to occur in asylums. What the older and even recent textbooks describe of raving mania has proved to be in a large percentage of cases a result of mismanagement. The classical excitements of the past are now limited to but few cases of various conditions in a well-conducted hospital and community. Excitement is therefore not a standard distinctive sign of a special disease, but apt to be rather an incidental fact.

Moreover, excitements, even in the form of exaltation, and depression are not mutually exclusive states. Many cases present both types of disorder alternately or in successive attacks, or even a simultaneous mixture of these conditions, and one would naturally want to look for a designation embracing both facts.

In another well-known rut of psychiatry, this scale of disorders was described as the typical course of a case of insanity: melancholia, excitement, confusion, dementia—a plausible formula which long figured in definitions and clouded the careful observation of things as they are, and made many a case pass through four and more diagnoses where now we see but one disease from the outset.

To identify a mental disorder with the type of manic-depressive insanity means to recognize it as a recoverable psychosis which is apt to recur as a depression or excitement or a mixed state of characteristic symptoms, but which rarely incapacitates the patient permanently and hardly ever leads to a real deterioration. It is possible to establish this important forecast through a careful analysis of the mental reactions. To establish the kinship of a case with the standard type of dementia praecox does *not* mean that the case is *hopeless*, but that it is very apt to drift into dilapidation.

With the recognition of these specific types goes the splitting-off of other entities worthy of differentiation, so that we now have groups with much more specific meaning. We no longer hold that there is but one big mass of insanity and only unessential differences of form; that it leads to dementia if it lasts long, or that the tendency to dementia depends on the degree of degeneracy and heredity, etc. Every one of these plausible deductions can be shown to be either tautological or inaccurate if not wrong. It is not the depression or excitement but the fundamental kind of disorder and the duration that decides the forecast; heredity is oftener found in those with recurrent recoverable psychoses; what is called degeneracy is to quite an extent the product of inadequate environment, etc.

One further step toward emancipation and absolute honesty has since been made. In order not to force anyone to class his cases under a set form, but in order to encourage groupings of the facts according to the worker's best judgment and to the extent of his actual attainments, merely a general outline of groupings—but with specific directions—has been adopted in the state hospitals with a great deal of freedom in detail left to the various staffs.

We thus avoid the lamentable consequence of the older tables, that even when the physician did make his diagnosis in terms of neurology and general medicine and modern psychopathology he had to throw it out when he used official language. We are now trying so to shape the classification that it will be an encouragement for efficient and progressive work, not the reverse.

Keeping those facts foremost which have the greatest importance in etiology, in the working out of the disease process, and in the prognosis, brings with it another important consequence. Looking over the disorders of mental activities as we see them in and outside the asylums, we find that almost every one may exist without implying conditions which constitute insanity in the common traditional sense of our social and legal compact. A true diagnosis must go deeper than the question of capacity for legal conduct and responsibility. In our dispensary work we come across cases of the essential deterioration or dementia praecox type long before the stage when the final catastrophe would show the existence of a serious calamity to a layman or to even the family. Many cases of manic-depressive insanity, if their periods of depression and exalted overactivity are within reasonable limits, are never committed. The diagnosis of the actual disease, however, remains the same.

The traditional psychiatry, with its legal definitions as a guide, is like a geology which would explain the formation of the Alps by studying only those regions that lie above the snow line. Numerous disorders exist as unsafe mental make-up and as disturbances in need of help long before one would pronounce them cases of unreserved *non compos mentis* [legally, of unsound mind]. From my medical point of view I consider it time that we recognize that the snow-line geology period is over. The diagnosis must be made irrespective of the legal issues. Legal issues are a practical question, certainly a very important one, demanding most careful study; but they are a practical question of non-medical character, for which the physicians should merely furnish the facts with the comment of their experience as a guide for the judge. On such a ground we can cooperate with the judge and the law without doing violence to our facts and without presuming to do the judge's work.

The fact that a commitment is necessary to enter a suitable hospital creates a decided obstacle to early treatment. I know one prominent neurologist who in one year lost three cases by suicide simply because of the peculiar barrier which tradition has built, and which in some way we shall have to adapt to our better knowledge of the facts.

The hospitals are becoming more and more hospitals and not mere asylums; the management of the numerous types of emergencies is infinitely better than most physicians and laymen have any idea of. Several hospitals have reception services which, apart from unessential luxuries, are in all respects on the level of what the best general hospitals and even private hospitals offer.

Psychiatry has been excessively institutionalized. Its definitions have in many cases been made at the wrong end, and thereby have delayed its practical evolution. Our institutions have not yet reached the climax of their efficiency, but they are worthy of high admiration and pride; their physicians do not yet enjoy the best attainable conditions of work, but their work is much more creditable and far-reaching than the general practitioner is apt to know. The patients are not quite as well classified as they will be under the newer provisions. Where admission is so difficult, discharge tends to become equally difficult. But most of the obstructive criticism comes from those who merely repeat the formulas of many years ago. Those who visit the discharged cases report an almost uniform gratitude and friendly feeling toward the hospitals.

Every one of our medical colleges should have its hospital wards for mental cases organized as clinics for model work, study, and teaching, as is the case with every Continental university, not only in France, Germany, Switzerland, and Austria, but also in Russia, Italy and other Mediterranean countries. There still are opportunities for the development of special hospitals for those who are not insane before the law, but who need psychotherapeutic help in habit training to forestall a breakdown, and for carrying to the public the knowledge of the best ways of living, not merely a gospel of healthy-minded contemplation but a gospel of healthy-minded life.

We need coordination of all those interested in a wholesome community. Only those who are leaders of the healthy can be leaders of those who fall by the wayside, and only those who take in the lessons of the failures of life will know how to shape normal life in the safest way. An interest in a few cases of after-care, some help in the work for the handicapped, will do more than any number of papers. To join in doing this work is within the reach of all.

After-care, long in use in European countries, is the most promising of all the advances made during the last decade. It opens the way to what was sorely needed: a closer relation between the hospitals and the communities, which have too long stood aloof, in mutual ignorance and lack of sympathy. It is bound to call on the forces that work for the best hygienic conditions in the community. It is bound to lead to an organization which will be able to meet that highest achievement of farsighted social economy—prophylaxis. After-care and prophylaxis necessarily draw upon the members of many existing organizations who may never have thought that they had anything to do for the insane, but who thereby gain much valuable experience and learn to apply preventive hygiene to those from whose ranks some unfortunates might otherwise be sufferers in the future.

AFTER-CARE AND PROPHYLAXIS

From a discussion by Dr. Meyer at the After-Care Committee meeting, Oct. 2, 1908, at Willard State Hospital, Willard, N. Y.; State Hospitals Bulletin, 1:631 (March, 1909).

The highest function and the highest ambition of the human intellect is undoubtedly the ability to foresee and to shape one's action so as to anticipate the future. The realization that something can be done in turn inevitably leads to a real feeling of responsibility. What then can be done in prophylaxis of mental disorders?

Nobody can engage in the work of the after-care of the insane without experiencing the awakening of an instinctive desire for prophylaxis. The two ideas are parts of one instinct; we might say: Prophylaxis is the climax and fulfillment of our endeavor in after-care work. At the same time I know of no better way of preparing for prophylaxis than by getting experience in after-care. The first step toward prophylaxis is to get a sufficient experience with what one wishes to prevent.

As a matter of fact, I have always felt that the term "after-care" in the name of a committee of this character is one that limits the field of interest below that which is actually the result. It is not only after-care as it was established in England, that is to say, one or two months' care for people who are discharged and need a boarding place or something of that nature, but it consists of finding occupation for patients who are leaving the institution and trying to live again in the community, and helping to make their reentrance into the community easy and safe against relapses. There we have the after-care movement turned into the prophylaxis movement; and anyone who once gets interested in the prophylaxis of recurrences cannot help but get interested in the prevention of the first attacks, and there you are in the center of what we must hope from this movement. It demands, it seems to me, an organization of all those people in the community who are capable of taking an interest in the insane and in methods of coping with mental disorders which arise in a community, whether they require hospital care or not. I certainly venture to say that there is more mental trouble causing unhappiness in the community than the hospitals ever get any idea of.

As I say, the after-care with absolute necessity leads to an understanding of prophylaxis. Working in after-care, you come into contact with persons who have distinct and concrete difficulties, the recurrence of which you want to prevent; that gives you the concrete material without which interest cannot be sustained. Practical concrete experience must give the backbone to efficient optimism. The majority of people think that insanity is a hopeless matter anyway; they say "Once insane forever insane," and all that sort of thing, which nothing can disprove as well as work in after-care, if at least the after-care does not simply deal with "those who are needy," as was originally expressed in the resolution passed in Albany.

Of course, that would only give one side of the picture. I really believe that the After-Care Committee might very well be taken into confidence concerning the fate of most persons who leave the hospital. A good many of the patients naturally will not need your help, but it will be a help to you to know about them; and others may be beyond your help, but it is nevertheless desirable that you should know how things stand so that you can form an opinion of the relative value of things yourself. Certainly, knowing the group of cases gives you an idea that some things can be done, and it helps you over the widely spread notion that insanity is a hopeless proposition.

We must get experience with those who help themselves or whose conditions are sufficient for success, and also the unfavorable cases, so as to have a sound balance and appreciation of the possibilities. Otherwise we are not entitled to convictions about what we can legitimately demand from the patients and their environment. We must learn to be sure about what can be expected and what rewards an effort or sacrifice will bring. Uncertainty weakens our determination about demanding the sometimes radical and even unpleasant changes and sacrifices, for we must feel sure of our ground to be able to prove our claims even to the defendant of the "mind your own business" doctrine.

The special reason why prophylaxis must appeal to us is that mental disease is much more easily prevented than cured, and that it is such a calamity that everything should be done to prevent it in its very inception. Years of observation have furnished us many facts; but the peculiar asylum habit of dealing with the insane in hordes has retarded the application of what conclusions we are able to derive from the experience. After-care carries the treatment of mental difficulties into the community again, that is, to the place where the prophylaxis must do its work, and we may hope that gradually a knowledge of the facts will bring to the thoughtful members of the community conviction and the means for prevention.

One great difficulty is that no mental disease is due to a single cause. It is extremely difficult to say in an offhand way what caused any one disturbance. Hardly one of the mental diseases is due to only one cause, and the consequence is that with many the "cause" given in any special case or disease appears not sufficiently convincing to warrant the frequently inconvenient and drastic measures which are required for prevention of recurrences.

There are certain forms of mental disorder in which the etiology is relatively simple. Certain poisons will produce mental disturbance of a transitory character in nearly every person, in some a little more readily than in others. We know that a sufficient quantity of alcohol creates mental disturbance; we know that certain drugs will produce hallucinations, etc. Many of these intoxicants paralyze sufficiently to throw the risks involved chiefly on the person intoxicated; and when others suffer, as occasionally in alcoholism, the American usage of law deems it justice to make the intoxicated person responsible as if no intoxication had occurred. That is, it leaves the prevention of intoxication on the grounds of personal moral suasion, or it attacks it indirectly, by punishment for the misdemeanors it leads to, or by prohibition or education.

The fact that not all drunkards become intoxicated and that not all of those who become intoxicated become insane, seems to lead many to actual doubt as to the causal importance of alcohol. There is no doubt that alcohol produces insanity only when certain conditions are fulfilled, and then different forms of the disorder result. In quite a few of these disorders the element of the constitutional make-up plays a role. As soon as that appears many wiseacres throw up their hands and speak of "degeneracy" and of "nature's way of weeding out the unfit," and all that sort of trash; and the interest in prophylaxis comes to an end.

Alcoholic insanities, like all mental disorders, are the result of at least two factors: the alcohol and the individual make-up, and probably always a certain number of other factors. Thus in the case of delirium tremens, we find, as a rule, that it is not only the fact that the patient has been drinking, as so many do without getting delirium tremens, but it is the association with gastritis and with insomnia that tips the scale and finally produces the condition that we know as delirium tremens—in which the fear of things, the imaginary hearing and seeing of things, unseats the mind. Or an injury or sudden forced abstinence that comes on together with insomnia, perhaps, may in an alcoholic individual produce the delirium.

In others, alcoholic abuses may lead to Korsakoff's disease (called by the name of the Russian alienist who described it in 1887), that form of alcoholic insanity which is especially marked, not by seeing things but by the peculiar forgetfulness and inability of the patients to remember what has happened one minute, five minutes before; a forgetfulness which they patch up by making up out of free imagination what they suppose they have been doing. For instance, a patient who has been for weeks in the hospital in bed, paralyzed with a neuritis—the condition is usually accompanied by neuritis with paralysis, or is part of neuritis with paralysis—salutes you as "Doctor Somebody Else," hardly ever uses the correct name, but has usually a correct appreciation that you are the doctor, the nurses are the nurses, etc. You say, "How are you?" "Very well." "How have you been getting along?" "Well, I just came up here half an hour ago" or, "was down at church" (many of them turn out the best sides of their past), or they give a vivid description of having been in the park with the children.

Or alcoholic abuses may lead to so-called paranoic conditions, that is, systematized delusional states, and that especially on account of the peculiar home conditions that are created by the alcoholic; for one thing, the alcoholic is as a rule exposed to all sorts of misdemeanors himself and he gets into trouble with the condemnations and friendly advice and scoldings that he may get at home, and then in a broad-minded way attributes his own failures to those who scold and makes up delusions—ideas of infidelity, etc., and then begins to imagine that whatever he sees has got to be construed along that line. Jealousy is one of the typical lines of the alcoholic, or it is persecutions by labor unions, persecutions by religious bodies; that is to say, the influence of antagonistic and restricting elements.

You see, therefore, that alcohol produces so many different things that we must be ready to look for contributing causes *and* the special tendencies of individual constitutions. Even if we should have to say that alcoholic insanities were due to a special temperament, the problem of efficient anti-alcoholic work would remain before us. In keeping with these facts, we realize that many things have to be looked out for in our remedies, not only the negative elimination of alcohol but helps in getting better pleasures and recreations, and giving the people at home a little advice as to how to arrange the home so as to make it attractive and a number of other things of that sort.

Another type of important etiology is syphilis. Depending on a number of factors, many of which are not known as yet, this infectious disease may disappear under treatment, or even sometimes without treatment, or it may remain and show itself in various ways—disease of the blood vessels of the brain or other modes of disorder. In every hospital we occasionally have a case in which cerebral syphilis is at the bottom of the difficulty, and far more often the affections called metasyphilis or locomotor ataxia and general paralysis. General paralysis produces six per cent of the admissions in the average hospital, and about twenty per cent of the male admissions in metropolitan hospitals. These are facts that cry out for preventive measures.

On the other extreme of causation of mental disorder we find those disorders which look more definitely like reactions to excessive demands on the capacity of adaptation, as premature wear, forms of exhaustion, senile deterioration, senile insanities, usually really lasting on the ground that the blood vessels of the brain become diseased, but also in part due to atrophy of the brain. Then we have all those cases of giving out, in the form of neurasthenia, depressions, and paranoic conditions. The most pernicious type is dementia praecox, of which my interpretation is rather different from the usually accepted fatalistic schemes.

The essence in these disorders where there is no poison or infection demonstrable is that the patient, through circumstances or through fundamental peculiar make-up, comes to react to the difficulties of life in ways which are bound to vitiate the life of the brain. We may well speak of the symptoms of insanity as disorders of *conduct* and *behavior*. Conduct and behavior constitute the mental life of the individual. Certain individuals have a form of conduct and behavior fit to meet many difficulties; conduct and behavior may be sufficient or insufficient; if it is insufficient it gets the individual into trouble and he will have to use the ways of nature in trying to get out of the trouble, by being afflicted with depression, which gives him a chance to extricate himself, or a breakdown, which gives him a chance to begin over again. One can really think of most diseases as an effort to right themselves and as giving the individual a chance to start over.

"Disease" is one of the means of picking up and getting straight. A normal depression is a state evolved to protect ourselves; as we are depressed, we want to be let alone more or less in order to get a chance to build up our fences again and strengthen ourselves instead of proceeding headlong in unfit action. Of course, you may consider this a rather optimistic view of a trouble, but it seems to me very well in harmony with the facts. Unfortunately, at times this normal method or reaction is used as a subterfuge. I know of neurasthenias which are a permanent excuse from having to carry the burdens of unwelcome duties. To cure them means to make the patient fit to meet the frequently exaggerated difficulties. Instead of working through to a solution of difficulties, the patient, owing to the fact that he has not the necessary funds of conduct and behavior and mental activity generally, or because he has not the physical funds, or because some poison or some factor disturbs the balance, works himself into various states of mind into which it is impossible to bring help, sometimes for long periods in which the brain may undergo deterioration.

Whether it undergoes deterioration depends altogether upon the factors which work together in producing the symptom complex of the disorder. There we may have to speak of "dementia praecox," but by no means all the cases of dementia praecox must be looked upon as cases of dementia. The term "dementia praecox" is a very unfortunate term. It really indicates merely the direction in which things may go if they cannot be stopped, and, of course, in some individuals, they cannot be stopped because these patients lack the ability to rally after things have gone so far; just as an individual may know how to balance himself if he be on his ordinary feet or on skates, but when he gets beyond his base all the knowledge of equilibrium will not help him—he will naturally have to tumble.

A great number of mental disorders present for quite a time a state in which the patient is relatively unapproachable. He over-uses the helps of the normal depressions, of the normal retirement, of the normal condition in which one would like to "crawl into a hole." We all know what that means; but he overuses it. We have to wait for chances of greater approachability and then use them with a knowledge of the difficulty the patient has to meet and fails in without help; and alas! often enough notwithstanding the belated help. Insight in these directions gives us some valuable points for prophylactic work. Unfortunately, we find that physicians have been overstating among themselves and before the public the importance of certain simple physical causes, and we have to learn to reinstate according to their actual merit those physical causes for which we have merely terms of conduct and behavior, terms of psychology, but which are nonetheless actual and real, the effects of abnormal application of mind or conduct and behavior, be it for the satisfaction of cravings or in unhygienic efforts to do what would be best if done with a proper adaptation of the aims to the means.

In every case the etiology is really best expressed as a constellation which must attain a certain balance without which the equilibrium of health is lost. Some of the matters are individual issues (plainly physical, or of that physical type which we call conduct and behavior), others more sociological.

After-care must begin before the patient leaves the hospital, and the After-Care Committee would, of course, be better off if its relations with the hospital were more frequent than once in six months. It is only while the patient is in the hospital that you can get the family thoroughly interested in their responsibility. It is then that the relatives should be brought into relations with the after-care helper, and it is only then that you can get the confidence of the patient absolutely and with certainty. It is by far the best and safest plan to get acquainted with the patients and the situation while they are still under control.

Looking over the alcoholics, we may depend on giving them strong enough interests, but you often have to use additional helps, through societies, by getting them into contact with organized abstinence circles. To do that adequately it seems to me that the After-Care Committee should have a directory of all the societies for anti-alcoholic propaganda in the district. Many a patient has got to be reached by people of his own level, as has been shown by the Salvation Army. The Committee ought not to try and simply be *it* and not take advantage of all the numerous people who would be perfectly willing to help if they knew how and where.

The suggestion that "if your subject happens to be a Roman

Catholic, you can do something" is a rather hard indictment of Protestant societies, and I think it would be well to let them know it and stir them up. In this country, I must confess, the matter of anti-alcoholic propaganda has been allowed to become sadly lax. It will, of course, always depend on one or two individuals in a community who have enough determination and personal inspiration. Professor Forel attained his purpose of finding a leader by putting a shoemaker in charge of a hospital for drunkards. That shoemaker had the conviction that something could be done (see *American Journal of Insanity*, 57:297, 1900). Forel himself told me he did not think many physicians could do it because they are not apt to have the necessary single-minded determination. If you want to have success you must have conviction.

It is indeed well to recognize the many different sets and types of social units and the types of persons that would appeal to them. This morning we saw a Methodist farmer who was converted from alcoholism and then gave others the benefit of his conviction, but unfortunately beyond his own balance. Such a man might do some good if properly guided and used. Certain converts are apt to be the most useful people; they work among people of their level very much better than educated people could do, who speak a different language. Use individuals who have the conviction, and help them; the strength and safeguards lie in organization.

A great function of societies lies in their bringing some fun and entertainment. This is one of those things prevention has got to be most concerned about. There are in the country and in cities difficulties in the possibility of having legitimate fun. The problem of creating possibilities of decent fun should be just as noble a task of the well-meaning people as to provide occasions for religious and moral exhortation.

Physicians, with the help of the after-care worker, might get the facts with which to correct misconceptions which, if left uncorrected, may play a rather disastrous role in later attacks. The after-care worker writes to or goes to see the physician who had the patient in charge. On Ward's Island that is done a great deal. Of course, it is easy there on account of the small distance, which also makes it easy to have the patient call on the hospital personally. Here it would have to be done this way: Induce some physician in the community who takes a strong interest in the cause to take an interest in the case, and the patient then might be told to go and talk matters over with him in case of difficulties arising, and then the physician may if necessary consult, or correspond with, the hospital, or may occasionally visit Willard State Hospital to talk over in detail some groups of cases. Or the after-care worker might consult such a physician and get advice from the local standpoint as well as from the hospital standpoint. It is a great deal to ask from a practitioner, but I think it would be well worth while and one of the ways to get physicians to outgrow their indifference toward insanity.

Very often patients come to a stage where they press for discharge. They appeal to the families, and the families begin to get worried and think they must take that patient out. I think an after-care worker who has seen that a number of times can give the family quite a little sound advice which they are more apt to take from a lay adviser than from physicians, because people outside always believe the physicians have an interest in keeping the patient. *There* is a misconception which after-care workers can help to uproot and by doing that they can also prepare the family to act more sensibly with regard to the discharge of a patient and to consider whether they are really ready to take a patient home. On the other hand, the after-care worker can materially facilitate the early discharge of certain other cases.

If a patient, after relative recovery, has a child, the matter needs quite a little looking into, and a little sensible advice from people who know better how to deal with such a situation would be perfectly timely, and I think a woman in that situation would take advice very well without having to be brought to a physician. I am inclined to think that is one of the best illustrations as to why after-care should not limit itself to two months. I suppose the fear of making dependents is at the bottom of that principle. As a matter of fact, there forms almost a life relation with those who had once found help and do not make themselves a burden. Many a patient needs an opportunity to make a friend, and usually a friend for life, if he deserves it.

Another important role which I have not mentioned so far is the relief of the feeling of prejudice and sensitiveness on the part of the patient or of the family. In one case of depression I find a note that there is quite a little sensitiveness about having been at the hospital, a feeling which should be straightened out; further, we meet with complaints of having been badly treated. It. is well worth while to take up the complaints and to give the patient the satisfaction of a fair inquiry. We must, of course, not join the flurry of indignation before we have seen how the facts are on both sides; but after that is done we can talk over the situation in the most sensible way. There are, of course, many different problems which a patient may have to settle, from love affairs to complicated troubles that nobody wants to handle directly; in such cases the best thing is to talk the matter over with the physician and then see what you can do with the patient.

Above all things, correct the impressions incurred at the hospital if they happen to be wrong. Keep in touch with the patient, favor correspondence with the patient, and encourage correspondence between the patient and the hospital. See that the patient visits the hospital once in a while to see his or her physician again, and see that occasionally the home is adjusted by providing a nurse or by eliminating certain people who are trying. This is very often possible. Accumulate information as to how successes were obtained with difficult situations, and discuss the failures. See that the distribution of etiological factors is watched in your district.

There further comes the difficult question of how to spread ideas of eugenics, and how to protect women, and potential candidates for marriage. Gradually try to prepare some popular pamphlets for distribution, which rise out of your experience and can be given out as general information; communicate your successes in a pamphlet which will interest some other people.

Last but not least—the after-care movement must also assist the physicians and supplement the impressions the physician gets from seeing only the patient and the relatives who are perhaps in a state of excitement when they arrive at the hospital, and may have reasons to misrepresent the facts. After the patient is discharged, help the physicians complete the picture of the patient by reporting to them the fluctuations you observe; it will always be to your benefit because you thus get a chance of talking over certain difficulties.

The more I see of after-care and prophylaxis, the more clearly do I see that it is in the interest of the hospital to be the leading element of the after-care organization and prophylaxis organization in its district. To my mind the hospital has been too much a continuation of the almshouse—doing the best it can for the cases that were brought in and dumped down. Today we know that even with the best of care we cannot rest there. The hospital is the place where experience is collected such as creates obligations, and the hospital ought to be under the responsibility to use that experience. We ought to have enough physicians to go to a locality and look up a situation, instead of having them grind year in and year out in the wards and at the desks. It is not well that those who should know most should be shut off from even a chance at preventive and corrective obligations.

I know very well that it is not well to invite too many responsibilities and especially that the hospitals cannot afford to take upon themselves the steps for correction; that is why outside workers must be had who do not bring legislative wrath down upon the hospital, if certain interests are affected by a movement for the correction of local dangers to mental hygiene. The question is asked whether it would be well to notify the After-Care Committee in all cases and to allow the members to seek out the cases that need their attention. It seems to me that this might properly supplement the present plan, since at the hospital we cannot always know what the needs of the home surroundings are. The selection should be made a matter of collaboration.

THE MENTAL-HYGIENE

MOVEMENT

From an address by Dr. Meyer, "The Birth and Development of the Mental-Hygiene Movement," delivered at the twenty-fifth anniversary dinner of the National Committee for Mental Hygiene, New York, Nov. 14, 1934; Mental Hygiene, 19:29 (Jan., 1935).

It was in the fall of 1907 that I received from our friend Stewart Paton one of his characteristic notes which always create new contacts. In this case he told me that he had advised a protégé of William James to bring me a manuscript that he felt sure would interest me and concerning which I might have some suggestions. Not long after that Clifford Beers appeared with the page proofs of his book, the vivid description of his memories and feelings and some plans for improving the institutional regime by means of legislative committees and through arousing organized public sentiment and effort. Clearly Mr. Beers was a man with a vivid appeal and a fervid devotion to a cause, and with a great human document nearly finished. On many things we saw alike; there were others, perhaps, on which our points of view were somewhat different; but we both felt equally keenly the opportunity of the hour. Active psychiatry and public sentiment seemed to be meeting on the same errand.

Psychiatric research, psychiatric teaching, and psychiatric practice had recently changed the Pathological Institute of the New York State Hospitals, born of interest in autopsies, into a workshop in the service also of the living and of real work with patients. Important things had happened in the years that immediately preceded and followed the opening of the twentieth century. In place of the passive descriptive psychiatry of the older tradition, limited to "insanity" and "asylums," and the mainly prognostic-dogmatic, diagnostic-nosological newer psychiatry of Kraepelin—concerned with classification rather than therapy—a biological, dynamic psychiatry which included the whole of human nature had arisen to pledge itself to research and teaching, based on an interest in daily work with patients.

From 1894 interest in child study and education and in the nature of the illness rather than in mere dry symptomatology and statistics of disease terms, and from 1903 active connection with teachers, schools, and homes, had come to give value to the patients' histories. From 1905, instead of the mere eleemosynary charity for after-care then recommended by Miss Louisa Lee Schuyler, psychiatry had introduced active social work for the patient and his family while the patient was still in the hospital and after; and organized recreation and occupation, instead of employment in mere ward and factory work, had become an essential part of the treatment on Ward's Island. And now came the voice of the sensitized layman, destined to bring physician, patient, and the public together and, with its equal appeal for humane treatment and a fair deal, to contribute a strong and vital impetus. Faith in the good will of hospital workers, and grave disappointment with the usually uninformed and often sensational attempts at public investigations and detrimental legislation, had made us eager for a positive, constructive program, with mental hygiene and mental health as a leading concept. To this end, the untiring and unswerving determination of Mr. Beers brought together a representative body of men and women, who first met officially February 19, 1909, at the old Hotel Manhattan in New York City.

It was a small but inspiring and inspired gathering that tonight's occasion leads me to look back upon. We had the presence and endorsement of Frederick Peterson, William James, President Jacob Gould Schurman, Julia Lathrop, Horace Fletcher, Anson

Phelps Stokes, Russell Henry Chittenden, Lewellys F. Barker, August Hoch, and Marcus M. Marks. They stood behind a judicious and truly workable program for a National Committee, to supplement the front-line work of state societies, which were to bring the public and the workers into live collaboration.

I wish you could all have before you the material that appears in the report of that first meeting. Among the aims proposed were: cooperation with the usually well-intentioned but poorly supported hospitals (not invidious investigations and further unsettling of public confidence, but wholehearted assistance); study of the patients and the personal and social factors responsible for their diseases, outside as well as in hospitals; sound after-care, and proper attention preceding hospitalization; the development of sound public attitudes and the provision of reliable information as to where those in need could go to get help; the interesting of existing health departments in mental health in schools and at large; and the promotion of intelligent legislation, removing false and unnecessary humiliations.

In the light of current experience it was not very difficult to see what would be the greatest obstacles to be encountered: (1) the dogmatism and air of proprietorship toward everything mental of church and school and university faculties, holding the human part of human nature in their grasp as the "humanities" in contrast to mere "natural science," claiming to know from tradition and revelation all that is worth knowing about man and his life (without adequate concern for biology), and often posing as the sole and only source of any real "idealism"; or (2) the equally rigid professionalized dogmatism of medicine and natural science, which had been allowed to go the way of mechanistic materialism and elementalism, orthodox and extolled so long as it left the mind and soul and behavior to philosophy and religion.

A rigid professionalism might allow medical leaders to lend their prestige as humanitarians to the cause of Mr. Beers, but would permit only a timid support to practical investigation and public instruction and research and demonstration on how to live and how to include mental health in a study of health, happiness, and efficiency. It looked as if an active stand in public would surely be stamped as self-advertisement or undignified. But really the main difficulty lay in an official agnosticism as to how to fit mind into what these medical leaders had learned and thought of as science in medical school. Actually our entry upon work with the public schools was delayed by fear of encroachment upon the field of moral teaching and denominationalism. The core of the new movement—respect for and practical interest in the whole, undivided live human being—had still to be assimilated, to take the place of the traditional dualism of mind and matter, or the tripartition of mind, body, and soul, with its confusing division of interest and of labor and training.

With this went an actual aversion to giving any serious attention to insanity as disease. I remember my distress, at the opening of our world-famous institute for preventive medical research on May 11, 1906—that monumental institute to be devoted to the study of the devastating ills of mankind—that no single reference was made and no status given either to the nervous system or to mental disease. Apparently there was a sincere unawareness of the fact that more hospital beds are maintained at public cost for mentally sick patients than for all other patients together, and equal unconcern and ingratitude for the often heroic and self-effacing work carried on in spite of the unblushing discrimination against the illnesses classed as insanity.

Somehow the medical advisers of the great humanitarian powers were the most difficult agencies to win over to a new and fair deal for the health of the human mind as the health of human life. It seemed impossible to get support for more than the humanitarian side of the problem. I say this not with any sense of blame. This is the apparently inevitable course of slow evolution and conservatism—the price we have to pay for stability. Man was and is the last object or subject to surrender to objective science, because thereby man has to surrender himself, not merely the child and the delinquent and the sick.

There was at the outset of the National Committee's work quite a question whether the truly serious work in the field would be able to keep pace with the demands of the lay movement for direction and guidance and its eagerness to turn from tradition and mere revelation to real experience, and whether the steadily growing desire for more knowledge was to be fed from sources of sound practice and research and teaching or largely from a flood of propaganda. There was a serious question whether an emphasis on lay development and lay organization would help or prejudice the needed reform in scientific quarters.

A middle road, with lay work as well as professional work, was decided upon.

Without waiting for perfection, with experience gathered in the front line, in a Connecticut State Society, there blossomed a local development, with Mr. Beers as the active promoter for the lay organization and its work with the community and at the university. Through Dr. William L. Russell, a member of the National Committee, Dr. Thomas W. Salmon became its medical director and started with a series of stimulating surveys of the care of the insane or mentally deficient in a number of states. When the Great War came, it was again through Dr. Salmon that the unexpected calamity found the United States prepared to give a neuropsychiatric service to its army, such as no other nation had provided. It was the war also that gave an opportunity to psychology, though still largely for its intelligence tests and not as yet in a clearly defined relationship to a health and efficiency service and to modern medicine generally. In the meantime (especially from 1921) the old interest in the child was revived (as a continuation of Mrs. W. F. Dummer's and Dr. Healy's work on the juvenile delinquent rather than of an expensive university experiment) and there arose the child-guidance movement.

But still there was something missing at the core. It had so far been impossible to secure the endorsement of science, medical and general, for the support of model institutes of mental hygiene such as would really represent an interest in all phases of mental health and its promotion in the young and the old and in the most active period, that of the adult. Even Dr. Salmon came from a conference without real support for a program of investigation, and was soon drawn into unimpeded practical work.

If science does not see that the time has come to recognize as

its central concern the whole of man, as individual and group, it
fails to do justice to its greatest task and opportunity. In its laboratories science has the privilege of following its own vision and
goals. But the attempt to legislate man out of its purview because
the study of man requires respect for facts not in the common
stock-in-trade will not overawe us much longer. We cannot distract human interest from man indefinitely by arbitrary segregation of mind and body and soul, and by an unfavorable division of labor among the various "faculties." We are quite sure
that man undissected is more real and more important to us than
the paradox of a divided individual. We are more inclined to
focus and train our methods on our facts as the facts need them,
instead of trimming our facts to suit mere methods. Any truly
human study of man will always include life history and situation
as well as function of structure and function of function.

Our School of Hygiene of The Johns Hopkins University received no active department of mental hygiene in 1919 because
neither the study of the available psychologies nor interest in
behavior had a recognized place among the medical sciences. This
was not a surprise to those who devote themselves to the modern-
ization of practical and research and teaching work in the field.
It had always been comparatively easy to stir the unsophisticated,
but not the dogmatists of psychology and philosophy and religion,
on the one hand, and, on the other, the equally dogmatic coworkers in the natural sciences and medicine, with their traditional
pharisaical alibi that the psychiatric domain had not as yet reached
a scientific status justifying support of its work—as if somehow
science had to precede commonsense, and as if the people had to
learn to swim before being trusted in the water—indeed, as if
nothing had ever been done that could have reached the judges!

We may frankly claim that what sense the sciences have begun
to show in our field came from the spreading of our commonsense
and not often from importations of ready-made science developed
for other problems, and also that orthodox natural-history study
rarely works with man as he actually lives. To be scientific one
had to leave out whole domains of human nature. Sex and psycho-

analysis somehow forced their way in, exploited in popularizing literature; but the large controlling factors of man and the historical organization of man's nature and life had to be forced into a statistical-mechanistic pattern as if it should be kept from showing, as part of his real nature, man's actual human nature, including his idealism and religious urges and attainments.

The same difficulty showed in the relation of our movement to the three big scientific advisory national bodies. Mental hygiene fell down between the National Research Council, the Social Science Research Council, and the Council of the Learned Societies. Owing to traditional prearranged divisions of labor and concepts, neither of the three opened the door of active support and participation and cultivation of the ground. Only a few of the official leaders could be interested, at the most sentimentally or somehow personally, in the whole of man and in the frank demand that we change the arbitrary dogma of science and study man with, and as, a living soul and full-souled body, as the center of research and concern, as a true unit or real individual, as such and in groups, however deplorably shunned or kept apart in the plannings of the older traditions; for after all, man is the most important issue that civilization of today should consider its concern, if we are to make the grade from a lapse into chaos to a livable society.

It was in the home city of the first state society for mental hygiene, and of Mr. Beers, that there came a first move in the direction of an Institute of Human Relations—or Human Realities —bringing at last under one roof those who work with man in individual and social life and those who are concerned with his nervous and mental equipment.

There is good news at the opening of this second quarter-century. For the first time in the history of the mental-hygiene movement, a sum of $6,000 has been allotted to a study of what actually constitutes the load of responsibility of mental-hygiene work in a community of 60,000, the Health District of the School of Hygiene of The Johns Hopkins University.

The work for child guidance is already under unusually good

coordination through the National Committee for Mental Hygiene under Dr. George S. Stevenson.

Fortunately, it is not merely or largely money that is called for. What is needed is the collaboration of many agencies already in existence today, recognition of work now being done that is worth coordination, and support for its immediate value.

THE PROBLEM OF THE STATE

From "The Problem of the State in the Care of the Insane," read by Dr. Meyer at a meeting held under the auspices of the Maryland State Lunacy Commission in Baltimore, Jan. 20, 1909; American Journal of Insanity, 65:689 (April, 1909).

There is in the fabric of our large sociological unit, the state, one great field in which the physician is the agency to be relied upon for proper work, although it is not usually included in the domain of the health officer. We find here the insane and the feebleminded and the epileptic and reformatory work. Very few people appreciate what the task involves. The whole modern change of front in the struggle against essentially chronic diseases in the direction of prevention and the radical transition of modern practical sociology from charity to efficiency offers a natural opportunity for a discussion of the question: "What has the state got to meet in the care of those afflicted with mental disorders?" We are today confronted with the problem of so-called state care in this state. That is but part of the whole problem. What is the specific problem?

A fairly large number of our people are exposed, or expose themselves, more or less constantly to conditions in which they jeopardize the health of their brain so as to endanger their individual and social plasticity and efficiency. Many of the resulting difficulties and disorders of balance are merely called nervousness; others interfere so deeply with conduct and behavior, and even the possibility of any regulated conduct and behavior, that the patient's judgment becomes so untrustworthy that to let him follow his morbid will or bent would be a crime—as much so as if you should let a patient in typhoid delirium go to ruin in the wandering of his mind and under its effect on conduct. Thus there are conditions in which it has been found best to give the patient even unsought protection against himself and against strangers, and at times even against his relatives; and it has become a law in most countries that a patient reduced in his capacity of self-conduct and self-determination shall be given the benefit of special supervision by the most impartial and also best organized authorities, and the benefit of care in hospitals which stand under a special pledge (or license), a few of them private, but most of them created by the state.

It is the nature of the diseases with their peculiar effect on the legal status of the patient that has led to the demand for a monopoly by our most impartial and most circumspect agency, the state, in the form of complete state care, and under these circumstances the state must become equal to a tremendous responsibility, and especially so under our modern conceptions of what the fight against relatively chronic diseases means. Not only must the state or the public provide for the best possible medical treatment and for the physical welfare and comfort of its large number of patients, but it must strive to make its institutions centers of progress, which must be concerned not only with meeting the emergencies of the day, but with the more far-reaching problems of prophylaxis and of stemming the tide of increase. The institutions for the insane must indeed become the nucleus of a far-reaching work for social and individual mental hygiene and mental readjustment.

What are the objects of this state provision?

When we mention the insane and mentally defective, the large number of even supposedly well-informed persons, among them many physicians, think of a mass of unfortunates doomed by heredity and fate, and hopelessly wrecked, to be segregated as much as possible, provided with proper care, but kept from complicating the life of the normal and from adding to the number of the degenerated.

I wish I could give you exact figures as to how many now in active and responsible life in the community have been in some hospital for months, or for one, two, three, ten and more years, and as to how much time of efficient life has been restored to them by the stay at the hospitals. Most of these facts are not obtainable owing to the insufficient way in which the data are collected by our as yet inadequately organized official departments. But we have some reliable figures after all. The number of cases admitted from their homes per year reaches the ratio of over one-fifth of the total number figuring as capacity of our [New York State] hospitals; of this number an equivalent of a little over twenty-five per cent leave the hospital restored to their previous standards, that is, recovered and capable of taking care of themselves; and easily twenty-five per cent more become well enough to get along at home, while the remainder does indeed swell the ranks of the more permanent hospital population, the nonrecovering more than balancing the deaths.

Actual hospital residence of the cases which entirely recover covers from a few months to several years; twenty-five per cent of those who recover have had hospital care for over one year and quite a few must perforce for two, three, four or more years be part of the more permanent hospital population, whose care therefore must be kept up to a mark, with an atmosphere of activity and hopefulness and not that of indifferent provision for mere incurables.

The grave responsibility of the work, especially with cases during the first year, is shown by the statistics of 1905 in New York, according to which the total death rate in the institutions per year was 8 per cent, and 40 per cent of all these deaths occurred among patients in the first year after admission; 15.6 per cent of those admitted die within a year. You thus see how the admission rate raises the responsibility resting on a hospital. Some of the deaths are inevitable; others are not, and may take away recoverable persons. That is a point on which we should have statistics to compare the efficiency of hospitals. How many recoverable cases are lost annually from avoidable causes?

Looking back over these figures derived from the experience in

New York, we evidently find that among those afflicted with mental disorders there are, to be sure, a certain number who form an essentially custodial problem, while at least one-fifth of the beds are occupied transitorily. We shall find the number of transitory inmates even greater in Maryland, hence my warning against merely speaking of a "class." Further, the fact that twenty-five per cent of the quarter of the admissions which recover do so after a hospital residence of more than one year, and that it is by no means possible to make a sharp line between recoverable and non-recoverable cases, shows why it is not likely that a clean-cut division into custodial asylums and treatment hospitals for the recoverable can be thought of. The insane are not a definite class settled for good or for bad. We must speak of so many beds required or occupied, and the next question is, "For what varieties of the diseases?"

The most rational grouping of mental disorders is that according to causes and their more or less specific effects. In a complex organism such as man, we can of course not expect simplicity and uniformity, but we always meet with a combination of different degrees and kinds of causal influences working moreover in different types of make-up or constitution, and with decided individual variations of type of manifestation, course, and outcome. But after all, the cases form natural groups of considerable individual significance. I shall merely pick out a few units of special importance which point to relatively plain differences in various strata of the community.

I studied the mental disorders due to alcohol in my observations at the Worcester Insane Hospital, Mass., and found striking differences in percentage. Among the patients of Protestant Massachusetts stock committed to the hospital only nine out of one hundred had some form of alcoholic insanity, while among the men patients born in Ireland fifty per cent had characteristically alcoholic disorders and, of course, quite an additional number had a record of alcoholism as merely a complicating factor—a striking evidence of the differences of the problem of prevention in the two units of population. Comparative statistics of country and city districts worked up by the Willard and St. Lawrence Hospitals bring out the fact that while a city of 120,000 furnishes fifteen per cent of its commitments with general paralysis, rural districts furnish only six or five per cent, showing the difference in the frequency of syphilis in these regions. On the other hand, the country districts as compared with the cities furnish more than twice the number of agitated depressions, strong evidence that the country has its own faulty ways of reacting to difficulties.

The recent racial statistics worked up by my associate, Dr. Kirby, on the admissions to the Manhattan State Hospital during the last year give additional highly instructive data. Here again we see striking contrasts: typically alcoholic mental disorders reach twenty-seven per cent among the Irish, while the Jews did not offer more than one case, and that one complicated. On the other hand, general paralysis figures with but seven per cent among the Irish, and with twenty-nine per cent among the Negroes, and twenty per cent among the Germans—a glaring signal as to where the work against the spreading of syphilis must be done. The functional psychoses, the direct disorders of mental hygiene and mental balance, show analogous differences—very high figures among the Hebrews, small figures among the happy-go-lucky Negroes. All this suggests that differences in types and in conditions make themselves felt and that the occurrence of insanity is not merely the fatal and unanalyzable result of our active life.

The suburban counties of the metropolitan district of New York have only from two to four admissions per 10,000 inhabitants per year, while the average for Manhattan Island is eight to nine per 10,000. Yet the commuter's life is far from being free of care, and the excess of the patients furnished by the more densely populated districts can hardly be laid altogether at the door of inevitable degeneracy.

Allow me to point to some ratios of recoverability. General paralysis (by the way, an absolutely preventable disease, to be stamped out by a truly efficient campaign against syphilis) leads to death with fatal necessity within a relatively short period averaging two years and three months, ranging from a few months to four or rarely more years. Senile dementia is equally ominous, a progressive and destructive condition. Among the alcoholic psychoses most forms are recoverable, the delirium tremens in a few days, the hallucinosis without plain delirium in a few weeks or months, but the paranoic or chiefly delusional and certain amnesic states last much longer and are apt to be chronic.

Among the most frequent mental disorders we find the excitements and depressions depending on inherited or acquired make-up and divided into the essentially recoverable forms, among which we find the so-called manic-depressive insanity, and certain types which have a strong tendency to lead to chronic defect, a group called dementia praecox. These are varieties differing in their causes, their prospects, their provisions and needs of treatment, so that indeed the so-called "insane class" ceases to be a unit of the population on which one could make quick and easy offhand calculations.

General hospitals used to be largely receptacles for the poverty-stricken and helpless. Today they are centers organized not as receptacles but as places of organized and efficient work. The provisions for mental disorders are still in the barbaric stage where legal certifiability, *i.e.*, the patient's actual incompetency or the discomfort of the environment is the criterion of admission, instead of the work to be done in treatment; thus we get only those types of cases together which appear forbidding to the ignorant, and this gives the whole problem of the care of mental disease the one-sided aspect of a specially odd field, for which the antiquated term *lunacy* has come down from the dark ages of superstition and still maintains an air of propriety.

The progress in the study of mental disorders according to their nature and not merely in bulk has brought many worthy consequences. The demands of the study of the individual case have been raised. We realize distinctions between the cases and want to determine them and attack the facts accordingly, and instead of the pretty-cloud effects of generalities we see more and more clean-cut problems.

The medical work in well-organized hospitals has thus become a more and more definite task. Today to ensure good work in a model state hospital, every patient is given a most thorough examination which must be much more painstaking than that in a general hospital, because our patients rarely can be depended on to draw attention to possible oversights such as are apt to occur and might be specially lamentable. Further, to insure accuracy and control, the results of the examination and the patient are, in such hospitals as the Manhattan State Hospital, presented to the entire staff, in at least three staff meetings and discussions. To do this well we have found it necessary to increase the number of physicians, and instead of making them merely physicians for intercurrent diseases—chiefly the archsupervisors of hundreds of cases sent them by judges for keeping and to be at least protected against hardship from the attendants—we urge them to take an active interest in the possible entanglement of the difficulties of every individual case.

No trouble is spared to get the facts for intelligent action and advice. An effort is made in cooperation with the State Charities Aid Association to have an agent in direct contact with the physician and with the patient, and also with the relatives outside while the patient is at the hospital, so that efficient simultaneous work can be expected in the adjustment of the conditions under which the patient had become ill, with a purpose similar to that of a board of health in providing for disinfection and quarantine in the sphere of the diseases that come under the charge of a board of health. We thus attain a collaboration beyond the hospital walls which is all-important with diseases which take sometimes months to develop under conditions which, so far, the hospital has not considered it its duty to investigate.

A thinking person must marvel at the thought that mental disorders are allowed to progress without skilled help on an average with a period of partial incapacity lasting from three to six and more months before admission, and with all this our state and private receptacles have no organized connection. Chronic diseases are not properly handled by mere patching up. It is necessary to go to the root of the evil, even if we come too late for prevention in a special case, to straighten out the environment, and to prepare the patient to be able to meet reasonably those difficulties which cannot be removed. That must in part be the duty of the state, but it can only fulfill it in cooperation with the friends and with the communities which must be taught to be or to become a healthy environment fit for anyone to live in, even for those with not especially favorable endowment.

To simply deplore from year to year the increase of insanity, and to get into periodic panics over the necessity of building more hospitals, is not doing the work at the right spot and to the best advantage. But to reach this modern goal we have to make proper provision and see that the work is actually done. We are inevitably pushed to the conclusion that each hospital must be the center of organized work in its district, with the help of the profession and all those who will take an efficient interest in public and individual health.

The wide call for psychopathic hospitals is not merely a sentimental cry to avoid the unfortunately existing notion of stigma; but it is a call to secure proper care for individuals who need it badly, a type of provision which every general hospital should be able to give at least temporarily, until the most suitable steps can be decided upon. How many states are really ready to meet their obvious duties? An equally urgent demand is the organization of communities for after-care and prophylaxis. Our hospitals must not only be the centers of curative activity and standards of maintenance but, since in all chronic cases prevention must come to the front, the hospitals must really use beyond the hospital walls the information they gain in the study and care of their cases. Our state authorities and the most intelligent and capable people should give all the support that a farsighted policy can give. This is a task hardly realized as yet, except by a few hospitals in which a so-called prophylaxis and after-care movement has been initiated, in the sense in which I discussed it in the New York reports.

To be equal to this task it is necessary to coordinate the forces properly. The state should consist of fairly definite *hospital districts*. The hospital must make it possible for the superintendent to be the organizer of the work not only in the business and medical arrangements of the hospital but really in the whole activity of the district. A man worthy to be superintendent of a hospital for the insane cannot have a higher incentive for efficiency. To make it possible he must have a medical staff capable of similar aspirations and adequately trained to meet the emergencies.

It goes without saying that institutions to be efficient must be of moderate size and located so as to serve a definite district. This is the only way to prevent the undesirable distances from the homes, compatible with the best principles of medical, administrative, and prophylactic efficiency. In New York and Illinois the coordination of the hospitals into a state unit has, moreover, made possible the working of a central institute which is not only a place of research but the place of training and equipment of the physicians for their special work until enough of the medical schools will be capable of providing adequate courses for all physicians and all their students.

This gives us a fair picture of the task with which a state must reckon:

1. The care of the insane is to be organized so that care is given at as early a date as possible, that is, *before* the time where nowadays commitment is thought necessary.

2. A system of notification of a mental-health board is to make organized activity possible; and adequate provisions with hospital nurses, not policemen and jails, must be available pending the transfer to the specially organized hospitals.

3. The special hospital must have adequate treatment divisions where it is possible to become thoroughly acquainted with all the facts about the patient before his transfer into the ordinary observation wards for a more lasting stay.

4. Even in wards for the supposedly more chronic cases, standards must be maintained that provide for the twenty-five per cent or more of recoverable cases whose illness lasts more than a year.

5. Adequate provisions must be made to become thoroughly acquainted with the outside conditions under which the disorder developed, and with the possibilities of an adjustment before the patient returns, so that such help or guidance as may be advantageous to the patient and to his friends on his return from the hospital may be extended.

6. General organization of work must be carried out in the locality, according to its needs, among the various types of the community, not only with regard to checking alcoholism and the spreading of syphilis, but also with regard to healthy methods of living generally; emphasis must be laid on keeping the minds balanced with a due share of recreation and rest, and *satisfaction* with the *returns* of everyday toil.

This, and nothing short of this, is the task for the care of the insane, as we understand it today.

The program now seems plain. We must use, and supplement, careful reports on the local distribution of mental disorders: A census of the probably custodial population now scattered through many institutions of greatly differing standards; a census of the incidence of cases requiring hospitalization, in the different districts; a study of the character of the disorders and their breeding places, and the best ways of coping with the care and after-care, and further prevention of these disorders.

The next step is the study of a natural distribution of the centers of care, *i.e.*, of hospitals and the organization of districts, not so much according to counties as according to convenience of travel, with the formation of committees of after-care and prophylaxis in which we must rely on the civic spirit of our ablest physicians and nonprofessional citizens and the press.

A necessary supposition of the proper working of the program is a high standard of work in the centers of remedial activity, the hospitals, and sufficient power vested in the coordinative agency, the State Commission, and I hope there will be enough liberality to make efficiency stand above mere temporary expediency.

Mental hygiene—and all that goes with it—is beginning to occupy the leaders of our nation and of our civic activity. Mental difficulties and mental disorders are not limited to asylums and never will be. The asylums and hospitals are, however, the sources from which the leaven of proper information and training must come forth. We must get standards and eradicate obstacles to wholesome development. It is not merely provision for hospitals that we are talking about, but provision for our citizens in times when they need advice, help, and remedies. For this we need the best types of hospitals from which to organize the community—and an abolition of the centers of indifference. Away with mere charity notions! Efficient organization is the only fit watchword for a democratic community.

CASE WORK IN SOCIAL SERVICE

From "Case Work in Social Service and Medical and Social Cooperation in Nervous and Mental Diseases," a paper presented by Dr. Meyer at the National Conference of Charities and Correction, Boston, June, 1911; Proceedings, p. 275 (1911).

Case work in hospital social service consists in procuring all the necessary facts and securing personal contact while the patient is in the hospital; in preparing healthy conditions in the home before the patient goes back to it; and in maintaining such conditions and continuing contact with the physician as long as needed thereafter.

No case should rest until it stands clearly before us as an experiment of nature, with especial emphasis on the factors which are to be faced, whether they be modifiable or nonmodifiable, and a balance to be attained.

This work requires good record keeping. My advice is: (1) to keep a thorough record of current notes and letters, etc.; (2) to prepare the case for discussion, to have the report at the discussion taken down in shorthand, with the final summing-up of the problem, the plan contrived to meet it, and the expectations in the case; and (3) when the case is subjected to the final review, to show how the facts were brought in line and what points in the expectations needed corrections and demand caution in the future, and finally (4) to list the case in the general group in which it belongs.

Concerning these records I wish to emphasize two points:

1. Records must bring out clearly the facts which guide our actions and not be a mere mass of impersonal statistical data spread over blanks. Our plea for records is not primarily for the future and for research; but the best record is the one which helps most in the handling of the case while the work is going on, and which allows other helpers to know, in the worker's absence, what the facts and the plan are, etc. A case record which is valuable in this line is bound to be good for research as well and needs but few routine supplements to be also statistically valuable. A case primarily planned for statistics is apt to be formal and empty of the very things which are decisive for the understanding of nature's experiment and our efforts to modify it. A distribution of the cases into groups must be done as one goes along, at least once a month, with the use of card catalogs and index files. If you leave the grouping and arrangement of the facts for more than a month the material overwhelms you.

2. My second point is this: Let the capacity of keeping a good record be the index of where you should draw the line on the number of your cases. Many a social-service department is a partial disappointment because the workers take too many cases. It is hard to refuse them, because one never can judge without investigation; but respect for the quality and effectiveness of the work demands a firm resolution not to give a worker more than he or she can handle and record properly.

The record is the bookkeeping of experience. Without records it would be difficult to know and difficult to teach others the actual growth of principles in our work. The occasional criticism that organized charities spend nearly as much money on salaries as on relief can best be met if the reports furnish full evidence of the results of case work and avoid bare unexplained figures or casual or too general statements.

The problem of medical and social cooperation raises all the questions of cooperation in any field. It will succeed if both the medical and the social ends are equally well organized and self-dependent and are not hampered by a fear of occasional overlapping. The fields under question are the social-service departments of general hospitals and dispensaries and the so-called after-care agencies in psychiatry. So far the social worker's end has been excellently attended to. The medical work is still unorganized and will be until our hospitals consider it as necessary to have a physician look after the extramural problems of the patients as to attend to the patients in the hospital.

When we come to the utilization of the actual medical information about a patient or a family, many points can only be decided when a physician has seen the place with his own eyes and his own experience. Many decisions must be made on the spur of the moment and cannot be put off until the social worker and the physician happen to meet again. Only the psychiatrically well-trained physician can expect to meet the emergencies and use the facts about each case to their full extent. Only a physician can judge what cases promise enough result to warrant the time taken from other promising cases. Then, with the medical end attended to, the social worker finds a better defined field of work.

In our great ideal of prevention, the physician again must bring better organization of his own efforts into the system of lay cooperation. In mental disease we do well to begin with the cases that leave our hospital and must be protected against relapses; or they come to us in dispensaries and may need a few days or weeks of rest and setting-right in a general hospital; or simple help in adjusting the home, or all these helps. These cases furnish us a concrete personal problem of (1) patients threatened, (2) families and conditions which are not safe. In that way we get a point of attack and a specific excuse to come in with advice and help. The whole problem of social hygiene (not only on its sexual side), the education of the living children and eugenics, must be tried out on well-chosen cases. A physician who supervises the work on a dozen foci of trouble, in the course of a few years, will be able to give better material for general education on problems of mental hygiene than the best intentioned lay person today could give, or the best intentioned physician depending merely on the tales of the relatives. It will take several generations to make a deep impression, but this is the great chance of pioneer work of today, of greater importance than even the work of Pinel—a real departure toward effective preventive study. I only regret that my numerous other interests do not allow me to throw myself heart and soul into this new line of civic medicine.

As some of you may know, I am advocating the creation of districts, keeping the patients and the hospitals as near the homes as conditions of economics and effective treatment will permit. We need provision in general hospitals for rest cases; convalescent homes in the suburbs or country with annexes for nervous cases; special reception wards for disturbing types of mental disorder; institutions in the suburbs or country for the more prolonged disorders and a relief of these from chronic cases in special divisions or annexes and in small colonies, which will allow us to keep the patients from each district within the district and within reach of the cooperative elements.

We must not forget that our present system of large institutions was the first crude effort to escape intolerable medieval conditions and exploitations by city or county politicians, at a time when no trained psychiatrists could be found and no standards were established. Today the problem takes a more natural turn. Small hospitals for definite districts and possibilities of organizing hospital and colony, general hospitals and dispensaries, and the civic and social work of a manageable district constitute a practical and manageable method, more likely to get at the root of the evil than our palatial and fortresslike great institutions in the remote corners of the state. We need the right kind of centralization of supervision and standards, with decentralization and corresponding organization of the work in working districts.

On the alienist to be chosen for extramural work will depend the public demonstration of the good sense and practical applicability of the plan. His efficiency and tact will do more to make the district idea with regard to the insane as obligatory and convincing as it has already become in social and charity work among the supposedly normal.

Much of what we need for the prevention of relapses and of new outbreaks of nervous and mental disorders is exactly what we need to make normal life tolerable and effective. Close contact between the workers among the normal and the workers among the sick is our first need, and to make it really possible I suggest that well-organized extramural medical work should prepare the way for effective coordination of medical and social work. I repeat that the secret of collaboration lies in an equally good organization of the medical as of the social camp. When the medical work is properly done, we can speak of true collaboration, free to overlap because there is good order on either side. When they can ever overlap freely, as they must to be efficient, we may be satisfied with the organization.

9

Action in Baltimore

"Orderly chance"—to use the phrase coined by Adolf Meyer—was at work. His own orderly progress in institutional psychiatry made confluence with a fount of medical learning, The Johns Hopkins Hospital, through the chance of a philanthropist seeking a new outlet of expression.

Henry Phipps, Andrew Carnegie's former partner in steel, had already given a large sum to the Hopkins for a tuberculosis dispensary, thereby showing faith when there was fatalism. Phipps was pleased with the results. On a day in May, 1908, visiting Baltimore, he asked Dr. William H. Welch, of the University Medical School, to suggest something else the hospital and its school needed.

Dr. Welch had long been listening to his crusading neighbor, Stewart Paton, an advocate of psychiatric clinics as adjuncts to medical education, and he was equally convinced of their desirability. Moreover, Dr. William Osler, in his farewell address on leaving the Hopkins for Oxford in 1905, had urged the Baltimoreans to think of departments of psychiatry, pediatrics, and ophthalmology as their next specialties. Welch took the first on the list and did not pause long before answering Phipps.

The retired steel magnate returned home to New York and then dispatched a request to Dr. Welch to amplify his suggestion. Welch in reply described the work and benefits of European clinics and also mailed a copy of Clifford Beers' just-published *A Mind That*

Found Itself, marking various passages for the busy man. Phipps found it "painful reading."

Impressed with the need of a place to study mental disorders in their earlier stages especially, Phipps acted. He asked for an estimate of the cost. The hospital committee, whose concept of research in psychiatry was limited to old asylum practices and German physiological laboratories, submitted a figure, and Phipps announced early in June his willingness to give $580,000 to cover the construction of a building with sixty beds and maintenance for ten years, along with a professorship and assistants. A few days later the trustees sent Meyer an invitation: the medical board of The Johns Hopkins Hospital and the board of medical advisers of the University had unanimously recommended him as director of the clinic and head of the new department.

For the past fifteen years Meyer had been in state service. He preferred a state hospital system to private hospitals. Here was an offer from "one of the foremost medical centers established and supported by private enterprise." How would he harmonize his orientation toward serving the community with the fact of functioning in an organization munificently endowed to pursue specialties and not having to wait for public appropriations? He was under no illusions as to the reason why they had chosen him. The Institute of the New York State Hospitals was still known at this time as "Pathological," and the Hopkins authorities took its administrative head literally, as one who fitted in with their view of the work of a psychiatric clinic. Although Meyer accepted, his vision reached further; in consequence he found their financial estimates too low.

Meyer met Phipps and gathered this picture of him:

An extraordinary man, modest, rather shy, ever quiet, but capable of thinking of things which his more widely known partner and colleague, Carnegie, would not have been able to see in his urge for quick action by spreading of knowledge through libraries and research institutes. Mr. Phipps was thoughtful of the things that took time; he was capable of seeing virtue in amelioration and not only in the solution—virtue in an attack on what could not be directly cut out and eliminated completely but was sure to require patient and long work—tuberculosis and that form of disease in the cure and prevention of which I don't believe many miracles are going to be achieved, but in dealing with which we are learning continually things that have an influence on the whole of our life and not only on a disease. That was the man he was—a man capable of patience with chronic conditions, the things that call for amelioration, for comparatives rather than for superlatives and the illusion of absolutes.[21]

After an understanding was reached, with Meyer to begin his new connection in October, 1909, he consulted with Phipps's architect on building plans and sailed to Europe with Mrs. Meyer for an inspection tour of clinics. He was forty-three. He was going to head the first university clinic in the United States that would be free to give preference to patients presenting diagnostic and therapeutic problems worthy of study. He would not limit admissions to mild cases. He did not want a feather bed.

Construction of the clinic was a long time in getting under way. He had the impression that a talk he gave in Baltimore offended influential persons there, who were a bit on the defensive toward outsiders and feared innovations. Meyer busied himself with the ramified task of preparation, though ground was not yet broken, and found time for much writing. From many sections of the country came appeals for advice on questions of institution management, but he refused to give *ex parte* opinions. In particular, he avoided being drawn into the Massachusetts situation, with its issue of expansion. Moreover, he had given himself a project—to make a detailed study of the various systems of care in order to acquire firsthand knowledge of the current status. But he began with Massachusetts at the instance of Dr. Vernon L. Briggs and canvassed the state in the summer of 1911; and when Governor Eugene Foss asked him to report his findings he did not spare anyone's feelings. Meyer sharply criticized "false centralization" of authority. District setups were needed. He deplored the conflict between administrative power and the urge for clinical study—the cause, incidentally, of his having left Worcester.

During this waiting period Meyer familiarized himself with his future milieu and met the brilliant men of Johns Hopkins. He was active in the hospital's outpatient department and continued his

The Commonsense Psychiatry of Dr. Adolf Meyer

studies in brain anatomy. Dr. Harvey Cushing observed his "sympathetic interest in our surgical performances" budding into a study of the mental aspects of some of the cases. This was an eye opener for the surgeons. They saw, with Cushing, "the great value of these analyses, which from insufficient training we had perforce neglected."

The dedication of the Henry Phipps Psychiatric Clinic on April 16, 1913, marked "the awakening of intelligent interest in man as an active, thinking being." (The opening year was not graven on the building, in a desire to avoid the number 13, Meyer has observed.) Said Dr. Paton at the exercises:

A great blessing was conferred by science upon humanity when the problems of psychiatry were restated in biological terms. Life was recognized as a process of adjustment, relatively perfect in health and imperfect in disease; while that metaphysical term insanity, arbitrarily reserved to designate certain forms of unsuccessful adjustment, was cast to the rubbish heap together with the chains, strait jackets, and handcuffs which had long tortured the lives of patients.

Sir William Osler, pleased with the realization of his prophecy, came to the celebration, which was attended by more than a thousand persons and lasted three days. Talks were given by Bleuler of Zürich, on "Autistic Thinking"; William McDougall of Oxford, on "The Sources and Direction of Psycho-Physical Energy"; Dr. Ernest Jones, then of the University of Toronto, on "The Interrelation of the Biogenetic Psychoses"; August Hoch, Meyer's successor in New York, on "Personality and Psychoses"; George H. Kirby, Cushing, and other notable figures.

Bleuler, whose term "schizophrenia" was to supplant dementia praecox, pointed to Meyer's emphasis on psychological mechanisms and himself took a biological stand. Hoch told of doing research on the shut-in personality on a cue from Meyer's habit-deterioration concept. Kirby, speaking of psychosis as the outcome of unhealthy adjustments, declared that "Professor Meyer was the first to show how clear indications of tendencies toward defective adaptation could so often be recognized long before the obvious breakdown, in many cases even very early in life."

What especially pleased Meyer were the reports given from the field of general medicine on closely integrated issues—the effect of disorders of the ductless glands and other internal organs, of anemia, pellagra, syphilis, etc.—

eloquent assertions of the share of general medicine in psychiatry, and their very extent shows how unlikely it is that we should ever come to distinguish sharply between mind and body in our field, because, after all, we face one large biological problem, the disorders and actual diseases of biological organisms and groups of organisms; and every one of the topics had to climb the ladder from the nerve-cells and tissue-cells to the reactions of the individual as a whole, which, for practical reasons, we call our mental life.[22]

Psychology had developed a broadening function of "rich amplification of facts and a mustering of these facts, not as tin soldiers of speculation but as a big, pulsating and real, live world which we must face and handle and which brings us new helps."

One of the tragedies of psychiatry, Osler said, had been its dissociation from centers of active medical and university life, its segregation, its stamp with an offensive taboo, for actually it was a department of medicine "with the closest affiliation with the life of the community." At the Hopkins it would take its proper place: a unit in the work of a university's medical school.

The Phipps Clinic was hampered at the start by inadequate financing. It had a laboratory for internal medicine but no funds for laboratories for either neurology or psychopathology. Under stringent economy a clinical organization was begun and the staff was trained to apply flexibility in the choice of procedures to fit each patient's individual situation. Meyer brought in as his chief aides two Scotsmen who had served at the Institute in New York, encouraged by their first chief, Dr. Alexander Bruce of Edinburgh. They were C. Macfie Campbell, as associate director of the Clinic and assistant professor of psychiatry, and David K. Henderson, who had gone home to Scotland after three years at the Institute post that Meyer had obtained for him and who now heeded his second summons, becoming senior resident at Phipps. In addition, the original staff included two assistant residents and five interns.

In Meyer's hands it worked as an apprentice system, distributing responsibility, reducing contrasts between teacher and pupil, and spreading the spirit of all learning together. They had the benefit of "continual stimulation of a critical curiosity which makes the study of clinical problems the main issues of research."

The first year was hardly one of leisure "or even of normal work," but there was no doubting the absorbing interest. The first patient was received on May 1, 1913, and on the same date a dispensary was opened for community service under Campbell's direction. A child-guidance clinic was a natural adjunct. Here were steps toward a social psychiatry, and Meyer wanted to develop "real research in social service." Under a $1,500 grant from Henry Phipps, Campbell undertook a survey of the school population in the immediate district, Locust Point. Meyer expected to take in other Baltimore neighborhoods and study them by indexing the cases coming in from each circumscribed area; but his wings were clipped when the Russell Sage Foundation failed to give him support.

The Clinic's first year of work was described by him to the members of the American Medico-Psychological Association who came to visit in 1914, for that year's meeting was held in Baltimore. There had been 370 admissions (only twelve under commitment); over one hundred were free patients, and twenty-five paid less than ten dollars a week.

"One of the great functions of the Clinic is the diagnostic sizing-up of the facts in a case and the outlining of a safe program of care with which many ventures of expensive and useless experimentation may be replaced by a plan adapted to the finances and the best opportunities of the family and the patient," Meyer told his guests.

The staff pushed their study beyond conventional diagnoses and into etiological factors decisive for outcome and treatment; next they looked to modify these factors for best possible adjustment in the light of the patient's assets. The year's experience gave them "keen insight into the frequency of minor mental adjustments," a matter of tremendous importance for the healthy development of individuals, their families, and the community.

The staff members were sensitive to the patient's sensitiveness.

They sought his collaboration during convalescence. They realized the need of overcoming the public's concept of insanity.

The great lesson the public needs to take to heart here, as in many other issues of practical life, is that no one is fit to be *absolutely* independent. We are social beings and members of a family and of a community, and act as a rule as agents of a commonsense consensus. Why should we not be able to harmonize with our dignity the conviction that there are times in every life when we had best accept the consensus of commonsense rather than our temporary feelings? Let us try and make the public see that alienists and our laws want to lead to a realization of this and nothing more.[23]

Campbell, too, struck this note. Reporting on the outpatient department, which registered 708 cases in the year (236 of them children), he said "the dispensary material emphasizes very strongly how much is gained by considering the individual in relation to his environment, not merely as a unit by himself."

Phipps's director did not regard himself now as an outsider among the state-hospital physicians. He objected to any contrast between these hospitals and the Clinic. He told them:

I consider that one of the best contributions I can make to the solution of the problem of remedial and preventive psychiatry is to draw our state institutions from their isolation in the eyes of the public and the profession. We have common aims and common duties, and we desire to work together on our difficult but after all most inspiring task.[23]

He offered students and hospital men opportunities for intensive work.

After the session at the Clinic, the Association passed a resolution hailing the new institution as an agency "of inestimable value for education in psychiatry" and of "noble, humanitarian work."

As to teaching, Meyer went beyond the little glimpse Osler had allowed himself of the Clinic's usefulness. Perhaps, Osler had said at the opening, it would serve to introduce fourth-year medical students to what he called neuropsychology. Meyer not only started with second-year students, he aimed to have them understand man as a person, a functioning unit. Eventually the freshman class would study personality while doing their anatomy and physiology.

THE HENRY PHIPPS

PSYCHIATRIC CLINIC

From remarks by Dr. Meyer at 24th anniversary of The Henry Phipps Psychiatric Clinic, Hurd Memorial Hall, Baltimore, April 17, 1937; in Contributions Dedicated to Dr. Adolf Meyer, *edited by S. Katzenelbogen, Johns Hopkins Press, Baltimore* (1938).

I realized at the outset the disharmony between the project and the estimates, and there were indeed five years between my appointment and the actual opening of the Clinic. The trustees were naturally reluctant to present to Mr. Phipps the revelation that in order to meet the task in an adequately balanced form, it was necessary to make somewhat unexpected provisions. I say this particularly because it is so important for those who are trying to think of how to introduce psychiatry into a university and into a community to know what actually became more and more essential in this particular experiment in its particular setting.

I was confronted with an idea of psychiatry envisioned by those expecting provisions only for a select type of "recoverable" patients "to be protected from a stigma," whereas I sensed the necessity of being prepared to serve any kind of psychiatric need and emergency, with provisions also for after-care and for convalescents and preventive work. I never was a believer in thinking that we could or should pick out just the "recoverable cases" and make a particularly magnificent achievement of the cases that could almost take care of themselves. It seemed essential for both clinical service and teaching to be able to serve psychiatric conditions as they are. In order to do that, we had to have provisions somewhat different from what the inexperienced well-wishers might have had in mind. It would have been like opening a surgical hospital planned as if you could exclude emergencies in the cases that might not prove easy successes but might disclose unexpected problems during the operation.

When, further, it was the intention to introduce investigation and the necessary space and time for thinking beyond the routine of the work, something of the experience that had become obvious in the work of transforming that so-called Pathological Institute into a real "psychiatric institute" had to come to expression. I soon learned that Mr. Phipps was most cordially prepared to meet the unavoidable fact that in order to have an institute for the study of psychiatry and the amelioration of the conditions involved, we could not live on wishes, but had to be prepared to meet the conditions of "mental disease" as they are, free of the old traditional discriminations and of any reinforcement of the notion of stigma if we excluded those patients who might need special care and protection, sometimes even with protection by commitment. There necessarily had to be concessions and adequate provisions. The building plans were accepted and carried through by Mr. Phipps's own architect (Grosvenor Atterbury) and Mr. Phipps's own Pittsburgh Building Company, actually at the expense of over $800,000, with the full approval of the donor.

Unfortunately, the recommendation regarding the working allowance for operation reached Mr. Phipps only after some disturbing delays and after the adjustment had been considered closed, which led Mr. Phipps to give the trustees the option of using the originally granted amount of $580,000 in seven years, or of adhering to the original budget on the ten-year basis. It was decided, and I think under the conditions wisely, to live the first ten years on the basis of the original estimate, with two dollars a day for patients (with an actual cost of four times that amount, spent in keeping with the standards of the rest of the hospital and the special needs) and the narrow margin of $14,000 a year for salaries and laboratories.

In the meantime there came the development of the full-time policy for the main divisions of the hospital, something that had been generally approximated in the practical handling of mental cases anyhow, although as a rule without adequate facilities, room, and possibilities of development in research. In those days laboratories for research were not as yet supposed to be a necessary part of any practical hospital, not even of a teaching hospital, so as to furnish the necessary laboratory provisions for the investigation of what had to be done from day to day, and also the ramifications of investigation.

There was also the problem of meeting the real question of how to shape the work of the hospital in the setting of a community. That relationship had to be a free one, and my dream of having an institute that was adapted for a particular well-circumscribed and organized district or community and a country division for more protracted disorders and for convalescents had to be adapted to the necessity of running a division in keeping with the rest of The Johns Hopkins Hospital, which also had no provision for more protracted cases and for convalescents.

All this limited us to some extent, not only in the funds, as I mentioned, but in the directness of interrelation with particular parts of the community, that kind of thing that I should consider eminently important for a normal development of psychiatry. Through a personal gift of $1,500 from Mr. Phipps, who was very friendly and actively inquiring, it was possible to start an investigation of the children of one district of Baltimore, which became the basis of the lasting relation to School 76. I had hoped that we might have special working relations with three districts representative of the differences of population of the city of Baltimore, but that was the only one we could develop, considering the small staff and means. Under Dr. Campbell's supervision a survey was made, very largely limited at first to mental deficiency in school children, which later led to the resurvey by Dr. Fairbank in 1931 with its illuminating results.

In 1915 Mr. Phipps spontaneously offered the University the sum of $50,000 for research provided that it was duplicated from other sources. When, after a year, the condition had not been satisfied, the offer was withdrawn and the amount turned over to the National Committee for Mental Hygiene.

As I say, it was my hope to create work in a community district and to effect an organization of the work within the hospital and within the district that might become a model for the graduates and students that had to work in it, and also an opportunity to get concrete contact with the conditions as they actually exist, with a reasonable adaptation to the status of The Johns Hopkins Hospital as partly a community hospital, partly a teaching hospital, partly a diagnostic research center.

Mr. and Mrs. Phipps had enough confidence and enough appreciation to give in 1923 one million dollars as an endowment for the running of the hospital aspect of the Clinic, on condition that the University should raise a similar amount for the maintenance of the staff and research laboratories and various other expenses of the department. To meet this condition we were fortunate to get from the Rockefeller Foundation the amount of $750,000, from Mr. Edward S. Harkness $125,000, and $125,000 collected from citizens of Baltimore—an endowment which then became the background on which the further organization with full-time regime became possible.

From remarks made by Dr. Meyer at the opening exercises of the Henry Phipps Psychiatric Clinic, Baltimore, April 16, 1913; American Journal of Insanity, *Special Number,* 69:857, 1079.

The existing hospitals or asylums for mental disorders have of necessity been too exclusively limited to the care of more or less extreme cases. A declaration of outspoken "insanity" with all its arbitrary implications was long required even for admission, and this barred out many and unhappily stigmatized those who entered. To be sure, even in asylum care wonderful strides have been made during the last twenty-five years, as has been shown in the recent mental-hygiene exhibit in this and other cities. In the face of great odds of overcrowding and undermanning and forced economy, they are playing a more and more active and helpful role in the community.

But now the time and conditions have become ripe for intensive research for an effective fight for care *and* prevention. The vigorous appeals of Stewart Paton, the magnetic influence of Dr. Osler and Dr. Welch, and the genius of the leaders of The Johns Hopkins Foundations, who realized that their hospital would do its work best with a medical school and the university, have all together created a unique soil in Baltimore—for an institute representing a true clinic, *i.e.*, a hospital for practical work, research, and teaching.

What is vaguely called insanity—a term which physicians would gladly leave to the lawyer if he can use it—is really a wide range of greatly differing conditions and diseases all playing havoc with our organ and functions of conduct and behavior. Many too-long neglected lines of research enter into it, and it is only to be hoped, now that the North Pole and the South Pole have been properly discovered, that there may be more interest in expeditions exploring the biggest asset and the biggest problem of individual and nation: the brain and its proper working.

The last years have opened up wonderful problems and opportunities for progressive work on the function and surgery of the brain, the important and more and more accessible role of certain glands regulating formerly mysterious functions; the control of the great scourges of humanity, the germs back of paresis and the actions of poisons; and at last science begins to take up with new and forceful methods the great problem of mental life in its narrower sense, the causes and modifiability of harmful cravings, and of poor mental habits, and the ways and means of helping people of widely different endowment to find their proper sphere. In all these lines the Clinic must work, investigate, and teach, and gather diligent students and workers around its patients and in its laboratories. But this work does not stop in the sanctum of the investigator. Just as bacteriology studies the water supply and the air and food of communities, schools, and homes, so we psychopathologists have to study more effectively the atmosphere of the community and must devise safeguards in the localities from which the patients come, and to which they are to return.

The Johns Hopkins Hospital has always kept its gates wide open, and as far as possible this new division will carry on the best traditions of the hospital. If we can, in part at least, devote ourselves to the close study and care of disorders affecting definite localities and definite conditions and difficulties of life which we may choose as the center of intensive study; if we are not forced to take in cases unless we feel reasonably sure of achieving something definite for the patient and of ourselves progressing toward our goal of better knowledge; if the Clinic is not forced to serve mainly as another crowded reception hospital, watching helplessly the endless procession of victims without time for thorough study, our Clinic will, of course, be most serviceable.

Even the ordinary current work will be at its best when we can study at close range the families and the environment in which the patient became sick, and to which he may have to return; and where we can really reduce the sometimes baffling troubles to intelligible principles of cause and effect, with all the helps of experimental pathology, therapy, internal medicine, neurology, psychology, and sociology. Our patients, their families, the students, and finally a broader public will thus gradually acquire safer ideas than those furnished by tradition, by novel and distorted impressions, a faith not merely in sensational stunts but in sane methods to prevent or adjust the many ways in which mind can be affected in concrete patients, a working-out of safe ways of mental hygiene and sound living for those who need special precautions, and ultimately a wider realization of what makes for the most efficient life for the community at large, and the best policy for our American cities and states.

Our general hospitals aim to create standards of sanitation, and a psychiatric clinic must create standards of how to spend a day and perhaps weeks in a way in which a mind can find itself again if it is at all possible. That is why our Clinic differs from the average hospital and why so much stress is laid on possibilities of sane living and social work, besides the direct specific curative work.

Above all things we must make it worth while to remedy and adjust small beginnings of trouble, which so far have received scarcely any systematic help. We must overcome the aversion to timely treatment created by the unnecessary wholesale declarations of insanity. We must show that the so-called insanities are not so different from so-called nervousness, that even ordinary impediments of our mental efficiency are worth a sensible adjustment, which is clearly valuable and more creditable to patient and family than groping about and shirking the helps available. We must do all in our power to see that physicians and students who see patients in their homes should become thoroughly familiar with and more broadly interested in the simple disorders, whether they be harmless or more serious.

Mental difficulties demand a great deal of patient inquiry into the conditions of the body and its functions and the personality and the situations to be met. Consultations and a study of the case in the outpatient department will suffice for some patients; for others a stay in the hospital for more thorough examination and for a start in a new attitude toward life and for special remedial treatment may be needed. Social work, *i.e.*, a study of the real life of the families, is probably needed in most cases. Few families know how to cope with the problems or else many of the disorders would not occur, and this holds for the well-to-do as for the poor.

This Clinic does not come to replace or make unnecessary our state and private institutions; nor can it be simply a municipal institution. Yet I trust that Baltimore will derive its full share of unquestionable advantages through the resources of the Clinic for individuals, for help and decisions in the work of the schools, of the courts, and wherever investigations of mental health and mental hygiene play a role.

All this is part of a large medical problem; but also part of a great civic problem. Progress in the mental-health issue calls for a great deal of the right balance between individualism and civic solidarity and a farsighted policy concerning the health problems. If we want to teach *some* people how to live, we *all* must realize that we have to give a chance to each according to his or her aptitude; the right to be *honorably* that which one is forced to be through the laws of nature and endowment, and the right to be stronger as a part of a well-fitted and truly amalgamated social body. Mr. Phipps has given us a wonderful center of mental orthopedics. With the help of the good will and active collaboration of Baltimore we hope to make it another of the great departments which may well be a source of pride and inspiration to every citizen, and a living and productive monument to this great philanthropist, Mr. Henry Phipps.

There is no field so much in need of a firm anchoring in specific concrete work as psychiatry, but also no field so much in need of a broad grasp with *plastic principles,* which guarantee an open mind and yet firmness and decision of action and of interests.

There is no field which must aim at having as great a variety of temperaments among its corps of workers and at the same time a most judicious balance of diversity and specialization on the one hand and sane and broad commonsense principles on the other.

There is no field in which more people have thought they can solve all the problems by imagination and reiteration of hackneyed generalities, and no field in which the products of mere imagination, even of the best guessers, fall more hopelessly short of reality. Psychiatry is a wide range of methods and problems of work to be *performed* and as little to be exhausted by talking as surgery or obstetrics or pathological anatomy. But the field is not simple. It appears vague to one who does not work in it, and an easy way to pass over what is difficult is often enough indifference or a derogatory remark about the methods and the field as a whole.

It may be that in psychiatry we shall always need to deal with matters which require an infinite amount of patience and of willingness to put up with far more relativity of results than most of the other domains of medicine. There might be something discouraging in this, but only to the lazy or to the one who believes in the false prophets of exclusive absolutism and cut-and-dried doctrines. Surgery requires its special temperaments, so do obstetrics and internal medicine, and certainly also psychopathology.

But it is not merely an issue of temperament and personal capacities. The last decade has also brought more concrete methods and objective facts within the reach of all than any previous period of psychiatry. Indeed, I feel that before long few physicians and students will escape the fascinating influence of the growing definiteness of the theoretical and practical problems which characterize the present phase of our science with its sane appeal to a broadened commonsense and more and more concrete points of attack.

There will in every class be students who want to take up the special kinds of problems and surely they cannot find a richer and more fascinating domain. I certainly venture to predict that, just as two or three decades ago neurology was the center of fascinating systematization, attracting some of the best minds of medicine, so this assertion in a fresh conception of the neurology of the highest integrative functions and the most vital business of man, to attend to the most efficient working of the functions of conduct and behavior and the mental adjustments, will attract a remarkable group of workers.

The recent observation of Noguchi, which at last brings an active, live element, the spirochetes, into the center of general-paralysis work, is a good instance of what is likely to happen. A fresh stab by an experimental worker helps us over a certain staleness of interest, and a new chain of problems arises which no doubt will demand part of that patience which comes with the study of the long-drawn-out diseases. In a zigzag line of give and take we shall work along. To be able to grasp fixed points or crystallizing material in this fluid mass of facts will forever mark the pathfinder. May we hope that more and more of us may lay our hands on *more* than descriptive material; cull out some salient factors, perhaps more definite than disorders of internal secretions or either "habit" or "complex," the combinations of the two in some special disorders, or newly conceived dynamic units—and we shall have more and more valuable lines for the analytical and constructive work which constitutes true pathology.

When we take into consideration the ramifications of psychi-

atry into the schools, social work, and the problems of legal conduct, we may realize that indeed psychiatry is expected to bring
a most important contribution to the rounding-off of a medical
education and to the very foundations of general culture.

Looking back over twenty years of work, I feel that the first
task, that of attaining sufficient average standards of psychiatric
work, has been fairly well achieved. The next ten years will no
doubt bring a further organization of standards, but mainly incidental to the development of much more clearly defined lines
of specific issues.

The distinctive trend of American psychiatry lies in the sober
attitude toward systematic nosology, and in the greater emphasis
with which the practical aims are pushed into the foreground. It
presents an essentially pragmatic attitude in the scientific program
as well as in the vigorous effort at a practical and scientific
understanding of the individual case. The whole fabric of social,
civic and medical and scientific organization around us is characteristically freer than that of the Old World, no doubt with many
a drawback, but alive with opportunities peculiar to this country.

American psychiatry on the surface looks like reflections of
the promising movements of the most varied parts of the globe,
yet without any sense for binding allegiance. One with even a
superficial familiarity with its work readily sees the dominance of
a fundamental confidence in commonsense and self-reliance, almost
crushed out in many foreign schools.

Concisely put, American psychiatry of the last ten years has
clearly branched off from descriptions and mere claims of analogies with aphasia or general paralysis, and from faith in a quasi-
exclusive salvation in pathological anatomy and nosology. It has
assumed the justification of dynamic conceptions even in the
mental life. It has reintegrated what was arbitrarily and scholasti-
cally split under the emphasis of psychophysical parallelism; it
has described some of the mental disorders in terms of habit- and
instinct-disorganizations and instinct conflicts. It first pinned down
the habit tendencies and their disorders; then it gave due attention
to the experiences which shape habits and trends. About that
time a most helpful concreteness was brought in in the recognition

of the so-called complexes of the Zürich school, and the formulation of certain concepts of Freud's studies (wish fulfillment and repression); and the next step was the assimilation of the nature and import of symbolic mentation. We may lay claims to a fairly broad capacity for readjustments in this rapidly growing development, if you consider that, over the general tendency in favor of psychogenic interpretation, the histopathology of the nervous system and the studies of internal secretions and the chemistry of the brain and experimental pathology in the sense of the Hodge-Crile school have been far from being neglected.

A country in which the so-called "brain-spot theory" and the "mind-twist theory" can coexist, each for what it is worth in the concrete case at the moment, or in special types of work; a country in which an anatomical, a functional, and a more or less psychodynamic standpoint are represented under nearly every roof in active hospital work; a country in which apparent aversion to the excessive social organization of the Old World has forced the call for some of the best efforts at *practical* social work—such a country has its own possibilities, its own pitfalls, and in the main a vigorous optimism and yet a keen eye for mere sham display. What other country could give us the peculiar gushes of independence and determined and energetic practical experiments so characteristic in the Jamesian emancipation in psychology, in Watson's appeal for the behaviorist's standpoint, in the eugenics movements of Davenport and Goddard, in the mechanistic formulations of Loeb and Herter, and in the equally strong functionalism in our own field?

The freedom and latitude of our methods naturally involve also very great risks. There is not among us the, in many ways, admirable discipline which turns out the stately numbers of *Schülerarbeiten* [theses] and dissertations, and papers for habilitation. The tendency is in the direction of more or less well-circumscribed issues, pushed with a great deal of free energy. Men of encyclopedic knowledge and capacity are and will be rare; but schools with many-sided representations of work will have to take their place. The American preparatory college, if any educational institution on earth, deserves the connotation of the

Greek word for school; it is a place where leisure in the best sense of the word is considered a virtue—the training for the proper kind of leisure on the one hand, and the training for concrete duties and an aversion against feeling too closely wedded to any single pursuit.

These are sound Anglo-Saxon and American characteristics which will be bound to find their rewards and returns in this marvelous boiling-pot of nationalities. Safer grounding in fundamentals without excessive grind, mastery without cast-iron frames, less and less even of the hidebound, and a wholesome amount of the right type of active leisure—these are conditions for which we look. Safety in a firm and reasonable grasp of actual resources of experimental work with a sufficient systematization of the best available knowledge in each fundamental science will do more than the sham perfection of examinations aimed at in the passing scholastic ideals. Our growth will depend on the cultivation and proper organization of leisure and on the practical contact with the many chances for work and experience.

Psychiatry in this country has a wonderful field important not only to the victim of disease but to all thoughtful people. It will have to furnish many facts for the experience on which we can build the elements of real culture. As soon as psychiatry enters upon the disorders below the arbitrary level of declared insanity; as soon as it pays attention to what has quite unnecessarily been left to untrained teachers; as soon as we become helpful in schools, in teaching how to shape mental life effectively, how to make the most of an individual's endowment instead of destroying him by attempting the impossible; as soon as we make our field a matter of obligatory study to the psychologist and create outlooks on the cultural benefits of psychiatry, the world will find psychiatry less like an initiation into a dark corner of human life, but more and more a broadener of commonsense.

I did not realize until these days of the opening how strongly I feel that at last another vital step, not merely in my career, but in my hopes for psychiatry, is achieved. The work of preparation and the many matters of solicitude in the shaping of the responsible task, the apparent impossibility of bringing home some of the actual needs of such an institution, the many uncertainties and the stern necessities of adaptation at every step—all that kept one wrapped up as the forest does as one climbs through the dense woods of a mountain slope until all of a sudden one reaches a fine open cliff on a height with a chance to look over the plains and the slopes conquered, and a usually very deceptive view of the heights yet to be climbed. A moment's rest, and again one delves into the woods on and up, until the camping ground is reached, to prepare for the further climbs.

There are many parallels in this simile. The climber sees ahead through the bush; he thinks he sees a top only to see another one beyond. Who has not had the experience? And who does not know the sensation of eagerness to conquer and the unbearableness of having to camp before the goal is reached?

Today we have reached a camp, not to rest but to work with all our energy, to recruit a body of workers, to convince those on whom we depend that our ideals are capable of taking good shape in the world of reality, and to make more people yearn and work for that which has been growing slowly and safely and will, I hope, never cease growing.

From "The Psychiatric Clinic at Johns Hopkins," by Dr. Meyer;
Medical Times, 44:188 (*June*, 1916).

Medical scientists have achieved a great success in creating a system of treatment that eliminates the obsolete methods of treating the men and women suffering from mental disease as criminals. This came about through the foundation of a type of institution, the psychiatric clinic, the first example of which was founded at Ann Arbor, Mich. [1906], by the late Dr. [W. J.] Herdman, professor of neurology at the University of Michigan.

The first conception of such clinics no doubt was founded on the general idea that the beginning of mental disease should receive the same type of medical care as the general hospitals could afford. A wide range of cases had scarcely ever come within reach of either the physician who worked in general hospitals or the psychiatrist who worked in the special institutions for the insane. For teaching, and for actual service to a locality, it appeared necessary to make provisions both for the severe cases and simple forms and for those cases which had developed to such an extent that the patients were in a serious mental condition. Neither type had so far been welcome in general hospitals, partly on account of certain risks, such as suicide.

Much thought was required to adopt methods of treatment which would be suitable in relieving the many varieties of nervous ailments. It was essential to provide facilities for the admission of any type of mental disorder from the very lightest to the gravest forms, patients who formerly were thrust into jails and lockups until they could be transferred to the padded rooms or cells of the asylums.

What is needed in psychiatry is assurance to the public that cases with any form of mental disorder can find proper care and treatment in modern hospitals. In the planning of a building such as the psychiatric clinic at Baltimore, it was necessary to take into consideration not only the immediate opportunities and problems but also the future in the development of psychiatry and psychopathology. The result was a set of plans which incorporate the best possible facilities of accommodation for treating a variety of disorders from the simplest psychopathological disturbances, which nobody would want to associate with the traditional ideas of mental disease, to the severe mental disorders; also plans for laboratory and research facilities in the internal-medicine issues of mental disorders, and in the neuropathological work and also in psychopathology.

The provisions for the patients include, first, an outpatient department with a waiting room, which is in part also used for occupation classes and for the social-service workers, and examination rooms, and a demonstration room for classes and instruction.

For the actual clinic, *i.e.*, the hospital division, is provided an admission ward, facilities for the care of specially excited cases; then a semi-quiet ward; a rest room for patients needing quiet, and a special ward for such cases as should not be brought into contact with the more mentally disturbed patients.

The front of the building looks almost directly to the north and only few of its rooms have sunlight. This side was, therefore, almost exclusively given over to the administrative department. From either end of this north front a pavilion of four superimposed wards extends to the south, the basement containing the hydrotherapy and mechanotherapy rooms and some orderlies' quarters. On the first floor, the admission ward is extended into a small division for more excited cases; the second floor provides for ten semi-quiet cases; the third floor for about sixteen quiet cases, and the fourth floor for eight private cases on each side of the house.

The top floor is reserved for the large recreation hall and for roof gardens.

The ground plan of the second floor gives a clear idea of the general organization of each ward. The unit consists of a ward with eight beds, and two single rooms, and a day room. One room contains two tubs for continuous baths. There are also a toilet and lavatory, the utility room, a nurses' room, clothes room, an occupation room, and a physicians' examining room. The first floor with the admission ward contains an examination room for the physicians, a small waiting room, and a cleansing bath, a utility room and pantry, a clothes room, and a nurses' room, a toilet and lavatory, a single room for a patient, and then the ward for eight beds. Beyond that, there is a division consisting of three single rooms and a small water section, and on the other side a small corridor opening into the court, and a bathroom with two tubs for continuous baths; next to this, a small room with one tub for continuous bath and closet, adjoining a room for a private patient. The end of this ward is reserved for a small day room for the cases of this division. The ward with the eight beds is subdivided by partitions so as to give a certain amount of privacy to each individual bed. The southern exposure of a middle part of the building is used for a reception room for the head nurse and her first assistant; for a small division for special cases with three or possibly five beds, connected with a bathroom. The fourth floor is taken up altogether with rooms and suites of rooms for private patients.

The second floor on the east wing of the north front is devoted to a large library, and the director's rooms, consisting of two offices, and two research rooms, and the lecture-room complex consisting of the lecture room proper, a waiting room, chart room, projection room, and a draughtsman's room.

The entire Clinic is an annex of The Johns Hopkins Hospital and Medical School. The food is furnished from the general kitchen. The nursing force is provided for in the general nurses' home. The nurses are partly trained at The Johns Hopkins Hospital, with experience in various institutions for mental cases, and others have had their training in private institutions.

The Clinic does not in any way want to form a fundamental contrast to the already existing aids in the care of mental diseases. It aims to be a valuable supplement, with the best possible facilities, conducted under the beneficial influence of continual use in teaching, in discussion, and under the eyes of colleagues working in the various specialties that have to be applied in psychiatrical work.

It must do its share to eradicate the widely spread notion of the stigma of insanity, not by making itself appear as something aloof from actual mental disorders, but by showing that any kind of mental disorder receives very intense and well-directed work, and not merely asylum care and shelter.

Among the most important effects of the working of such a hospital is the opportunity it affords to the medical student, and to some extent to postgraduate workers, to obtain an intimate experience with the manner mental cases are studied and treated. It is not fair to leave this whole question to untrained commonsense. Psychiatry really has so many perplexities and difficulties, and also adequate methods to meet them, that it would not do to leave these conditions any longer to the guessing and mere human ingenuity of physicians and lay persons.

To spread a knowledge of these facts we must have opportunities to obtain actual practice in the wards and their laboratories and in research. It is very much to be hoped that in the near future physicians who are to be given the license to work on mental cases should have to demonstrate that they have actually studied and treated a certain number—at least a dozen or two cases personally and completely—under adequate supervision before they are allowed to pass on mental disorders in the form of commitment or to take charge of the treatment of such cases.

THE AIMS OF A

PSYCHIATRIC CLINIC

From papers read by Dr. Meyer in Transactions, *International Congress of Medicine, London,* 1913; *Sec.* 12, *p.* 1, *and pt.* 2, *p.* 9.

The last decade brought forth the first attempts to introduce into Anglo-Saxon communities and medical centers a type of institution called "psychiatric clinic." The term "clinic" suggests bedside teaching; a psychiatric clinic, therefore, is a hospital for teaching as well as for treatment and study of mental disorders.

At the time when clinical teachers in surgery and general medicine could find natural homes for their work in excellent general hospitals in the heart of the medical centers and usually closely attached to the medical schools, those who wanted to teach psychiatry had to cope with the fact that there existed a well-organized system of institutions usually placed in the country, large and unwieldy and far away from the other teaching clinics. Humanitarian and administrative-economic conditions had necessitated the organization of these hospitals at a time when relatively little research and teaching work had been bestowed on this specialty.

When teaching psychopathology more widely to medical students became a general desideratum, the communities seemed to be provided with the most satisfactory system they could afford —a type of institution to which it may seem superfluous to add another type which would be more adapted to teaching and investigative study. There is no doubt that the great amount of administrative responsibility heaped upon the medical superintendents of the existing large hospitals for the insane was a considerable obstacle to the promotion of such investigation as would have encouraged teaching, and especially teaching for the practitioner who had to deal with the patients under home conditions, and we may say that English and American psychiatry has developed its leaders in the face of many unusual difficulties. The European and South American continents were provided with special hospitals for the teaching of psychiatry much earlier than England and the United States.

The ideal of any modern medical school is to furnish a comprehensive representation of the practical work and research in all those directions in which a physician should have firsthand experience. The ideal of psychiatry is to bring such practical work near the student, exactly as is done in surgery, medicine, obstetrics, etc.—a chance for practical work and investigation.

The creation of psychiatric clinics evidently was greatly furthered by the conviction that the public does not merely want large "asylums," but that physicians will always want opportunities to see the patients treated in or near their homes by means of local hospitals. There is no doubt that with proper facilities many a patient can be tided over difficult periods or be started on adequate treatment without an official declaration of insanity. Moreover, if we wish to teach physicians matters of general value to them, we must show them how to handle patients *before* they are admitted to the asylums. Otherwise we might as well leave the whole problem of teaching psychiatry to the institutions that care for the cases, and go on the principle that the average practitioner does not need any special training in this field beyond what is needed for commitment.

Our first problem, then, is to make accessible to the student the experience with treatment of cases as they present themselves in the community to the physician and to the social worker; that is to say, with that type of case that might by no means necessarily be willing to consider himself, or would not be considered by others, as sufficiently disturbed mentally to require removal to a state hospital or asylum. Such a function can be fulfilled by outpatient departments and dispensaries. As soon, of course, as teaching and investigation must be combined with the ordinary practical work, it becomes obvious that a somewhat more elaborate organization should spring up; and it is this demand that is fulfilled by the creation of clinics.

The characteristic traits of a clinic for mental diseases according to my conception should be, first, service to the patient rather than to an administrative system; second, elaboration of the study of the diseases rather than of means of wholesale handling of patients; third, possibilities of following up the study of nature's experiments beyond the hospital period, and preventive work through (extramural) efforts outside of the hospital; and, fourth, possibilities for medical students and graduate students to take an instructive share in the three main fields of the work, *viz.*, the study, the treatment, and the research. For reasons presently to be discussed I consider it of the greatest importance that the clinic make itself responsible for the mental-health work of a fairly well circumscribed unit of population, so as to make possible studies of the social situation and of the dynamic factors which lead to the occurrence of mental derangements which must be attacked for purposes of prevention.

The advantages and needs of the patients, the needs of the community and the physician, and the needs of the educator call alike for these same principles, as we shall now try to show in detail.

Of all diseases those affecting the organ of mind and the function of behavior hold a special position. In ordinary diseases, as those of the heart, of the kidney, or skin, or in ordinary exhaustion, the function of behavior is not necessarily involved. On the contrary, we find that some trouble in any one of these fields is apt to make us do better in heeding the rules of hygiene and in adapting our activities in work and in play. Indeed, disease brings us to our senses: we begin to heed the needs of our heart or of our digestion, exercise our bodies, strengthen our resistance to cold, train ourselves to have our normal appetite and other functions at the right time and with sufficient regularity.

If the organ of behavior suffers, if its delicate regulation by the feelings, by fear or desire, by knowledge and habit, by personal wish or social custom or actual laws, is interfered with or upset, the patient becomes more and more liable to do the wrong thing. He is no longer able to use mere good advice without practical help; he finds it hard to admit his failings and to consult somebody; and often enough he is afraid of being considered unbalanced and of being committed or certified, as the phrase is in Great Britain, or at least of being forced to do things which he does not feel equal to and which he has been dodging.

Unfortunately, some of the very things which seem to give temporary relief prove to be the very worst things in the long run. The use of alcohol as a solace, and many of the modern resources of pleasure and excitement, like moving-picture shows and vaudeville, furnish but temporary satisfaction and relief, often enough at a cost of increased restlessness and yearning for even more alcohol and possibly unhealthy stimulation. Depression, often aggravated by the continual urging and advice of eager friends, is apt to lead to a craving for solitude, which in turn favors the very brooding which is half the trouble. Again, when we meet the feeling of exaggerated well-being of an expansive patient, or the cocksureness of a person with a beginning paranoic development, cooperation becomes clearly possible only if we succeed in making our help attractive and acceptable even to the shaken or twisted confidence of our patients.

Our large asylums for the care of mental disorders apparently throw together all kinds of diseases, and shock in that way the already sensitive patient who fears the worst for himself and dreads the very thought and the possibility of the sight of patients who are past help. The very admission to treatment comes with an outspoken official declaration of insanity, an expression which carries a humiliation to the patient and bruises the sore feelings.

By means of a psychiatric clinic, a department for consultation and the treatment of outpatients can be obtained near the home. Into such a clinic a patient can be admitted for at least a few days, during which time a thorough examination can be made and the patient taught the desired regime. The facts can be collected, and where possible a close acquaintance between the patient and the physician can be established, pending a careful investigation and possibly adjustment of the home environment. We cannot expect that the physician's advice can be followed without considerable help and guidance and supervision. More effective help will tend to overcome the prejudices of the public, of the healthy and of the patient alike. The frequent failure of early treatment, and especially of home treatment, comes from the unusual amount of supervision and help required by the average sufferer from disturbances of the organ of behavior. Propinquity and a feeling of familiarity with the hospital are essential conditions for success, and this brings us to the demands made by modern social work in the mental-health problem.

If we wish to be true to the modern spirit of medicine, which demands work of prevention as well as of cure, I should consider social work connected with the hospital as one of the fundamental and most important factors of progress in psychiatry. Social service, as we call this work in the United States, is the agency which reaches into the home and makes it its duty to supervise the conditions outside of the hospital and the activity of the patient in relation with the family and the community. As opposed to the detached eleemosynary after-care system developed in some countries, the majority of our institutions have developed special departments, usually in the hands of one agent with several helpers looking after the home conditions and outside interests of patients while they are in the hospital, but also working on prevention in those who have not yet reached the hospital, and in the interest of those discharged. These hospital agencies work in a way very closely akin to the modern work of the federated charities or social work of our large cities.

To make the work satisfactory the field of work of all these social agencies has to be divided into relatively limited districts, so that the worker may gain an intimate knowledge of the district and so that there may be as little scattering of effort as possible. The hospital, with its social-service department, must therefore work as far as possible with a well-circumscribed and well-defined limited area, and a more or less distinct unit of population.

In order to be a model of psychiatric activity a clinic must make itself primarily serviceable to the immediate community in which it is located. The size of the hospital and the size of this community, or locality, or district, must be determined by the number of inside and outside patients and conditions which can be easily handled under one management.

Today our more densely populated cities and towns furnish nearly one actual commitment per thousand inhabitants per year. As soon as we make the conditions of admission and treatment easier, the number of candidates for treatment will at least double, especially if care be offered to those who are now merely managing to drag out a painful and inefficient existence, painful to the person, to the family, and to the community, and too often leading to social as well as to hygienic fiasco, although not necessarily reaching the high-water mark of certifiability. The number of persons who need experienced help in the hygiene and care of their organ of behavior is really nearer one per hundred than one per thousand, especially if we consider the fact that probably two per cent of the school children—that is, one out of every fifty—is decidedly in need of investigation by a trained psychopathologist.

This consideration throws important light upon the most advantageous medical organization. Each person requiring a mental examination calls for a most painstaking medical examination of the functions of all the individual organs of the body, besides that of the coordinating mechanisms which constitute more especially the mental life or functions of behavior. Each physician can only attend to a limited number of such cases, and it would be unwise to make a staff of workers too great for a leader to keep in practical contact with the concrete work of his associates. The ideal would be to undertake the work of an organized clinic for a unit of population of from 200,000 to 500,000 inhabitants as representing the maximum of what could be coped with as a reasonable unit.

A clinic must have some of the features of a school, and while we do a great deal to make each other forget that the school is an institution in which the work can be digested and assimilated and given a reasonable latitude of interest, which is the best feature of leisure, each case presents such a large amount of work that only a staff with unusual proportions is able to do justice to all the facts at hand. I know full well that there are always persons who claim that too much time is spent on the individual cases. It may be that we might be going from one extreme to another, but it appears to me that if the spirit of work is not only random accumulation of data but an obligatory digest of the facts for purposes of teaching, there will inevitably evolve means of control and of prevention of useless work.

The responsible leader of the clinic must not become a mere administrator of medical work and research, but must be able to keep a grasp on the work actually being done—a task making much greater demands than that of an ordinary medical and surgical service which deals with much more clearly pointed and classifiable issues.

So long as this type of hospital remains relatively rare, demands from regions far beyond a normal special-service unit will come and tempt us to receive patients from beyond the district. Allowing for a certain need of compromises, I should like to see a clinic give one-half of its beds to intensive work on a limited district, and bestow the other half on intensive work on special clinical problems, but not scatter the work by accepting too many cases which would pass too far from one's supervision and control, owing to great distances. Poor work will result from drawing patients from remote districts, owing to inability to size up the level of the stock and environment from which the patient comes, and owing to the ignorance of the difficulties which he has to meet again. In a limited district many patients can be treated at home with only an occasional or temporary stay at the hospital.

We now pass to the discussion of the internal organization of a hospital serving this purpose. In order that admission to the clinic may not be a shock to the patient, we must see to it that the clinic has sufficient subdivisions. Even in a compact hospital there must be a sufficient variety of types of environment for a number of types of cases—for those with delirium, for those who need above all things rest, and for the rank and file who need a routine of simple quiet occupation and play, amusement, and recreation—in order that the note of helpfulness and not that of coercion be uppermost, and a sound foundation be furnished to the specialized treatment.

We call here for provisions which are absolutely essential for our work, whereas in the average general hospital they can be neglected on the supposition that any normal person has internal resources with which to stand forced rest or restrictions imposed by disease to a reasonable extent, and that as soon as the actual period of sickness is over the convalescent can go and again look out for his or her own needs. The readjustments which we have to strive for usually take days, weeks, months, and sometimes even years of active treatment, or at least of protection. For some cases the average hospital methods, like rest in bed, and feeding and drug treatment, will be the best; for others a stay in a more homelike environment, or possibly in an institution adapted for subacute and chronic care and habit training, or at least a place where a patient can be in the open air and yet away from the temptations or attractions alluring to his morbid appetite, longings, and fancies.

The clinic must be able to meet a wide range of individual requirements besides being a place of distribution of the patients to other institutions and agencies offered by the community. After all, the clinic can only be one part of an organization in the mental-health problem of a community. It must be able to receive *any* type of case, but it should have in close association its convalescent home and school for habit training or mental reformatory, its homes for those mainly needing protection. For some of these functions provisions are furnished in our existing state hospitals or asylums, for others not.

The clinic must be the center of the mental-health work of a sufficiently circumscribed community and work in close harmony with the larger suburban asylum or hospital, which if possible should also observe the principle of work for districts. For sound practical work it is decidedly advantageous that the clinic and its district as far as possible keep its successes, and also its failures, within easy reach, especially where teaching and research are among the primary tasks. The right kind of teaching is showing how to do things in each case from the start to the finish, and the right kind of research is work which keeps all the facts within reach and in sight, and among these is the study of the failures as well as of the successes.

Large complexes like New York or London naturally need special provisions, monstrosities perhaps to fit the monstrosities. Even a city like Baltimore, with its 700,000 inhabitants, is almost too large to be taken up as a unit. Yet even now London is sub-divided into districts with special asylums. Within these districts it would not be difficult to erect special admission and treatment services within closer reach than the asylum itself, from which to take up intensive social study, and to facilitate dispensary work by a system of social service.

All this, I think, should make it clear that a psychiatric clinic takes its field in a sphere in which it can strengthen the work of the average physician and become an agency where work is most telling, both in its remedial possibilities and in prevention, and consequently also at the point where investigation promises to be most fruitful.

Psychiatry deals with the social organ of man and is bound to become a prominent part of the field of social medicine, which so far has limited itself mainly to the infectious diseases and to the toxicoses. We have come to recognize the need of the study of each patient, not only from the point of view of the study of the function of each of his organs but also from the point of view of his being or trying to be a member of a community. A great part of the practical responsibility of psychiatry is social work and social adjustment, and in shaping a clinic or a hospital for model work it becomes essential that it should be planned so that the social work as well as the study of the individual case from the point of view of individual medicine should be as prac-ticable and effective as possible.

Nothing will teach as much as the propinquity of the right kind of working hospital in the midst of a medical center. Today I can foresee more and more clearly a psychiatry and psycho-pathology working in the pre-institutional phase, in the schools, in the mental hygiene of the communities, and in the families which have had grave and possibly disastrous experiences but learn to face the facts without fatalism. This decentralization and refocusing of psychiatry in the centers of community life and research and teaching is the most important new aim of the new type of institutions, to be cultivated side by side with the problems of the now-existing hospitals or asylums.

IO

Training the Doctors

Because psychology was neglected in medical education Adolf
Meyer strove to establish its place.

I take it to be one of the most important tasks of my life to make
sure that students and physicians and the public can, more quickly than
I did, get a natural sense and interest and curiosity and determination
to *know* when and how those human problems come up which even
today are dodged by medical and general training but which may
complicate or undo the chances of many a good start in human health
and success.[1]

The curriculum must include "the person." A physician must be
able to appreciate personality problems of the rank and file of
cases throughout the branches of medicine, whereas in his unfamiliarity he usually passed them over as digestive, gynecological,
or vague nervous disorders, or products of mood and weak will
—and the unhappy patients resorted to quacks.

But there was opposition to the introduction of psychology,
as well as uncertainty. Apart from scientists who had what Meyer
called "psychophobia," psychologists themselves disagreed on the
relation of psychology to the sciences, and some injected further
confusion by splitting into camps of psychopathology and patho-
psychology.

Psychology was a natural science, a branch of biology. It met
the demand of science for strict objectivity. The "subjectiveness
of the past" must remain in the past. Behavior, its mechanisms,
the performance of biological adaptation—this was the material

for investigation. "We study not an ego but the mentally connected activities, the dynamic biological processes of the whole individual."

Even where the practitioner recognized the "complaint" as belonging to psychiatry, he was likely to ask only whether it was a psychoneurosis or a psychosis, and if a psychosis, whether an organic one (such as paresis) or manic-depressive or dementia praecox—thereby betraying an interest going hardly further than prognosis. Such were the fruits of inadequate schooling. Meyer looked to the brighter day when doctors would be sensitized to other questions: "How much and what (if anything) is structural? How much functional, somatic, or metabolic? How much constitutional, psychogenic, and social?"

He began a long crusade of speaking and writing and conferring—besides developing standards at The Johns Hopkins Medical School—with an address in 1911 before a joint session of the American Psychological Association and the Southern Society for Philosophy and Psychology, held at the Government Hospital in Washington. This conference recommended that psychology be made a part of the medical curriculum. The next year a meeting of the American Psychopathological Association in Boston provided expression of various viewpoints on the nature that a course in medical psychology should have. Dr. Morton Prince, Dr. Elmer E. Southard, John B. Watson, and Meyer participated, and it was evident that distinctions were still being made between mental reactions and the physical kind, instead of mental and nonmental. In other words, the nineteenth-century (German) conception of the science of man had not been outlived.

But the year had brought hopeful developments, such as Bleuler's psychopathological formulation of dementia praecox as schizophrenia, and "a certain clearing of the relations between Freudian and general psychopathology." These relations promised, oddly enough in the face of Anglo-Saxon traditions, said Meyer,

to be much more genuine and far-reaching in our continent than in Europe and will, I hope, not lead to antagonism but to a give-and-take of neighborly and common work by persons who are ready to admit that they may be of different temperaments and capacities, but that they can leave the acceptance of their methods to the test of trial and experience rather than doctrinal persuasion or dogmatic taboo.[24]

At the 1912 meeting, which Meyer addressed as president, he advocated adoption of the British plan of a diploma in psychological medicine testifying to proficiency. But our medical profession was not ready. The American Medical Association acknowledged that psychiatric training was inadequate, and attributed this to the paucity of time given to the subject and to the lack of special clinics.

Poorly taught, this chapter of medicine was mildewed with old traditions perpetuated because "they make the physician's ignorance less conspicuous," Meyer observed. "Popular opinion is unfortunately not founded on experience but very largely on traditional misinterpretations, and especially on such reports from patients with imperfect insight as would rouse the sympathy of the average person, not so much for the illness itself but for some of its consequences, and justify the aversion against hospitals." [25] The vicious circle of hopelessness included the great research foundations of the day; even the Rockefeller Institute ignored psychopathology in its opening program.

The first course in psychology for medical students at the Hopkins was a triple-jointed attempt in 1914 in which Watson (whose laboratory was at Phipps on Meyer's invitation), Dr. Knight Dunlap, and Meyer side by side expounded their views—Watson with his mechanistic behaviorism, Dunlap with his experimental "scientific psychology" (using "scientific" in contrast to the chief's human emphasis). It was hard on the students, this obligation to harmonize the teachings of three professors, and some of the young men who "imitated the older members of the profession in giving psychiatry just as low a rating as they gave psychology . . . went to the dean's office to find out whether they really had to buckle down to work out what was asked for, and they were given the assurance that nothing would ever happen to them in any examination in this new chapter of the curriculum." Meyer gave up the scheme as too complex and handled the next year's course by himself as a "just human attempt to combine scientific psychology with a certain amount of philosophy and sociology and practical contacts with human entanglements."

Even so, he continued to encounter resistance among students who did not see that behavior was connected with the study of medicine; especially doctors' sons, who were least interested in what could not be observed in a test tube or under a microscope. Medical training had always begun with the dead. It ignored what the students brought into class: knowledge of their own lives. In psychiatry they preferred case work to the analysis of personality, which started with their own "personal history in the making"—a detailed charting of the elements entering into their make-up, for a synthesis of the forces. Meyer could easily have captured the men's curiosity with dramatic bedside demonstrations, but their job was to master their materials. Personality-studies and life-charts prepared them to apply the same procedure with a patient in order to get at the biographic determinants of the "complaint." In this way the illness would become sharply etched as a series of progressive pictures telling the story of "how it happened," each case a Hogarthian "Progress," faithful to life and strong in social implications. The positive and negative values, brought to light, would be used for therapeutic ends, the patient redirected away from dependence and toward competence.

As the program evolved, Meyer added the personality-study to the first year's work, a study of complaints in the second year, practice in methods of examination and formulation the third year, and a follow-up of six or more cases and their treatment the fourth year. The student was cautioned against facile spotting of causes. Though given freedom in his formulations he was advised to think through his material and not follow any psychiatric bellwether. Impatient to apply therapeutic measures, he was taught to recognize that "even the examination, the relation to the patient from the first contact, is apt to be a part of the treatment, *viz.*, the imparting of a sense of security in reality and factual perspective and in *doing* as well as in talking." Meyer found it useful to be on a conversational basis with the students concerning their own daily lives—"it is an advantage for the student himself to have been sensitized to normal happenings before he runs away with the idea that 'this may be all right in patients but it doesn't concern me.' Even in the study of patients it behooves us to give as much attention to the normal assets as to what must be remedied." [26]

One elective feature of the course (and it was never passed up) was a supper conference at the home of Dr. and Mrs. Meyer. On Thursday nights a group of about twenty students were invited (Mrs. Meyer did not have any trouble, as the meal was standardized and the servants knew just what to do), and after the pleasures of dining came open discussion of problems that needed expression. For the professor-host this informality was better than a platform monologue because in conversation one can use "the hearer's own trend of thought and experience as one goes along."

The value of studying "man as a person" was presented by Meyer at the 1915 session of the American Medical Association in San Francisco in a paper, "Objective Psychology or Psychobiology, with Subordination of the Medically Useless Contrast of Mental and Physical," after a first reading before the New York Psychiatrical Society. He had hoped it would help physicians to act with an understanding of the patient's personality at work in the illness and make them "less likely to drive a lot of sensible but misguided people into obscure mystical cults and ourselves into passing fads and fashions and empty squabbling before a justly distrustful public." And if psychobiology (Meyer's term) were made a part of the curriculum, there would be no call for the newly arisen tribe of medically untrained "clinical psychologists" who were venturing upon the field of abnormal conditions with danger.

Asking for the reinstatement of psychology among the natural sciences, Meyer brought his justification of psychobiology to the American Association for the Advancement of Science and declared,

The division of sciences lies between those dealing with the dynamic biological processes of the entire individual (as opposed to the activities of detached parts) and those dealing with adynamic logical relational connections. . . . It must be possible to study the activities of the level of mental integration in others as well as in ourselves.[27]

He delivered the presidential address of the American Psychopathological Association again in 1916. Here he reported that despite the difficulty of defining the medical profession's attitude toward psychopathology, there was a growing tendency "to stand for a frankly objective psychobiology which deals with concrete assets and performances of biological adaptation. Psychology, with its modern bent, turns from mere philosophic discussion to practical questions along lines of dynamics, with a gradual elimination of the parallelistic dogma."

Meyer was now asserting his main energy in psychobiological training and was working to make its medically useful principles more generally acceptable and teachable by means of a systematic body of facts and methods. He set forth these problems: to determine in a patient

1. The assets and adaptive tendencies and difficulties.

2. Their reduction to nonmental and mental factors.

3. Their orderly use for education and reeducation.

4. The readjustment of conflicts, inhibitions, or one-sided fixation of reactions, by reeducation and by the use of capacities unnecessarily checked, by immunization to morbidly sensitive complexes through a better understanding or through suggestion.[28]

In quest of the core of the mechanism of balance in a person, the student was taught to steer clear of traditional disease entities and be

as concrete and individualizing as the cases may suggest. In some of the cases we find frequently recurring acquaintances in the form of special reaction-types or in the form of provoking situations or etiological constellations; but there is no call for extolling symptoms spelling diseases and for expecting nosological glories to flourish in this field. Both physicians and laymen will have to learn this lesson. Nor should we expect that any one-sided method will get at all the facts or that any simple scheme of therapy will be effective to the exclusion of others.[28]

Among many psychopathologists Meyer found exclusive dependence on some panacea: hypnosis, hypnoidization, persuasion, synthetic treatment of the results of tapping the subconscious, or analysis with free use of dynamic principles and free recognition of substitutions and symbolizations. As an antidote he suggested "migratory training" of talented students to enable them to get a working acquaintance with prevailing views and methods.

Let us not hide too much behind the adoration of personalities. The great problems are *time* and *patience* and *determination*, and the first step a freer contact among the teachers and the workers in the various schools.[28]

To attain clarity in a common body of facts and methods, a systematic shaping of the literature would help—

with less of the trite vituperations and with less risk of the misrepresentations which disfigure our journals and discussions. No field of biology is more in danger of verbosity than ours. We still write as if we were the first apostles and the only ones giving quite the right facts and statements.[28]

As Meyer developed his pedagogic principles he eschewed verbiage for concreteness. "Facts and functions must be the issue, not words." So he avoided textbooks and written instructions, and did not let the student

think of, talk of, or work with anything that is not clearly established and connected in his own experience. . . . By getting away from a burdensome terminology and from endless detail, and by teaching him to work unyieldingly with the facts he can grasp and put together into a practical whole, the student is emancipated from the chaotic and bewildering task usually forced on him as he is required to combine and survive the diverse teachings of the different courses in his training. . . . At no time is the student permitted to lose the view of the whole living biologic organism.[29]

In my psychobiology course I begin with the request, "Give the steps of evolution of your own personal attitude with regard to the nature of 'mind' from childhood up and your understanding as to the nature of the facts dealt with under the heading of psychology." Similarly, I feel like asking any inquirer, student, or worker in psychiatry, "What has been the evolution of what you thought psychiatry was and is?" [1]

Fellowship students, besides studying patients at the Phipps Clinic and The Johns Hopkins Hospital, were required to spend three months in state-hospital service to become acquainted with the vast differentiation of cases.

In Minneapolis in 1928, as president of the American Psychiatric Association (the new name of the American Medico-Psychological Association) Meyer made a plea for a board which would be authorized to certify qualified psychiatrists. "Our British colleagues have for some time developed a method of encouragement and standardization of the workers in the form of courses of study and diplomas." Contact with British psychiatrists so trained had convinced him that the system created workers with a grasp on the practical tasks and a preparedness for progress. It would stimulate our medical centers and the men and women in our hospitals; it would provide an impetus for our leaders to focus on the best possible curriculums. "We want plastic and progressive standards rather than a set form. We want the right to individuality but with a recognition of a responsibility for a consensus."

The desirability of diplomas for proficiency and achievement in psychiatry did not square with existing facilities, for a great many medical schools had no clinics and a great many more lacked adequate staffs; but it set a mark. It stirred inquiry and a thrashing out of standards. The association appointed a committee (Dr. George H. Kirby, Dr. Edward A. Strecker, and Meyer) to study the proposal. Strecker, reporting at the next meeting, noted that the demand for trained psychiatrists was now greater than the supply, and there was a temptation for inadequately prepared men to enter the field. A new committee on graduate education was named (with Meyer as chairman) and it reported in 1930 in favor of an examination in both neurology and psychiatry after a comprehensive course.

A psychiatrist or psychopathologist who does not recognize diseases of the brain, and a neurologist who does not understand the role of personality functions, are alike a danger to the patient and to the cause of medicine.[30]

At the end of the year a meeting of psychiatrists held in New York under the auspices of the Commonwealth Fund agreed that a board of psychiatry should be established. The movement advanced rapidly, spurred on by the National Committee for Mental Hygiene, which with the aid of the Commonwealth Fund and others set up a special division of psychiatric education; Dr. Franklin G. Ebaugh, director of the division, conducted a survey of the medical schools. Meyer, who was honorary president of the National Committee and chairman of the division's advisory committee, was able to report in 1934 that other medical organizations were collaborating on plans for improvement in undergraduate and graduate training. For the division had assembled a conference on the subject, and the forces of the American Psychiatric Association were now merged with those of the American Neurological Association and the American Medical Association.

By the close of 1934 the American Board of Psychiatry and Neurology was a reality. It consisted of four members each from the three associations: H. Douglas Singer, C. Macfie Campbell, Walter Freeman, Louis Casamajor, Clarence O. Cheney, Franklin G. Ebaugh, George W. Hall, J. Allen Jackson, Adolf Meyer, Lewis J. Pollock, Edwin G. Zabriskie, and Lloyd H. Ziegler. The Board's functions were to determine the competence of specialists, arrange examinations to test the qualifications of voluntary candidates for certificates, and to issue certificates to successful voluntary applicants.

Not only was a level set for the aspiring practitioner of psychiatry, but isolation from the rest of medicine was dissolved. The subject won the status of a fixed phase of medical training; organized postgraduate instruction was developed, with fellowships granted by the Commonwealth Fund and the Rockefeller Foundation, and postgraduate institutes for state-hospital physicians came into being. General hospitals provided for psychiatric divisions and thus coordinated the speciality with the over-all program of health. In the interaction on the general body of medicine, attention became focused on "the nature and need of the live person . . . the consideration and collaboration of the patient and the social setting."

Meanwhile the advancement of teaching methods was studied in annual conferences sponsored by the National Committee. At its 1936 sessions, held at the Phipps Clinic with Meyer in the chair, representatives of twenty medical schools discussed their methods of undergraduate instruction. They set as their goal, "stimulating the student's sense for the personal reaction and problems of the patient in any medical, surgical or obstetrical case, not only in the obviously psychiatric or psychoneurotic patient."

This was a far cry from the indifference of schools and students which had obtained when psychiatry was limited to the issue of a patient's sanity to determine whether the state could commit him.

THE VALUE OF PSYCHOLOGY

IN PSYCHIATRY

From a paper read by Dr. Meyer at a joint session of the American Psychological Association and the Southern Society for Philosophy and Psychology, Government Hospital for the Insane, Washington, Dec. 28, 1911; Journal of the American Medical Association, 58:911 (March 30, 1912).

Most of us would probably shrink from a dogmatic psychology consisting of pure principles. The domain is the field of psychological experience, and the science becomes specified according to the methods employed. On this point I feel strongly that psychology as a science must work with as many different types of method as are necessary to reduce the events to well-defined experiments of nature. In other words, it must cope with the problems of introspection and also with the other problems dealing with the biological, physiological and even anatomical conditions of mental life. Without this an unwarrantable gap is left between psychology and the medical sciences.

Psychiatry inevitably has to deal with the mental facts presented by the patients. We call their conditions mental diseases because the mental activities are involved, either in a leading way or incidentally to disorders of nonmental functions of the organism such as metabolism, circulation or direct damage of the brain. As one deals with psychological facts it is, to say the very least, desirable, and I should say essential, that one should use such methods and standards as will pass muster in the light of the critical, or if you please, scientific observation of such facts.

There was a day when the mental manifestations were over-rated and misinterpreted in a system of archaic conceptions of chiefly moralizing character in many ways quite remote from actual psychology, *i.e.*, from the laws and conditions of behavior and mentation. We often hear Heinroth quoted as the archfiend acting against good sense and science, owing to his emphasis on sin. He used psychology as it existed in his day with its moralizing standards of qualitative evaluation of the reactions of his patients. Then came a period when practically everybody believed that psychology at its best could serve only in description and for symptomatology, furnishing merely highly untrustworthy "signs" of "real diseases back of the symptoms." Huxley's own view of mental life as an epiphenomenon rests on this same standpoint. The average physician who insists on translating the plain functional facts into neuron-mythology practices systematically mere neurol-ogizing tautology. Today we fail to see exclusive sense in either extreme. We describe facts in terms of objective observation, but often in the form of functional valuation and in terms of utterances or expressions and automatic or volitional activities and reactions, which we are forced to treat as a record of psychological material; and we also use and induce reactions such as suggestion or habit training or helps in clearing up mental tangles, directly as dynamic agencies in the readjustment of a normal course of mental life of our patients.

The evolution of psychiatric literature gives little clearness in this matter, because for various reasons the issues are slurred over, or, to put it more correctly, not yet clearly in sight.

Kraepelin started his career under the influence of Wundt, and with an effort to get critical accounts of the effect of drugs, etc. The result is the use of the curve of work in various forms, the ergogram, the addition series, etc., in the main with but meager application to his actual psychiatry, which represents the facts under more or less schematic set headings: apperception, orienta-tion, hallucinations, delusions, sensorium, attention, memory, re-tention, stream of thought, judgment, affective life, disorders of volition and application, and the physical symptoms. Kraepelin may well be classed with those who, notwithstanding an interest in experimental methods, study the psychological facts in their patients as mere symptoms of more or less hypothetical diseases back of them. Aschaffenburg's study of associations, continued by Isserlin, and the work of other pupils of Kraepelin remain in this setting. The Würzburg school and Sommer were more intent in the direction of inventories and standards of recording; the book of Störring was the German Wundtian statement of the material covered in a much less strict manner by Hyslop in English. The French school of Ribot and Binet and Janet followed a descriptive classificatory trend, but with a strong biological leaning and a gradual emancipation from neurologizing tautologies. Then came the Freudian movement, powerfully reenforced by the work of the Zürich school; while in this country a number of more or less systematized lines of interest and work have pushed their way to the present discussion.

The chief facts today are (1) that the division between psychoneuroses and insanities has become less marked, so that psychopathology has become the scientific definition of psychiatry generally, and with this an acknowledgment of the importance of psychology is guaranteed; and (2) that a number of workers urge closer contact with psychology proper, but are apt to find a categorical separation of a strictly emancipated laboratory psychology, everything else being called "applied psychology," or no psychology at all, as I should infer from the statement of a psychological leader who wrote that the psychiatrist can get along without psychology. We admit differences of emphasis in the interests of laboratory men and what we might call fieldworkers, but urge the importance of making the most of the common ground. On this common ground the psychologist may follow up his pet studies, or the psychopathologist may stick to problems of his own; but the sooner we agree on common ground, or even on a formula and plan as to what we shall call the common ground, the better it will be.

Some of us feel that in the life of the individual and in interindividual relations reactions occur and determine developments to which neither anatomy nor physiology in their narrow sense can do justice, but in which we are forced to speak in terms of a psychology or at least a biology which is able to scrutinize the reactions of behavior and mentation, the conditions under which they occur, and their effects in the course of life and behavior of the organism that shows them. We study deliriums, depressions, dominant ideas, delusions and obsessions for the role they play, the conditions under which they arise, the effect on the stream of mentation and mental balance, and their modifiability. We are confronted with facts which cannot any longer be passed off as mere manifestations of mysterious things back of them; but which stand more and more clearly as well-defined reactions for which we have only psychological terms and which represent momentous units of dynamic psychology. A suggestion once induced in a patient may be the central part of a biologic reaction which cannot profitably be split, to the point of nonrecognition and unintelligibility, into mental and physical facts in keeping with a self-evident and overemphasized and distracting logical frill of psychophysical parallelism. Mental facts taken as biological reactions of the type of mental integration play a decided role and we must meet them with—to say the least—respectable methods.

In speaking of "mental integrations" I imply the whole of our attitudes and activities, including the respiratory and vasomotor and circulatory and cerebral activity involved, and also the situation in which the reaction takes place as a process of adjustment. The "integrations of the nervous system" would thus form an essential link in the broader "integration of the personality."

Our first task is to make ourselves and our students describe critically and correctly whatever involves the reactions of the type of behavior and other objective manifestations of mental activity. This is no small task even with students who pretend to have some training in psychology, since it usually was psychology of a less matter-of-fact type, and the students do not necessarily know how to use the foot measure of simple observation through having used the chronoscope. Our first problem is to learn to describe ordinary events of behavior, and the description must as far as possible render the facts so that if the same conditions were reproduced, we should be forced to expect the same results, whether they be normal or abnormal, such as an automatic or peculiar act, or evidence of amnesia, or an obsession or delusion or a delusional system or a wave of depression or what not. We must be able to see an event as an experiment of nature, study the conditions, the modifiability, the role of the various integrated parts of the event, and the probable mode of dynamic hanging-together of the facts; and this is a thing to be acquired by practice in concrete situations.

To my mind, psychopathology and psychology have to study mental events and their settings and their effects in terms of activities of behavior. There may be a psychology for any one teacher's or investigator's sake divested of all but the introspective conditions; to us physicians psychopathology and psychology demand studies with a clear command of the biological settings and a definite sizing-up of the mental dynamics and also of the nonmental dynamic factors. This gives all the desirable space to the most microscopic introspective analysis and to any other lines of interest; and it will be up to the devotees of the various standpoints to bring forth types of work which will make themselves acceptable and inspiring to the workers who must live with a psychology which works and lives rather than a psychology easy to teach or easy to write.

That psychopathology sees a value in psychology, from all I have said, is above question. The special lines I chose to emphasize may of course appear somewhat perplexing and confusing in the eyes of the normal psychologist with his narrower laboratory problems—they must be experienced on concrete cases to be fully understood and appreciated, and I should urge that we accept that condition and give and receive a mutual promise of good faith and tolerance and gratitude for mutual help.

Within the field of studying psychopathological cases and branching off from it, there are many lines of psychological research and training which the medical student will learn to acquire with interest, not as amplification of the obvious and sheer accumulation of details, but as a clearing of issues striking at the very roots of the dynamics and of the estimates in the field in which he works. As long as he makes it a rule, as far as possible, to record events together with the conditions under which they arise, the description of the event, and the results, and a sizing-up of the time and of the influences needed for a readjustment of a state of balance, the worker is on the safe side and sure to record valuable material, no matter how complex the facts may be from the point of view of a detailed analysis in terms of structural psychology.

How to use the reactions, either as mere signs of broader disorders or as dynamic factors, must be learned in the study of cases and by experimentation. In this connection I should urge that we avoid depriving the field of its freshness and concreteness in courses to undergraduates by teaching abstract systems of psychopathology merely illustrated by the parade cases of the literature, and leaving them with dyspepsia when confronted with our plain hospital cases and the less sensational disorders.

It is equally uncalled for to describe psychopathology merely as "applied psychology." We do not call pathology "applied physiology" or autopsy work "applied pathology." For the establishment of some fundamental facts the simple autopsy is sufficient; for others it is the starting point of deeper work, possibly demanding an experimental reconstruction of the facts. In psychiatry the so-called clinical observation and clinical conversation and routine examination with its record in questions and answers is the basis for the various ramifications, and the more we cultivate safety in these ordinary starting points the safer our position. Psychopathology is not applied psychology. It is a field from which psychology may expect just as much broadening out as psychopathology can expect help and experience from the methods of so-called pure psychology. If, for instance, we can work with dynamic principles in psychopathology, all the better for psychology as a whole; but even on neutral ground with methods already current in psychology, valuable collaboration is possible and offering friendly companionship of interests.

I repeat: Psychology is the only field of experience from which we can get the proper designation and understanding of many reactions which we must learn to describe, to differentiate, to understand for the conditions under which they arise, for the share played by the different integrative factors of the reactions as a whole, for a reduction to terms of an experiment of nature, and for the study of its modifiability. Even in its most dogmatic form psychology offers methods and precautions to our workers; and the more we learn to know where we can safely depend on qualitative tests of our reactions and where quantitative tests are possible and worth while and the more we use the dynamic aspects of the facts, the greater will be the appreciation of a demand for psychology on the part of medical students.

On this ground, it would seem desirable to have a member of the staff in psychopathology add to the course in physiology an outline of psychology of normal life, and to the course in pathology an outline of psychopathological fundamental experiments and reaction-types, so that when psychiatry is introduced the student has a firsthand experience with the fundamental facts and methods.

CONDITIONS FOR A HOME OF PSYCHOLOGY IN THE MEDICAL CURRICULUM

From the presidential address delivered by Dr. Meyer before the
American Psychopathological Association, Boston, May 30, 1912;
Journal of Abnormal Psychology, 7:313 (Dec., 1912-Jan., 1913).

There is no doubt that the teaching of psychology and psychopathology in a medical school must in the first place get its trend
from the lines in which the available worker is accustomed to work.
Few are in the fortunate position today of having the broad fundamental preparation which we now want to give our own students;
and therefore there arises the problem of how to round off the
task so that the special lines of preference of the individual worker
and teacher do not give a one-sided aspect such as will provoke
misleading contrasts and especially also undesirable criticisms on
the part of those who want to protect the students against an
excessive curriculum, or even take an a priori stand against the one
or the other school or perhaps against all psychopathology.

As a matter of fact, we need only look over the available textbooks of psychology and psychopathology, or chapters on psychopathology in various works, and the journal contributions of the
possible candidates for chairs of psychopathology to realize what
a difference of standpoints the students will have to face. And when
we add to this even a modest list of what the medical practitioner

and the public expect psychopathology to cover, or what they have fatal prejudices about, you will agree that the task presents features worthy of at least a summary discussion.

As you know, I expect the best results if we succeed in making psychology and psychopathology a natural extension of common-sense psychology and of the student's interests in normal as well as abnormal mental life, by encouraging the biological attitude and conceptions, with equal respect for the objective as well as the more or less subjective or introspective material that presents itself to the observer. I say "more or less" subjective because to make the so-called introspective material an object of science, we certainly do all we can to pin down the evidence of its existence and nature and to prove it before others as well as before ourselves by just as searching evidence as physics demands for sound waves or electromagnetism. In the measure that the introspectively most evident reactions obtain evidence of objective validity in the interplay of objective events can they become a valid topic of the science which describes what its objects are and do.

It is extraordinary how the short period since the human race has actually evolved and practiced the methods of science has tended to corroborate a dualistic tendency which is exploited by some in ultrabiological claims and speculation, and in turn forces the scientist and the average man to accept our mental life naïvely as a mere world of subjective values, and to respect them as scientific or at least as dynamic only when translated into terms of various kinds of modern brain mythology.

The change of attitude on this point is very slow. We are still looked at with suspicion when we claim that the emphasis on the so-called psychophysical parallelism is no longer obligatory, and that if we make a contrast it should be that of mental and nonmental biological reactions and not the illogical contrast of mental and physical. Only few admit, what we all assume in practical life, that we might well listen with some respect to the concepts of the plain man who speaks of mental forces, of mental causes and their effects. The firmness with which the orthodox parallelistic attitude is officially adhered to was strongly brought home to me at the recent Berlin Congress of Experimental Psychology. The type of psychology which prospers within these restrictions is certainly impressive, but such an ever-growing and ramified structure of detail that one might cry out with Möbius the cry of hopelessness as to our finding common ground.

Psychology and psychopathology in medical schools will succeed in the measure that we can offer a clear formulation of a body of facts enriching and balancing the commonsense experience, and assuring a well-defined gain over the untrained. It is natural that we should start with the disturbances in which even our common-sense work has recognized a need of accurate methods, in the form of a mental status, in the defect states a reliable carrying-out of the Binet tests, memory tests, and association tests. This is bound to lead to an extension into a study of processes and tendencies and their conflicts, types of conduct and attitude and their de-termining factors, and this inevitably to the mooted material which does not present itself clearly in the patient's mind, but which we have to learn to disclose, partly in terms of reminiscences or lines of more or less automatic reactions, or through evidences of inter-ferences, resistances, symbolic disfigurement, etc. This inevitably necessitates the study of already analyzed and interpreted material of kindred cases and practice in the analysis of one's own life.

All through the conditions had best be stated as conditions of *adaptation* to more or less clearly defined situations with a certain constitutional and experiential material, and the degree of success determined and reduced to the terms of an experiment. The chief steps beyond the ordinary medical attitude are that the aim is not merely a determination of certain fixed symptoms which dictate a diagnosis—a procedure which is justified enough for preliminary orientation where the facts are simple—but actually as close a reconstruction as possible of the mental and nonmental factors which determine the course of events and the various reactions.

It is quite obvious that this requires a decided broadening of the horizon and method of critical reasoning beyond what the student is usually trained for, and it seems to me worth while to formulate an important step—the surrender of absolute quantities and absolute effects for relative or conditioned quantities and effects which, moreover, the student must learn to handle by seeing them not as independent entities but as parts of balancing processes.

What discourages the layman or student most is the *relativity of all the factors* with which he has to deal in our field. He is trained chiefly in the so-called accurate or absolute sciences, in which the mass, the specific weight, temperature and the chemical constitution and form, etc., determine about all that defines the nature and potentialities of the object. Moreover, he assumes that a factor must act like a set dose of a chemical and produce certain effects, or *if* it does *not*, it cannot be considered as a cause and becomes unreliable and negligible.

To learn to work with the highly conditioned entities he must be given a standpoint on which the conditioned character of his facts remains plain, and on which he nevertheless learns to appreciate safe relative measures and standards of test and control.

Biological forces and especially psychological forces have this in common, that the quantity of mass and energy expressible in chemicals and in stored energy plays a relatively unessential role as compared with the qualitative features which show in the different associations and which I might call "the fitness for the task."

As James says: "The measure of greatness here is the effect produced on the environment, not a quantity antecedently absorbed from physical nature." To give the student an idea of these forces, we must show him the reactive mechanisms and available reaction-types whose triggers the specialized force is able to pull.

The problem thus becomes the introduction of accuracy into a field which seems to resist the common methods of the simple and more purely objective sciences.

A tendency which has worked itself out in quite a few minds (Mach and Kirchhoff in physics, Roux in morphology, Verworn in physiology, von Hansemann in pathology) is the transformation of the naïve causal conception of events and facts into a more modest conception of determination of conditions free of the presumption that, by stating the one element of a variation of a state or process, that determination of the one element alone would be a complete and accurate statement of the causal value in any situation under consideration.

The relativity of individual factors, the conditioned value of every one of the factors with which we deal, puts psychology on a basis where much more caution is needed than in any other domain of human experience and analysis, and for which we also have special helps. The average individual *is* a good enough reagent to react reliably and safely and in keeping with the laws of probability and absolute pitch, but the safety of the predictions is only relative, almost always conditioned by more factors than we can control. The point is that we should and do react sufficiently safely to determine certain important conditions of events.

In this direction nothing will help but training in a similarly safe conditional presentation of any facts which we must look upon as the parts integrated in the whole of *any* biological, neurological, or general physiological reaction. While the elementary sciences pride themselves on getting along with elements which stand by themselves, embodying as it were with fatal necessity all the effects into which they can be led, the living organism, owing to its complexity, baffles the demand for regularity in many points. Hence the temptation to fall into the mistake in which men like Loeb get involved when they believe that only a rigid mechanistic conception of nature can eliminate mysticism, and that any recognition of conditioned reactions and any temporary acceptance of a measure of factors in terms of the effect produced in the completion of a known process, in an *Aufgabe* or task, is teleology.

Simply because there really occurs in benighted quarters such a thing as unwarranted mystic teleology, the entire logical formula of seeing parts in the light of a whole is to be replaced by, however hypothetical, constructs of elementary units, or is at least to be discredited. I should, on the contrary, urge that the training in physiology put much more emphasis on the definition of the conditions under which ends are attained.

The student needs practice in this form of presentation in matters where errors would be easy to *demonstrate*. Only with such preparation will he then learn to see the conditioned share of bacteria in infections and symbiotic reactions, the conditioned effects of poisons such as morphine which a cow can eat without narcosis; the conditioned effects of serums, and the conditioned effect of the so-called causes of nervous and mental disorders, and the variability of the form of appearance, and especially also the nature of symbolism, which seems to be as the red flag to the bull to the orthodox critics of modern psychopathology.

This has many important implications which I want to illustrate briefly. Psychology is forced to get square with that simplistic temptation to take detail reactions such as sensation, or any other relatively independent units of response, and to give them at once the independent position of reaction of a special independent organ or of nerve-cell groups, even independent of receptive and effective organs.

I thus should have to ask for caution at the very foundation of the teaching concerning reflexes. Reflexes are the simplest processes of neurobiological adaptation. As a matter of fact we demonstrate such fundamental reactions as reflex activity at its best in a spinal frog, or in a detached lumbar animal, *i.e.*, enough of a central mechanism attached to receptors and effectors to be sufficient for a reflex entity. We can, of course, penetrate further and study this fundamental mechanism in more detail. We can take the nerve-muscle preparation, or the Kühne experiment, or since we know from anatomy and histology types of neurons and groups of neurons of special type of appearance and connection, we think of the independent activity of these types, perhaps with insufficient regard for the fact that however independent they may appear from the point of view of growth and maintenance, neurologically they have their position not as such but as parts of mechanisms.

To reduce the data to the schematic reflex arc, and especially to individual neurons, means cutting it down to a conceptual minimum inviting dangerous conceptions of simplicity from which many a student cannot recover, and which he carries wholesale into the field of the more highly conditioned psychobiological reactions; especially because the latter are already prepared in a similar way so as to work with independent units and elements—the independence of which must, however, be surrendered when we make of psychology the science of mental activity and its disorders in the sense of problems of biological adaptations.

Perhaps the best analogy and guidance for the medical student comes from serology, dealing with a similarly high biological reaction-type which exposes one very little to the hope that we can assign the specific function to definitely known parts in the immediate future; a type of reaction which must at this stage be considered in terms of regulation and adaptation of the organism as a whole.

We deal with systems of balance and systems of adaptation; and within these we may push the details of reaction referring more especially to sense organs, or to motor mechanisms, or depending more on the central organization and the material of constructive imagination, and the adaptive play of emotions; but after all we do well to avoid the simplistic notion that we can dispense with the reference to the whole system and to the *Aufgabe* or task. We study the detail as relatively independent integrative factors, and train the student to observe the essential fact of how much of the personality must be intact for a function, and what situation or task it fits into in the performance of its function.

The next consideration on which we must demand better training in the student is that of time, *i.e.*, that of the necessary steps and sequences for the assurance of an adaptive reaction, a point concerning which the student must develop his scientific conscience if he wants to be true to the world of events, and if his predictions shall carry correct prognostic values. We must relieve him of the feeling that scientific simplicity demands a kind of telescoping which is apt to lead to serious disregard of the actual chronological sequence of the various factors or conditions.

If we are to become clearly helpful to the medical student and physician generally we must help him complete his ways and methods of sizing up and handling usual and unusual mental states better than he can now under the dogma of neurologizing tautology—that vain feeling that there is an independent world of physics, but that only those facts are scientific which can be reduced to terms of brain cells, and also the notion that all facts of pathology worth knowing can ultimately be telescoped into the notion of some lesion, whereas we really always find most safety in series of events which may differ according to the sequence in which the elements enter into function.

We must be able to help him give a reliable and helpful and suggestive description of his cases, and not merely a rigmarole of faddist terms and phrases which change from man to man and from year to year. We must be able to carry the conviction that we point to observable facts or factors without which the vital conclusions about a case simply cannot be drawn correctly enough. A feeling for economy and safety must of course mark our methods of examination and also a direct applicability of the results to our diagnostic and practical conclusions. We must give the student guidance in the static and dynamic sizing-up of personalities and situations and conditions, and courage to use his native sense.

Like every other science, psychology and psychopathology must show that it brings safe facts not already equally well known without all the work it calls for, and not merely amplifications of the obvious, and we must furnish the understructure in the form of safe data of the evolution of the *Trieb* life, such as the evolution of the sex life, and of related or of more independent trends and their conflicts, the craving for various gratifications, cravings for protection, for revenge, for justice and what not, or the conflicts between imagination and reality.

Personally I look in the events for the factors of psychobiological reaction, and study them for the conditions under which they occur, the differentiative marks of the different conditions, the factors principally at work and the means for their modifiability. The facts thus singled out must then be studied under various modifications of conditions. We find most accessible to our study those that can be produced at will, sleep and sleeplike states, states of hypnotic dissociation, states of fatigue and of toxic modification; and on the more essentially mental side, states of preoccupation, of conflicts, of cravings, of wish, of substitutive gratification, of repression, of symbolization (*i.e.*, facts which cannot be grasped by those who have raised the scientific use of elements to the point of negation of larger units, in the light of which alone such a fact as symbolization can have a sense). The chief weight is to be laid on the known conditions of modifiability of the integrative factors of adaptive reactions.

A serious issue is a safe knowledge of the extent to which reactions can be induced and can be made to play an active part in the problem of adaptation of the personality *to* the situation and adaptations *of* the situation to the needs of the person. Thus we learn to single out certain mechanisms, functional if not structural, representing the clinical entities worth differentiating and forming safe settings for details. We should above all things impress the student and the public with the fact that *the nonmental factors and the mental factors are made of similar stuff*, and that they cannot safely be viewed apart or entrusted to anyone who has too strong a bias or deficient capacity or training in the one line or the other.

There are sad tales on both sides. I am thinking of a case of butchery and mutilation, so qualified by the patient herself, perpetrated in a woman with a psychosis from sexual maladjustment, but also an occasional case where too ready and final assumption of a hysteria sealed the chances of a brain tumor, or of a merely apparently defective child, or of a symptomatic reaction. In justice to the patient and to medical experience we should also keep account of the at least relative value of approved traditional ways of handling reactions, the pharmacological effects of a timely reduction of tension by bromide and other helps, and at the same time the existence of reactive tendencies which would require functional investigation and adjustment. We can make it plain that a functional statement of the facts does not and should not disregard the organic facts involved; that sometimes the *nonmental* integral components and sometimes the *mental* ones offer the most effective modifiability or offer the explanation of why they are or are not modifiable. Moreover—and I say this without being an advocate of a medical trust—only the broadly trained physician can remain free of the charge of opening the door to the *a-scientific* if not *anti-scientific;* nobody can fail to recognize the responsibility of adequate knowledge about all the integrative material with which we work. On the whole we do well, I think, to advise our psychological friends to choose at least as an avocation a medical training which I hope will some day figure as a worthy source of general culture, and as a good way to learn to know the human machine and its vicissitudes in the broader relations of life.

Critical control of the induction of mental states, such as suggestion, persuasion, etc., should furnish one of the best means of measuring the relativity of the dynamics of mental forces. Judgment on this point is, however, difficult to obtain. As a matter of practice, it is desirable to make sure of the actual facts personally or through a third person, by controlling what the patient understood and carried away from medical advice—a duty unfortunately shirked as a rule but at the cost of a great deal of the superstition and gossip that surround medical advice, and at the cost of much imagination on the part of the physician.

The great responsibility of investigating and regulating the sexual life of patients and the extent to which sexual life has proved to be of importance all through the pathology of neuroses and psychoses, and the prominence of so-called moral principles in the work of mental hygiene and cure naturally throws another burden on the teaching of psychopathology. The physician must here, as in the teaching of the nonmental physiology, transgress the customary aloofness of Science with its capital S. Without tact and a clear foundation much harm can be done. Matters have come to the point that the position of a physician in a new hospital recently was made dependent on the disgraceful condition imposed by the trustees that neither hypnosis nor psychoanalysis be employed. On the other hand, teachers and ministers have carried dangerous inferences into the schoolwork with the inevitable result of grievous misunderstandings if not worse consequences, and a setback to a simple and steady growth of our work.

Psychopathology is bound to be the agency through which many excessively rigid and cut-and-dried rules of traditions of conduct of one's personal life and of social conditions will be broadened out. A few years ago in some lectures at Ithaca I spoke of the solidarity of mental hygiene and ethics. May this be made possible through a sane accumulation and utilization of facts and a gradual evolution of helps making for unification of biological and ethical views, and for a broad orthobiosis. That this means a departure from the purely mechanistic and purely statistical views of the world and a restitution of a perhaps more temperamental conception of things with acknowledgment of the mechanistic and statistical methods in their proper setting, need hardly be questioned.

Among ourselves we have to cultivate a true and direct formulation of the lay concepts, their presentation in our trained view of the facts and only then a transformation into technical concepts until we shall have worked out ways of certainty that we see, mean, and handle the same things. I should especially urge those who work with Freud's methods to be somewhat sparing with the use of terms with too many implications, such as *Übertragung* [transference], unless they are sure that the hearer has had his foundations adjusted.

A general idea of what training in psychopathology should be has been mapped out in connection with the English plan of creating a special diploma in psychological medicine. The best formulation will no doubt be the work of a psychopathic hospital. There we get the concrete problems and the organized efforts to get square with them. They will, I hope, implant in the public, and especially the medical public, such a familiarity with concrete facts as will correct the outcroppings of fantastic literature and one-sided conceptions and expectations of the domain of psychopathology, and also shape a natural curriculum in our new courses.

OBJECTIVE PSYCHOLOGY OR

PSYCHOBIOLOGY

With Subordination of the Medically Useless Contrast of Mental and Physical

From a paper read by Dr. Meyer before the American Medical Association, San Francisco, June, 1915; Journal of the American Medical Association, 65:860 (*Sept. 4, 1915*).

I asked my students to state what relation psychology had in their minds to physiology and pathology. I was at once confronted with a lack of definiteness and agreement which is the inevitable consequence of the fact that there is but little mutual understanding among the teachers of psychology, and little applicability of what is taught either to the plain man's needs in viewing mental life or to the physician's needs.

I found that most students had the conception that psychology deals with the mind as physiology deals with the body. They contrasted mental functions and physical functions, and had more or less vague notions of the doctrine of psychophysical parallelism which has governed science during the last fifty years or more.

I am not surprised at this state of affairs, for when I look around among my colleagues I find few well-defined attitudes. There are those who see no sense in studying mind beyond what is done in the physiology of the brain. There are, however, others who recognize the facts of suggestion, the role played by the emotions not only in hysteria but even in Graves' disease; but just how the thing works, many believe to be beyond human ken. One of my colleagues expressed his views in last year's address before the Medico-Psychological Association, in which he emphasized the subjective character of the mental facts, suggesting in fact if not in words that mind can be of use to the physician in the form of symptoms but not as causes and objective facts like the other objective facts of medical observation.

The difficulty lies in the hesitancy to accept a frankly biological view of the reactions and behavior of man. "Mental attitudes" and "mental activities" certainly are doings and activities of definite individuals; we see them and prove them to be present or absent or changed, as attitudes and actions of others as truly as we know them in ourselves. We may know some of our own mental states in more detail; but that which counts is attitude, activity, and behavior, observable in anyone and sometimes rendered more accessible by inducing the subject to amplify his activities verbally or in other ways until we know the facts—*i.e.,* until they have been made objectively evident.

What is of importance to us is the activity and behavior of the total organism or individual as opposed to the activity of single, detachable organs. It is more than cerebration; we must take our domain broadly as behavior and passive and constructive adaptation of the entire individual. It differs from the ordinary physiology because it represents an integration of biological activity on a specific level through its having the characteristic of more or less consciousness and because of its hanging together by associative function.

From the point of view of science, behavior and mental activity, even in its implicit or more subjective forms, is not more subjective than the activity of the stomach or the heart or blood serum or cerebrospinal fluid or the knee-jerk. Each individual has his own mental activity, but to say that we cannot see it and make it accessible and understand it in others is a philosopher's scare like the statement that we can never know whether the world exists because we know only mental states and processes. Commonsense has never worried about the reality of the world.

I hope we shall soon be agreed on the fact that we need not worry about the psychobiological reality and the objectivity of those actions and internal workings of living beings which we call mentation and behavior. I should quit being a physician and a teacher if I felt compelled to doubt the possibility of my studying and knowing your minds and those of my patients well enough to draw practical conclusions from such knowledge. If solipsistic philosophy, *i.e.*, the assumption that one can know only one's mind, were true, one might as well retire into absolute solitude. By making of mind something like the religious-philosophical concept of the soul, something opposed to the body instead of a function of the individual as a whole, traditional philosophy and psychology have rendered us a poor service.

The first step in a course of psychology for medical students is to restore in them the courage of commonsense. It is not necessary to start the course with a discussion of the unconscious and the subconscious, and with hypnotism and psychoanalysis and other specialized and more or less unfamiliar domains. On the contrary, I urge the student to trace the plain life history of a person and to record it on what I call the life-chart; the result is a record of a smooth or broken life curve of each one of the main organs and functions, and, in addition, a record of the main events of the life of the whole bundle of organs, that is, "the individual as a whole," and of the facts which determined and constituted his behavior.

This realm of objective and determinable facts of the individual as a person constitutes what we as physicians need to know as psychology. The science dealing with these facts I call psycho-biology, in order not to step on the toes of the introspectionist who might want to reserve the term "psychology" for the traditional types of subjective psychology. Its facts are behavior in the widest sense of reactive and constructive adaptation of the completely integrated organism.

We ask, "What are the individual's assets: the reactive and associative resources in the form of effective and expressive activity and its abortive economizing forms, conations, affections, cognition, discrimination, and reconstructive and constructive imagination? Under what conditions are they apt to go wrong and under what conditions can they be modified again for the better?" You can readily see that we are dealing with absolutely objective and positive facts, peculiar only in the way in which they hang together by association in the wealth of equivalents and combinations, and in the varying extent and depth to which they implicate the parts of the integrated organism.

As an instance of the study of assets, we take up the Binet-Simon and other genetic standards and survey the successive epochs of human life and their psychobiological problems: infancy; then the period of acquisition of signs and language; the early childhood passing into what Joseph Lee calls the "Big Injun" stage and the school childhood; the period of adult aggressive life; the period of maturity; the matron's period; and the period of senescence—each with its own psychobiological features and problems.

Within this broad and clearly biological frame, the student becomes ready to see a proper setting for the more detailed and specific chapters, among which I take up first the cognitive-representative data: reactions to things present (sensation and perception), reactions to things absent (memories and images), reactions with ideas and words and concepts; all activities depending more or less directly on the collaboration of brain and sense mechanism, and serving the function of orientation. Then we take up the affective processes which determine the general trend of association and involve, besides the brain, mainly the sympathetic system and internal secretions, as Cannon has so well shown lately; and then the overt actions, specified as effective and expressive, and the laws of habit formation, memory and association, and conation or will and its relation to instinct. We then consider the various degrees of consciousness and attention; and we introduce the data of hypnotism and the subconscious and dispositional determining influences shown in the association experiment.

On this ground we take up the genetic account of several leading functions or instincts as given in Pyle's *Outlines of Educational Psychology* and incidentally the psychobiology of sex life.

A review of the nonmental components of the mental integrations, the foundation of fatigue, and walking and sleep states, of the share of the circulation, of internal secretion, and of brain organization, rounds off the course and leaves us with a well-checked outline of examination of the mental resources and reactive tendencies of any patient, to be used and developed in the third- and fourth-year courses in psychopathology and psychiatry.

Psychobiology as thus conceived forms clearly and simply the missing chapter of ordinary physiology and pathology, the chapter dealing with functions of the total person and not merely of detachable parts. It is a topic representing a special level of biological integration, a new level of simple units having in common the fact of blending in consciousness, integrating our organism into simple or complex adaptive and constructive reactions of overt and implicit behavior.

I contrast (1) mentally or more or less consciously connected reactions, and (2) nonmental reactions of individual detachable organs which may as well be studied in the test tube and isolated and then certainly give us no evidence of consciousness. With this frank contrast we avoid panpsychism and solipsism and absolute subjectivism and all other bugbears confusing the medical and lay mind and the would-be scientific psychologist. We keep on the ground of commonsense and teach the student to study individuals or persons, in addition to making a study of the special organs, and in this study of individuals we deal definitely with objective facts which we must learn to specify and demonstrate, to account for genetically, to study for their effects and for means of modifying them for better or worse, just as we study the heart functions and not only the murmurs and the lesions, and the kidney function and the carbohydrate regulation or any other objective fact of biology and physiology and pathology. Reduction of the essential facts to terms of an experiment of nature, and study of the modifiability of the experiment, is the fundamental law and aim of medical science, and this holds clearly enough for the psychobiological assets as well as any other type of reaction.

In harmony with this conception, the concepts of mental and physical must undergo a readjustment, as the concepts of sunrise and sunset had to undergo a reinterpretation. Science deals with a world of things, facts, and relations appearing in several distinct levels or types of integration. Physics deals with one set of aspects of matter and ether; chemistry with another, namely, the laws of behavior of atoms and their affinities and combinations; physiology with a biological level, that is, those objects and their parts which grow by reproduction and metabolism; and as psychobiology we treat the functions of total organisms which blend in more or less consciousness in a manner constituting a special level of integration which has been especially and most characteristically enriched by the interindividual and social development of language. This level of integration we treat as psychobiology when considered as actual functioning and behavior of living organisms. All that constitutes psychobiology to the physician is, therefore, physical as well as mental. We can further recognize an ultrabiological level of facts when we consider the products of such functioning, as logic and mathematics or theory of relations, or realms of fact, philosophy, and religion. In this way we obtain an orderly perspective of the various sciences, but eliminate the contrast between physical and mental.

It is desirable, I think, to make the student feel that he does not have to draw too sharp a line between mentally integrated and nonmentally integrated activities. Many reflexes or instincts or reactions can appear on the physiological level or on the psycho-biological level. The difference lies in the hanging-together, the setting and the extent and kind of possible interrelations.

On the physiological level the reactions last as long as the stimulus, are commensurate with the stimulus, and occur as it were according to the laws and requirement of contiguity.

The entering into the psychobiological level brings in a more extensive scope of potential links and interrelations, with the laws of consciousness and of associative relations.

The reaction becomes part of what I describe to the student as a burst or geyser of daily activity, with laws of blending and laws of falling into trends laid down according to the principles which experience with this special level of biological regulations must furnish us. The student must realize that the mechanisms of the psychobiological level are not limited to the type of conscious-ness which we know in waking life and which most psychologists cultivate exclusively. Watson's work shows that there are many problems which can be studied accurately with practical disregard of the "contents of consciousness" as we are apt to call the "implicit" links of action. Many conditions will, however, become intelligible only if we take into consideration the special characteristics of special types of consciousness, such as the dream states, half-dream states, states of distraction, hypnosis, and special affective states, the study of which can do full justice to the fact that some of these special states will prove open to explanation and reproduction or at least facilitation by the introduction of detachable physiological lifts, chemicals, narcotics or internal secretions, of which we know that they can produce modifications of the hanging-together of psychobiological trends.

To sum up: From time immemorial the physician has been urged to treat not only the diseased organs or the condition, but also the patient. And of late years we have learned to realize that indeed some disorders can be explained, and treated, as abnormal and unhealthy ways of the person rather than as disorders of any one special organ; rather as disorders of the combination and its behavior. Every medical teacher gives some advice on this topic of doing justice to the personality; oftenest, and probably too often, he feels that the talent for dealing with personality must be inborn and cannot be hammered in by any training.

Of late years the difficulties in the total unified adjustment and behavior of our patients have been more and more reduced to intelligible processes: defects of development, intellectual, affective, or conative, improper use of assets, etc. Instead of mere vague ideas, of something requiring special handling, we have today a growing body of facts in the way of habit-disorders, harmful substitution and the like, which must be heeded in helping the patient to reach his best ground. How can the student be helped to command these facts most quickly? We teach him physics and chemistry and biology and physiology. Who teaches him the elements of those reactions which we call behavior and mentation? He enters on this field with confused and confusing notions; how is he to straighten them out?

The first condition for productive work in this field of psychobiology as in any other, certainly, is controlled procedure and methods of description and record and experimentation which come up to definite standards. It is clear that psychobiology and psychopathology have principles to offer which go beyond the dilettante realm and form a fairly clean-cut body of methods and helpful procedure: not only safe neurological methods and safer methods of work with internal secretions as such, but also safer methods of inducing and directing associative and nonassociative processes and associative material serving the best demands of the various types of make-up.

The difference between modern psychology and the older forms is that we can no longer be satisfied with mere plausible statements and amplifications of the obvious, but must test and verify objective facts under controlled conditions and controlled modifications.

In my own teaching I am determined not to put curiosities and the sensational to the forefront. Students whose interest goes toward such sensational things can in time be reached even with this conservative scheme if they have the right stuff in them. On the other hand, stagy psychology can be maintained to advantage by but few teachers and few workers and it fails with the bulk of our clinical material. We must discourage the ever-lurking interest in the occult and semioccult and replace it by solid confidence in reliable methods and by determined interest in matters obviously calling for serious objective study.

This hasty survey might easily gain by further amplification. I trust it may give an idea of the entire practicability of a course of study of objective behavior and mentation useful and essential to every student and physician; likely to give a sure balance and to furnish protection against extreme and one-sided vagaries or equally unnecessary psychophobia, which have so long marred the efforts of physicians in their working with the personality of the patient as well as with the individual organs. Saner views will make us physicians juster and more capable and less likely to drive a lot of sensible but misguided people into obscure mystical cults, and ourselves into passing fads and fashions and empty squabbling before a justly distrustful public, and they also will make unnecessary that new profession of "clinical psychologist" and efficiency psychologist for which a medical training will become obligatory if we physicians show the sense and capacity to furnish the needed psychobiology as a necessary and obligatory part of our training.

PROGRESS IN TEACHING

PSYCHIATRY

From a paper read by Dr. Meyer before the American Medical Association, New York, June, 1917; Journal of the American Medical Association, 69:861 (*July* 15, 1917).

No real physician is altogether specialist and no real specialist fails to define his share as part of the great problem of helping the sick and troubled patient. The psychiatrist may at least say that he has found himself. Instead of being singled out from the rest of physicians as what used to be called an asylum man, pure and simple, he has found his sphere in the special study of the *patient as a person*, the special study of the total activities and total behavior, the kind of thing which cannot be singled out as merely the function of any one detachable organ, not even of the brain itself.

In the medical curriculum the student is led to take man apart and to study the structure and function of these parts; it then falls to the brain physiologist, and ultimately to the psychologist and psychiatrist, to show the student how these parts and functions are integrated into that whole which we know as the personality of the patient, the subject of the life history, the entity to which we as physicians appeal when we give advice and map out a routine behavior and adjustment; that entity which we try to bring into health- and success-bringing relations with ourselves, the environment, and personal life problems. We deal not only with organs but also with the integrated and integrating personality and its functions. The psychiatrist thus deals with a wide range of facts usually left to untrained commonsense, but now available as a more and more organized body of facts, methods of study and methods of therapeutic procedure.

An important advance in teaching comes from this gain in a more natural definition of the field. As I outlined two years ago in my contribution to the San Francisco meeting, the second-year student gets an introduction into the methods of taking a life history, a study of the assets and determining factors, a general discussion of the intelligence tests, the usual mental status, the method needed in examining a case of aphasia and the principles of getting at the dynamic determining factors of the patient's life, with a study of the orientative activity, the associative processes and resources, the affective assets, and habit formation.

With this preparation the student begins his third year with a study of the principal reaction-types which he has to learn to understand and distinguish from one another. We may begin with the organic reaction-types with their memory and judgment defects (very specifically brought out in the parenchymatous brain syphilis or paresis, in senile dementia, and in the Korsakoff reaction) and the epileptic and epileptoid reactions. The epileptic and the Korsakoff reactions lead over either to the delirious hallucinatory reactions, which are mainly toxic as in the drug and alcoholic deliriums, or to reactions with a more constitutional groundwork, as in the acute and chronic hallucinoses.

The next reaction-type discussed is the affective one, either tending to appear in attacks constituting the manic-depressive and cyclothymic disorders, or leading over to the substitutive, less diffusely affective disorders of hysteria and psychasthenia, and the deeper substitutive disorders of the schizophrenic type with its more benign and graver forms. Next we find the paranoic disorders, and the constitutional disorders of balance and perversion, and the development of *defects* such as idiocy, imbecility, etc.

The student is told from the outset that while each reaction complex tends to have its own structural etiological and prognostic implications and meanings, the various types are not necessarily exclusive of each other in one and the same patient and that we must learn to recognize combinations.

Each patient is studied specifically for the etiological factors (exogenic, somatogenic, neurogenic, psychogenic, and constitutional); and for therapeutically responsive features, so that ultimately the patient stands before us as an experiment of nature, sometimes simple, sometimes complex, not an entity deriving light or meaning from the pigeonhole of some classification, but an orderly set of facts inviting the physician to recognize more or less clean-cut problems of adjustment: the somatic therapy, the rest treatment and graded reeducation, and the study and re-adaptation of psychogenic and constitutional problems. The third-year course thus familiarizes the student with the essential types and problems, so that in the fourth year the student is prepared to meet the rank and file of the outpatient and house cases and is able to follow the more detailed discussions of the psycho-pathological, cerebral, general somatic and endocrine components of the cases as they are met, and also the problems of management, of commitment, etc. No student is admitted to the final examination without having personally examined and reported in writing a minimum of six cases.

The most fundamental departure from current tradition is the emphasis not on the question whether the patient presents one or another of a set of diseases, but rather on the question how many factors and conditions enter into the state of the patient, what reaction complexes are recognizable as relative entities and what psychopathological, cerebral, general somatic, endocrine, toxic and infectious components; in other words, we take the same attitude which modern pathology has assumed in general medicine. We get away from the dominant notion of classification of each patient as having just one exclusive disease, and that usually a rather artificial traditional entity but rarely realized completely in any one case; we prefer to urge the student to consider whatever group of facts and factors he actually finds in the patient before him. We certainly would not classify our necropsy patients according to one single cause of death, and neglect to do justice to the other facts and factors present; and why should we not train the student of psychiatry to learn to appreciate and trust the facts and factors by themselves and in combination as actually found? It is absolutely essential that he learn to use all the means of general medicine at his disposal and also to work safely with the psychobiologically integrated part-phenomena and functions, as well as with the frequently more or less artificial units of nosological disease entities.

Our general medical, clinical, and necropsy diagnoses no longer fail to specify the combination of facts to be dealt with; and psychopathology and psychiatry are at last reaching the same principle. We may have a right to speak of manic-depressive psychoses and of dementia praecox types of mental disease in order to designate certain broad categories similar to the terms used when we speak of Bright's disease, or of valvular disease; but such terms would hardly be regarded in modern medicine an adequate and sufficient "diagnosis," but a suggestion in the direction of a proper search for infectious sources and their working. Similarly we have to train the student of psychiatry and psychopathology to heed the structural facts, the toxic and endocrine and serologic facts, the constitutional and psychogenic facts, and to learn to work with them, individually and in combination. Even the simplest general diseases, the acute infections, are no longer viewed as an issue of the mere presence of a microbe; they present an infection plus a problem of constitution, or of more or less immunity; and similarly the disorders of the psychobiological adaptive processes must be viewed as the resultants of a group of facts and factors, and by accepting this view, we get on a natural working basis.

To sum up the present trend of teaching psychiatry:

1. Psychiatry cannot limit itself to the traditional asylum diseases. It has become the medical study of all types and forms of disorders and involvements of the total behavior and mentation, from the simplest, we might say normal, defects and difficulties of adaptation to the more sweeping affections, some of which *may* disqualify the patient for being his or her own safest guide and adviser and then may enter the category or temporary phase of committable disorders.

2. The second-year course of the medical student includes the methods of recording a medically useful biography, of using the standard tests of intelligence and motor performance, of making out the principal facts and determining factors of a normal individual's make-up and reactive tendencies.

3. The third-year course deals with the standard reaction-types or reaction complexes of psychopathology and the factors entering into them.

4. The fourth-year course takes up the general routine of cases, and the study of special problems of at least six cases by each student.

5. The principal departure from tradition is the inclusion of normal psychobiological adaptive problems, and the getting away from the dogmatic notion of "one person one disease" dictated by a classification-ridden tradition, and from a nosology which neglects too many points important for the understanding and treatment of the actual patient.

6. Hence, we should say that the student is led to recognize the facts and factors entering into the simple entities and combining in the more complex disorders, so that he may get a dynamic as well as a structural conception of the patients whom he is called on to treat.

One of the principal consequences of this mode of instruction is that the students frequently find patients in other divisions of the hospital who, according to their impressions, should be referred to the psychopathological or psychiatric department, especially many of those patients who, according to the internist or surgeon, "have nothing the matter with them" but who should not be sent away without a study of their psychobiological adaptation. It is probably not practicable to transfer all these patients; hence, why not get accustomed to *use* the psychological training wherever it is needed? We have to realize that in all branches of medicine physicians are expected to apply psychopathological methods, just as modern psychiatrists make use of all the methods and experience presented by the other departments of medicine even if the patients have mainly psychopathological problems.

Another consequence is that quite a few students begin to see, in conditions which are looked on as normal or as merely nervous, possibilities of readjustment which may become of inestimable value to the patient and be to the interest of preventive medicine and hygiene because the worker is put into the position which enables him to deal with the component factors before the full-fledged traditional pictures have established themselves and have begun to overawe both patient and physician.

THE AIMS AND MEANING OF

PSYCHIATRIC DIAGNOSIS

From a paper read by Dr. Meyer before the American Medico-Psychological Association, New York, May 29, 1917; American Journal of Insanity, 74:163 (Oct., 1917).

To guide the student—and one's own work—as directly as possible to the facts which really can be studied and worked with and which are the safest expression of the nature and depth of the disorder and of the points of attack for treatment—this, to my mind, must be the ideal of the teacher and practitioner and investigator alike.

On the other hand, any system which aims mainly at the traditional accumulation and enumeration of "symptoms of disease entities" tends to create entities for mere identification and from there on to suggest mainly deductive reasoning. One thinks of the disease in general and not of the facts presented by the patient, and reasons from that more or less abstract something or assumed entity.

There are, to be sure, fields in which the worker must be willing to run a risk, to run ahead of his facts, to shape his aims for what he wants to attain rather than according to the facts at hand. We must have the courage of hypotheses. I do, however, feel that this should be encouraged chiefly among trained workers and where research is stimulated, and not in the systems which are to be the equipment of those who are mainly students or practitioners.

Our facts and our ambitions lie in the structural field or in the functional field of description, and in the fields of etiological or causal interpretation and the fields of prognosis and of treatment. Let us consider the first, *i.e.*, the condition of the structure of the nervous system and especially of the cerebrum, and of the sensory-motor equipment and of the vegetative and regulative mechanisms of the body, *i.e.*, the internal secretion organs, the foci of infections, etc. Whatever facts we can get in this structural level are undoubtedly most dependable, controllable and lasting. Sometimes they are a complete explanation, where we can reproduce them experimentally, as in beriberi; or they may be empirically clear enough and safe, as in parenchymatous syphilis or paresis, where we feel sure that the histological findings have precedence over any other form of examination in ultimate dependability; or in the senile processes, although there the principle is not so clear; or in epilepsy, which leads us to still more uncertain ground.

Pragmatically, the structural supremacy would be accepted as clearly established where we might declare ourselves willing to trust the study of the living patient as is done in cancer and of late in the study of the thyroid. Where this test is not considered dependable, we might do well to turn to a functional pathology, either in the form of reactions of the body fluids, or in the form of various functional tests, including glandular, neurocerebral and psychobiological functions.

This second—the functional—field might roughly be divided into the physiopathological and the psychopathological ones, at least if we agree on certain revaluations of these terms, as was done in my article on objective psychobiology [see page 397].

In the physiopathological sphere we may distinguish the serum reactions, in which we really withdraw a sample of the fluid body tissue for structural or chemical tests or for biological study, as in the complement fixation or Abderhalden reaction and the like; or we may subject certain functions of the organism or of parts either to tests in the way of establishing certain conditions, such as pulse, temperature, and respiration curve, the gastro-intestinal and secretory and metabolic regulations, or in the way of pharmacological tests as in the study of vagotonia, sympatheticotonia, etc. With all the general progress of late years, the physiological or physiopathological chemical tests have hardly obtained a leading position except in a limited sphere and for the determination of part-disorders, as in the measuring of emotional trends by the blood sugar and the like. The serum reactions or biological tests have been more fruitful. The field has, however, hardly been touched in the most promising line, *viz.*, that of experimental-preventive pathology; and the problem of internal secretions unfortunately still is on ground on which an undue amount of speculative guesses obscures the lines of safe and well-controlled work.

The psychopathological field has made the most remarkable strides to record. Since the analytic-synthetic dynamic viewpoints have asserted themselves, the psychopathological problems of man lie before us in a much more humanly comprehensive form. Not only the so-called psychoneuroses or minor psychoses, but also the more bewildering and apparently unintelligible types dissolve themselves to a far-reaching extent into reactions not so foreign to normal human experience. We find not only "method in the madness," but many common links with the normal, where the passing generation vainly sought for exclusive salvation in the urine and feces, and in the sham comforts of neurologizing tautologies. With critical work on the facts and a little less quibbling over pet theories and a little less vituperation of the contrary-minded, we can today show the student and the patient material that leads us into the midst of where things happen. Even simple description of the overt and implicit activities of the patient takes us a long way toward an understanding of what is right or wrong in the condition, and toward the third viewpoint of prominence, the etiological, that of the causal and experimental interpretation.

This is undoubtedly the ground of real pathology, *i.e.*, the ground of real explanation of disease. The chief gain we have to record here is the gain in tolerance of the *multiconditioned character* of all the conditions with which we deal. We always have to reckon with at least two factors, the more or less specific causal agent and the constitutional make-up; indeed, merely to mention the latter forces us to accept a multiconditioned experimental equation. We cannot speak of alcoholic insanity except as a general group of a multiplicity of disorders in which alcohol plays its various roles; we cannot speak of syphilitic and para-syphilitic disease any longer without much more additional quali-fication; even a simple brain injury or an emotional difficulty must be studied as one of many dynamic factors, and the upshot is in the recognition that a purely etiological explanation is either too summary in many of the cases, or it is too complex to be practical.

This is why, ever since Falret and Kahlbaum, the combined descriptive and etiological and structural conceptions have been welded into "clinical entities," entities for bedside use, with vary-ing sagacity and reserve. Today the majority stand under the standards of German nosology, and, with the good old tradition, physicians and students sort out the *patients*, not the facts, and label the men and women as cases of "manic-depressive insanity" or "dementia praecox" and a few other entities, created by Kraepelin in a fit of indignation against Ziehen, and praised to the world owing to the prognostic virtues and ultimate simplicity of his nosological schema.

To bring in prognosis as a leading feature in a nosological system is about as wise as to bring the issue of religious denomination into an election. Even the cocksure attitude about paresis is wav-ering. We still have to remember Stanley Hall's bright taunt, that those who talk so glibly of dementia praecox should call paresis thanatic or deadly dementia (*Adolescence*, 1:305). I, for one, am determined to subordinate the prognostic verdict to the inquiry in a more constructive question, that of the problem of therapeutic modifiability, which in turn is subordinated to the study of the working of all the dynamic factors and the struc-tural and functional descriptive facts. Looking over my experi-ence with this in view corroborates an early impression that few patients have but one abnormal factor working in them. That which is one big calamity, one disease, resolves itself usually into groups of facts, none of which is the unique and unequivocal cause or force "back of it all"; but each combination has its dominant feature and subordinate features open to study, and some of them open to therapeutic readjustment. And since we are far from omniscient, we do well to ask: "Will our salvation come from any unitary Kantian *Ding an sich* or noumenon, that which is back of the practical nosological entity, apt to be made a starting part for deductions, or from a better grasp on that which we can work on and not merely think about?"

I do not share the holy horror of the *Ding an sich* or noumenon entertained by some people. It is well that we should have our concepts and words for the totalities even if they can never be fully realized as wholly indisputable entities. For both scientific and practical purposes, it is, however, wisest to choose one's noumena or ideal entities and bedside terms as closely as possible to where one actually can work, to choose them where their help is needed and not to sacrifice our progress to the old notion of unitary one-name "diseases" where many facts call for consideration. While, in a way, I look for what is back of the surface, that which is back of it all in the sense of being the essential and fundamental fact really answers better to the call: "What is there *in* it and what is there *to* it?"

Hence, where structure expresses any facts, I bow to structure, and I bend all my energy upon an understanding of the conditions which explain and can—or cannot—modify that structure. If the structure is subordinated, the mere necessary background of the battle, not well known, or only incidentally affected, I turn to the other battling elements.

In order to be able to draw upon all the helpful elements for the understanding and handling of the condition presented by a patient, I force myself first to get my facts concerning the total reaction or reaction-type or reaction complex, whether it is organic, or toxic-delirious, or affective, or paranoic, or a benign or a malignant substitutive process, or a constitutional defect or perversion, or a mixture. The reaction complex is then qualified by the statement of the etiological or dynamic factors at work; it is next weighed for the possible structural involvement and the therapeutic opportunities and the prognosis; and, finally, according to whether the case does or does not coincide with a well-defined practical type, it is classed as identical with, or akin to, a standard unit such as we keep for our statistics and for elementary teaching.

One thing is certain. We have to get away from the idea of "one person one disease." Where would general pathology stand if it had to conform to the reports of the so-called cause of death without qualification? That our own committee on statistical classification should at this late hour have sworn allegiance to the German dogma without provisions for mixed and merely allied types was a somewhat distressing surprise. Fortunately, we still constitute a free country and have reason to hope that if a cause is just it will ultimately find a majority.

THE LIFE-CHART

From a paper by Dr. Meyer in Contributions to Medical and
Biological Research, *dedicated to Sir William Osler, in honor of
his seventieth birthday, July* 12, 1919, *by his pupils and coworkers,*
2:1,128, *Paul B. Hoeber, New York* (1919).

The two big sins of the physician against the psychoneurotic are
apt to be the dismissal of the patient with, "Nothing the matter
with you" (with perhaps a hint that he or she had best go to
Christian Science or to some cure-all), or the statement: "What
I find is enough to account for all your nervous symptoms."
Either statement is apt to encourage neglect in the examination
of the psychopathological and the situational status of the patient.
Well-directed attention to these settings will make the verdict
safer for the patient, and ultimately also do better justice to the
responsibility of the physician.

How, then, can we pin down the pertinent facts? How can
we get them in a form which will be a safe, dependable formulation in terms of an "experiment of nature," or of a problem of
functional pathology, suggesting more or less well-defined non-
derogatory therapeutic modifications?

Medical psychology consists largely in the determination of
the actual life history and experiences and concrete reactions of
the patient, and the gaining of a safe and sensible perspective, so
as to adapt as far as possible the aims to the means and the means
to the aims, and the personality to the situation and the situation
to the personality.

The facts which really count are as plain and tangible and concrete and controllable as those in any other part of the record and examination of the human being. Unfortunately, they may be unwieldy, and form a "long story," and before we can say that we have a clean-cut and practically useful view of the fateful bias indicated by the history, it must be shown by careful scrutiny of the facts that the allegations tally with what the person actually shows objectively by behavior and associations and with the history furnished by the friends. It is the length of the records and their apparent lack of pointedness that make many physicians shun the task. It is, furthermore, somewhat difficult to control the time relations and causal interdependence of the events.

To facilitate a concise final review of the facts I use a device which, I hope, illustrates not only our practice but also the entire philosophy behind it.

The patient who comes to the physician is naturally examined, not only for the history and present condition of each organ and function, but also for the development and condition of the integrated personality. In order to record the facts in a graphic manner, we can use a life record for each of the principal organs, giving sufficient space for each year so that we can record dates at least accurately enough to indicate the months. To give a rational background to the scheme, the weight-curve of the most readily comparable part of each system is charted. For the nervous and mental conditions we use the growth-curve of the weight of the brain; for the respiratory apparatus, the weight-curve of the lungs; for the circulation, the heart; for the digestive apparatus, the weight-curve of the liver; and similarly we add the curve of the kidneys and that of the thyroid, thymus, and sex glands. The whole forms a tracing of the life-curve of the entire organism, whose integration in its relation to the environment then becomes the basis of the so-called "mental record," which is entered in terms of situations and reactions.

We begin with the entering of date and year of birth so as to be able to read off easily the individual age and the corresponding calendar years (the age being entered on the right and the years on the left); we next enter the periods of disorders of the various organs, and after this the data concerning the situations and re-actions of the patient. The space on either side of the tracing of the organism is used for explanations, but specially for the data which constitute the principal situations and reactions expressing the "mental" record, permitting various degrees of completeness. On the right border near the edge we may note the changes of habitat, of school entrance, graduations or changes, or failures; the various jobs; the dates of possibly important births and deaths

YEAR.		BIRTHDAY: Jan. 11, 1895	YR.
1896		Youngest of 17. Mother--second wife. Learned to walk and talk in the first year.	1
1897	Cholera infantum		2
1898	Broncho-pneumónia		3
1899	Croup	Well developed; large for his age.	4
1900	Usual exanthemata		5
1901			6
1902		Began school.	7
1903		Open disposition; friendly, but quiet.	8
1904		Preferred staying at home to playing with others.	9
1905			10
1906	Autoerotism continued to present (1916)		11
1907	Malaria	No worries	12
1908		Only close companion a cousin of own age--very wild boy. Intimacy continued to present time (1916).	13
1909		Dredge-hand in boat of brother-in-law Left school (7th grade)	14
1910		Industrious, saving money.	15
1911		Bought boat. Crabbing, {Summers at home. Winters dredging oysters {in Balto. with brother.	16
1912		Quarrels with brothers; thought he was abused, being the youngest.	17
1913	Illicit relations. Neisser infection	Went with girls often, but no serious love affairs.	18
1914	Autoerotism increased		19
1915	Depression	Feb.-Refused admission to lodge; kidney trouble. Depressed; stopped work; worried over illness. At home.	20
1916		Worked 6 weeks. Unconscious in boat (Aug.) Peculiar words and behaviour. Reproached sisters for immorality. Hears voices; uneasy; frightened; then dull. At home.	21
1917		Development of semi-stupor and indifference. Entered Clinic.	22

Labels within the tracing: Sex Life, Thyroid, Thymus, Digest. & Liver, Kidneys, Heart, Respir., Cerebrum, Reflex Level

A Case of Schizophrenia

YEAR: BIRTHDAY: May 27, 1885.

Year	Left notes	Center labels	Right notes	YR.
1886				1
1887				2
1888				3
1889				4
1890				5
1891			Beginning of headaches.	6
1892			Private school	7
1893				8
1894				9
1895				10
1896	"Typhoid"			11
1897			5th grade repeated	12
1898	Menstruation irregular		Headaches partly menstrual, partly reactive.	13
1899				14
1900				15
1901				16
1902				17
1903			Marriage	18
1904	1st child died 6 mos. old			19
1905	Complications of sex-life.			20
1906				21
1907				22
1908			Indifference of husband? Pains about the heart; globus; depression; exhaustion	23
1909	2d child lived 2½ days.		Growing invalidism. Need of sympathy.	24
1910				25
1911	3d child living.			26
1912	Operation for fallen stomach. Appendectomy.		Invalidism; mostly in bed. Call for sympathy reinforced by call for operations.	27
1913	Removal of ovaries and tubes.		Lavage of stomach by mother every 10 days for 2 years. / Exhaustion; pressure in head. Marked fatigability, backache, pains about heart, shoulders and limbs; numbness on left side; sensitiveness to noises; poor sleep.	28
1914	Hot flushes.			29
1915	"Menstrual" headaches.		In hospital from Feb. 9 to July 31, 1915. Recovery.	30

Center vertical labels: Sex Life — Thyroid — Thymus — Kidneys — Digest. & Liver — Respir. — Heart — Cerebrum — Reflex Level

A Case of Invalidism

in the family, and other fundamentally important environmental influences. Brackets indicate the duration of some of these features. Any specific trends of special importance in the evolution of the illness had best be underscored with different-colored inks.

It is well to put on the left side the entries concerning special diseases, the sex life, etc. In case the details of illness require more space, certain periods can be charted on a supplementary chart so as to make the space represent months instead of years.

The two accompanying examples will explain the plan better than would extended description.

The first chart presents the data of a patient with schizophrenia. The second gives the facts in a case of invalidism in which a recovery might possibly have been obtained without mutilation.

In the latter case you find from the age of five a habit of headaches, a dependence on others, lack of emancipation, a tendency to appeal for sympathy by her complaints; then after her marriage and the birth of a child and subsequent interference with her normal instinctive life, fear of losing the affection of her husband (a friend of the wife had come to live in the house), and more invalidism; then several unfortunate and mutilating operations, a real evisceration without any evidence of a study of the facts in the case, but finally a readjustment under a treatment establishing better habits, a better understanding of difficulties, and an end of making the remaining organs, the stomach and the head, the scapegoats for the failure of adaptation.

This brief note may illustrate the objective practical procedure of modern psychopathological studies, and how simply, controllably, and suggestively the facts can be brought into a record.

PREPARATION FOR PSYCHIATRY

From "Preparation for Psychiatry," by Dr. Meyer, Archives of Neurology and Psychiatry, 30:1,111 (Nov., 1933).

As psychiatry is much broader than psychoanalysis, the latter is to be regarded as an incident in the broader training, to be limited to specially talented physicians and well-chosen patients; it is not to figure as the all-pervading principle of actual psychiatric practice. A question that provokes the greatest diversity of opinion relates indeed to the scope granted or required for psychoanalysis in a scheme of training in psychiatry. Unless a physician has a special urge, need, or talent in this direction, it is a question whether a routine requirement of psychoanalysis does not become a distraction and disruption of the habitual procedure and orientation for both the patient and the physician.

This should not, however, imply a disregard of the broadening of the rich material of content and motivation that the psychoanalytic workers have contributed. Indiscriminate mixing of principles or a belief in exclusive salvation is, however, often detrimental to both practice and patient. In the main, in spite of the value of personal experience, I am a bit suspicious of those who have been psychoanalytically trained chiefly because they needed to be psychoanalyzed on account of their own maladjustment or who had to be aroused by the lure of the revelations.

To be able to be a sound psychoanalyst requires an exceptional combination of elasticity and critique and medical training. I should advise a good training in the most rigidly disciplined psychiatry and psychobiology before the intensive training in any form of psychoanalysis if this is still possible and compatible with actual practice and conditions of work. For the rank and file, training in distributive analysis of the determining factors and synthesis of the physician's and the patient's positive and negative assets is the best that can be offered and used.

In addition to the ideal complete program there naturally must be opportunities for shorter courses, as well as visits to differently organized centers, with the obligation to report the special observations.

Teaching centers are most advantageous for training, but periods of work in centers for intensive practical work are also essential. Whenever possible, the psychiatrist-in-training should also have experience in teaching, so as to make himself responsible for well-organized formulations.

Intrinsic understanding of the patient's state and situation, reconstruction of nature's experiment, and constructive handling of the "pathology and therapy" in specific cases and groups of cases must be cultivated above all things.

As to laboratory techniques, psychological or otherwise, I believe that in the main no "tests" should figure as urgent and convincingly valid until they tempt the ward physician to try to master them himself. While some work may be left to technicians, it should never get far beyond what the physician should be able to do or to know thoroughly in its principles and to sense the value of. Otherwise one drifts into the present-day superabundance of work that "can always be done" but is often done as a mere show of thoroughness without regard for the patient or for economy of time or money.

The training must have as its goal a preparedness to meet the rank and file of practical cases and the emergencies of psychiatric experience. And to reach this goal, graduate study in psychiatry should always take the form of assistantship, and the assistantship should be of a type that allows time and opportunity for the digestion and supplementing of the practical work with a reasonably systematic course in which a more detailed study of personality and laboratory work in neurology and in psychobiology and in all the fields drawn on in behalf of the patient find their place and time for assimilation.

Whatever one may wish to learn in psychology or psycho-biology, the first step must be to organize what commonsense knowledge one possesses and whatever methods the student brings to his patient. I heartily disagree with those who so distrust even the most critical commonsense that they ask for new oversystem-atized concepts and terms with a clean sweep of all the old. With regard to terminology, I consider it easy to show that the precipitate of human experience shaken down in the natural development of language is infinitely closer to reality than the "high-brow" use of special terms would often indicate. There is no objection to any real enrichment of language and modes of presentation, but the first step is what might be called an interest in the facts close to reality and life, and the use of the best available terms, with plenty of exposure of both the language and the facts to the critical sense demanded not only in Missouri, as the phrase goes, but as a general commodity. The days of verbal magic are unfortunately not over, but it does not overawe the average person today. Plain facts and plain words are needed first, to be supplemented by what corrections prove necessary in the light of constructive and critical experience.

No student who has not a sense for meanings (be it of looks, of utterances and posture, of behavior, of characters or of means of helpfulness) should enter psychiatry. And by "sense" I mean a natural and practical critical-minded and not merely verbal response. Whoever has to be stirred first by the extraordinary or by his own psychobiological discomforts and preoccupation is hardly the best material for psychiatry. The psychiatrist as a mere "diagnostician" or as a mere sympathetic bystander comes closer to being a racketeer than a physician. There is the greatest need for imagination and its critical—and especially its constructive —use, but it must rest on a solid basis of well-disciplined common-sense.

As soon as the rest of medical training recognizes its obligation to pay reasonable attention to the person and to personality-function as part of all physician-patient relationship, it will be possible to consider an internship in one of the general medical branches an important part of the foundation for psychiatric graduate training. When but inadequate emphasis is given to the human problems, special postgraduate training in internal medicine and other specialties might as well be inserted later when the psychiatric aspirant has acquired his own sense of relations and proportion.

Anatomy without ample study of the living, physiology without ample inclusion of general biology and respect for the psychobiological total-functions, and internal medicine or neurology taught by persons not also at least psychiatrically intelligent would not be altogether sound or safe or desirable unless there was serious contact with the psychiatric staff.

Above all, one needs in psychiatric training a sound blending of the study of things as they are found in patients, and not only a study of what one finds in the contents of the test tube and in special experimental preparations. Nobody can furnish or find that sound blending in an atmosphere not friendly to the present-day views of man and a natural science including man, "body and soul"—not for mere possession as one's patient or one's autopsy material, but for work.

How much internal medicine should be studied?

From the angle of observation and study it is especially important to know the "normal" and also the unavoidable variations of functions which the average physician is taught to disregard so as to avoid being misled into false diagnoses. The psychiatrically intelligent internist does not disregard but learns and teaches how and where to assign "functional" symptoms and "nervous" signs and complaints of the various organs and functions. Whoever specializes in psychiatry must know the range of variations of heart dullness, heart sounds, and heart rhythm, indeed all the things which the beginner is taught not to mistake for evidence of lesions (or as medical jargon will have it, evidence of "pathology"). The same holds for the gastro-intestinal tract, the skin, metabolism, the endocrine glands, and other organs. Present-day pathology is not only anatomy and histology but fully as much a variant of physiology, and is greatly interested in findings that are often tossed aside unused by those devoid of a genetic-dynamic orientation.

This same point holds for neurology. Many a good "organic" neurologist is a poor trainer for the neurology needed by the psychiatrist or average physician. It is often the "insignificant" and "noncontributory" variants that count and with which one must be familiar, not for the purpose of discarding them but to give them their due. With all my love for the structural facts in neurology, I greatly deplore the paucity of help and training offered in the organization of functional data. My introduction to anatomy of the brain [*Archives of Neurology and Psychiatry*, 7:287; *ibid.*, 19:573] is one of broad functional lines. Function demands a training that should become available simultaneously with the anatomical and physiological discussions and clinical study. Moreover, the closer one comes to the sympathetic and parasympathetic balance and the postural reflexes and to the problems of aphasia and apraxia, the closer one gets to common interests and common needs of the anatomist, physiologist, neuropathologist, and psychopathologist.

Even pathological anatomy—unavoidably sadly managed by the general pathologist not clinically trained—is safe only in the hands of one trained in a psychiatrically intelligent neurology.

Deplorably little is being done along the lines of complete investigation of autopsy material. Good and convincing experiments of nature and accident are rare. They should not be lost under the impression that all the work has already been done. There is too much teaching not constantly controlled by study of actual material. Practically no material of vital importance has been added to the study of secondary degenerations coming out of experience in the World War. The International Brain Commission has gone out of existence, and systematic studies requiring special laboratories are scarce. This is bound to revenge itself on the quality of teaching and preparation of the new generation.

The first condition for sound psychiatry consists in the gathering and recording and coordinating of the data with which one works and by which one is guided from day to day and through the lifetime of patients.

It is fairly well agreed today that the facts must be accepted in

the form in which they are most distinctive and also most controllable, either by corroboration in reobservation or, whenever
possible, by test, *i.e.*, by performances obtainable at any time. The
latter desideratum must be recognized as only partly attainable.
Man is an entity that does not respond in an invariable manner.
Even in the organically definable disorders, only a limited number
of performances are constant and obtainable in a uniform manner
at all times. Almost all reactions are apt to vary somewhat from
day to day, and a large number are bound to be relatively unpredictable, but reasonably true to type if one makes allowance for
the obligatory relation to situation and the personality. The most
characteristic and personally distinctive data must be gathered and
accepted as personal and considered in the light of a history. To
discard the historical specificity of human life and development in
favor of the nonhistorical physiology would be fatal to accuracy.

Statistics do not give more than probabilities. Each specific case
and instance calls for a summary consideration of the specific
problems, assets, and issues, and the type of combination. Consideration of these points then leads to the genetic-dynamic conceptions if one aims at dependability of the inferences, and to a frank
espousal of reaction sets which must not be taken as finalistic
diagnoses without a checking-up covering the various sets of possible relations—exogenic, organogenic, neurogenic, constitutional
and psychogenic.

All this requires a capacity to master one's actual range of data
in a dependable manner. Moreover, for the organization of one's
experience, it is essential that one should have a body of sufficiently
long-controlled cases. Indeed, one should have enough cases that
have been seen through to the end and to autopsy, and, I trust,
some time, studies of a number of generations.

Within this setting, and only within it, is there a place for
research in the realm of part-disorders or part-functions in the
physiological and other special realms.

The desire to introduce chemical and internistic work by persons
not trained in the psychiatric patterns and settings and not in touch
with the daily variations and the long-term perspective leads oftener
than not to disappointments. Yet hope in these directions must be

fostered because of the far greater dependability and accessibility of the quantitative and unconditioned data.

My experience leads me to the following conclusions: Whoever wants to do research in psychiatry must have a basic general training in psychiatric observation. Without that the special worker will lose himself in grinding the organ of extraneous methods and problems, usually with scant bearing on known psychiatric issues. Far more has been achieved in the gains from detailed long-term study and efforts in real psychiatry than with the methods indiscriminately introduced from general medicine and other special domains. Even the modern treatment for dementia paralytica came from a psychiatrist and not from a specialist in syphilis.

No one can say a priori along what lines genuine advances are to be made. Nevertheless, when one reviews the attainments of the last sixty years, one finds that progress has been partly in the direction of a more determined and intelligent use of the personal assets along individual lines and also along the lines of socialization and personal adjustment. There is need of a singling-out of conditions within which special helps can be determined and introduced; the procedures are largely individualized and are by no means as strongly "mechanized" as certain psychotherapeutic formulas would lead one to expect.

The future of psychiatric research will depend partly on chance, but largely on the creation of sound conditions for practical psychiatric work satisfying and attracting good workers with enough interest in training for specialized work.

Research in neurology and psychiatry serves cultural rather than immediately practical usefulness. Most of the special work of inquiry goes beyond what the individual patient should be forced to pay for. Nevertheless, to be a good neurologist and psychiatrist one cannot remain a mere routinist. Considering the amount of opportunity to learn from experience in neurosurgery, the habit of securing and maintaining follow-up work that cannot properly be charged to the patient deserves more extensive support than it has today, as part of neurophysiological training and research. All this depends on sounder methods of working together, sharing opportunities, and conveying to the agency able to support research a sense of where support is needed and the responsibilities for progress lie. What can be more important than more knowledge of the integrative functions of man and human life? Can one go on leaving it to the philosopher and theologian on the one hand and the physicist and chemist on the other, and missing the experiments of nature with the actual human being? How can one give opportunities to see the actual working of psychiatry unless one can overcome the systematic ignorance and inattention with regard to the nature and working of human nature?

It is quite probable that for some time to come a reasonable amount of continence in publication is more of a virtue than a cause for reproach. Particularly in the direction of "mental hygiene," publicity, and promises of therapeutic boons, a more conscientious adherence to what can be proved and used is greatly to be desired. It is all the more necessary to secure adequate support for publication which may require more space than the average medical article or monograph, on account of the need of specification of the settings and the great differentiation of the psychobiological data and the checks introduced from contributing fields—so valuable, provided that they can be said to be contributive.

There is room for many different temperaments. There is a demand for administrators, who must know the needs of both patients and physicians and also the general public, and who must, moreover, know fiscal conditions. Intimate therapeutic work with individual patients is one thing, the talent for socializing hospital treatment often another. There are socially interested psychiatrists working in outpatient departments, schools, factories, and courts, all in need of sound knowledge of the generally accessible facts in the cases and also of the needs of families, friends, and public and trends at large. There is need of safe, constructive-minded relations to the community. There are coordinators and persons who take to details. In the end, all have to acquire a capacity to review and grasp the broader relations as well as the more and more specialized hobbies, and to build up a genuine consensus with freedom and solidarity.

Some difficulty arises from the need of defining the spheres of work of specialists and also of lay workers. To the nurses belongs the cultivation of what makes for the best twenty-four hours of the day, supplementing rather than imitating the physician's work—a sphere of great usefulness, if they take seriously their unique opportunities without the burden of the detail confided to and demanded of the physician. Taking histories and seeing relatives and friends should not be relegated to nurses. It should remain an important opportunity of the physician. Psychologists must find it difficult to outline their sphere if they reach into the practical working with patients. McDougall justly advises that all those who wish to work with mental disorders should supplement their psychological training by an adequate medical training. The analyst usually takes over the patient altogether; so does the theological healer. There are frequent complaints that psychiatrists fail to understand the cultural aspects and the sociological aspects of the lives of their patients. Much damage to medical usefulness comes from this gap—something to be remembered in cultivating the premedical and extraprofessional interests.

The outlook for a career, as in any other field, depends on the personal equation and capacity for service. A growing range of institutional and personal work is open with promise of a very worth-while position professionally and socially as a teacher. Perhaps, when more persons become educated, not in natural sciences only or in the humanities only, but especially in the study of man as he actually grows and functions and becomes an asset or a handicap to self and to living humanity, one may look for the support of psychiatry and its contributive sciences as a task of advancing culture even if the benefit to the individual sufferer cannot be as individually gratifying as one would wish. Man grows but one brain in a lifetime and is thereby likely to be limited in his personality development. One cannot let progress in psychiatry depend merely on its earnings from its cases in the same sense as progress in surgery and many other branches of medicine does. On the other hand, cultural advances based on scientific rather than on emotional revelation will be needed to meet the basic conditions for advancement of the race, and, having to depend largely on "experiments of nature," one can expect worth-while experience from the psychiatrist who does not have to cater to fashions and to emotions as much as has been the case in the little more than a hundred years of the existence of psychiatry as a planned pursuit.

Psychiatric training calls for a plan of apprenticeship with enough systematical presentation and amplification of the concrete work with individual persons. It rests on experience with personality-study of normal persons and of persons with special complaints and problems, the reduction of the history and examinations to terms of an experiment of nature, with emphasis on the balance of the plastic modifiable and the nonmodifiable components of the person as a unit, in contrast to either physiology or sociology.

It is an intrinsic part of all medical work.

Specialistic training includes apprenticeship in a teaching center with an adequate range of practical experience in ward, laboratory, and field work, liaison activity, and theoretical organization of the material.

It assumes a sound conception of the relations of pathology and therapy in a setting of biology recognizing psychobiology as the division of total-function or personality-function.

TEACHING PSYCHOBIOLOGY

From "Scope and Teaching of Psychobiology," by Dr. Meyer,
Journal of the Association of American Medical Colleges, 10:93
(March, 1935*); and from his paper "Psychobiology in the First*
Year of Medical School," ibid., 10:365 *(Nov.,* 1935*).*

Until recently the behavior and functioning of the individual has
been divided between psychological and physiological, with most
of the emphasis placed on the study of the various organs and with
a certain helplessness in bringing in a more or less timid use of
psychology or resorting to one or another cult of psychotherapy.
Too often the mental developments and mental factors are brushed
aside or they are exaggerated or misjudged. Some patients who are
seriously ill are treated as mere complainers and as being hysterical
and hypochrondriacal; in other cases serious emotional disturbances
are concealed and overlooked. Much of this is due to the deeply
ingrained tendency to consider mind and body apart and to failure
to see that this splits human functioning out of keeping with reality.
When we speak of emotional problems, we know very well that
they include a strain on the heart, the visceral functions, the appetite, digestion and attention to the bowels, the effectiveness of sleep
and of recreation. We therefore come to speak of psychobiology,
which includes the living body in action and describes all that
behavior to which we must pay.attention.

When someone draws our attention to a case of gastric ulcer
and we look into the mode of living of the patient, it is not merely
a case of suffering and, perhaps, a fussy or troubled soul in need

433

of consolation and verbal advice, but a call for a change of activity and behavior. Why, then, talk of psychology as if it occurred without a body, and of the mismanaged body functions as if they were not part of the disturbed emotions and behavior, to be corrected by equally real and physical normal behavior?

Is this psychology? Yes, but a psychology that is biological and that takes life as it is without any splitting into something mental and something physical. We study behavior not merely as a function of the mind and of various parts of the body, but as a function of the individual, and by that we mean the living organism, not a mysteriously split entity. When we see somebody eating or drinking too much or too hurriedly, or overworking, with inadequate recreation, we want to know why and how this occurs, and we modify it not merely as a state of mind but as behavior. That is what we imply by psychobiological—undivided and direct attention to the person and to the function, health, and efficiency of the person as a living organism. We talk of real organismal function and behavior and its understanding and management, and offer a course in practice of sound and controllable commonsense.

The medical student needs preparation to assume responsibilities with human beings. He has to know many facts not now taught because neither anatomy nor physiology can afford to preoccupy itself in these directions, yet it is clearly also his responsibility to work with man as an organized entity, as an individual, as well as with the structure and function of various parts. We demand specific experience with man and his needs in surgery and medicine and we are beginning to realize that we must deal with human nature and functioning by appropriate methods. There is a lot of idle talk of psychiatry and psychoanalysis and psychotherapy, and the physician has ultimately to bear the brunt of a great deal of criticism if he does not know what it is all about. Over and over again, we hear that forty per cent or more of the patients coming to a dispensary are sick in their personality-functions rather than in any particular organ or function; yet we are not making any effort to teach orderly management of them, and we allow the student to flounder instead of developing sound habits of using trained commonsense. We cannot afford to allow him to toss aside his twenty or more years of experience because of any wrong notion that he must wait for the coming of an unusual science.

There is much confusion between conflicting schools of psychology, often with unwise dramatization in teaching certain subjects like hysteria, hypnotism, and theories of psychoanalysis by instructors who have never worked with patients, and without any opportunity for the student to see the facts first, or even to see the actual clinical material. For this reason, some of us turn frankly to the sound Huxleyan definition of science as being organized commonsense. In a field in which nearly every adult has more practical experience with human nature and human functioning than is set forth in most textbooks on psychology, it seemed wisest not to add so much theory but to make certain that the worker learns to use all the plain facts. We want to start out deliberately to help the student organize what he knows about personality facts and the way to determine, record, and use them, to supplement data and methods, but above all to reenforce and organize his best sense, to help him determine the assets of the individual and to see what is the share of the individual and what is the share of the parts or special organs or special situations. Let us review some examples.

If an individual does not get along well with a job, it may be because of fundamental personal incapacity or because the situation prevents it, the competitive ways of the people around him, the attitude of the foreman, or what not; or it may be his own irregular life or some emotional preoccupation, some memories, or some anticipations or fears; or there may be something the average person calls "physical." Most probably all the things mentioned are also physical, if they are real; they are, at least, organismal as well as environmental and physiological. Any attitude, emotion, or activity, all our behavior, must be studied for what will make it intelligible or manageable. Certainly, some of the "physical" difficulties, such as insistence of perspiration and a feeling of faintness, or gastro-intestinal upsets, will be understood correctly as being parts of fear and can be corrected only by treating the fear as one treats fear, by promise of protection and security, and behavior in keeping with the best commonsense considering the situation, *i.e.,* using the individual's best resources and understanding and capacity to see and use the facts—without losing time over splitting the facts into mental and physical. We deal with psychobiological facts and methods, as far as possible of ordinary life, and, where needed, of additional technical training.

When we come to the behavior of the gastro-intestinal tract, we know that, for instance, vomiting can be due either to direct irritation of the stomach, to misuse of the stomach, such as over-filling with inappropriate food, to a drug like apomorphine, to sea sickness, or to pregnancy or fear of pregnancy or even a delusion of pregnancy. In some cases it is the stomach that initiates the condition; in the last-mentioned case it is the individual who gives the clue and the setting, and we must be able to determine what is operative and causative. Is the origin of the vomiting in terms of the structure of the stomach, in terms of its function, from actual disgust, or in terms of anticipation or fears or, perhaps, something about which the patient is not at all clear in his own mind? There are patients with pregnancy delusions or pregnancy fears who will hide them and make the physician believe that they blame the diet and want relief from nothing but the stomach distress.

It is obvious that for our needs we require a psychology that can deal directly with what we use in everyday life. We study the facts (a fact is anything which makes a difference) for what they mean in actual life, and by that we mean the life of a "somebody." He is to us an organism with a life history, a biography. Psychobiology comprehends all those functions and performances which cannot properly be said to be the function of merely one or another part of the living organism, not even merely of the brain. Anyone will best understand and study and manage it as the functioning of the individual, the person, the "he" or "she," not as a mere mind, but as a live entity with the flesh and bone of anatomy and physiology. This includes all that which has always been studied as psychology. To leave no doubt, we speak of psychobiology. How can this be taught and kept in a form that does not merely become a theoretical affair?

The field of human total-function or psychobiology is probably the one domain of science that presents not so much a mass of new information as primarily training in using what everybody knows. I regard the course as one of organizing the best critical common-sense in a form usable in record keeping and in serious work with patients. It is not merely a preparation for psychiatry; it means to serve all our dealing with human beings. It is not diluted psychiatry, nor diluted psychopathology.

We stand for the principle of keeping the first-year work within the purview of the normal. The course is based on a questionnaire furnishing the student an outline with which to review the deter-mining facts and factors that lead the individual to be what he is and to behave as he behaves. In order to dispel the traditional idea that personality-study is all introspection, we insist on studying the ordinary lives of others as well as our own. We ask the students for a characterization of the three most different classmates. We feel that such a personality-study is as important a procedure as the dissection of a cadaver and naturally an important supplement of all training with the living. Through this experience the student is prepared to extend his work to patients, whether psychiatric or seeking help anywhere else. The student studies life facts and life situations in the many differences of the normal and later in his patients. This leads from interest in more or less fixed diagnosis to an interest in the understanding of the whole patient and his prob-lems. In the psychiatric case, the student follows genetic-dynamic considerations instead of attempts to classify and pigeonhole his patient. He studies life situations and reactions and formulates his views in terms of facts and events which can be utilized to under-stand and modify the adaptations of the individual. The student singles out distinctive reaction patterns in his attempts to under-stand and group the essential demonstrable facts underlying a mental disorder.

The actual course consists of eight two-hour afternoon sessions. It consists of the completion of the personality-study, which is the equivalent of a laboratory experience, and which activates the material for our discussions of life, without allowing the student to remain in the abstract. Experience has emphasized the usefulness of the following topics which constitute the objective nature and functioning of the personality:

OUTLINE OF PERSONALITY-STUDY

I. General personality survey (jobs, hobbies, activity with family, friends, religion, education and politics as examples of performance; type of rest and satisfaction obtained after effort).

II. Special analyses of the psychobiological assets (intelligence and memory functions, action tendencies, emotional rises and balance).

III. Range and fluctuation of fitness with regard to work, play, rest, and sleep.

IV. Social relations in family, and the relative role of self-dependence and social dependence.

V. Sex development.

VI. Synthesis and balance of personality (personality type, role of less directly accessible influences, the position of any "unconscious" determiners).

VII. Difficulties and handicaps.

VIII. Specific disappointments and reactions to them.

IX. Assets and tendencies, favorable and unfavorable, traced to heredity, special sense-organ development or motor abilities, etc.

X. An enumeration of the events, experiences and situations in life which constitute special dynamic complexes or determining tendencies, in the form of an index of the significant results of the personality-study.

The goal is a natural-history basis and at the same time a sound appreciation of the human character of the facts educed. It aims at clearness of concepts and methods, with freedom and open-mindedness in the acceptance and use of these data, and is as devoid of dogmatism as is possible; freedom from a priori assumptions of extreme mechanistic or extreme humanistic conceptions, an orderly balance and correlation of the material and working with the various sciences, free of any unnecessary mixing of data and issues, or of premature dabbling with psychoanalysis and other overspecialized interests.

The whole course is a reorientation, which can be amplified on an elective basis with varying emphasis on child study, on sociological questions, on special lines of inquiry and research and applications, such as are mentioned in Prout and Ziegler's suggestive "Study in Psychobiology" (*American Journal of Psychiatry*, 13:1,227).

The student will get out of it what he puts into it, but in an orderly and intelligent and usable form. There will be those students who want to get by, but even they will not approach human facts again in a wholly haphazard fashion. And those students who are serious about the work find themselves in possession of reasonable methods of turning to facts that prove themselves without dogmatic proselytism or involvements in cults. The pragmatism involved is critical and the attitude one of function and progressiveness, active, creative and open-minded, ready for collaboration on as sound a commonsense and scientific basis as the facts and demands make possible and mandatory, stimulating imagination and a scientific conscience and urge for work.

The second year is granted eight two-hour sessions for an introduction to the examination of patients in a "mental status" and an outline of psychopathology. The latter does not start with what one knows least about but with the minor deviations from average functions. The student is taught to begin with the layman's complaint, and his own examination of the history and of the patient. His task is to bring the raw material to terms of an experiment of nature, to be studied for the conditions, the factors, their working, results, and modifiability. The upshot is that of a functional pathology, experiential and experimental. Basic reaction-types are discussed, abstracts of case-studies are offered for group study with emphasis on the "mental status" and the genetic-dynamic formulation of the case as a basis for therapy and diagnostic-prognostic guidance.

There is unanimity of opinion among teachers of psychiatry that these pre-clinical foundations, psychobiology and psychopathology, are essential in the medical curriculum. This is especially so because they meet the primary objectives of producing, on completion of the medical course, a practitioner who has acquired a sound attitude toward his medical duties and responsibilities along with an ability to deal reasonably well in the early days of his practice with the rank and file of patients presenting mental phenomena which he will see in his daily work. Such a foundation in the first year is essential for the undergraduate clinical instruction in the third and fourth years as well as for graduate training for those physicians who plan to enter special practice in various fields. Teaching of this kind is in accord with the recent outstanding studies made of the medical curriculum (Rappleye, League of Nations, British Medical Association).

For centuries man has been held up as standing in many ways outside and above nature and natural-science methods. What Galileo did to physics and nature has at last come to be done to the study of man and to that very feature of man of which it was said that it must be beyond human ken, that it is the one part that cannot become diseased or the subject of pathology. Within our lifetime, we might almost say overnight, there has come a tendency to put aside the mystery attitude and to use the same "sense" that belongs to the scientist as well as to the man in the street, an essentially objective and sensible way of using and treating plain facts with plain methods, by avoiding a split which has too long retarded a getting-together of those who must assume responsibilities with man. They want to do it frankly and honestly, without new mystifications, and without creating impressions of any great puzzle or secrets up one's sleeve. Instead of puzzling over the ultimate nature of mind and soul and life and man, we can occupy ourselves with the availability or absence of capacity and the performance in the demands of life and the conditions under which they do or do not operate.

It may have seemed to some as if, all of a sudden, psychiatry had come to parade before the public and to usurp the field so as to be called a real danger to commonsense in more than one discussion. Just at the time when every pediatrician began to feel that he was getting hold of important problems formerly left to the grandmothers, he feared a blast of hot air was being injected into his domain until it became clearer and clearer that it was not a question of a revolution but of organizing a rapid growth of commonsense and observation, of useful work which he did not have to lose or surrender to a new set of specialists, but could, to quite an extent, absorb and cultivate in the regular courses of training as a physician.

Psychologists like Yerkes joined those who speak of psychobiology. The last two generations of American psychologists have split off from the tutelage of metaphysics and have come more and more definitely into the camp of the naturalist, where the physician is also getting his training. What had long straddled between a better knowledge of brain and nervous system, and untrained commonsense about the functioning of man, is coming to stand on both feet and to "talk sense" and to work with a plain desire to want to know and see things as they are and to see them at work speaking the language of performance. We begin to treat our knowledge as being one of how to watch and do things, as well as how to talk and describe, and to try out things, instead of creating new mystifications. Instead of waiting for amazing revelations, we organize opportunities for experience, in dealing with the facts and growth and development of body and soul and mind and behavior, the child, the person, the indivisible unit or individual, and the groups in which man appears to us as the child, the adolescent, the adult, and the aged, and the partly well and the partly ill, just as we find them in real life and practice. The main point is that we turn to concrete objectivity and specificity, to the facts that speak through their performance in the service of life, hence the term psychobiology.

What we do is very simple. We want to make certain that while the student dissects the dead body, he also cultivates an interesting natural-history exercise with the living. We have so far been intent on teaching him to work with the parts; now we also want to teach him to work with the man. It is odd that we have not even a simple word for this man except the person, *i.e.*, the mask he speaks or sounds through. Do we really only study the mask, the Great God Brown, or do we study from the outset the real person we actually see in the flesh, alive—I again have to say the person—which we can make intelligible even in a movie and just what we term "he" or "she," or "you" or "I"?

The special feature of these entities or objects called human beings is that they are so specific and individually differentiated that we get to know them only when we know their name, the family name, and something of their history. When we come to meet a person or a new group, we try to get the name with a bit of real acquaintance, of an *accognitare*, of getting closer to the facts. But what is it that we want to know? The wherefrom; the whereto or line of activity and interests, and what we may have in common, and what may be specific to the entity or individual and to the family and to the groups to which he belongs!

There is no mystery about what we want. It is a question of what material the person is made of and how he uses what he is and has and what he does. We should like to know his experience, *i.e.*, what he has gone through, and what he has done; what he usually does, is, feels, thinks, and also what he does, is, feels and thinks in emergencies and special tasks and demands, and when left to himself and his own spontaneity. These are not hard conundrums. Then, if there are special—or actually queer—things, we deal with them as we do under all such circumstances: we want to be sure of the facts and events and what we are talking about, ascertain under what conditions they appear or occur; what facts enter as factors; how it all works, with what effects, and how it can be controlled and, when necessary, modified. And where the facts are not at once sufficient, we look either into the broader settings and understandings or into the inner detail of the organism and its working, or both, but always without surrender to the obsession that we should look for something else when we should really first try to see what is at hand. We make it our habit and duty to single out what is the capacity and its actual use, not only in general, but specifically in the service of the individual or group in real life and lifetimes, working for better or for worse.

We still are too definitely brought up to think that what goes on in us is a kind of extraordinary epiphenomenon, and that what really counts can be limited to the events in the body which must be thought of in purely physiological structure-function terms. As a matter of fact, we cannot afford any longer not to keep the two together and to include also the situation without which the personality and its behavior would not happen and could not be understood. The medically trained worker has to learn to think more naturally and concretely and differently from the traditional mind and body, or body, mind and soul. The "person" is not a mere abstract and reflector and not merely either a body or a spirit. It is a body in action; an organism alive with flesh and bone, doing exactly what he is and does and feels and senses. Mind is organismal action. Being is the doing, feeling, sensing, wanting and refusing of the actual and real person and never only a mind or only a body. We may speak of "mentation" (when we deal with that being and feeling and sensing and dreaming and planning in their most economizing, maximally abbreviated but richly amplified form called imagination), as shorthand attitudes and performances, but originally made up of full-fledged performances.

We forget that every mentally integrated activity, as it counts in life, is just so sufficiently different from what could be started by reflex stimulation, to be at once recognizable as the action of a more or less conscious person, a real action of the person, a piece of behavior, an ergasia in contrast to what the physiologist singles out; with its meaning in a personal life, and with its meaning-function in group life; more than a mere series of twitches, because it is part of a flow of function more or less smooth and but little broken up, in spite of its tremendous differentiation, always to be measured as part of the day's or the hour's or the moment's activity of a specific person or group, if we want to be accurate; and it is for that that we have terms usable for the shorthand of mere imagination (or economizing symbolization), as much as for the full-fledged behavior: our doing, our walking, and breathing, including also the action of the sense organs and the brain and our muscles and glands as integral parts of our total behavior—the person, indeed, as the self-integrator, that which furnishes the subject of our predicates and our various "ologies." We cannot report this behavior in terms of mere sensory-neuromuscular performances, but we do it in terms of action, disposals of situations, performance of tasks; and this is something we must learn to practice, just as the work in physiology and in anatomy, on the basis of objective concrete material, instead of just thinking and talking.

We must establish the habit of scrutinizing the facts and factors in their bearing on the life of any person under consideration. It is certainly not mere physiology. It is felt and remembered and anticipated and thought of in settings for which physiology does not have any terms, and for which it does not cultivate adequate terms, whereas we have no difficulty in using the hundreds of terms to be found in our dictionaries dealing with human life and per- formances and discriminations, desires and aversions, felt as our own and those of others or of all of us, but in a way to be treated as we treat fractions, with obligatory reference to the person described and describable in terms of a specific life record serving as the denominator of each fraction. No pertinent fact would be exactly the same thing in different periods of the life of the same person, not to speak of their meaning in different persons. This requires experiences with both facts and methods. There is so much of it so lightly handled and experienced and performed that in one's untrained moods one learns to pass by every morning the news of a few murders and some gloomy events of mismanaged finances, and the ruthless doings and undoings of untold numbers of people, enough to make us callous and inclined to treat even our own share without sufficient care of detail. To cultivate sound discriminating attention to human nature and human facts and doings and experi- ences is our job. And this requires supervised practice and not mere "thinking" and reading and talking.

Yet, it is just this kind of functioning which we may have to review, be it in the reconstruction of the picture of success or failure, which we usually call by the results without detail, such as the flunking of an examination without attention to the pertinent preparatory lapses; or our running into a nest of syphilis with hardly more than a "606" in the mind of a physician. We must learn to turn to where vital things happen, where they have their beginnings and developments. And this is not so simple, as we can readily see when we ask somebody, or try ourselves, to describe the human facts and to understand what has happened and what would be necessary for the event to repeat itself—or to be prevented or changed.

How many of us could give a really useful and searching and telling and usable description of what happens in a tantrum of a child, or in a mood of boredom that leads a person to drink, or to where he catches syphilis or ruins his chances with a job or comes to commit suicide? We are accustomed to mention these things for scolding or comment or for giving advice and preaching; but who renders them in a way which could be of use in the processes of prevention and understanding and making the events unnecessary and unlikely and others preferable and effective? Out of one hundred patients who come to the physician we realize that at least forty come with complaints that must be scrutinized for a larger setting—for what we term mental—if they are to be treated for what they actually are, as incidents to conditions which can only be described in terms of life, or events, of performances and neglects, of dissimulation and little insidious and sometimes morbid ways of directing attention away from where the real troubles are going on, the dissatisfactions, the unhappiness in a home, the distrust of one's security and one's health, apt to be covered up under a desire to blame something harmless for which one might get a remedy and some comfort even if one did not go to the source. To reconstruct the real events without the now-fashionable months of costly searching in an unconscious, we must have experience with actual life, with facts and factors that play their role in these hindrances to human comfort and efficiency and happiness and in resources of natural betterment. The bulk of disturbers do not make the front page of our newspapers, but we must know them and know where to put our finger for timely understanding and management. When we hear a physician give an account, we want it to be direct and better than that of the untrained layman.

It is natural enough that physicians prefer to deal with what saves them the trouble of such concerns. They are trained to work with what can be given a distinguishing name and treated with a prescription. They have trained the public to expect that. But that will not stand muster any longer. There was a time when there was but one Richard Cabot. Today there are many such men who are ready to betray our foibles. And there are huge forces of false education at work. Many patients and many normals prefer a well-advertised and unblushing promising quack medicine or recommended procedure to a Latin prescription or to plain advice; they look to what they think they can understand, to the chiropractor and the osteopath, who pounce on the spine to relieve "the pressure on nerves" and save one from endless rehearsals with inexperienced physicians of what consists largely of dissimulation of the plain realities. A great deal of what is wanted is plain life experience for which it is not necessary to reach for costly analyses. The first foundation is not psychiatry; it is trained commonsense and is needed in all work with man. That the psychiatrist proposes to assume the task of teaching this field comes from the fact that to know the range of the normal one does well also to know the less normal; but one does not need to begin with stories of bankruptcy and crime to get a wholesome picture of the demands of ordinary life and the bulk of what can be bungled so as to lead to trouble.

We do not at once narrow ourselves down to a course of "medical psychology" and consideration only of the extraordinary or what may hold for the other but would have nothing to do with the average and one's own self. We base our discussions and concrete work on what is observed as happening in concrete personality-studies and observations and doings of specific persons, to be described and used in the terms which will touch what we actually find and use and see used.

The difficulty with some students is that they are too erudite and preoccupied with their special panaceas of science and mechanistic elementalism. The difficulty of others lies in sheer indifference. But there are those who want to get out of a tangle of uncertainties and like to get their own house in order. It is not only the psychologists who have all sorts of schools, which Dr. F. M. R. Walshe terms the fifty-seven varieties in his discussion of the training of students, but there are also all kinds of prejudices and blunderings in the other sciences. To have but a modicum of work with a human biography, with the working out of a few of the essentials determining the life of the day or year or one's job or one's habits and urges, will not only do no harm but can be kept close to what everybody can control and try out and correct in the process if it is ineffective or disturbing or a mere complication. The student will be the better off for being familiar with the most essential sets of facts and terms and concepts, even if the terms and concepts are those of ordinary life and experience, supplemented here and there by a perhaps not as commonly used expression but one meeting the requirements and saving a lot of blundering.

If we happen to use "ergasia" for particular items of function and behavior because behavior does not have a plural nor a satisfactory adjective, we do no more than every other science does that looks for telling terms. The root *erg*—the Greek word for work—is known to every educated person and is used not only in physics but when we talk of energy as being the inherent working force.

When I talk of mentation instead of mind, anyone with some sense for language feels that I talk of action and function and not of a substance.

When I talk of subject-organization, I mean the person in action at any specific moment or in any specific situation.

When I refer to personality-organization, I immediately think of the many component traits and assets and possibly also handicaps that constitute a person.

When I speak of "person" instead of merely a mind, I mean a biological entity, with a name and life history and inner continuity and actual record, an entity spread over a lifetime between conception and death and natural periods and phases and rhythms of action and rest, wakefulness and sleep, phases of maximal fitness and states of repair.

When I speak of particular performances, I know that each one has a history, an apprenticeship, an accumulation of experience and preparedness for use.

We lose no time over puzzling about the nature of consciousness, when we take it scrupulously and with its real content as we find it and cease talking about something devoid of facts. It is the continuity of the flow of our functioning at high pitch or at low pitch, and we take the facts as we should take to the study of the fluids after we speak of wetness or any other word ending in "ness" as the sign of its special meaning.

When we emphasize one or another special component of function, we want to know the role it plays, as well as the condition under which it recurs, and ways it operates and the results—the means of control and modification.

We group the actions that count and the emotions that tend to regulate them and the data of intelligence that give differentiation and selection, and we view the items for the sense they have in an actual life-picture. It is their sense or meaning that is so specific in the personality-function, and so we come to consider psycho-biology as the study of the meaning-function in the process of life.

If, then, we have the habit and, perhaps, a need of looking further, beyond, at the beginning and at the end, and the ultimate goals, there is no need to worry lest we might have to neglect the soul and the factors constituting some of our most cherished directing lines. There is nothing in these views and concepts that would hinder including ourselves in the broad sets of family, community, state, and the continuity of generations and of their civilization, culture, art, philosophy, and religion.

II

Social Aspects

The First World War advertised psychiatry, with mixed blessings. The war both sped up and diverted its course.

Faced with the task of maintaining the health of a gigantic army, the medical profession was heavily drained of personnel, and an elaborate military psychiatric service was established to screen recruits and cope with mental casualties. This brought wholesome collaboration between neurologists and psychiatrists in a lasting blend of neuropsychiatry. There were other developments: the enlistment of psychologists and social workers in a foundation for new community service, the public's awareness of so-called shellshock victims and their need for separate treatment, and public recognition of psychiatry as a servant not exclusively in asylum practice.

But the war brought also a breakdown of conventions in a feverish quest for freedom. A seemingly gay revolt took place against represssion. Popular fancy snatched phrases from psychoanalysis and waged a postwar war on "suppressed desires." Psychopathology came to mean a Freudianism whose promise of emotionally healthier life was borne on a lusty literary wave. A new psychology arose, spelling sex, salesmanship, and success. It sidetracked interest in general psychiatric research, in the supposedly hopeless psychoses, and in controlled hospital psychiatry, for the sake of more alluring expectations in the reform of sex life, family life, and child guidance. Medical leaders and philanthropists alike failed to support facilities for rigid scientific research and

449

creative work—objectives temporarily eclipsed by work in "more popular but little controllable spheres," Adolf Meyer reported.

The great gain was "a wholly unprecedented burst of dynamic interest in man and in the role of the 'mental' and human factors." Now the functioning of the human organism as a personality was in focus. "The specific contribution of American psychiatry, the growing understanding of mental disorders in terms of *life problems*, proved a great help and it was also recognized that work with soldiers and ex-soldiers would be bound to be inadequate without a safe setting in the civil organization of our communities with the help of the right kind of social work." [31]

Dr. Thomas W. Salmon, chief psychiatric consultant to the American Expeditionary Forces, told Dr. William L. Russell, the director of Bloomingdale Hospital, that Meyer's influence had been at work in France. Salmon said that a New York State psychiatrist in army service usually could be identified at headquarters by the character of his reports. (Meyer himself had not been called upon by the government to render war work.)

In the years that followed, Meyer's activities were reminiscent of those of his teacher Forel. He gave much thought to social problems and to organized groups grappling with them, for medicine and sociology were interdependent and both must make the community their central concern; but hospital work was his base. A model community hospital was his ideal for service, for teaching, and for research. He had long advocated partitioning states into hospital districts, each with its mental-health centers and dispensaries growing out of local organization. The centers would work with the parent institution, but without being coordinated into robots.

This idea was carried out to some extent in Baltimore. Before the opening of the Phipps Clinic, Meyer had encouraged the Maryland Psychiatrical Society in a movement of "extramural psychiatry." Dr. William Burgess Cornell was given charge of an office supported by state hospitals and the Sheppard and Enoch Pratt Hospital, to provide after-care for patients and parolees and to handle cases referred by the city's social-service agencies. Preventive work was also done. Later, members of Phipps's social department visited patients' homes before their discharge, in order to pave the way to readjustment. In 1915, when the National Conference of Charities and Corrections met, Meyer outlined his community plan; and ten years later, when it convened as the National Conference of Social Work, he repeated his plea—but with awareness of the current mood of individualism and the "temporary revolt against organization of the type I looked forward to."

The emergence of a special class of psychiatric social workers as a war product, sponsored by the Smith College School for Social Work, and the postwar switch of the mental-hygiene movement into the narrowed field of child guidance and delinquency, precipitated a rivalry between hospital psychiatry and independent clinics. These clinics operated with a standard unit of psychiatrist, psychologist, and social workers. Meyer felt they were running ahead of rigid checking-up and could not flourish scientifically out of contact with psychiatry's main stream.

It will never do to focus too exclusively on the child at the expense of interest in the psychiatry and hygiene of the adult in whose hands the fate of the younger generation lies. There has to be an appropriate distribution of attention to wherever disorders develop and can be reached.[32]

Hence he stood for leadership by hospitals serving definite districts. "The hospitals which receive the more difficult cases will always give us in the end a means of checking up on the actual attainments and the economic and medical values of the various efforts." Sufficiently staffed, each hospital could spare one or more physicians to make regular visits to community centers and see cases and causes in developmental stages, in contrast to their own institutionalized cases whose personal characteristics were usually smothered by the pattern of an advanced disorder. These men would train their eyes to see many features that transcended the importance of hospital classifications. They would acquire familiarity with the community's recoverable and nonrecoverable eruptions and thereby gain a safe guide.

Of course, it was desirable to develop consultation centers in courts, schools, churches, jails, employment and vocational bureaus, and even advisory stations for child guidance and family relations apart from hospitals, where the goal was "a general conscience about health . . . with less dependence on teaching by advertisement of quacks or by the equally extreme self-protective pessimism of the general medical profession." For these duties the modern social worker was better oriented and better trained than the average physician, according to Meyer.

But he advised social workers that they could learn more from normal life than from "dime-museum oddities." The trouble with intellectuals and average mortals was that they took their views of life-functioning largely from the abnormal and the unusual. This was a dilettante approach to knowledge of health, unfortunately the method used by "certain therapeutic cults and especially by psychoanalysis."

Life is not simply a by-product of sex yearnings and outcroppings of a repressed unconscious, Meyer told another conference on social work. In his own patients he looked for "what is normal and working," for the capacity to use their assets, more so than the overspecialized psychopathologist did. "In training social workers I should frankly espouse the task of looking in each personality-study and case record for the plain, actual personal problems." Psychoanalytic generalizations had best be put on a pragmatic basis. "I for one shall try to make more and more convincing and attractive the study of the accessible facts and their use in contrast to that of the exotic and largely dogmatic." [33]

The great calamity of the nineteen twenties was the loss of a sense of restful satisfaction; in its place had come an unending craving for stimulation and excitement. Meyer sought to nurture a capacity for "constructive composure," which he defined as "putting oneself together in rest for new activity and new responsiveness." He bade social workers steer the way to a less haphazard or theory-ridden existence; to help people to "find their place in nature and in the social fabric . . . to cultivate cause for confidence rather than juvenile chafing and suspicion of interference where we really just want the right kind of order and self-regulation; to attain poise and to attain satisfaction under a creative rather than violent revolutionary regime—that is what most of us yearn for at heart." [33]

The era carried its banner of rebellion with the sanction of a pseudoscientific edict against repression of instincts and drives. Two conventions of the Progressive Education Association afforded Meyer openings to penetrate the fog of misconception. He admitted: "Psychiatry no doubt shares the responsibility for the present-day revolution against traditional principles of human conduct and education." But the notion was wrong that all repression was hazardous, that repression was bound to destroy genius, deaden initiative, and even lead to insanity; that repression was at the bottom of all psychogenic nervous and mental disorders. "I showed on the ground of the principles of science that it was largely inadequate choice, inadequate decision, and inadequate elimination of what had to be rejected that made most of the trouble." [34]

He heartily sympathized with the progressive educators' program of natural growth without forcing, "provided that the essentially social nature of the child is recognized and the compatibility of freedom and discipline is acknowledged"—and he reminded them that the word "discipline" came from the same root as "disciple." Extremists, "artists in the matter of protest," were in vogue, impatient with all fundamentals. They obscured the necessity for participation in responsibility and for a give-and-take between children and adults. The best benefit from the pioneer schools, in a world "infinitely harder and more complex than anything our own generation had to face," was the development of plastic preparedness for an efficient, serviceable life in the midst of many problems.

I have never been satisfied with the attempt to relate all the troubles of adult life too exclusively to the troubles of child life. Commonsense tells us that in the adult we deal with many new functions and many new problems and new difficulties which we should treat on their own ground. In the end, the guidance of youth has to be undertaken by adults who are often groping and in need of setting their own house in order.[35]

This brought Meyer to study maturity as a measure of dependability, of growing ripeness for a specific course of action, and of ability to adapt one's changing self to the changing scene. "A great deal of every biography is played upon a stage beyond the individual's control." A balance must be struck between one's own nature and the demands and opportunities of the world. "Rise to the occasion" was an apt expression.

Only if we have a sense of the meaning of maturity for all ages and stages of life can we form a true picture of the particular maturity we call adulthood, without which emancipation becomes just a claim to a "bill of rights" with little understanding of basic conditions and responsibilities. Education must some day furnish more adequate qualifications to every phase of life and every grade of maturity.[36]

In the nineteen thirties he still saw pressure in some educational circles to cultivate premature independence and burden the child's capacity for choice and self-direction. Overloading, no less than thwarting, could cripple a personality. And why foster futile self-assertion any more than excessive submission? Why lead children into the basically selfish pattern of overconscientiousness?

We are prone to forget that emotional growth does not always keep pace with intellectual growth. . . . There is a wide gulf between the full life a child may live within his own sphere and the overshadowing round of temptations thrown in by eager or thoughtless adults. The ideal is preparation for the eventual assumption of responsibility, rather than for indifference and those evasions which come from overstimulation. The capacity for responsibility spells freedom, and freedom cannot thrive without responsibility.[36]

In the groping of that period, tradition was abandoned before new understanding was on a firm footing, and Meyer objected.

We are just now in the midst of an attempt to replace old authoritative dependabilities by an obsession with popularized anthropology and ethnology and a preoccupation with sexuality. . . . We still interpret life in terms of right or wrong, of guilt, remorse, fear, threat, and the legalistic attitude based essentially on precedent. All this is lacking in prevention except as punishment acts as a deterrent. Scientific interpretations, on the other hand, are couched in part in terms of dream analysis and the "unconscious" or in terms of the supposedly obligatory stages of development which must be absolved so as to avoid "fixation"; or in conceptions of the personality as working under various bribes, corrections of conflicts, and false compensations; or through a new therapy which explains and digests experiences by reconsideration and reexperience.[36]

Especially in the realm of child guidance Meyer cautioned against premature invoking of the Freudian concept and borrowing trouble. The essence of this work was objective observation of the child's performance "without our putting stereotyped meanings in it." Get a solid, socialized background, he urged. "Only when one knows that status is one in a position to know to what extent one wants to get closer to the child." [37] There was too much concern with pathological cases. Meyer was skeptical about the wisdom of letting teachers develop an attitude of "sniffing and snooping" instead of open-mindedness; for teachers could give, after all, only inadequate and biased data such as constituted psychiatric records of the beginning of the century—"largely the complaints of the attendants as to the annoyances they were put to by the presence of patients. That is not hygiene." [38]

Crediting research by Dr. William Healy in the Chicago Juvenile Court with revealing the close relation between mental conflict and misconduct, Meyer called for a broader base. (Some workers limited mental hygiene to infantile sexuality.) Investigators paid insufficient attention to the child-producers. Glib reports on "successes" could only be evaluated properly twenty-five years later, whereas the need now was scrutiny also of adult life and real centers of sound, exemplary work.

When the National Committee for Mental Hygiene gathered in New York to celebrate its first quarter-century, Meyer was delighted to observe that its vision was not confined to a narrow field of exploitation. The direction of the Committee's activities had been put into the hands of people engaged in psychiatry instead of being left to persons trained in "a mind-shy science" or to "plausible propagandists." There had been too much reiteration of "uninformed pessimism," too much of a backdoor approach instead of a study of man as part of nature, "too much hiding of one's unfamiliarity by claims that psychiatry is not mature enough and that it is not scientific unless it limits itself to the concepts and methods that the traditional sciences use." [39]

The National Committee was beginning its second quarter-century with new zeal, new goals, a growing understanding in the humanities and objective science, Meyer happily noted. The new leaders realized that the study of nature was sure to be incomplete

when all the sap of spiritual reality and vital biological meaning is ignored in a mechanistic-statistical dogmatism or withdrawn into unassimilated supernaturalism. We cannot so divide human nature. Our souls have bodies and our bodies have souls—or should we rather not say: Our souls are live bodies, and our lives are our souls? [39]

By 1940 mental hygiene had come to face the enormous problem of promoting the health of personal functioning in a world shaken by another war. "Fear can no longer throw the whole of humanity into a huddle of abject defeat." (Meyer was elected president of the National Committee that year.) Psychiatry had risen to the occasion in 1917, and now he said:

Today it is much more than an army that concerns us. It is the sense of security of mankind that is at stake, and it is our share and our duty, to contribute to the sanity and security of our own people. [40]

ORGANIZING THE COMMUNITY

From "Where Should We Attack the Problem of the Prevention of Mental Defect and Mental Disease?" read by Dr. Meyer at the 1915 Baltimore meeting of the National Conference of Charities and Correction, Proceedings, 42:298 (1915); *and from "Individualism and the Organization of Neuropsychiatric Work in a Community," read at the 1925 Denver meeting of the National Conference of Social Work,* Proceedings, 52d annual session, p. 444.

As the distinctive ideal I am anxious to emphasize the need of attacking the work in small enough units of communities and neighborhoods, of making the *attack at the source,* by community organization in addition to legislation, and by making the best use of our available opportunities in these directions.

First, the existing agencies and their proper use.

1. The hospitals. A number of our states have today a very elaborate and efficient state-hospital system. In the minds of the general public these hospitals are still asylums—that is to say, places to which people are sent with more or less certainty that they will either die soon or stay there for the rest of their lives.

It is high time that the community should recognize that a hospital's most vital function is curative and constructive, and that the principle of segregation is not the leading issue. About twenty per cent of those who are admitted are returned home in their previous working capacity, and twenty-five per cent more able at least to live at home under protection. It should be made clear to the people and to the legislatures that these hospitals must be located and officered in keeping with the aim of constructive and curative work.

A modern hospital must get together the facts with which to reconstruct the patient's life. It must be in touch with the patient's home and be helpful to the family in the attempt to create a wholesome environment for the returning patient. This inevitably means the organization of social work and home visitation, and help to the heredity-tainted family; it also means that the staffs of the hospitals must be chosen from men devoted to constructive and creative work, not merely to administrative interests; and that there should be enough physicians actually to do the work and to bring it to the point of efficiency and success beyond the hospital walls.

2. Our second type of agency is the *dispensaries.* Either in connection with hospitals or independent, they must make it easy for the patient to get advice for home treatment. The ideal arrangement would be to have in connection with a dispensary at least one physician able to visit homes, assisted by social workers trained for investigation and for giving guidance to the patient and to the family and social unit.

3. In some communities it has been found best to organize special *mental-hygiene organizations,* using the available dispensaries as far as possible, doing emergency work and work in the form of after-care and placing of patients returned from hospitals, and serving as advisers in the decision as to where to place patients and preventive cases or where to direct them.

4. The fourth already-existing agency is the *school system.* It is true that most of the school physicians are trained mainly to discover infectious diseases and possibly the defects of various organs, such as sense organs, but more and more attention is being paid to the mental defects and to the disorders of the personality and of behavior. How much there is to be done in this field is clearly shown by the survey in one of the school districts of Baltimore made by Dr. Charles Macfie Campbell, a survey which brought out as the principal result the fact that at least ten per cent of the children are clearly not fitted for any public-school curriculum, and that another fifteen per cent or twenty per cent should have a curriculum more especially adapted to the endowment of the pupil. What vocational bureaus can do in connection with schools has no doubt been brought out elsewhere.

5. In a few cities *juvenile courts* begin to have as adjuncts trained psychopathologists whose work it is to study the mental condition of the children brought there. Prisons and jails should be centers of preventive work; the judges would be more even-handed in their decisions if the prison officials aimed more to utilize the period of detention of the prisoners to the best advantage for some sort of reconstructive work. Punishment, in order to attain its end in correction, should be punishment which *does* correct. For genuine preventive work along these lines we shall have to wait until the legal profession and the public accept the fact that a good many individuals are best served by prolonged detention or permanent care of some kind, since every relapse, or at least every repetition of offense, is really a blot on the efficiency of justice and often the result of a wanton assignment of responsibility to persons unable to carry the burden.

6. It would be wrong to pass over the interesting work which is being done by those *boards which control the issuance of working permits* for minors under the age required by the child labor laws; further, the activity of many of the constructive workers in the *charity organizations,* and no doubt also the work of *church organizations.* I have heard it stated repeatedly of late that since the wider use of dispensaries for mental cases, the point of view of charity workers has changed considerably, and that a great deal of what appeared as mere "cussedness" is becoming more and more a matter of investigation and of examination by dispensary and other physicians.

Now let us briefly review the special causes against which we should fight. It is in one respect a comfort, although to those concerned a matter of distress, that mental disorders depend to a very large extent on heredity and predisposition of the stock. This is significant not only for eugenics but also for the proper education of children and the choice of their careers and the need of hygienic precautions. Preventive work must not be too vague and diffused. It weakens the movement to preach too much to those who do not need it. Preventive work must have its places of attack; and the first places are the families that through experience with mental disorders have had their interest awakened in averting trouble for other members of the family.

Finding the right level of occupation and aspiration is the great difficulty in the hereditary cases and, naturally, equally so in those whose trouble is not necessarily on a hereditary foundation. Too many people aspire to positions, or are *driven into* positions, which may be too hard for them to fill; but a certain amount of success is as much a need for our health as our food and clothing and shelter. Those who are trying to obtain occupation for the handicapped and for the slightly defective realize the great obligation resting upon the community to create respectable and satisfying opportunities for the handicapped, and for those not able to face the full struggle of life. Any civilization can offer jobs to the strong worker; it takes a well-organized civilization to take care of those less favored.

From the difficulties of finding one's level we turn to the more specific factor, that of alcoholism. Alcoholism has been minimized by some and even praised by some as a help in the elimination of the unfit. Here, too, perhaps there has been too much talk when it was not greatly needed. It is important that the public should know that the frequency of mental disorders due to alcohol differs very much among various nationalities and the several strata of the population. In the much maligned state of Maine there is absolutely no doubt that alcoholic insanity is relatively much less frequent than in any other state that I know of; and when we study the nationalities of any one community, as I did in Massachusetts and as Dr. George H. Kirby did for New York, we find that those nationalities that indulge largely in the social habits of alcoholism or in ordinary use of alcohol recruit the largest numbers of cases of alcoholic insanity in our hospitals. The percentage varies from less than one per cent to thirty-nine per cent of all the admissions from the various nationalities. Alcoholic insanity is very rare among the Hebrews, who, for reasons worth studying, furnish a model standard; it is most frequent in nationalities accustomed to strong liquors. There is an average of about twenty to twenty-five per cent of alcoholic insanity among the male admissions in wine- and beer-drinking communities.

Another fifteen per cent of the patients are undoubtedly accounted for by syphilis, which presents a gigantic problem from the point of view of prevention. Large numbers of individuals, by no means hereditarily predisposed, get swept away in the best periods of their lives by general paresis, which during the last twenty years has been clearly demonstrated to be a syphilitic disease of the brain. That over thirty per cent of our patients have serious difficulties with the adjustment of their sex life is a further reason why sex hygiene should be as broadly conceived as possible.

Let us now turn to the constructive program. Some of the specific items just mentioned are general problems which all social workers have to wrestle with. Any effort to fight alcoholism will help us as much as it will help the criminologist and the charity worker, because it is not merely an individual problem but really one of communities. What I feel most keenly is the necessity of organizing in our communities societies for total abstinence, to which it would be possible to join individuals who are recovering from the warning effects of disease. Unless recovering individuals join groups of normally living persons maintaining standards of total abstinence and providing social compensations for drinking habits, it is not often that they will resist for any length of time the attractions of alcohol and of destructive social companionships.

Constructive work for the prevention of syphilis is another issue of prophylaxis which inevitably meets far more than merely psychiatric needs. Even with the most optimistic conception of our ability to treat syphilis at the present time, there is always a great possibility of the lingering of the infection so that prevention here continues to mean ever so much more than cure. As far as I can see, the close association of syphilis with commercialized vice points out very clearly what is needed. It puts upon us the obligation of eradicating all those attempts of the solution of the prostitution problem which hold up to the young the idea of public sanction of commercialized vice, and which, especially in the form of segregation, form a permanent advertisement and an official exhibit of the supposed necessity of "wild oats" and promiscuity. More than anything else, a more serious attitude of our adult male population will be necessary to bring about a reform.

In the ultimate analysis, both the prevention of alcoholism and the prevention of syphilis have their greatest ally in the improvement of the program of education. I have great confidence in the teachers being able to solve their problem if they are well trained and promoted according to merit, and given adequate support by the community. I have often felt that probably our community would be better off with regard to the school system if every citizen made it his duty to visit a school once a year and to spend at least half a day there. Without such firsthand acquaintance few of us realize what admirable work is being done and how much more support the community ought to give to the school system. Let us encourage teachers to teach pupils to do what they *can* do, both in work and in recreation and rest, instead of making them the half-obedient servants of a system often killing the native interests and inculcating habits of serving time, rather than doing their work efficiently.

Let us learn something from the study of the frequently perfectly normal truant and other revolutionary spirits of the school age. And let us get over the notion that only the bad pupil needs attention. A thing that is less often thought of is the fact that the so-called "very good pupil," the extreme at the good end of the scale, is very much more likely to be endangered by mental disease and nervous states than the frankly and outspokenly bad and happy-go-lucky child. School excuses, headaches, and attempts to get relieved from various studies ought to be subjected to the attention of the school physician much oftener than is the case at the present time. The requests for dispensation from various courses are often the first signs of a need of attention.

On all these points legislation is but a partial help. Statewide efforts become dilute. They are essential to make activity permissive, but the work ultimately must become intensive in the real place of attack, in the natural units of community life.

Without an improvement of the principles of the grown-up

population we must not expect the young to change by mere school training. Children learn more from what they see and hear than from what they are made to do at school. Without an improvement in the sense of the personal responsibility of each individual for community conditions, many reforms will be changes in style rather than changes of heart.

In such a matter as the prevention of mental troubles due to heredity, I maintain that although we know that a large percentage of mental cases have a history of heredity, there is not a sufficiently decisive body of facts established for us to be justified in making sweeping rules against the marriage of those who have had mental trouble either themselves or in their families. Indeed, we might thereby run the risk of doing a grave injustice to the race as well as of infringing on the rights of the individual. We can do justice to the individual as well as to the race by making some practical conditions for such individuals to marry and have children: if they can feel and give to their own sense and conscience reasonable assurance of giving a family of four children a wholesome, healthy environment and education. If any unfavorable heredity should crop out, it would be highly probable that healthy and capable brothers and sisters would be able to assure the protection and care of the problematic individual. Eugenics, in its present development, has no right to attempt to enforce a stronger negative policy than that. If it does so, it does so at the risk of depriving the race of individuals who are a benefit to it. I certainly should not like to miss some of the brothers and sisters of certain patients from this globe, nor even some of the patients.

But I cannot emphasize too strongly the obligation to refrain from offspring, resting upon those individuals who are incapable of giving a reasonably good environment and opportunities of education to a family of four children. That this cuts out the sanction of marriage of imbeciles, most epileptics, and most psychotic persons and individuals constitutionally below par, is self-evident; and the principle formulated in this way has the advantage of pointing directly to some crucial measure of practical efficiency without any harping on pseudoscience, of which so many reformers and many patients know more than of plain sense.

For the sake of concreteness and clearness in our aims, let me point first to our peculiar difficulties, which suggest some radical efforts such as I do not consider beyond our reach. Our American communities are probably the most individualistic aggregates of population. Mostly descendants from constitutional dissenters and nonconformists, temperamentally jealous of government, we form communities divided from top to bottom into the most individualistic groups. In the field of leading ideals, in religion and ethics, we seem to be as far as ever from solidarity and unity; we seem to have more hope in the salvation of our souls than confidence in the ways and hopes of our neighbor, unless he pledges himself to our own dogma of exclusive salvation. I know that in a recent gathering many ministers from the same district of the city did not know each other. What community spirit can we expect then, if this holds for the heads of what should be the most social and the most large-hearted of our social organizations?

The next grouping, that of citizenship of civic interest, we have allowed to become a matter of concern of the professional politician, who has about the same ideal as many a lawyer who frankly cares little for justice and principle, but mainly for winning his case. Our standards, punctilious in dress and fashion and table manners, are outspokenly individualistic and deficient in common ideals and solidarity, in the very essentials of religious, civic, business and intellectual life. The one common principle seems to be the primitive scheme of boss system and one-man power, which makes one person responsible for good or for bad and releases all other individuals from further responsibility. Under these conditions it is somewhat difficult to think of a utopia such as I insist on dreaming about. My hope lies in bringing together that which *is* together: manageable groups and districts with enough common interests to create a community spirit, fostered not only in the head of the boss whom we see hailed as the chief or turned into a scapegoat, but permeating the district in the form of customs, standards, and principles and ideals easily enough attainable to become the dominant rule.

The districting of our cities is at present carried out in different ways for different purposes. As far as I know, the political wards and the police- and fire-department districts, the school districts, the criminal- and juvenile-court districts, the districts of the charity organizations, all are apt to follow different lines of division. The ideal will have to be an organization so made that as many districts as possible may form reasonably complete households within themselves. Such an arrangement would make it possible for more people actually to realize what the *community* has to make itself responsible for, and it might become practicable to have district problems, district committees and district meetings, such as the political parties have long been shrewd enough to maintain in their wards.

However much of a dreamer I may be, I pride myself on having seen a good many of my dreams come true. Can you see the wards or district organization? With a district building instead of the police station, with policemen as constructive workers rather than as watchdogs of their beats, a district center with reasonably accurate records of the facts needed for orderly work; among the officers, a district health officer, and a district school committee and a district improvement and recreation committee, a district tax committee, a district charity or civic-work committee, a tangible expression of what the district stands for.

With a system of helpfulness and fairness and true democracy, avoiding bureaucracy as well as militarism and its primitive residual, the boss system, this country can safely go on developing methods tolerant of individuality and yet effective in its essential purposes.

There is not a solitary line of preventive and constructive work in which we do not sooner or later run up against insufficiency of community work, of registration, of collaboration, and even of mere acquaintance of those who should work together. Over and over again we become guilty of the common mistake of every good worker being given a bigger field than can possibly be covered. I long to get the means and the privilege of trying a few mental-hygiene districts, no doubt best shaped, as things are now subdivided, so as to have the school of the district as the center of attention; with a specially trained physician and two or three helpers living in the district, without any trumpets and without legislation, as far as possible inconspicuous, but charged to obtain the friendship and cooperation of the teachers, the playground workers, the district workers of various charity organizations and the physicians and ministers of the region. They would have to know their districts as a social fabric and they can do so if their districts are not too large; they must become helpers of individuals and families when they are in a mood to listen. The physician had best be chosen who can be acceptable as school physician, able to work in a quiet and inconspicuous manner, and devoting all his time to this wonderful opportunity without entering into competition with local physicians.

The work may cost $6,000 or $7,000 a year for the district until it can be handed on to local representatives, who may not be so privileged and may be less expensive, but who can use the results of the trained pioneers. It is work which does not pretend to make unnecessary the city-wide and state-wide movements; but which will want to do justice to its own local job. The use of dispensaries and hospitals and centralized helps like vocational bureaus which cannot be duplicated everywhere gets a local reinforcement and safe soil, and it becomes possible to implant in the locality that which we are too often content to put on the posters of our mental-hygiene exhibits and on letterheads. Sound knowledge and actual performance are, after all, the best ground on which science and practical life join hands.

When will our intelligent leaders begin to realize the agony to which we psychiatrists are put when we have to watch, too often helpless, the long illness and frequently the irresistible fading-out or perversion of human minds, sometimes in the wives and husbands and children of our nearest friends and sometimes members of our own family; hampered on all sides, always with half-officered hospitals, half-trained staffs, half-equipped laboratories; and less than half-organized communities? When will some sensible concentration of effort become possible which will allow us to say: Here is something like an agricultural station; here is a small community doing the best that can be done today and trying to determine in a quiet, unostentatious way the value of the various claims in vogue, so that those who can do but little can at least be guided in the choice of what will do most good?

A kind of rear-guard psychiatry is what we have been teaching physicians and medical students up to the present, rear-guard defense, and defense in fortified asylums. Today we occasionally hear such words as "pre-paresis" and "pre-dementia praecox"; and I hope the time will come when we shall attack various predisposing factors, not merely because we want to head off war, but because we have higher constructive ideals of peace than that of keeping the enemy cowed. There is plenty of room on this globe for many kinds of people. The art of community-building begins with the cultivation of community centers and community ideals, for the small as well as for the big units. And just as I hope the police work will pass more and more from the level of scouring the community for misdeeds to that of constructive community work, so I hope psychiatry will pass more and more from being merely our patient's attendant to the work of teaching people how to find their levels and how to help in bringing a constructive tolerance, and in establishing a constructive habit of wholesome life for community and individual.

Where, then, shall we attack the problem of prevention? By reinforcing the existing helps, the hospitals, the dispensaries, the special agencies; by adapting the methods to the needs of the pupils; but, above all, by starting a quiet work of community organization, building up manageable district units, and by inspiring a constructive atmosphere among people who can know and understand each other and who have common needs. Let us find the individual at home and the chances for concrete work at the source from which both the wealth and the misery of the nation flow.

We are at times made to believe that all our mental-hygiene work and effort aims largely at the prevention of "insanity and crime," just as the early advocates of psychopathic hospitals made it look as if, through the creation of a psychopathic hospital in each state, the existing state-hospital care would then be made less expensive and perhaps in part unnecessary. To be sure, early work means a heading-off of some of the disastrous depth of aberration and deviation, and much unnecessary blundering. But the chief goal is much more direct: it offers prompter and more and more enlightened help to both patient and family and the community in respect to really new problems, largely left to themselves before; it is a direct service to the positive needs and opportunities of the community in behalf of what I reemphasize as health, happiness, efficiency, and social adaptation.

With the espousal of mental hygiene a totally new conception of problems thus comes before us, many of them problems concerning which the older generation was held in line by rules from above—by rules of authority and tradition, of law, and of strict group regulation, whereas today the individual claims his right to his own decisions and to freedom from domination and from the hard old principle of "bend or break." It does not do much good to debate which regime is better. We have them both, and rigorous scientific statistical methods will some day tell us what mixtures will do best for the various temperaments. Mixtures they will be.

In the days of our grandparents and parents, the measure of everything seemed to lie in tradition and in obedience to more or less unreasoned and undisputed standards of custom and undisputed spirituality upheld by the culture of the day. When explanation and change of behavior were looked for, it was only rarely that one thought of calling a physician. Today many issues that were formerly simple problems of morality and custom have become issues the individual wants to settle for himself or herself, but also issues in which the individual should be able to look to the physician as a helper and adviser, because the physician thinks and works in terms of study of cause and effect, and not in terms of tradition and authority. Medical help in life problems may have started with tonsils and adenoids, but soon developed also regard for sleeping habits and for emotional maladjustments and the like.

A number of other developments conspired to bring home the dynamic-genetic trend of things. In the education of children we hear little today of "breaking the will" and blind obedience; and in the management of labor new principles of maintenance of happiness and efficiency came into prominence, no doubt to quite an extent feeding on, and in turn producing, new conceptions of philosophy and morality and biology in general. The example of economists like Carlton Parker, and of educationists like Colonel Francis W. Parker and John Dewey, and a growing confidence in commonsense, and perhaps also in modern psychopathology, put more and more emphasis on the inner needs of the individual and far less on the necessity of merely conforming to traditional authority-determined patterns. The child and the adolescent were ever more encouraged to develop confidence in their own nature. There is no doubt that with all this the retort "I can't help it" and "I can't change myself" became more and more general and also acceptable, or at least was condoned; excuses by heredity and by various external and internal influences began to count beside the traditional exclusive appeal to responsibility and obligation alone. The whole sense of discipline, that is, the ability to learn and to follow the leader, was perhaps too hastily reversed into a doctrine of mere growth and self-development.

However that may be, the problem of happiness and success is becoming recognized to a greater extent as a problem of hygiene or health, and not merely one of conformity to the teachings of tradition and goodness alone; moreover, hygiene is found to depend to an overwhelming extent upon the condition of the organism, heredity and eugenics, the proper nutrition and growth, the habit training—and not only on the acquisition of knowledge and of some practical resources, but also on the emotional attitude, the development of one's innate capacities; and a reasonable respect for the instinctive desires and tendencies. Not that we would claim that what we call hygiene should or could allow us to disregard all the wisdom of ages laid down in tradition. But many traditions, even when handed on under the authoritative stamp of revelation, have been found to have flaws and to profit from consideration and study, akin to the work or the problems of hygiene generally. Even the fundamentalist is willing to see imperfect, although sometimes very wise, attempts at hygiene in Deuteronomy, attempts which, with growing knowledge and insight, he has long adapted to new times.

With the habit of studying facts in manageable parts and not mainly as systems of philosophy and of dogma which had to be swallowed as wholes, more people have become confident of their own ability to form reasonable opinions. (We have there the same evolution as in the attack of the sciences of physics and chemistry on vitalism.) This same evolution and growth is what had, during the last 400 years, led to the formation of new groups of religious and social denominations, and to some extent to greater individuality, especially among the Nordic peoples. But most of the groups still are held together through the venerable bonds of revealed authority, and the criterion of "fitness to belong" with the elect remained, whether or not the individual was able to swallow the prescribed dose of forced belief and dogma. With the recent change the force of these influences has lessened tremendously, and it is actually up to modern mental hygiene to bring back on the new basis a new respect for a new spirituality and morality and conscience.

The question now arises: "How can we actually make good in such a situation? What is there that we can put at the disposal of the individual?"

Individualism has brought us a remarkable gain in frankness and also in a demand for consideration of personal rights and dignity.

The first point we have gained is an assurance of respect for individual differences and the abstaining from invidious comparisons. Not that we have reached perfection on this important point. Last year I heard one of our leading officials explain the selective distribution of immigrant labor, based on the principle that we need foreigners to do the dirty work and to attend to the undesirable jobs. In any civilization there are all kinds of jobs adapted to all kinds of intelligences, and none so small or so big that it would not be honorable to anyone who does it honorably. It is a kind of snobbish reasoning that creates the reverse foolishness, the idea that a chance for a college education should be called the ideal for everybody. Why not stand for the good sense of fitness and respect for fitness?

Most people are interested in Binet-Simon tests of others—and in their own only if they come out well. To get these tests on a level of acceptability and real usefulness we have to show that we do not use them to label and brand people, but to give them the right kind of start, help, and guidance for fitness and happiness, constructively and in a spirit of helpfulness rather than for any condemnation or for an invidious classification of inferiorities.

It looks very much as if there were developing a tendency to accept the fact of difference between individuals with a less brutally competitive attitude. We learn to be more objective and thoughtful. The intelligence test is but one line of human evaluation. No matter how keenly we may favor the more intelligent types from a eugenic point of view, it is about time that we recognize that there are perfectly good and useful imbeciles and that it is the use, and not only the quantity, of the assets which decides individual desirability. Similarly, we see wide difference in the lines of sensitiveness and capacity to do various things, and with the proper thought and understanding we recognize greater possibilities of finding and using opportunities for the unusual, as well as the ordinary, make-up.

Similarly, it is again the helpfulness and resourcefulness of the investigator that will determine the acceptability of inquiry into any blundering, and the study of personality problems and the need of advice, according to whether it is handled in a spirit of superiority or of service.

All this constitutes a fundamental and necessary adjustment of attitude.

To advise anyone to see a psychiatrist is less and less like a charge of insanity; it is an occasion to take stock with the help of one with a wider range of experience, used not for incarceration, but for helpfulness toward one's best place and one's health, happiness, efficiency, and social adaptation. The *New Republic* recently [May 27, 1925] added insult to injury with its discourse on an imputation of "insanity" in the request by the President of Princeton University that the writer of a scurrilous article in the college paper retire or have himself examined by Dr. Paton. The President would no doubt have done better to investigate the problems of the student quietly before suppressing the paper, instead of allowing the examination by Dr. Paton to be turned into a quasi-punitive measure. But why should a progressive journal indulge in rehearsals of archaic, superannuated and incorrect associations with the obsolete word "insanity"?

In the face of all the difficulties, there is no doubt that increasing numbers of people are reaching out for help, perhaps not always with complete simplicity of purpose. All those of us who are sometimes consulted in connection with problems of marriage know very well that one is oftener consulted for corroboration of decisions already secrectly made, or for the corroboration of doubts which the one or the other has not the courage to utter, than with any genuine readiness to get a review of all the facts and to use them all for clearer thinking and clearer decision. There is an intrinsic tendency to favor the romance of the moment and to minimize the responsibilities of experimentation. One is too often consulted merely to strengthen the authority of the parent, and even the teacher, and that before all the parties concerned can have their say and their show. On the other hand, there is no doubt an immense amount of good coming from the widespread encouragement to seek at least discussion, and with this recognition comes a great sense of obligation on the part of us teachers to provide a body of advisers standing on well-scrutinized ground.

We have today an ever-growing number of would-be helpful agencies and enterprises, most of which, however, have all the characteristics of pioneer work. They are exceedingly individualistic and in many ways an expression largely of what the leader would like to do for himself or would like to have obtained sometime for himself. What is needed is a clearer and clearer recognition of the objective needs, irrespective of one's own personal yearnings, and a singling-out of problems which everybody can recognize as topics requiring objective study, a body of concrete facts generally applicable concerning such matters as the balance of work and play, and rest, the management of discontent, of disappointment, the acceptance of one's grades and the proper reaction thereto, the reaction to criticism, the family problems, the choice of time and conditions for pregnancies, the economics and practice in the care of the mother and infant, the care of the child in the family, in school, during adolescence, and the care of that greatest duty of the adult, that of being a reasonably helpful and steadying, rather than disconcerting, example for the growing generation.

There is a great gain in concreteness, and with it in the possibilities of learning and teaching the needed facts.

None of us can boast of enough knowledge concerning human behavior and adaptation, and not enough opportunities have been created to learn more and grow more. Most of it is being learned on a more or less patient or impatient public by variously judicious beginners, unfortunately under all kinds of enticing futuristic propaganda, with an eager public looking for the millennium.

The best sources of training today are those which provide experience in the whole rank and file of pertinent problems, such as only few centers can bring within reach. Unfortunately, contact with every one of these fields requires considerable time. It may partly be condensed by attendance at the meetings and participation in the work of the welfare organizations, some contact with schools and with juvenile-court and domestic-relations court work, some work with the habit clinics, and last but not least, some contact with the psychiatric dispensaries and with the psychiatric hospitals and their social work.

A number of ways are open to meet the natural difficulties. It may be some time before we can attain an organization of the community into the ideal districts suggested by me ten years ago; but there are several nearer ways open to hasten progress.

First, the most perfectionistic scheme is that of the trial clinics imported with means and personnel from the outside. This is no doubt a favored situation, and it will succeed in proportion as it brings about also the coordination and utilization and training of local workers.

Second, a simpler scheme, not sufficiently used as yet, would be that of having a specially trained organizer bring about an organization of the workers and interested persons of the community, such as teachers, nurses, physicians, and various social agencies of churches and the like, for regular demonstrations and discussions of the common problems. A great deal of mental hygiene is like grammar and composition, something to be acquired incidentally in every branch of work. An experienced fieldworker could readily elicit from workers in all possible spheres the material for most stimulating discussions of the ever-returning questions. Here and there a local leader will arise, and a group will form.

Third, in either plan one will have to see to it that as soon as possible we bring most of the trial work on a basis that can be maintained in any community, and not only in the specially favored ones. Much can be learned from the experience in spreading other health problems, such as the fight against hookworm, calling for an arousal of interest in all the active strata of a population.

Along with this principle of greater economy I want to urge that of simplicity and the cultivation of sane commonsense as the most telling measure of wisdom and balance of a program. I am a little bit suspicious of those who claim too much of a special "psychiatric technique." There is no doubt that experience teaches us certain procedures, but as soon as they fail to present themselves in terms of plain commonsense I wonder how much is sound in these theories and in their use. I advise the rank and file to keep hands off from both elaborate hypotheses and elaborate methods until the methods and procedures are sufficiently clear to be really incorporated in plain though critical commonsense.

The wisest help will therefore come from developing specially talented fieldworkers and field instructors, and these had best be trained in what I might call survey of surveys, *i.e.*, in the dispassionate study of work performed under all kinds of conditions, including those that figure as models but also the simplest. Some good beginnings have been made in following up the usefulness of dispensary work, of the boarding-out of children in contrast to institutional care, and the like. Yet we still are deplorably ignorant of the actual results of our good efforts and good intentions, and since our experiments take years to allow of an estimate of the final returns, we have to favor all the efforts to make the work controllable and fit for subsequent study, and to cultivate investigation and investigators. I am anxious that every organizing agency give adequate attention to providing a margin for the reviewing and evaluation of its work and the results thereof. We have to create the foundations for the work with the modern statistical methods that will bring us a necessary and helpful check, with a wholesome perspective of the needs and the available opportunities and the effectiveness of our efforts.

Hand in hand with improved organization of work and workers will have to go the development of a sane public opinion. Today the public is sadly overfed by propaganda and also by the specially fashionable present-day antipropaganda of sneering, always suspecting wholesale attacks upon the rights of the individuals, and raising the defense against so-called "uplift."

We no doubt have an exceedingly difficult task before us to live down the opprobrium of "uplift" and of "job holder." It has become a very popular slogan used mercilessly by the press to gain popularity with large numbers. There will always be far more potential victims of "uplift" than uplifters, and more subscribers to the newspapers to be gained by catering to the large numbers through flattering their supposed independence—from playing on the rights of the individual, up to the playing on states' rights. It is easy to speak of religious and political freedom, but fatal to help sinister forces use the strongest weapons in mass psychology, the spreading of vague fears and suspicions, against all those who have the courage of convictions and cannot remain everlastingly passive. The only dependable remedy on our part is a clear and intelligible demonstration of what we do and aim at.

It is always a good rule for missionaries to make sure that they succeed first at home, and certainly we social workers have to furnish a specially good accounting for what we stand for. It is especially and preeminently important that we should be able to prove ourselves well balanced and especially thoughtful also in the great task of dealing with the accumulated wisdom with respect to habits of life and habits of thought and habits of feeling, esthetic, moral, and religious; capable, when called upon, of a helpful vision of spirituality and morality and conscience.

We all have—or surely most of us have—almost instinctlike thought and feeling tendencies which represent the very soul of human nature, and which we want to learn to understand in each other and share with each other—if possible without dogma and without insistence on specific revelations, because others may have grown up to live by other "revelations" than those of our own personal leaning.

The social worker and mental-hygiene worker has to meet and coordinate very heterogeneous elements. To do so he has to have an unusually well-balanced philosophy.

The problem of how to blend allegiances to group convictions and to the great ideal of political and religious freedom for which our Constitution stands is no doubt the most difficult problem to rise to. Yet I include it in the program of the mental hygiene of community, town, state, and nation.

Present-day individualism unfortunately has a tendency to maximalistic extremes. In its Russian debauch it has landed in one of the most highhanded forms of minority rule, akin to the "head-on" or "head-off" rule of the French Revolution. It becomes a more or less benevolent group despotism. In the Fascist methods in Italy and in the Klan methods of this country, individualism loses itself in a more or less strongly organized and more or less well-intentioned, but after all very dangerous, usurpation of government by groups, and with principles not accountable to the whole. Sometimes it is Bryanesque self-sufficiency falling back upon sectarian assertions of revelations of the past. Sometimes it is the futuristic gospel of elimination of all "repression," and the idolatry of the instinct, where we might well develop more faith in the irrepressibility of real genius, remembering that real genius is not lawlessness, but shows in the natural and spontaneous espousal of what comes nearest to reality.

Here again I feel that our mental-hygiene philosophy is ready to meet individualism without antagonism. We admit that groups have a right to enter upon agreements as to what they would like to take for granted with those who claim to "belong." But groups have to remember that they are groups among groups, and that conditions of belonging should be open.

It is not wise to talk too glibly of one-hundred-percentism. Nobody can know just what that is or should be. What we want is wholeheartedness and fairness and a willingness to learn to understand and know one's neighbor. But it is also our duty to try to make ourselves understood. This, I feel, we can do without the big stick of authority, and without enforced dogma, either political or religious.

One of the biggest conflicts today is that between two types of fundamentalists—those who seek their foundations and facts in revealed tradition and those who, with just as much respect for God and God's creation and true religion, seek the foundations and facts in the ever-progressive revelations of objective experience. Even revelation has its growth from primitive to more mature forms. A sense of intuition and revelation will always be an essential experience of human nature. There have been inspirations at all times. Unfortunately, too many think of inspiration and revelation only where some mysterious influences claim to be at work, and they do not sense adequately the still greater happiness over every step that will lead us closer to observation and to the utilization of generally observable fact in constructive work.

I recently had my attention drawn to a dictum of Commodore Maury, one of our great government scientists: "When, after much toil," he says, "I have discovered a law of God's nature, I feel that I have thought one of God's thoughts, and I tremble." One might well tremble at such an exalted conception of science—calling it thinking God's thoughts. One might tremble at the thought that someone might want to see more in the thought than in the fact, and turn it into a dogma. Dogma is a law of agreement and acceptance of authority and discipleship, but it does not, or should not, take the place of our reverence for fact. It should fade when it ceases to point to clear and obvious fact.

To claim anything as revelation is a responsibility before which, to use Maury's phrase, it is becoming in man "to tremble." With all respect for intuition and revelation and the flights of aspiration, the social worker wants to keep, wherever possible, to what speaks in terms of facts that bring themselves to unrelenting scrutiny and test.

The alternative slogans of the day are devolution, revolution, or evolution. Devolution is the assumption of original perfection and a struggle against a supposedly imposed wickedness of nature. Revolution is the costly application of a peremptory, impulsive policy of "head on, if with me" or "head off and decapitation, if not with me," repeating the terribly costly methods of world improvement of France in the eighteenth and Russia in the present century. Evolution is the faith in growth and development—neither optimism nor pessimism, but meliorism, an ever-growing betterment. We have good reasons to mistrust any agency that wants to work largely with force and fear. We may well choose; and let us hope that we choose well in turning to the faith in that type of evolution which is the philosophy and gospel of growth.

If then I may sum up my discussion, it is that, in the organization of neuropsychiatric work in a community, the present-day rise of individualism urges us in a number of valuable directions. It keeps before us a philosophy of evolution and growth, an ever-closer appreciation of the importance of the concrete components of real life; it cultivates a respect for individual differences and a desire to understand and use individual qualities. It encourages teaching by doing, and confidence in the worker, encouragement and fostering of the local efforts, training of teachers by the study of old, seasoned, and new experience and, if I may give a new meaning to a misused word, a cultivation of a truly fundamental and creative and progressive new fundamentalism, as I said, with faith in that type of evolution which is the philosophy and gospel of growth.

REPRESSION, FREEDOM AND

DISCIPLINE

"Normal and Abnormal Repression," address delivered by Dr. Meyer at convention of Progressive Education Association, Baltimore, April 7, 1922, Bulletin No. 13 (Sept., 1922); and from "Freedom and Discipline," address by Dr. Meyer at Progressive Education Association conference, New York, March, 1928, Progressive Education, 5:205 (July-Sept., 1928).

The problem of the parent and of the educator during our period of reestablishment of stability is not easy. What we are groping for in these days is a new standard of freedom. The process naturally involves a certain amount of uncertainty, of trial and error and perhaps of floundering. Some of the floundering is due to mis-understandings of what we mean by discipline, which I would like to have mean nothing more or less than the art of being a disciple and of helping others to be disciples—disciples of the best available knowledge and wisdom, no matter whether it be one's own or whether it comes from others, provided that it is a discipline and doctrine based on a common understanding by the teacher and the taught. Within this problem of discipline there comes up the problem of control and repression, not as principles held by one set of people over another, but as principles pervading all life and all ages, a problem of the individual and a social problem.

I suppose we are all agreed upon one thing—that it is not authority through awe and fear, but a common understanding, a consensus of the best knowledge, that builds up the most desirable rules of the wisest discipline. The same holds for control and repression: it must come from a sound consensus of safe knowledge.

But why speak of control and repression in the same breath with "a new standard of freedom"? Why not leave off this negative feature? Because it lies in the nature of things. Freedom is not chaos; it is choice, and choice implies rejection as well as espousal. We cannot go forward and backward at the same time; only a deluded person or a fraud can claim to be in more than one place at the same time; we cannot keep the cake and eat it. We must be able to forgo in order to gain. We must learn to grasp the truth that the "better" can become the actual enemy of what may long have been accepted as "good." We must learn to repress what may be most tempting for the moment, because of the greater call of the ulterior good. It is not so hard to realize that many an apparent repression of a momentary impulse is an obvious gain. It may be harder for some children and for some adults to learn the art of repression than for others. Repression may cause some frank outcries and disappointments until the bigger or more lasting good is clearly felt and understood and the push which works back of unfulfillable desires is directed into more successful channels.

Some time ago in a lecture on psychoanalysis I remarked,

A very frequent question raised is that of repression. Repression no doubt is a measure of wisdom, to counteract evils resulting from license. To show that mere repression may still leave unguided the fundamental tendency and drive, and that certain poor ways of handling repression create trouble, does not mean that we should at once flop over into the ranks of mere license or superciliousness. It merely means that there are bad ways of trying to be good just as there are bad ways of indulging in license; and there are perfectly good ways for most people to keep from between the devil and the deep sea.

A reporter added to this remark, as if it had come from me, "but sometimes repression causes mild forms of insanity." I should emphatically say, only mismanaged repression and mismanaged desires and mismanaged conflicts under mismanaged conditions. It is not the repression but the mismanagement that does the harm.

Shall we throw all commonsense to the wind just because both the methods and concept of repression have been stupidly used?

What I am concerned about is the difference between revolution and evolution in the progress of a truer freedom. Revolution usually is a spectacular, terribly expensive process and the mother of reaction. It is always evolution that has done the real work attributed to revolution. It is not likely that a revolution ever does more than decapitate the conservatives and put the unchastened in a position to try themselves out and learn, and then to turn into a new conservative group, or class, themselves. The revolutionist starts with the fervor of some apparently impregnable or at least convincing theory and finally modifies it—while all might have been done, with more foresight and less disorder and with reasonable result, by a people with a sense for a better type of freedom.

The present-day emancipation from a false authority of fear and dogma and from the self-satisfied, dogmatic I-know-it-all-best attitude of the elder toward the young, borrows much of its fervor from a new fear, the offhand or unreasoning fear of repression of individual desire. We are led to take well-nigh for granted that the ideals of the elder person cannot possibly be as safe and good a guide as the natural trend of the young in its unhampered state, and in this many are driven further because they fear there is always arbitrariness inherent in traditional repressions. To me our period looks like one of accelerated evolution, and not of revolution, and one of the factors under concern is, as I said, a new and more livable freedom, with maximal respect for the natural drives of man but also for accumulated wisdom of the race—a freedom demanding also reasonable responsibility, that which in civics means "freedom and solidarity." My special concern here is a modest but nonetheless emphatic call for a thoughtful and sensible warning against wholesale dread of repression or control, provided we can find control by consensus, by understanding and collaboration.

Repression has been overadvertised as the source of terrible consequences. Repression is an essentially normal necessity and at the same time, like everything else, it may be turned into a chance for harm to society and a chance for harm to the individual. The fundamental difficulty is that, in certain individuals and under certain conditions, it is apt to lead to conflicts and sometimes to conflicts which are mismanaged. Fundamentally, then, we may deal with a problem of *mismanagement* of conflicts and desires.

How did the concept of repression get such prominence? Most of us were probably brought up under a regime in which repression played an altogether excessive role. Then there came a decided letup in the strictness and bitter-endedness of control, until finally a wholesome commonsense and good will attitude prevails among parents and teachers. Now, in this day of popularized psychoanalysis, repression is decried as a danger and horror.

As a part of an ingenious and remarkably fertile theory of psychology, itself to my mind the product of a one-sided generalization of certain pathological disorders, repression has been made a one-sided explanation of all possible normal commonsense facts. The fact that children do not remember as adults do and that we do not remember much of our childhood is called the product of a "repression." That we forget and mislay an object is shown to be due to a "repression"; the hysterical person has his or her fit and palsies through "repression." Deny yourself a wish and you will suffer from the "repression." The most remarkable evil effects are laid at the door of various so-called repressions in the sex life. The dream is represented as a labored and camouflaged welling-up of repressed topics.

Now there is some truth in much of this, enough to justify the advice to the student to search for the facts along this line where real facts suggest such a procedure. Yet there is no need of making the principle a pedagogical and ethical dogma of the necessity of gratification of everything that might be called an "instinct."

We deal here with an upshot of a dynamic psychology or, we might say, a biological psychology with its recognition of appetite or need and its satisfaction lying at the bottom of human nature as well as of life generally. Everywhere we see action-tendencies which McDougall in his *Social Psychology* has put together in very readable form in a system of "instincts." Somehow instincts, especially as they occur in the higher invertebrates, are highly complex action-tendencies and reflex chains which, through simple heredity of the structure of the organism, tend to take their full serial course, whenever set off. The overconfidence in the existence and especially the necessity of satisfying so-called "instinct," more than any other fact, has led to giving modern psychology the impress of the existence of quasi-immutable and obligatory demands, patterned, without further discrimination, after the facts prevailing in hunger and food instinct.

It is clear enough in the case of hunger and thirst that they determine the attitude and action-tendencies of the entire individual. Like respiration, hunger and thirst are a blatant necessity. Whether all the other "instincts" should be viewed as quasi-immutable and obligatory demands, the interception of which would be harmful, is, however, another question.

As we consider human life, the "instincts" are combinations of part-activities, hardly running with a machinelike course or set cycle. Not even the reflexes in the frog run in an absolutely machinelike, nonvariable course. (See Baglioni.)

In man we deal undoubtedly with a definite dissolution and modification of "instinct" probably similar to the modification of certain ordinary reflexes. One of the best examples is the grasping reflex of the infant, by which it can at first carry its own weight, but which gradually ceases to work automatically and gets relaxed and transformed into free activity in proportion as the hand is used for many purposes. In my psychology course I give my students a table of the equivalents of instincts in the development of man showing how every tendency or instinct, so-called, develops individual habit or performance types, as the result of the working-together of the inheritable preparedness or tendency and the influences of social usage and individual opportunity. John Dewey in his new book on *Human Nature and Conduct*, published by Holt, treats the so-called classification of instincts with the conclusion that there are no separate instincts in man.

What happens is the development of a much wider range of foresight and choice, and therewith the call for discriminations, for espousals and repressions, and gradually the type of organization we know perfectly well in ourselves—not a fatalistically acting machine, but one in which we expect a gradual training of discrimination. Unfortunately, science has been built up with such an exclusive interest in physics and chemistry of an elemental kind and of late in some biology and special physiology equally elemental, that the conceptions of science became and remained unduly mechanistic and unyielding, with an unnecessary expurgation of all the larger concepts of mind and soul that we meet in ourselves and in our fellow beings.

We are led to believe that this whole problem is all worked out and glaringly brought out in the problem of sex repression. There is probably no other so-called instinct burdened with more half-baked and dogmatic inferences than the "sex instinct." Is it repression or mismanagement that causes most trouble? Every child can see that the adults are floundering as much as the young.

In this matter I am convinced that we have reason to trust a freedom with solidarity, a full sense of responsibility and adequate control through breadth of outlook. A view of the gradually attainable goal—family formation, which can be held up before the child with a natural and judicious range of detail, but in its full-fledged form and goal from the start—some knowledge of the occasions for blundering, some knowledge of means of rehabilitation and correction of blundering, a little more confidence in the probability that most people will try to do the best they know, a sensible appeal for the safety of one's sisters and sweethearts and mothers and daughters and wives, and for the boys and the men and even for oneself, plenty of room for wiser freedom and less impulsive and uninformed bungling and pessimism or equally discouraging perfectionism, frankness on a melioristic basis, with good practical evidence of a willingness to find out and do—that is what will help here as in other pursuits of life.

I am fully convinced, let me say again, that there are perfectly normal and also abnormal ways of repression.

Abnormal repressions are no adequate excuse for skepticism concerning the feasibility of cultivation of conditions for normal management.

What is wanted is more willingness to study the facts and to create perspective, and less authoritativeness.

The quest for a new standard of freedom is somewhat exploited by our younger friends whenever they see the supposedly mature uncertain and groping. Many adults are far from having found themselves on solid ground, to mention only the dancing and Volstead and automobile problems. As long as large numbers of individuals and of the press speak only of the restrictive aspect and the retaliative excesses and hardly ever of the constructive opportunity of a practicable freedom from alcoholic and other supposed necessities, there is bound to be much floundering among those who cannot be expected to have all the vision of the causes and opportunities of a new state of affairs. If really constructive and informing statements of facts and their settings are handed around, one may expect some clearing of the atmosphere. As it is, one sees only the general frame of the what's-the-use attitude and the lingering idea of the "physiological necessity" and the hint that if you do not give the people one intoxicant they will want other "dope," and all that immature yielding to a doctrine of pseudo-scientific fatalism and mechanism and necessity.

As parents and teachers we are apt to get what we call for. It is well that we should remember with a recent reviewer in one of our periodicals that grownups lose the ability to read the child intuitively as the child can read the adult. Parents and teachers may quiz, but it is often useless to ask a child a direct, or especially a plainly jeopardizing, question about things of importance to himself. The child, however, has a penetrating observation of emotional attitudes difficult to escape. It is one of his chief resources in the control of the environment. He can make himself a great nuisance, or, on the other hand, so endearing that he temporarily manages his milieu. Parents and teachers have to recognize this and to lay aside that fatuous sense of superiority which often makes them so unequal in combat. Any dogmatic and dictatorial way of picturing what is and what ought to be has a hard time today and at the same time it is dying hard.

What, then, are the ways of control, correction, and normal repression?

The first point is development of habits which can be thoroughly satisfied in harmony with the environment and with ample opportunity for satisfaction. For the pedagogue it is essential that he should recognize where false foundations are present: daydreaming of a morbid kind, introversion of a morbid kind, and habit developments which are apt to cut out the trial-and-error method and correction in the open. We cannot let a youngster narrow indefinitely the range of what capacity he has for conforming to the best sense of the environment. There must be habits of work for which there is a market and a call, habits of care of oneself in keeping with the probable opportunities, habits of recreation easily enough dovetailed with life, habits of melioristic self-culture—social, educational, civil and religious habits and contacts.

The next thing is an early cultivation of familiarity with what may ultimately satisfy the representatives of the various temperaments.

It would be better for youngsters to spend with their teachers one day a week in various shops and business establishments, farms of various kinds from the simplest to the most perfect, in various industries and in places of amusement and recreation, rather than give all their schooltime to an artificial curriculum.

Do not let us forget that the report on the part-time pupils in one of our leading cities had to be suppressed because the results with the part-timers were better than the results with those who had to serve the full term of each school day.

Let the school show the pupil how to work and play at school instead of making the pupil complicate the home life with piles of homework which should really be done in school.

I am heartily in sympathy with the maxim quoted by Seashore in his discussion of sectioning classes on the basis of ability: "Keep each student at his highest level of achievement in order that he may be successful and happy and good." Have in each grade a group for the best endowed, a group for those less endowed but nonetheless alive and able in their way, and a middle group; then tasks may be fitted to each student.

There is no need of false comparison and stressing of inferiority or superiority. We are not all alike. We have to do our share with very different endowments and learn to be true to ourselves and develop our own best type of a day's activity.

Nor is it necessary with that scheme to promote capable children into higher classes beyond their social age merely because their intellectual age points higher and demands greater intensity and abundance of work, but not association with older children. To furnish this greater intensity and abundance of work is not easy. It puts teachers and parents on their mettle as nothing else would, and if they play fair, the young generation will play fair as well.

It is freedom based on a broad outlook that we have to cultivate, a freedom which does not have to shy from training in repression and choice, but a freedom that is true to nature as seen in the individual, in the social groups, and shaped, not by momentary whim or impulse, but by one's best outlook and vision.

What I feel under special obligation to warn against is the false assumption that the so-called new psychiatry has in any way removed us from the need and obligation and right to use our plain commonsense subject to trial, or that it has given us a superior type of intuition and magic. It is real critical commonsense that is enriching the practical life in both education and psychiatry. It is a desire to do real justice to the child and to youth under greatly altered conditions of life that guides us toward the recognition of the necessity, as well as wisdom, of *well-managed repression* and a sound balance of freedom with its absolutely essential partner, discipline. It is a practical working together and sharing of practical experience and not an exotic pathological theory alone that most of us live by. There are a few basic principles which daily necessities and daily experiences are bringing home everywhere: the possibility and therewith the desirability of attaining early self-determination and independence in self-care, furthered by the use of nursery schools for the education of both the parent and the child; the elimination from education of unnecessary traditions and coercions. The child of today has learned to resent what many adults themselves are too slow to give up. A new influence asserts itself through a spirit of participation of the young and the elder in real life and a mutual rather than a one-sided respect.

The human being is by nature and necessity an intensely social as well as socially dependent individual. In this sentence you have the quintessence of the problem of freedom. We have here a problem of reality of relationships, the hardest thing to acquire, and to maintain where you have it, and to develop as you need more.

When one speaks of discipline, the thought of punishment is apt to enter. Punishment feels to me like an anachronistic residual and whenever I *do* have an inclination to think in terms of punishment, the mere first step toward carrying thought over into the action makes me halt. When the other day I looked up the history of the word "discipline," I was delighted to find that the Latin dictionary of Lewis, so meritoriously careful in its etymological helps and in its analysis of meanings, shows that "discipline," a term for training, learning and order, had nowhere in the classical Latin any of the reprehensible implications of punishment. See what a period of zealous doctrinal and highhanded authoritativeness and hopelessly archaic legalism and militarism and preaching has done to a perfectly wholesome concept! The art and practice of helpful training is all that the Romans saw and intended the word "discipline" to convey, and that is also what I have in mind—the capacity and opportunity of being a disciple and winning a disciple. Discipline that is not also self-discipline and a discipline of participation as opposed to merely authoritative discipline ought to be called something else.

Somehow, just as freedom is being extolled as a panacea, so we find discipline and growth under direction beclouded with inherent suspicion. If the adult turns freedom into license, and discipline into vindictiveness, the child and the youth become rather wary and class-conscious beings. The freedom school will be either a training for sound democracy in the sense of freedom with solidarity and self-government, or a training merely for revolt. The very concreteness of the work of these schools creates not a wild futurism, but a philosophy which includes and cultivates history and outlook alike, in a conscience about today and tomorrow, with a philosophy of interdependence and participation according to one's best means and capacity, a frank and honest give-and-take and fair play in harmony with the golden rule.

Man has found his place in nature and is learning to respect the nature he represents in his ideals expressed in practical life as well as in word. From being brought up as not a merely potential but a fate-doomed candidate for eternity and with a corresponding type of too ulterior self-concern, man has learned to see himself in his fuller actuality in the successive stages of threescore and ten years or more or less. From conception, he is an entity having a right to the respect of all and playing his part in the world of flux, a part very real at every moment and not merely significant under a sign of eternity and predestination and what not. He is a positive factor in the social participation we call home and community, school and life, a positive factor in—shall we call it democracy? Yes, most emphatically, provided that we interpret the "cracy" or "ruling" as collaboration and solidarity. In my adolescence we used to talk of a new aristocracy in the sense of the rule of the best principles under the leadership and guidance of those best fitted. Today, with the very concrete trend of modern life, we should speak of the best consensus, the best conjoint understanding—to be measured by vote?—but measured above all by a sense of the best working together of individuals and groups—freedom and discipline, freedom and responsibility.

I cannot give a better example of what I mean by this demand that even the child be drawn into our consensus than our experience with Americanism. The real Americanization of us foreign people is best achieved through the children who go forth from the foreign home and then bring back to it more of real American life than any teaching by word and press and the complex examples of adult life would bring home to the adult. Is there not a world of meaning and strength in "a little child shall lead them"? My hope lies in the same achievement among us all—the child is more than ever destined to make his contribution to the spirit of the home, and to a less tangled philosophy and practice of individual and social life.

The best teaching is opportunity for reciprocal participation and in this the adult has the burden of shaping a tenable civilization, fit for old and young to live in side by side. I doubt whether we should be right if we assume that the young generation should begin everything afresh and organize a completely self-created world. I do not share Bertrand Russell's fear of imparting to the child convictions and precepts as long as they are not imposition and display of false plumage. Rousseau and Pestalozzi have to take their place among mere theorists and beginners; something much more scientific and also much more radical is sought after and, in this search, overspecialized branches of psychiatry are too often exploited and extolled as the oracle. We are going through a kind of postwar inflation period and are beginning to look for means of stabilization, for a safer currency. What shall it be?

I wonder sometimes why there is such a zest for saving the child from becoming just a plain human being such as most of us are, subject alike to the laws of nature and the opportunities of growth and occasional blunders. It looks almost as if we were playing ourselves up as the sole originators and creators of nature, not content with finding our place in nature.

I suppose the world has always considered the conflicts and problems of the moment as the most upsetting and disturbing phases mankind ever went through. One or two generations ago works were written on the warfare of religion and science. Today it is a philosophy of radical emancipation from everything that might be suspected of having been considered true in the self-righteous Victorian era—customs, policies, ethics, philosophies, and religion being almost too personal and too antiquated to be even mentioned. Because some people make a mess of democracy we question not the people but the democracy; because many people make a mess of the home, some question the justification of the family; because there is much foolishness in imaginary obligations, all obligations have to be questioned; because some people make a mess of repression, all repression is dreaded. We may well learn to profit from, but not to emasculate, these accidents of abnormality.

Fortunately there is a positive, constructive philosophy as well, that of a John Dewey, that of progressive education, that of commonsense psychiatry. Fortunately there are children everywhere in a world of life and action, their very presence forcing upon us a daily need and daily urge, a daily opportunity to take up the child and the youth as a collaborator, and this with a true sense of freedom, freedom united to discipline, makes possible a joyful rather than a scolding and suffering discipline, a true freedom with true solidarity.

SCHOOLS AND MENTAL HEALTH

From a lecture by Dr. Meyer, "Mental and Moral Health in a Constructive School Program," delivered for the Joint Committee on Education at the Civic Club, Chicago, Feb. 24, 1917; in Suggestions of Modern Science Concerning Education, by Herbert S. Jennings, John B. Watson, Adolf Meyer, and William I. Thomas, at p. 103, The Macmillan Company, New York (1917).

There is clearly a very potent stimulus of my interest in the schools in the fact that in all my work I am constantly confronted with the question, "What has been the share of nature and of nurture, and of home and school, in the lives of the patients who form the subject of my medical work?" My great desire to learn more through close contact from the many workers whose life interest lies in the shaping of the school problem and my interest in a prospective experiment with a school as a community center account for my yielding to Mrs. Ethel S. Dummer's appeal to undertake a humble discussion of what the psychopathologist might have to contribute to a constructive consideration of the relation of the school to mental and moral health.

There are periods when some of our human institutions are blindly accepted by tradition as if they were the revelation of immutable truths; and other periods come when there is debate and a conviction of possibilities of growth.

To be sure, every human institution such as a school system has to have its frame of stable and dependable organization if it is to hold its own among the many other factors making up organized civilization. But, as it serves as one of the organizations of the growing and ever-changing world of mankind, the frame and the structure as a whole will always have to be more than dead bone, a living adaptable part of the great biological and social integrations of human beings into organized communities, and success will always be judged by the great criterion of the mental and moral health of its products.

I feel strongly that the educator and the physician have more and more common ground on account of the great progress made both in the school and in the medical sphere. Since the days when I took my first plunge into practical adult life in Chicago and Kankakee, momentous transformations have occurred in the life-work that I then chose. From having their main and almost exclusive field in hospitals largely for committed patients, such as that at Kankakee, the psychiatric interests have broadened until one of our most inspiring activities is now extrainstitutional work in the community and especially at the point where the individual first enters community life—the school.

Today we study mental activity and behavior—the topic of psychology—as the function and activity of the unified organism, just as we view physiology as the science studying the behavior and function of the various organs and parts. The study of the *total behavior of the individual and its integration as it hangs together as part of a life history of a personality in distinction from the life history of a single organ*—that is our great interest in psychology and psychopathology.

No words of mine can give you a more graphic picture of the concreteness of what counts than the life-chart [see page 420], a record, on the one hand, of the condition and of the performance of the various bodily functions and special organs and of the role each of these plays in shaping the biography or life of the person; and, on the other hand, the various experiences expressing the lines of habit-and-resource formation constituting the accumulated mass of habits, memories, and the reactive resources of the individual. The result of this integration is not an abstract mind but a living body in action, a unified personality, an individual with capacity for reflexes and instincts and habits and memories and imaginative reactive resources.

A life can be presented graphically as a record of the special organs (arbitrarily represented in the form of a weight-curve of the principal parts) and at the same time as a record of total behavior. The interrelation of the parts and the whole, as I said, constitutes a system of integration. Thus we can appreciate the fact that the respiration has to serve properly the total need of oxygen and the elimination of carbon dioxide, but the same combination also has to serve the functions of voice and language production as integrated by the nervous system, and this has to blend with even the larger needs and aims of the total organism, since most of our thought is couched in language, forming an important part of those habits and trends which we specify as "the mental and moral life" and its resources. Thus we see in thought and speech an integration of an organ simultaneously serving simple physiological demands and also serving such a function as the one I am at present engaged in, in a full-fledged observable mental activity.

The great advantage of this simplification, of viewing mind primarily as the adaptive and creative activity of a biological organism in terms of a biography and record, is that it gives us a practical way of putting forth our facts and problems—whether we try to educate a person or whether we apply mental orthopedics to the correction of behavior, whether it be in connection with any special organ or any special function, or activities involving the whole personality. Moreover, it gives us a valuable sense of proportion between what counts in the life and what is purely incidental; the overt and demonstrable brought out by overt action and expression, and the mere thoughts; the performance rather than the mere knowledge; the results rather than the mere step to it.

Besides the practical emphasis, the simplified scheme shows us human life with its material and spiritual aspects as a consistent whole. We are no longer worried and confused by the apparent chasm between nature and the world of human life and its ambitions, which seems to have staggered even Huxley so that it drove him into the transitory stage of agnosticism and doubt as to the possibility of harmonizing the laws of nature and of life with the great human world of ambitions and of dreams of perfection and ideals, the laws of the mores, or ethics, and religion. As we said before, a complex and yet simple organization of natural and creative forces into actual living individuals is what we have to deal with—an organization starting from lowly origins but reaching as high as its support will carry; the product of a long process of growth and function, an unfolding of instincts and their application and transformation, a readiness for and attraction to many experiences and performances, an evolution through a wealth of reactions and capacities gradually wrought into habits and resources, rising to full-fledged individual and social life with its heights of appreciation and creative attainment. There is but one way to learn to know such an organism and that is through its life history, the record of past and present reactions, from which we are to foretell the range and capacities of the future.

In comparing the simpler biological organisms and man in respect to growth and education, we are at once struck by a contrast which is very significant and which entails the great preeminence of man in the scale of evolution but also a great risk in the sphere of health. The development of language and its symbols, the development of the silent language, and language-memory, and imagination in terms of language, gives man at once the great privilege and the great task of maintaining the proper balance, so much more difficult than where life consists more conspicuously of overt and direct activity, as in animals.

The ability to store knowledge in terms of word-memories and principles, in terms of written and transmitted doctrine, creates the human atmosphere and brings with it the temptation to change the system of education from that of training to one of teaching and instructing. So great is this temptation that the traditional scheme of education has limited itself almost exclusively to this one type of human attainment, and indeed there are many who would not like to see the school do anything else; and all this in the face of the fact that our very nature is a product of the growth and nurture of an organism in which impulse, instinct and differential activity and performance make up what counts in the biography or life record. Activity is the natural setting and the very nature of all mental growth. As has been said, "The laws of mental health and of character require the completion of thought or feeling by expression in action." Mere feeling and thought and fancy which are not brought to the test of action, to their fulfillment in action, tend to become one of the danger points of human nature.

Even in the pre-biological period of human thought as among the Greeks, the school aimed at the development of the entire organism and the development of all-round fitness for adult life. Later the medieval tendency to treat an abstract mind as an entity by itself, and the sectarian tendency to keep important aspects of life out of the curriculum, tended to focus attention upon but one feature of the personality. When we look at biographies, the schooling clearly gives the main setting to a long series of years. Even if the ideal of the scheme of education aimed mainly at knowledge and at the acquisition of the arts of reading and writing and arithmetic and a certain amount of historical, linguistic, and natural-history information, the period of school life is the time during which the habits acquired in earlier childhood become more definitely shaped. Between home, social environment, and school, the young citizen spends six, eight or more years to attain the ideal of education of his or her generation. The traditional school aims at conveying systematized knowledge, the results of centuries of human evolution—the paper money of experience, a set of capacities which a democracy must be able to expect of its citizens, and which life at large would supply only unsystematically. For this purpose the school practically takes possession of the child and the adolescent, and it determines the principal features of that period of life. Need we wonder that it is more and more concerning itself with a broader conception of education than that of mere "mental training"?

The questions we might ask about a school system are: "Can the result be called well rounded, making for preparedness for an efficient and wholesome thirty or forty or more years of adult life? Does the product of such training know what he or she is fitted for;

what he or she wants and will try to do as his or her share of the work of sustenance and productiveness? Is the school training in harmony with our best knowledge of the integrated human organism and personality: does it satisfy the principle that life ultimately be judged in terms of biography of objective achievement and that knowledge is merely an incidental asset and telling only when it shows in effective or expressive activity? Does it succeed in forging the natural assets into power? And finally, what share can any type of school have in favoring or damaging the individual chances for mental and moral health and efficiency?"

There are two ways of being interested in health; the common one is that of making a list and plan of all the things that are good and desirable in life and giving the best possible description of utopia and perfection with recommendations as to how to get there. The way of the worker in modern hygiene is that of making a survey of the actual activities and conditions, and then of taking up definite points of difficulty, tracing them to an understanding in terms of causes and effects and to factors on which fruitful experimental analytical and constructive work can be done. The first type leads mainly to moralizing; the second type leads to conscientious and impartial study and to constructive experimentation. It is one thing to study the problem of mental and moral health in the abstract and another to take up the definite points at which the human being is apt to fail and to trace them specifically to factors which can receive consideration in experimental creative work and in a constructive school program.

To get help from the field of abnormalities and difficulties of children and of methods of teaching naturally requires familiarity with the well-studied overt major and minor mental disorders and the methods of getting at their understanding—and also with the aims and methods of pedagogy. These are quite obviously matters which can be acquired only by practical work and collaboration in the fields concerned. What I can survey here is merely a sketch of some fundamental facts and principles to show possibilities and methods as a basis for recommendations of organization.

Let me state as the first requirement that the school physician should have a clear conception of the school child's nature as an organism to be studied in its parts and also as a psychobiological whole, a personality and individual—a conception which implies training in psychobiology for at least a certain number of the school physicians. The school physician who has the analytic-constructive biological conception approaches the pupil with due attention to disorders of eye and ear, of the breathing and possible adenoids, and the state of nutrition; but he also knows that the pupil brings to the school an endowment not merely of special organs but also of habits of total-function; good or bad food habits expressing themselves in appetites and more or less orderly habits of feeding and of digestion; a more or less adequate equipment of habits of sleep and waking and resting and activity; the kind of life characteristic of the infant or child or adolescent, different from that of the adult or old person.

He recognizes individual differences in the scope of endowment and resources; endurance and concentration and interest; or weakness, distractability, and indifference; a varying ability to control with foresight the momentary notions, temptations, and desires; a capacity of contentment and satisfaction, or of unrest; habits of self-dependence or of dependence upon others and a craving for attention; habits for teamwork or a lack of social instincts; an ability to mix, to respond to others and to make them respond—an ability to understand and to be understood and to enjoy and be enjoyed. Within this large sphere of resources and activities and qualifications we may further single out features such as varying preparedness to meet the unusual or perhaps the undesirable, such as sickness, and varying amenability to discipline and to guidance, and capacities to assume responsibilities and duties. Here there is a mass of vital facts requiring consideration if the child is to be put into the best balanced situations.

Until we shall have our nursery and childhood laboratories, might we not be guided in a helpful manner by the grave school of life, with its exhibits of the blundering of human nature?

The reason why I should like to give you a bird's-eye view of the varied troubles of the adult is this: There is a widespread notion current among the public, and possibly also in the medical profession, that what you have to do in these disorders is to get a formal diagnosis as the result of some more or less specific and remarkable test or trick, and that this diagnosis is then used to prescribe a very particular treatment. If you mean by diagnosis a knowledge and understanding of what the moving forces are and how they *work* and how they can be modified, you are on safe ground; if, however, you think you have gained much when you have found a name for the condition, you deceive yourselves. If I may turn once more to the life-chart, you find there in brief the record of a patient who was driven into invalidism through many misunderstandings [see page 421]. Call the condition neurasthenia or hysteria; the fact is that you only describe and classify it dogmatically that way. In order to understand it you have to trace the various factors. In this case, as in many similar ones, the school missed an opportunity to trace the situation which tolerated and possibly encouraged the persistence of the habit-headache, the reason for the dependence and lack of emancipation, etc.

Does this recital of concrete medical experience suggest to you the close similarity of the problems of the physician and those of the teacher, those of all life? What you see in this brief sketch of our adult patient is what we must learn to determine even in the minor disturbances and especially also in the disciplinary difficulties of the child; we must not be satisfied with mere descriptions and with distress over the regrettable difficulties and with offhand efforts to apply traditional measures of correction which may not fit the case or may only smooth over the trouble. But we must devise methods of getting at the facts in a judicious, helpful, and constructive manner, and that means the systematic use of what we physicians and you teachers alike have learned to recognize as obligatory—a study of the individual case in the light of his or her development and home and school situation.

Where nervous and behavior disorders are corrected by attention to special organs as in eyestrain, or adenoids, it is of the utmost importance not to neglect, in an optimistic mood, the weak spot in the psychobiological balance which may show again under some other strain or which may persist as evidence of deficit or of sources of irritation.

There are problems of management of life in and out of school and there are always ways of getting at the facts and of adjusting them. The school undoubtedly has its share in producing or favoring the disorders of balance at the bottom of the smaller and greater failures of adaptation. It is my impression, however, that the modern school is open in the main to fewer charges of commission than to charges of omission. Most abnormalities undoubtedly have their foundation laid in the home, by heredity, and by a poor start in habit formation. In the European schools there is much concern about the *Überbürdung*, the overtaxing of the school child, a problem which might be considered an exception here, except where a child does not know *how* to work and how to play. The school is apt to furnish a more or less innocent aggravation of more deeply rooted difficulties, traits which come to the front as much or even more in the extrascholastic life of the youngster.

A more specific school problem is the frequent recurrence of weariness and ennui, with puzzling and meandering in thought mazes. With this goes a tendency to develop false standards, habits of putting up a sham front of performance where the pupil is doing hardly more than serving time; a formal obedience and formal attention without any real interest and performance. This actual training in the intellectual dishonesty of maintaining appearance of interest and work where the interest is plainly wandering inevitably warps the development of action and its appreciation and incentives. It stunts the appetites and capacities the child actually has, and it creates pockets for dangerous ruminations, fancies, and daydreams which are not apt to be drawn out into the world of activity, test, and correction. Even among the best we have to face a pitfall that comes from man's unique development of mere language and thought habits favoring a difficulty of balance of thought and fancy on the one hand and the capacity and output of performance on the other.

It is a striking fact that in the main the more serious and conspicuous disorders are much less frequent and less glaring in children than in the adult. But we see all the more clearly the possible roots from which the smaller and the graver disorders arise. The most frequent disorders, if you disregard for the time the defective growth of the nervous system and the infections and toxic affections of the nervous system associated with feeblemindedness, epilepsy and kindred defects or retardation of development, are due to defect of balancing resources, unevenness of endowment and of assets, often with tendencies to overreach—with deficit and disappointment reactions—or briefly put, the big problem is that of poorly balanced yearning and desires. The greatest problem is not that of feeblemindedness. There are plenty of good and well-behaved imbeciles. The point that concerns us all is that back of everything lie the yearnings, the penchant, the leanings of the individual's make-up and the equation of balancing factors of the individual and the social group—the capacity to balance the resources wherever there is a choice or a need of proper adaptation and substitutions.

Disease shows us along what lines human beings are apt to break down and what man is not made for. It points inexorably to any existing discrepancies of balance, and errors in the working out of one's economic safety and efficiency. Some diseases are a community disgrace, still others must be charged to the stock (poorly guided habits of mating) and to the life of the family, and still others to the individual. Most diseases are chargeable to the unwillingness or inability to face realities of make-up and situation and to shape one's life in keeping with them. And the same holds for the major and the minor difficulties one meets in the schoolroom and playroom, the shyness, the fears, misbehavior, temporary inefficiency, etc.

It is here, in the apparently trifling signals of something being wrong, that the psychopathologist may be able to offer his share of help in the form of methods developed in the study of mental disease. Thereby he serves two purposes: that of helping the pupil, possibly for a lifetime, by aiding him or her to assume harmony between means and ends, and, second, that of fostering inspiration for a broader view of the teachers' working sphere.

But why all this interest in the abnormal? The main problem of the teacher is the healthy child. My contention is that a natural interest in all things human helps us to a more broadly biological and more broadly human and unified understanding of facts and methods.

THE RIGHT TO MARRY

From an article by Dr. Meyer, "The Right to Marry: What Can a Democratic Civilization Do About Heredity and Child Welfare?" The Survey, 36:243 (June 3, 1916).

What we speak of as heredity in the sense of influence of the parent on the constitution of the child is oftenest the sum of three factors: (1) genuine heredity, that which comes with the germ cells and is itself inherited—a property of the chromosomes; (2) early growth and nutrition; (3) early training and habit formation. It is impossible to separate these three factors in man very clearly, owing to the long period of gestation and infancy during which the nutrition and training problems are combined. There is, however, at times a fourth factor, more like true heredity: *i.e.*, germ damage at the time of conception, by alcohol, febrile disease, and the like; or by temporary subnormalities of the parent, producing an inferiority of the stock, different from the transmission of "acquired characters." In other words, the germ plasm can be damaged permanently or for many generations by poisoning the germ-cells; whereas individual injuries or experiences do not influence the stock.

Who is entitled to progeny? We pride ourselves on living under the sign of a generally and freely voiced responsibility to be well ourselves and to enter upon parenthood only when there is a fair chance of giving reasonable health to the child. There may be persons who do not care and who live blindly by instinct and tradition. There are, however, many who do some thinking and feel under obligation to use their intelligence in matters of parenthood. No parent today would consider it right to give origin to a child during sickness; nor during intoxication; nor in such rapid succession as to exhaust the mother and to make her unfit to be what she ought to be to a child. And we claim that some persons should not marry at all and others only into stock distinctly better than their own.

To give a concrete picture of actual problems, I have had put together the material of four interrelated family groups in one of our school districts. These families are represented at the public school by thirty-five children, fourteen of whom were found to be defective. These families were studied as wholes (about 522 persons); and then specifically, the 104 children that constitute the products of twenty-four matings and among whom are the thirty-five children in the public schools studied.

It was deemed best to group the children according to whether both parents were normal, or only one or both abnormal. The parents of the first group thus are normal or at least afflicted only by characteristics which are acquired by association, *i.e.*, likely to be the product of nurture rather than of nature. Thus we gave alcoholism and looseness of sex life the benefit of doubt, as a condition not necessarily denoting abnormal stock, but apt to be the product of unfavorable environment.

With this understanding, we found eleven matings to be those of practically normal parents; in four of these matings both parents were, however, tainted with defect—that is, having in the family cases of mental disorder or defect referable to stock and individual make-up, rather than to external causes, such as injuries. These parents show one or two defectives among their progeny, besides from three to six normal children. In the other seven matings of normal parents, of whom but one was tainted, the result was correspondingly better. In other words, it is not enough that both parents be relatively normal; but if an individual be tainted by heredity, he or she should guard against marriage with another tainted individual.

In a second group of nine matings, one parent was actually defective. Those married to normal but tainted persons produced about equal numbers of normal and defective children; whereas the six defectives married to nontainted persons produced two defective, six uncertain, and fifteen normal children. Here again, a tainted person aggravates bad parentage; a nontainted mate reduces the risks.

The third group of matings consists of four matings where both parents were defective. The result was twenty-one defective, one sex offender, four uncertain, and one normal. In other words, prohibition of these matings would have meant the loss of but one normal person against the prevention of over twenty-one defectives.

As far as we know, the great-grandparents of these families, who years ago moved into the neighborhood studied, were practically normal people, but through unfortunate cumulative matings, ignoring combinations of taint, the result described above has been obtained.

What holds for such defects as imbecility and epilepsy holds also for a number of other mental and nervous and other diseases. Only there is fortunately not the same inheritance of an actual condition but usually only of a disposition to abnormality.

We are, of course, concerned here mainly with the question of preventing further cumulative mischief by reaching the proper persons with our advice as to marriage or nonmarriage.

Attempts have been made of late years to regulate this problem by legislation. The great question is, "Who is to decide? A certificate exacted from a physician for two or three dollars, as was advocated in Wisconsin? Or the good sense of the community? Or a free and sensible collaboration of the responsible parties, the good sense and good will of the community, and when needed the help of the expert physician?"

These are days of leagues of personal freedom and leagues of medical freedom and leagues protecting the privilege to get drunk and to get sick and make others sick whenever and however you please. The worst enemy man has is his own unbridled passion and unbridled craving; and it is unbridled craving and childish fear of interference which under the glamour of freedom keeps us all the more strongly in bondage. Opposed to these there may be regulation leagues, but as intermediaries we want at least to be sure to cultivate plain good sense and a fair chance to use it.

A careful student of the literature and of the facts of eugenics realizes the complexity of the problem and the reason why we should be cautious about pushing everything to the point of legislative regulation. It is in the interest of civilization to provide principles and customs rather than laws, and to give the plain sense of the individual a chance to develop and to become effective. Give the people the facts and some help to think and the right sources of advice, and there will surely be results.

I am tempted to emphasize the fact that those who have had trouble and conquered have often been the most helpful and effective pioneers and the most thoughtful agents of constructive reform. We need persons willing to struggle and able to struggle. We must strive to avoid wanton disaster; but we must also trust our ability to save good traits and to provide against any possible mishap such improvements of our marriage standards that the undesirable traits may be bred out as often as they used to be bred in.

Somehow I cannot be a fatalist. I am, therefore, very cautious about the advice to suppress nature's promptings for progeny unless I consider the mating doubly charged and the parents unfit to create a home.

What might a helpful civilization do toward preventing such disaster as we see in our figures? The first help is protection of the foolish against playing with the holiest of all sacraments—with marriage.

Under the heading of personal freedom we indulge in this country in the acceptance of common-law marriage, and marriage on marriage licenses which are, as far as I know, a mere farce, since they evidently can be obtained without any guarantee of control. The clerk can insist on forms and on a fee, but cannot guarantee controlled facts. The statements are made on oath, but I have not heard of any prosecution for perjury on the part of the state. Licenses without a provision of control have no sense.

Why not provide methods which would make control and advice at least possible? Personally, I grew up as one of a people (the Swiss) which has had a republican form of government since the year 1291—a time preceding the discovery of this continent by 200 years and antedating the Declaration of Independence by 485 years. In that country, which certainly does not foster paternalism and disregard of personal rights, no marriage license is valid that has not been posted for three weeks by the civil authorities and published in the papers. Runaway matches and marrying parsons have no place under such conditions.

Is it asking too much in Uncle Sam's type of free country to have the sense of the people so roused that they prefer to have their personal freedom guided by three weeks of calm consideration rather than by the mere passion of a moment and false romanticism? In the families cited above, there were one girl and one boy married at fifteen years, the boy's being a decidedly unsatisfactory marriage.

Or if, in such a critical period as the consideration of marriage, we should have no confidence in our families and neighbors and in their good sense and good will, why should we not, in the ceremony itself, put the proper emphasis on the real issue of marriage? Why not replace the much-discussed question of obedience by the question put to both parties to the life contract: "Do you want this man (or this woman) and no other to be the father (or mother) of your children?"

Not until some question as pointed as this is, in all cases, expected and squarely asked and squarely answered as a matter of general and frank concern as soon as marriage is considered, will the rank and file of people realize the needed obligation to deal fairly with the problem of health and parental responsibility before the knot is tied. Let it be a legitimate and obligatory question and more couples will give some serious thought to what is often enough passed over because of false prudery or for lack of sense of responsibility.

Now the other point: Do not let us obscure the issue by encouraging intentionally childless marriage. The more I see of childless marriages the more I feel their intrinsic wrong. Nine times out of ten they mean that one of the partners is exploited and condemned to forced sterility and stolen away from less selfish compacts of life. How are you going to help that? By the community's undertaking to make possible a greater measure of economic security among all classes, through sickness insurance, through the provision of medical care and of vocational training, and by practical demonstrations in the schools of the way in which the economic problems can be faced and family life made possible on a limited income.

My second problem is: What is the duty of those who have become parents but with hereditary taint?

Nobody can have absolute guarantee of healthy progeny. All parents need a good dose of preparedness to accept whatever fate may bring to their children. The progress of the world has done much to guide us if we are wise, and, fortunately, on the constructive side as well as on the preventive. Let us not forget that those who may have a tainted stock and some cause for worry may be able to make good and render valuable service to all. Those forewarned are more likely to be thoughtful about the child than those who play ostrich and make it their practical and even religious duty to be blind to the great facts of experience. And when the forewarned improve the chances of their own children it will be for the good of all.

As far as the child itself is concerned, give it a chance to grow and to develop naturally, and consider it a duty to protect this growth and to guide rather than force it. Few realize what a hell a child's life must be when it is continually cut into by the whims and momentary or untimely good intentions and peremptory expectations of adults. Heed the many sensible suggestions which are available in such valuable documents as the publications of the National Committee for Mental Hygiene and the Federal Children's Bureau.

I want to limit my special advice to tainted parents to two points: First, do not allow yourselves to cultivate any sensitiveness about learning the facts and facing the facts about your children. Do not assume an attitude of defense or offense when anyone gives you the helpful truth. You need not talk to everybody about your grief or tears; but do not let your own false pride or conceit stand in the way of helping yourselves and the child by means of proper advice. When you see that your own resources fail, why not go

over the trouble with someone who knows more about it? Why
not hand over a difficult child for a time to a trained person, a
school or an institution, and why not be willing to take a few
lessons in child management?

When you are in doubt it should become less and less difficult
to find a medical and an educational adviser with whom you are
willing to work out a careful record of the assets and of the
difficulties, and of the failures and the successes of various plans
tried so far. You can then expect to guide your children toward
what may be best for them at the time. It is in this connection that
I should like to urge you to expect ever-improving services from
our schools.

Our schools must become the places where the first attempts at
grading and at standardization for life should be started. Civilization
is not one simple scheme and rule, but depends on a wonderful
coordination of the safe knowledge and wisdom of generations on
a wide range of human needs. Among other things, real civilization
includes a public morality and a public spirit which looks upon
schools not as part of a system of political favoritism and exploitation, but as one means of bringing order into community life, of
training and trying out the child in the capacities of social behavior, and of learning and working under impartial standards.

The proper collaboration of home and school is less and less
vitiated by false ideals of freedom and false fears of meddling.
Parents are perhaps still too ready to consider their parental feelings
hurt and to withdraw the child from school when they are tempted
to attribute lack of progress to the teaching or to the school. Instead
of having the matter looked into by a competent and impartial
inquirer, the parents and the child still are too apt to rule the
situation and to blunder.

I know of parents belonging to the intellectual aristocracy who
will not let their child be given a Binet-Simon test; they do not
want to know the facts and prefer to be led by sentiment alone.
Children who become inefficient at one school are apt to be sent to
another or to work; whereas it would be in the interest of the
community and the children if they were standardized and advised

and taught to be respectable members of the community on their own level.

Bureaus issuing labor permits may do excellent work on this point. If a child has the misfortune of being defective there are still some ways to be effective. To be helped to bring these effective ways to the front and to find one's level is better than being forced by foolish parents to live on bluff. In these defectives we can also train ideals and a conscience and can give them satisfactions adapted to them, instead of letting them outmarry the marriageable and outmultiply the fit.

I am skeptical about the possibility of general segregation of all those who are defective and dangerous because they are apt to reproduce their kind. We can increase our training schools and colonies but slowly, in keeping with the growth of the confidence of the people. But if we have compulsory school attendance and compulsory standardizing at school, we can certainly learn to help more persons find their sphere or level in life. This does not mean branding the child; it does mean helping him to find a sphere in which he can attain his best level in perfect respectability.

The second point of my advice to tainted parents is but an extension of this point: Train yourselves and your children to look upon physicians and hospitals and trainers as constructive rather than corrective agencies.

The most difficult cases to help are those who distrust hospital and physician and adviser, we may say, constitutionally. Familiarize yourself with what hospitals and training schools are doing so that you may feel ready to accept their help when you need it; and inculcate in the young the right attitude toward the resources our civilization offers us.

You have little idea how many people believe training schools and mental hospitals are for what they call "the really insane" or "defective" of other families, but their own children and friends are certainly not of that class. What do people know of "classes"?

Go and teach yourselves and your children and your neighbors the fact that when anyone gets nervous and unequal to the difficulties of life, we have in our midst dispensaries and hospitals to help us on the right track, hospitals serving as asylums from which fully twenty per cent may readily come out better entitled to be called normal than if they had missed the opportunities offered by our states, and from which many apparently hopeless wrecks emerge with a gain worthy of our open gratitude instead of our frequent desire to hide the facts and to swell the false traditions of stigma, the absurd relic of fear and superstition.

If I felt that I had to conceal the fact that my own mother had two attacks of melancholia from which she recovered, I should thereby tacitly corroborate the false efforts at concealment of many others who could not conceal the fact of mental diseases in their family if they tried. Why am I able to speak freely to my own progeny about it? Because I have a conviction based on experience and on facts that many a mental disorder is much less ignominious than more than fifty per cent of other diseases for which people have to get treatment; that many a nervous or mental disorder is the result of struggling honestly but unwisely; that many a former patient becomes a wiser element of the community when restored than the luckier and possibly thoughtless fellow.

If there is some hereditary taint which causes you apprehension, try to prepare your offspring to live all the more wisely and to make themselves worthy of the healthiest mates. What we call insanity in a family must not be a wholesale warning against marriage. It means greater care in education and more appreciation of truly healthy strains and then either fitness to become attractive to the untainted or a choice of a life of usefulness outside of marriage.

After all, what we need most is to teach the child to wish to be well and to love the healthy. Love is very justly nature's and mankind's ablest matrimonial agent. Love plays many pranks and is said to be blind; but love, like any other capacity, can be made to grow better or worse. It certainly is taught badly or indifferently or wisely through the way the parents love each other and through the ideals implanted in the child.

Let me state once more the main points of my appeal:

First, help me in fighting the foolish game of trying to conceal the facts of heredity and of catering to the cruel notions of stigma. A man or a woman is primarily what he or she is, or can do; and the knowledge of heredity will help in guiding the understanding or management of inborn traits. All this secrecy about heredity only means that other people cannot mention the facts to your face, but behind your back will talk of the skeleton in your closet. By thinking more of the safety of this closet than of actual needs you may cheat your own people out of their best chances of getting timely care in the beginning of any trouble, and throw at the same time a slur on hospitals and on other patients, and ultimately it will fall back with a vengeance on your own family.

Second, let us not indulge in vague notions about heredity. If you want facts, let someone work up your family records as we have worked up those described in this paper. It will not do to go to a physician and ask, "What do you think of heredity?" But you must say, "I want somebody put on the job of getting my family record worked out, and then I want your advice on various questions." No physician should prostitute himself by giving his opinion without having the family studied properly.

Third, the conclusions from heredity study cannot be codified in the form of legislation. We can, however, lead people to be more responsible and to do better thinking. My two suggestions are: Turn the marriage license again into something which calls for three weeks of sound and open thinking and which is worth more than a fee and an invitation to frequent perjury which the state tolerates, thus lowering the sacredness of an oath before an official. The second suggestion would be regarding the marriage ceremony. Have it understood that in this solemn hour you have to answer the question whether you have really chosen the person whom you want to be the father or the mother of your children.

Fourth, let parents who know that their children may have a taint—a latent disposition or actual defect—find their compensation in the conviction that theirs is the burden of being specially mindful of the saner and sounder education of their children; and especially also a saner and sounder education in the question of what and whom and how to love.

This is not a hopeless problem. It is the biggest and finest problem of humanity.

EUGENICS RESEARCH

From "Organization of Eugenics Investigation," presidential address by Dr. Meyer, Eugenics Research Association, Cold Spring Harbor, N. Y., June 22, 1917; Eugenical News, 2:66 (Sept., 1917).

Several factors have conspired against my bringing to you a well-defined personal contribution to research in eugenics. The fundamental reason, undoubtedly, is my reserve against accepting the applications of the Mendelian rules as more than a stimulus to research until we shall have safer definitions of unit characters and safe life records in our material showing Mendelism along some of the more controllable lines and not only along the lines on which we are anxious for results.

Since I have not much use for skepticism which does not lead to some activity and constructive reaction, I should like at least to make an appeal for the constitution of several committees which might become the coordinating centers for certain definite lines of work which would get away from the more questionable generalities and focus the attention upon a few definite points of obvious importance in our field.

My skepticism about premature Mendelian simplicity in the etiological explanation of psychobiological disorders has two sources. In the first place, I am one of those who see too many explanations by more *direct nonhereditary* causes in many of the defects and disorders of total behavior which we meet in our practical work. We know much more today than the nontrained outsider knows of the factors which enter into the production of defect of development and disorder of psychobiological functions, without having to appeal to ultrarecondite and formal explanations; and while I most heartily encourage the search for fundamental facts of human make-up in terms of inheritable units, it seems to me best not to prejudice observation and analysis of facts too hastily by claims which tend to paralyze further investigation.

At the present juncture it seems so much safer to work on individual patients as hard as possible with methods and factors and purposes which one can actually direct and modify, such as the analysis and recasting of habit developments and the regulation of the organs entering into the psychobiological integrations. On the other hand, I want to be equally sure that this quest for factors modifiable in the patient does not dull our attention to those firm and unshakable facts embodied in the heredity of growth, organ, and equipment with resources, which the genetic method can attack.

When I compare the standard of study required for a reasonably good understanding of any one patient with the summary estimate with which fieldworkers have to be satisfied when they hear of a nervous breakdown, or alcoholism, or insanity, I am staggered, on the one hand, by the naïveté which would be needed to ignore the mass of facts of an ontogenetic nature seen in the individual life, and on the other hand by the sweeping simplicity of the few points picked out for heredity statistics.

As soon as we use the standards of the best knowledge we have of our cases, our confidence in the explanatory forces of the available laws of heredity for the understanding of the disorders suffers considerably. We have no right to rest our case on over-simple statistical hypotheses where so many variables are involved. I feel that I can best express my attitude by a comparison with what we require in other hypothetical biological tests, such as the Abderhalden reaction. We demand that each unit of study be tried on a number of no-longer-hypothetical tests of the same method in order to give the specific and questionable new test a dependable comparative background. In other words, we shall have a few really Mendelizing human factors as controls in our human series if we want to use the material for our new hypothetical thrusts into the unknown.

This method of control does not retard practical progress. The undesirability of reproduction of the feebleminded and obviously too unstable is granted even without resorting to Mendelian claims which tend to minimize the wide range of types and origins of these conditions. The main practical test, I take it, in actually using Mendelism for our guidance will have been brought out when we shall be able actually to claim reasonable germ purity and freedom from transmission tendency for some individuals and not for others, and reasonably safe facts for the breeding-in and the breeding-out of traits, helping us beyond what is already brought out by the unpretentious survey of the family tendency as a whole and by the practical estimate of the individual as a possible parent and educator. Only in a few conditions are we able to say, "Here we can separate definitely the taint-free from the tainted members," or at least prove that there are taint-free individuals who would breed or already had bred true normal descendants, in contrast to those who, as tainted, may have to be limited in their matings or directly considered unfit. There is here a most important field for patient and tenacious research.

When we come to the actually practical application of our data of heredity in our social fabric, we must evidently be able to build on more convincing evidence than that available today if we are to get the wholehearted support of our political and social organizations. I do not know what the present status is of that wave of marriage regulation which collapsed in the Wisconsin law. Personally, I am not pessimistic about a really more far-reaching human collaboration—even after the present sad relapse of humanity into a trial of pseudoprogress by general destruction—at least if we go about it correctly.

The jealous protection of the right to individual impulse in such matters as marriage can only be met by a much greater lucidity in marshaling human aims and human assets than we have ever imposed upon ourselves in our erudite and scientific work. Unfortunately, our personality-studies and family-studies are not lucid and perspicuous enough to be taken in at a glance and yet to be convincing, and we expect the average public to do what we ourselves would not want to do, *i.e.*, arrive at a conclusion on faith and general impression where really the actual facts should be more clearly digested and brought home in a convincing demonstration with evidence of adequate controls. I am absolutely certain that the eugenics movement has so far worked mainly by its appeal to natural human meliorism and that very largely negatively; it has mainly helped some people to rationalize their preexisting hesitancy in regard to marriage and progeny; it may have raised the fear of tainted families, but only to a lesser extent a wider and a clearer knowledge about them.

One of our practical aims must be to give more students a grasp on sorting out personalities and life records in a more convincing and more graphic way and to require a most scrupulous demonstration of the facts on which we want to make statistics. Dr. C. B. Davenport's very stimulating revival of the concept of simple temperaments comes nearest the generally intelligible, as far as the points of emphasis and direction go; but I certainly have in myself to overcome certain fundamental revulsions against such exceedingly simple and general assumptions as the heterogeneity of push and inhibition on the one hand, and cheerfulness and depression problems on the other, which if not just one general trait, certainly are most strongly interlaced in our experiences, and by no means in evidence or absent in pure culture in most of the affected persons whom we know well enough. To assume that a depressive reaction would have to mean a melancholy temperament and absence of the C factor, would be clearly contradicted by my knowledge of the sunny and happy temperaments of many patients who, as people say, were "the last persons ever expected to develop melancholia"—and these are by no means so rare that they would be overruled by statistical results.

The division into interchangeable components of manic-depressive insanity was tried by Weygandt. It is well that they should be tried out; but we should no doubt learn more from bold dismembering than from timid suspense.

Now a word with regard to the collection of data. Looking over the whole ground, I feel there is much call for enthusiastic work, but undoubtedly we must first be willing to work practically for the sake of safer and more readily demonstrable knowledge, and we should encourage especially those who will sift the data as they are being collected, those who show talent to single out the facts impressed upon them to adjust the methods for the collection of new data as their knowledge increases and as they become more familiar with possible objections and doubts. This is a very different procedure from a supposedly random collection of facts and then a trying-out of various theories derived from efforts to satisfy certain laws. The great demand ultimately is to satisfy the call for such clear-cut presentation of complex facts as will convince the layman and the scholar alike through getting beyond crude impressionism and its dogmatic counterpart, the arbitrariness of over-simple hypotheses.

My own psychiatric tendency, with its taboo on oversimple nosology, might further exemplify what I mean. It may be disquieting to some, but I trust it will after all be a stimulus toward safer and more profitable work. I do not shrink from using most of the standard notions of disease entities in psychiatry and psychopathology mainly as more or less frequent combinations of events and facts, and not as set and final entities, and demand that we accept frankly the composite character of many of the conditions which we now aim to treat as units, as if they were the evidence of one central fact, for which we would have to invent, if we do not find it, one kind of "lesion," the discovery of which would relieve us of all further call for the consideration of other facts.

For the advancement of our movement, in order to avoid both useless diffusion and arbitrary dogmatism, it would seem wisest to create and constitute certain centers of intensive discussion or committee work on various topics as they arise from time to time; centers for the concentrated sifting of issues pertaining to the special topics, committees known as such to the Association at large and serving as recipients of facts and suggestions with a view to furnishing surveys of the questions and suggestions raised. Thus we might well have a committee on simplified presentations of personalities and standards of facts; a committee composed of geneticists and psychobiologists should work intensively on what can be proposed as promising and tenable unit material and allelomorphs; and further, on the practical side, which we can never afford to leave behind, a committee might focus on a study of the lines of responsiveness of the public to a more than impulsive interest in practical eugenics, such as the attainment of a reform of marriage customs and the best possible investment of the undoubtedly existing natural tendency to do the best one really knows.

From a practical point of view such centers or committees should in part be made up of neighbors forming a natural group that can meet often and freely, with something like corresponding members in the other research stations (or at least act with those specifically interested) and occasionally conjoint meetings, especially at the time of the annual conference or other favorable occasions, and furnishing well-digested reports for the annual meetings. The Record Office [Eugenics Record Office, Cold Spring Harbor] has its quota of special and natural lines of interest in definite topics. Let it be known what they are and the Record Office together with a sort of steering committee of the Association would see to it that the group work gets furthered in the best possible way.

BIRTH CONTROL

From preface by Dr. Meyer to Birth Control, *edited by Adolf Meyer, p. v, Williams & Wilkins Company, Baltimore* (1925); *and from paper by Dr. Meyer, "The Obligation of Procreative Hygiene,"* 1923 Baltimore Conference on Birth Control, *ibid., p. 1.*

Our primary concern is the development of a conscience concerning procreation.

Owing to some of our laws the topic has to be excluded from the textbooks and discussions of professional journals using the mails and there is neither research nor proper teaching on this topic in most medical schools.

Hence the formulation of the problem to the effect that it is a matter of conscience not to indulge even in the consideration of sex relations in which the possibility of conception would not be acceptable with a full sense of responsibility, since the notion of depending on abortion as a remedy of lapses has to be kept out of the public mind on account of the dangers to the mother, if for no other reason. It must be clear that contraceptive measures are given consideration partly in order to prevent undue suffering in a civilization which includes a great deal of indiscriminative and obtrusive sex stimulation, and partly in order to prevent the frequently disastrous way of allowing the possibility of abortion to figure as the corrective of undesired pregnancy.

We are convinced that the greatest opportunity of mankind, that of recruiting itself and reproducing itself, ought to receive the benefits of experience and thoughtfulness such as man puts on every other interest. We want to reinforce our conscience for the quality and health of human progeny.

We are aware that there are conscientious but loving and after all human married couples who, we feel, should not suffer the often agonizing fear of unjustified pregnancy in the climax of their natural affection. We ask for frank investigation of life as it is actually lived by the rank and file of our people and of all the ways that make for better living. Social happiness, the health of the individual and development of the progeny—it is these three points which furnish the basis for any consideration of sex and birth control.

To approach this goal we really ask for little—merely the right of the physician to be allowed to give his advice and guidance where his judgment calls for a sensible regulation of the chances of pregnancy.

We realize that we are dealing with a tendency and usage that occurs in very concrete forms in nearly every household and it is not an abstract question. We have to admit frankly that we are concerned with a respectable percentage of the rank and file of marriages of today and not with exceptions, and that this state of affairs creates a source of much floundering and unhealth. Like the prevention of venereal disease, the prevention of unwelcome and especially potentially harmful and dangerous pregnancies certainly is a serious and highly responsible medical and individual consideration.

Opponents of birth control evidently want everyone to depend on his or her own limited experience. They want to keep the world good by keeping it ignorant and by mere precepts. They mistrust anything short of absolute prohibition of sex relations without intent to impregnate.

We are interested primarily in the wholesomeness of marital life and in including in its ideal the duty to provide for the health and the future of the progeny, and are not mainly concerned with the mere begetting of children, with the calming of concupiscence and the fostering of that type of conjugal love and affection that we find emphasized under the title of "conjugal obedience."

We definitely state that sex relations even with contraceptives should not happen where there is not a willingness to accept a pregnancy if it does occur.

Personally, I am one of those who would like to work for a gradual readjustment of human cravings and self-control. I should like to see a man rise above the animal or attain what some animals do naturally, as far as possible by concentrating the sex urge upon the occasions of a climax of affection when progeny is wanted or at least welcome.

I should like to see better outlets for human ambition than play with the potentially most responsible of acts. But having such an ideal should not blind one in the meantime to the facts as they are. Could there not be a more reasonable harmony between our laws and our usages, and a wiser attitude of confidence in a fundamentally melioristic philosophy of the average person when he or she is given the facts and the best knowledge and outlook?

The main point is that physicians shall do what they do with such habits of supervision, study, and control of the effects of what they do that we may grow toward a better knowledge of the facts. Let us remember that the modern ideal of freedom is a freedom with obligatory responsibility, but responsibilities dictated not merely by dogma but by the best possible wisdom of the facts and opportunities for betterment.

We urge that physicians be protected against unjustified prosecution when they follow their medical consciences, that physicians discuss the actual results and effects of their advice, so that a body of facts and frank comparisons of experience can become a guide for practice and progress—not an arbitrary blundering along, but a readiness to correct the mistakes and to work for even wiser foresight.

THE FAMILY SETTING

From remarks by Dr. Meyer at First International Congress on Mental Hygiene, Washington, May 10, 1930; Proceedings, 2:644.

The family is an old institution, biologically and socially determined, and, as an institution, not likely to work well without some effort and forethought. Yet it seems to be one of those human possessions which are latest in becoming the object of constructive-minded study, and, like the heart, seems to be something one hardly heeds unless something goes wrong with it. The bulk of the present-day literature dealing with the family, like so much of the psychological bases of hygiene, is too largely a study of pathology and bankruptcies. What is needed is a study of more of the successful families and the conditions at work in them.

The family is the nest in and around which the basic development of the character formation needed for certain levels of civilization seeks its best chance to take shape. Through similar tastes and yet enough mixtures of traits, family formation furnishes to the siblings and the parents and the relatives the familial combination of ties and opportunities, a school and a test of affection, of tolerance, of cohesion.

Within the relative intimacy of the *family group* and its radius of friendly and neighborly contacts, personal lives and their goals and standards can shape themselves better than in any other promiscuous group or one not based on blood relationship. The school provides a more or less select setting for a wider socialization, the racial and church sets provide another, and the civic and political national setting a still more comprehensive one. The question is the extent to which the individualistic personal instincts and personal experiences can shape themselves into a personal outlook and personal habits, dependable regular and emerging resources and what we call character. While the concept of the family carries with it taboos and hazards and quasi-instinctive fears and conflicts, it includes both basic biological and ultimately social attainments, with opportunities for a strong sense of belonging, of security, intimacy, and understanding of life. It can never cease to be the prototype of primary grouping.

For centuries marriage has been held to be one of the sacraments and as such kept under a system of religious obligations in a none-too-good system of social customs. Today there exists the urge to throw off the tradition-born order, but liberty based on mere revolt is not necessarily a guarantee of progress. It may be a gain, but we may well hope for something better than mere trial and error and mere lessons from excursions to the South Seas.

Something as complicated individually and socially or as fateful as marital selection, and something as important as parent-child and child-parent and intra- and interfamilial relationships, naturally cannot be expected offhand, in scientifically, biologically and humanly true terms, with the few generations in which the modern mind has taken the chance to apply itself seriously to a really dependable study of man with a view to shaping its own destiny.

The ideal of science demands (1) observation of the facts and happenings, and (2) formulation fit to be used in the next step, which has to be (3) tested by actual performance; and it will take unrelenting and prolonged labor to arrive at a good and safe picture of a creative pattern as dependable as the authoritative one is at its best, but at the same time more open to individual choice and creativeness.

The time may come when we shall have enough sets of dependable facts to let them speak for themselves, instead of our having to express our interest in family study largely in terms devised for the plots and stories of "best selling" literature or in terms of exhortations and the more modern style of revolt and remonstrance. Because of the great role imagination plays in human life, man's constitutional endowment shapes itself along the lines of experience and fancy, but in experience and fancy man usually follows patterns of example and fashion rather than any particular creative capacity. The successes and failures are open to study, however, and the results of study are used in leadership. The basic condition for successful family formation is undoubtedly the degree of maturity in the choice of a mate.

The present trend expresses itself too exclusively, to my mind, in terms of one ideal sex pattern. I would emphasize much more strongly the sense of security, of belonging, and of the various forms of affection. It is inevitable that there will always have to be quite a number of livable sex and life patterns. It is obvious, too, that they must be made more appropriately communicable for the different ages and life periods coexisting in a family— where we have side by side the immature child, the restless adolescent, the variously mature, the senescent, the married and the unmarried, the well and poorly balanced.

The family is apt to offer the individual member examples of the varieties of contacts, which have to be managed with foresight, in terms of both freedom and thoughtfulness and as affections with and without sex function, resting on a basis of experience more and more capable of including the fruits of critical objective demonstration; integrated in literature and in art, and sound religious and sociological thought patterns.

Civilization is not compatible with unlimited promiscuity, or any other purely individualistic willfullness. The family is the place where the processes of training in socially required differentiations of affections can be worked out and cultivated.

It is natural and desirable that the deep-rooted sentiments—conjugal, parental and familial—should be the principles underlying marriage. Let us know the factors that are constructive and those that might become disturbing. One of our greatest tasks will be the creation of special formulations suitable for the different ages of the members of the family and for the social spheres, as well as the most personal spheres. The family is also most likely to be the best ground on which to acquire a balance for the two, by no means incompatible and yet definitely distinct, modes of discussion—the broadly public and the more private and personal. An appeal for more tact and thoughtfulness in literature and in art and science is not a sign of prudery but is due to a wish for less difficulty in separating in a reasonable way what can be public and what, in a way, must be private and attainable only with maturity. We are certainly graduating from secrecy and mystery, but without any corresponding understanding for the right time or the right place. In the family we may learn to sense what we need to make the living-together of old and young wholesome.

A nation and a civilization need taste as well as efficiency. Today, with the tremendous variety of communications there is more than ever a need of patterns and of philosophies and a forward-looking conscience, in the sense of what the individual and the group can be conscious of in moments of emergency, and may well make others conscious of.

CHARACTER EDUCATION AND
RELIGION

From an address, "What Can the Psychiatrist Contribute to Character Education?" delivered by Dr. Meyer before the Religious Education Association, regional conference, Baltimore, 1930; Religious Education, 25:414 (May, 1930).

Psychiatry has no dogma to offer. It builds on a willingness to learn from experience. It strives to develop a science of man under the sign of experience and creative experiment. It has to begin with those who come to the physician on their own initiative, or that of others, because they are in trouble. When we, the supposedly healthy, come to study ourselves, we begin with the differences and variations in behavior, in the intellectual and emotional tendencies, and in the capacity to accumulate and to use experience; and, furthermore, with the differences in the lasting traits, the temperament and character. We know character is a matter of growth (of nature and physique) and of experience; and this is the mutual understanding on which we join hands with the educator on the policies of guidance.

Here we find two main routes: The interest of the minister is largely one of guidance from above; ours is largely attention to guidance from the roots, but by no means exclusively so. The psychiatrist, at any rate the social-minded psychiatrist, knows that human nature includes all of that which belongs to the reality and actuality of human functioning and settings, from the roots to the fruition and from one stage to the other. When we speak of character we look for dependability—that is, orderliness—and for discipline—which is the capacity to use guidance—and for a certain security and maturity. We aim at whatever favors getting the best start, the best guidance and, finally, the best opportunities for the character to endure when we have got it.

There is such a thing as character really true to nature—ringing true to our best sense. There is also such a thing as imposed character—which is apt to fail in emergency.

We have a session on character-building probably because we are in a period when there seems to be a lot of uncertainty about the meaning and worth-whileness of current methods of character training. Our ideals are uncertain, and the ways of attainment seem also to be uncertain. Perhaps we are justly in an inquiring mood. Our spokesman of American intellectuality, John Dewey, finds himself pondering over the justification and wisdom of all the "quest for certainty" and expounds to us the need of a better sense for relativities. There used to be a quest for truth, whatever it might be. And, in these days of gambling, we speak, with a hope for relief, of a quest for "certainty" as if it could be a fixed and final something. But today we are not so sure that we should seek absolute truth. We are a bit suspicious of those who claim too loudly to have it.

The most besetting difficulty of the present day seems to be a kind of haste in the direction of individual willfullness, with a desperate determination to assert this willfullness, without any very clear ideas as to what one wants to be willful about. We see it in feminism for feminism's sake. We see it in the popularity of Max Stirner's will to power and in the hold of Nietzsche's philosophy and his superadolescent urge to tell the world the bald truth and to cut out all "illusions." We see it in the way people lose their heads and their constructive judgment over the alcohol problem and in the fact that writers consider it a drawing card to a big audience to announce their wisdom in terms of suspicion and derision with the question: "What's the matter with this and what's the matter with that?" And we see it in talk of the bankruptcy of democracy and marriage and religion and science—usually having for its objective the taking of the backbone out of all time-honored institutions, which are depicted as if they could be of no good at all because they do not prosper without some real effort and sense of responsibility. There is no stand-by of a hundred years ago that has not had its "survey" and prediction of the need of the famous Nietzschean "transvaluation of all values." All this means instability and marks a philosophy rather of revolution than of growth and evolution.

What do we think we mean when we talk of character? We mean "the unity, consistency and distinctive individuality of feeling and thinking and acting of a person."

Character, I assume, is not merely what the Greek word implies, the scratch on a stick (like the simile the German uses for writing with letters, the *Buchstaben*), the mark or stamp impressed. It means the intrinsic essence of the peculiar nature of a person and, evidently, his dependable features or traits—that which one has to expect and can expect in the light of his make-up—the person's outlook and philosophy in action. It is the factual upshot of balance between what man is, by structure and function of the parts and the person, and the vision of what he wants to be or can see himself to be.

Temperament refers to the dominant trend of rapid or slow, weak or strong, emotional and volitional reactivity. Character refers more to the trends of motivation. Character is, I should say, the capacity to stand for things. For what? It is the capacity to identify oneself with causes and principles, or, if one has not any of one's own, with certain persons and groups.

There are, then, two prerequisites, a capacity to see worth-while causes and goals and a capacity to embrace them in thought and performance.

I am reminded of my first attempt at discussing a plan to help nervous people, the first paper I ever read before a medical society, in February, 1893. I asked those whom I expected to help me in the discussion: "Can you tell me what types of occupation will arouse and hold the interest of American women and men when they become self-concerned and neurotic and in need of therapeutic occupation?"

I still ask the same question: "What is there for my patients, and for average young Americans, to choose as their goal, to build themselves up with?" Shall we trust sheer "self-realization," according to the modern gospel, and let it go at that? I still should say: "What worth-while causes have we to offer, what interests and principles and real performances, to which the various personalities can pledge themselves? What does an age of success in machine work and occasional success in the stock market and salesmanship offer for one to identify himself with?"

Character is not an abstract virtue. Like the mill, it has to have its grist. We have the reputation of being the land of the dollar, with a civilization based too much on the doctrine of success, and this measured, in the end, by what one is worth in dollars and cents. It is a bit difficult for a young man to know for what he should prepare himself, except for pursuits in which the success can be measured by money. What else do we usually mean if we speak of bettering ourselves? What do we mean when we permit to pass, without question or remonstrance, the claim that every man has his price? What is worthy of being made a man's goal? It is very difficult to prepare for a career or for a life's work as long as the gamble counts for more than does the endeavor—the result is more due to chance than to character.

We pride ourselves on our civilization of action and hustling. How about the equally necessary capacity for composure—freedom from excitement, satisfaction even in natural sobriety?

Somehow, a certain degree of composure is the necessary cradle for substantial new starts. We need the ability to collect our thoughts for rest, as well as for venture. What, then, promises satisfaction, even in sobriety, rather than in kick and thrill? Neither the sociologist nor the economist has a simple goal or method to offer.

Let us now turn to those who study not so much the economico-sociological staging as the agents, the actors of the drama.

The physician, unfortunately, has, true to his title, been too long the guardian only of the body. Today we are interested more and more in the body in action, in the body as a person.

For the broadening of human interest in medicine, you might

be interested to know—it could not have been mere chance—that of the several psychiatrists especially interested in character, quite a number, like myself, are ministers' sons. Lavater, one of the first characterologists, was a Zürich minister; Dr. Jung, also of Zürich, the characterologist who has given a name to the introvert and the extrovert, is a minister's son. Zürich also was the place of training of Rorschach, a psychiatrist who died young, but who left to us his test of personality make-up, based on what the person can read out of apparently meaningless spread ink spots. The daughter of the Zürich novelist, Conrad Ferdinand Meyer, gave shelter and help to Klages, the graphologist, who today offers a most pretentious characterology to the world. And it was another minister's son, Kretschmer, a Swabian, who pointed out a most striking relation between body structure and stature and character. He showed clearly that man's physique determines largely his character. It is materially important that some are round and stubby and deep-chested and others are lank and more like a wedge or a spade. His was a clever vision and objective demonstration of well-founded relationships between physique and temperament, already sensed by the ancients, with their doctrine of temperaments, and by Shakespeare in Julius Caesar's words: "Let me have men about me that are fat." Another Zürich psychiatrist, Bleuler, has coined the term of syntonic and schizoid traits of man for Kretschmer's two main types: the emotionally clean-cut, easy and natural mixer, or extrovert, the syntonic; and the more odd, seclusive, shut-in person, the introvert and schizoid.

In my teaching I am inclined to contrast the people who live in terms of "we," the thoroughly socializable, the syntropic, with those who always have to be concerned with the self, the egotropic, not readily socialized, who then fall into the groups of the active aggressive and the passive subtypes.

Psychiatry, of course, has to deal largely with the persons who deviate, who get out of the groove of the normal. In psychiatry generally, we speak of the syntonic and cyclothymic or manic-depressive syntropic (outgoing) temperament, with its pyknic (heavy-set) stature; of the paranoic aggressive egotropic and the submissive passive but remonstrating "schizoid" introvert (more asthenic and lank); and of the dystonic or dystropic, usually also dysplastic, not well put together. We speak of the hysterical—wanting to be noticed; and of the epileptic, usually an openly or quietly egocentric character.

There is another group of physicians today and especially, also, litterateurs, that exploit the endocrine data, the glands, as determiners of character; others, the visceral data generally. There can be no doubt that what we grow to be we also act and feel and have as part of our fate.

There is no getting around the great significance of the very nature of types of physique. It is an inherent fact of the nature of man that on the one hand what we mean verbally and literally by nature (*i.e.*, what is to be born) and by the physical (*i.e.*, what becomes what it is by growth) means a great deal and is basic and is sure to determine a great deal of what is given to us as the spirit and the range of the meaning of man.

The attitude of modern psychiatry in matters of character study and in all of this both keeps and adds to what commonsense experience has long taught.

Man's nature and physique imply what he is born from and into what he grows. The very word *natura* points to "what will be given birth to" and what we grow to be. And so does "physique" signify that which goes with and comes through growth, *physis*.

Most of us, in this way, take seriously also the fact which even language brings down to us when it speaks of our animal nature, pointing to *anima*, the breeze or breath, as a basic, inherent feature of animal life; and we do well to remember that all the words designating our mental and spiritual functions are expressed in terms of breath: *psyche* is breath; the Hebrew word *roach* builds upon the primarily life- and spirit-giving nature of breathing, the concept of spirit and inspiration and life.

But how about the air which we breathe and give others to breathe? What are the dependables we offer to nature and physique to shape itself for?

Let me make myself emphatically clear on this point. This is a period when everyone wants to pick on and tinker with the child, although in reality we know less about the child than about the adult, and when it is very unpopular to ask the adult to mind first his own business. The adult is supposed to be the mature fruit of all nature and nurture; and he, in turn, is the dispenser of all that is good in material and experience and endowment for the next generation. If he wants to do this well, the adult cannot shirk assuming a great responsibility for creating the necessary atmosphere.

The student of nature sees in nature the process, the becoming. Nature, as I said, is literally *natura*, that which is to be born. Hence the adult will have to create the best conditions of birth and growth.

We have to begin with the stock and give the first thought not to special forms of companionate and other readily dissoluble marriages but to the choice of a mate worthy to be the parent of the child and of the next generation. This is the first step of character-building.

We have to create conditions—as the phrase goes—for "physical, mental, and spiritual" growth or life—conditions for life today and tomorrow, for this generation and for the next. And perhaps we should have a little less conceit about any ability to possess and to hand out the keys to eternity. We have to create a world of adults fit for the young to be born into.

While imitation in the ordinary naïve sense has probably been overrated, there nevertheless have to be conditions for socialization of these primarily self-willed organisms called children and adolescents.

A little less worry over the child and a bit more concern about the world we make for the child to live in; an inclusion of the child in a life of which the aim is not merely to earn money so as to become independent of the job; more love for wholehearted, creative work and progress that will make possible what we all can share in; with these conditions, the adult and the young both will have a better chance.

As a basis for child guidance, let me say that character-building has to begin with our own. Let us pool what features of character we can offer to the other and wish to accept from the other.

Science, that is, the systematic work with facts and the best possible verbal and technical formulation and retrial of the facts, has had but little chance so far to work without bias, hindrance or fear in the field of human nature.

As long as mystification tries to keep man altogether out of the field of scientific understanding and scientific responsibilities, at least to keep vital parts of man outside of nature, as belonging to a supposedly wholly detached world of spirit and morality, it is difficult to lay the foundations for a healthy and broad perspective and sense of proportion. When we were young, it was a theoretical quest for a philosophical solution of the mind-and-body problem that created unnecessary puzzlement. Just now, it is the matter of sex that looms up out of proportion. There is a deplorable lack of sense of proportion, with a false doctrine that separates the physical and the mental.

Today we include man in the realm of nature and objective reality, body and soul. If it kept the soul out of nature as a kind of proprietary stronghold of another, unknown world, theology would inflict on mankind a questionable service. A wholesome agreement on idealism and realism, with a truly religious faith in the dependability of what we live by, will make it much easier for strong characters to crystallize and to maintain and develop themselves.

Can we, who should be the leaders, wonder at the bewilderment of the average thinking man and woman? Are not some of the best intentioned would-be leaders among the worst sinners, defeating efforts to create a dependable vision for the growth of sound dependability and character and a communion of common goals and common faith?

Many of us are baffled by the remnants of the doctrine of exclusive salvation by dogma. Unless we are born to a special sect it becomes very hard to swallow the conditions of admission to a good general setting for faith in a common progressive ideal. The pity of it is that many a serious and thoughtful scientist feels himself shut out and is unwilling to add any other sectarian group to the too many already existing.

Modern science is not body-shy, nor is it mind-shy any longer. Or to turn it around: Modern religion can no longer be one-sided. It can offer increasing freedom from conflict and from cultivating logic-tight compartments. It does not think largely in terms of eternity but recognizes that one of the intrinsic characteristics of man is his time-bound opportunity: we all have our date of birth and our date of death and a span of life spread over valuable years of growth and maturity, and we all have plenty of need of dependable character and also of reward for character. The respect of religion for the now and here has grown and is growing with more immediate attention to spiritual goals. We learn to respect the hours of mating and infancy and childhood. Jesuits have long claimed that if they have the child during the first seven years they will not worry for its future. We learn to respect the formative years, and while Minot, the Boston embryologist, has told us that we begin to get old at the moment of birth because the nuclei of the cells begin to get smaller, we also take confidence from the fact that to the last breath it is the nature of man to accumulate and profit from experience, as long as man keeps his brain in order, a-functioning.

Throughout the whole of individual life there is a place for character training, and certainly the most urgent and the most constructively potent will always be the character training of the adult, the should-be mature, for his own sake and for that of the growing generation. Hence my interest not only in child hygiene but especially also in the nature and values of the mature, as a necessary setting and prerequisite for educational character training.

MATURE LIVING

From "Maturity," by Dr. Meyer, in Child Study, 7:225 (May, 1930).

Two questions that set me pondering over our American standards of maturity are, first, the difficulty of knowing—with our widely differing economic, denominational, and largely success-determined origins—when maturity will begin and by what we can judge and measure it; and, second, our inadequate consideration of grades of immaturity. Assumption of maturity seems to be a matter of individual choice; it is very like the belief that one is a specialist as soon as one begins to limit oneself to learning or working in a specialty, and as such is entitled to either a fellowship or a salary for the mere intention. To talk of immaturity is taboo, because with our Pollyanna fear of "repressing genius" we are afraid of reminding anyone of possible limitations. Because there were some bad ways of treating children, the child is treated as a would-be adult. Because there were some bad things in apprenticeship and its equivalents, we do away with apprenticeship and replace it with curriculums and examinations and helps to "get by"—often enough with the very soul left out. We educate our youth and allow them to surprise us with the strange use they sometimes make of their erudition and "maturity."

One of the most fateful and responsible steps of life, for which we might care to require maturity, the step of marriage, we leave to the false romanticism of the little ivy-clad church, or to the justice of the peace. We demand only a license, obtainable without any great scruple or obligation, sometimes by hook or by crook, and without any controlled inquiry. All this may be lack of maturity of a civilization rather than of individuals. The individual is powerless against the atmosphere created by the financial success standards ruling the printing press, the movies, the automobile, fashions in drink, and all the other ubiquitous problems for the immature, whether adult or younger. To this we must add often overestimated theories of repression.

Is not all maturity a relative and still progressive attainment even in the adult? Does not all maturity have to be maturity *for something?* And when does it become maturity in general?

We look for maturity for jobs and play and rest, for poise in composure and in active composition (the reader will pardon the play on this word root which spells "safety of position"). We look for a fitting relation of personality and situation in individual, family, social and civic life, in the flow of ever-new time and ever-new opportunity. We look for maturity of choice and discrimination and decision (suggesting the cutting-off of what is not chosen), and of a sense of what is reality and what fancy in opportunity and desire.

Those who do not like to bother with the more abstract and comprehensive might make a collection of very immediate issues of maturity—for using a car? for using the day and the night in unsupervised life? for the ventures of life or for making laws as the wisest formulations of customs, and handling them for community health, happiness and efficiency?

When we come to sex maturity we deal with far more than the complexity of the individual sex development and the demand for adaptability required in the individual, whether in marital or in bachelor life. We also deal with one's role as a sample and a potential factor, in meeting the curiosity and susceptibility of the younger generation. They should find a respectful and sensible consideration from earliest childhood and receive understanding answers to frank and sincere questions. Lectures or pamphlets cannot be expected to be generally effective. We need preparedness and patterns to meet concrete situations; not merely beautiful talk about beautiful flowers, but answers to actual questions and situations.

A word must suffice concerning our obsession with the false obligations of supposed or imposed maturity. Most of the traditional steps toward maturity are imposed rites, in which our present-day emancipation still indulges—of having "experience," being "like the other boys and girls," lest one might have missed something essential for one's evolution and self-realization. What are the merits of such rites and displays? What happens when they are neglected? What do they bring into life? How far shall we artificially push "self-realization" when, as it exists, it is actually group realization?

Many adjustments in tolerance will be required before the rank and file of humanity can live by the dictates of objective patterns rather than of intellectual and emotional bias. It is a pity to see the supposedly idealistic considerations of life "cornered" by conflicting groups entrenched in dogmas of exclusive salvation, and to see the often refreshing radical forced out of contact with the best creative groups and into making his appeal largely to the immature.

Maturity implies quite definitely a dependability assured not only by practice and drill, but one that is intrinsic, ingrained, expressed in terms of growth. For this we have unfortunately few direct measures. It is remarkable that even for such a very obvious fact as fatigue, science has not as yet found any dependable correlation of structural, functional, and effectual data.

Expressions of mature living are the balancing of expectation against reality, and the capacity to fit into groups: in business; in home life, with its nonsexual affections as well as with its visions of sexualization; in our allegiances as well as in our emancipation. It implies the capacity to accept illness, disappointments, bereavements, even death, and all that which is largely beyond our own control and influence; to accept our own make-up, the perfections and imperfections of self and others, success and failure, sportsmanship, and the social comparisons which we call advice, criticism, and authority. Finally, maturity assumes a philosophy of objectivity about the past and a vision of creative opportunity for the present and the future.

Maturity requires a capacity to recognize limitations without being hindered in using what one is and has; a realization that there are grades and stages of adequacy, and where the more obvious grades and stages of growth and education have been allowed for, there are still fluctuations of efficiency. It includes the capacity to appreciate one's place in a scale, and to sustain the tension needed to attain one's ends. We have to realize that all of us have to attain certain conditions if we are to obtain what we wish. We have to maintain a certain degree of an ever-present holding to a tenor or pitch, to keep an average for action as well as for rest, and for what we assume ourselves subject to in the direction of letdown or of rise.

Maturity of the individual and of a civilization presupposes the dependability of certain standards, and standards do not stand without attention, force or effort. Without a certain normal tension no civilization is tenable. In short, wherever we turn, we meet the question of preparedness and capacity for effort.

This social self-guidance is based on insight and foresight and a helpful type of "hindsight" or capacity to use the past, and not merely to suffer from the past. These three combine as a forward-looking conscience in the modern sense of the word. Probably its severest test is capacity to create, and to participate in, a consensus, based on understanding others and on making oneself understood— consensus in contrast to domination, literally a capacity for more interest in common ground and less in one-sided emphasis on differences and digressions of opinion.

Education may one day sense and furnish more adequate grati-fications to every phase of life and every grade of maturity. To maintain a progressing civilization may then become more possible and with it will come a more natural organization of the leaders and the led, and more happiness as well as efficiency within what each individual actually can be and do.

12

A Science of Man

"Think in terms of a science of man." Adolf Meyer made this appeal to researchers in nervous and mental diseases. Think in terms of the life of man. Our own life, our own thoughts. Get on "commonly intelligible ground," without the great many confusing words which befuddle the workers themselves and plunge them into mystery when they should be using language to say what they do understand. "We have to debunk in medicine and in our ordinary way of thinking and in the various sciences—we have to debunk the things that cannot harmonize and that are not merely the expression of our experience." [41]

Man's notion of man often was not only unscientific but partly antiscientific and "full of unjustified presuppositions," especially the idea that mentality could not be treated, like other facts, objectively. In the early efforts to establish psychology among the sciences, the mind concept had been dropped and an attempt had been made to win status by showing that psychology could use quantitative methods. It studied sensations and work-curves, flirted with instincts, but avoided "all the most truly dynamic interests of life." And so psychology became wedded to "sensation-derived symbol production" when it should have had a concept for action.

Mentality, Meyer said, meant "mind as it appears and works," a product of both the individual and his habit development as molded in social contacts. Mentality was objective concrete performance, to be studied not for the limited purpose of intelligence tests or for a reduction of man's life to sex and the unconscious, but for a full review of man's responsiveness.

While Freud courageously insisted on attention to mankind's struggle for happiness and gave "a broadening and humanizing of our conceptions of mentality," his preoccupation with the unconscious, his emphasis on the sex instinct and later the ego instincts, went to the other extreme from timid evasion. His theory bespoke absolute determinism of life.

The consequence of these psychometric and psychoanalytic developments was, on the one hand, a tendency to rule-of-thumb measurements . . . largely neglecting if not belittling the personality features, just as had been done by the soul-shy and mind-shy factions of academic psychology; on the other hand, a humanizing psychology, but one getting its impetus largely from the lessons of mythology and hysteria, where we might prefer a confident front attack upon average man as we all should know him.[42]

Psychobiology started with the premise that the one trait common to man was his individuality and inequality. This remarkable variation and variability made obligatory a review of specific samples of a person's whole wide range of activities, and more—his capacity for satisfaction and for "constructive composure."

This gives us a science which would mean the acceptance of man as the product of physicochemical, biological, and finally psychobiological interpretation, an intrinsically social type of individual, the heir, structurally and culturally, of a succession of civilizations.[42]

The practical application of psychobiology was a systematized study of the working of the various determining factors in mental illness, resulting from disharmony with environment, and a search for factors of adaptation.

The greatest difficulty in life, the greatest source of disharmony, apart from the influences of heredity, infectious disease and poor feeding and poor chances for growth, is the discrepancy between impulse, yearning, and ambition, on the one hand and the actual opportunities and the actual efficiency of performance on the other.

Many persons come to grief because they are unwilling, unable, to "accept their own nature and the world as it is, and to shape their aims according to their assets." Meyer described them:

Failing with what is frequently impossible and undesirable anyhow, these persons develop emotional attitudes and habits and tendencies to fumble or to brood or to puzzle or to be apprehensive, until what students of the functional diseases of the heart call "a break of compensation" occurs, a break of nature's system of maintaining the balance, with a more or less sudden slump and implication of collateral functions.[43]

In some cases vicious circles were set up, damaging various organs or the brain itself. These conditions were established by emotional conflicts and bungling attempts to fit incompatibles together and by "disregard of the strain on the various organs which participate in the integrated reactions and in the biological adaptations."

The great difficulty of psychiatry was finding dependable and worth-while topics of work. Meyer advised against making it appear that techniques were psychiatry's essence and against claiming one's own brand of psychopathology the one and only. "Psychopathology is and will for some time be a rather individual affair." [44] He instanced Forel's hypnotism, Prince's multiple personalities, Freud's elaborate analytic system, Jung's system, the symbolism of others, the nosological ventures of Kraepelin, and other methods, including that of "the more pragmatic workers with the facts as we find them." This aspect of psychiatry could resolve itself by having doctors of diverse temperaments accept training in all the fundamental lines of neuropsychiatry.

But in the quest for solid topics of work—in dementia praecox, for example, where Kraepelin posed the hypothesis of sex-gland malfunction and Dr. Elmer E. Southard of the Boston Psychopathic Hospital held to a brain-spot theory—the rational course was to "take up intensive and experimental work on whatever clues lend themselves to positive investigation." The vast problem should be separated into many subgroups. Persons tending toward introversion, for example, could be studied for the development and the conflicts of their sex life. The catatonic reaction, to take a single aspect, might prove to be not a deterioration but a positive asset, a defense mechanism, indicating the person's constitutional make-up, with the forces at work turned to therapeutic use.

The means of approach have got to be adapted to the facts at hand, and nothing is more sickening and unpromising than the tendency to assume that we ought to wait until some very practical, simple, and single thing is discovered which would then explain what may, after all, be largely an imaginary entity. The study of epilepsy is a similar problem. Those who expect to solve it by hunting for a button that can be pressed hold up the progress of the world by throwing a lot of pessimism on the work that is possible and inviting when we accept the fact frankly that we had better speak of epilepsies as a general expression of specific features worth studying by themselves.[45]

Anatomical studies, metabolic studies, and pharmacological experiments were certainly welcome, but the definite problems must be singled out and related to definite psychobiological reactions, not to a hypothetical disease entity, and these reactions studied without prejudice.

It had taken a great deal of persistence to shake faith in the tempting convenience of disease entities; in Kraepelin's "tour de force and psychiatric revolution" that had swept the imagination on the promise of a prognosis. Acceptance of course and outcome as a fixed fate in any type of disturbance was unprofitable, Meyer held, unless the nature of the process could be so discerned as to be measurable. Despite his reasonable reservations he had more than one critic objecting to "all this nosological bolshevism and nihilism."

The challenge to the profession came from Southard. As president of the American Medico-Psychological Association back in 1919, after declaring that "no greater power to change our minds has been at work in the interior of the psychiatric profession in America than the personality of Adolf Meyer" and calling him "a ferment, an enzyme, a catalyzer," Southard said: "No American theorist in psychiatry of these and the immediately succeeding decades but is compelled either to agree or else—a thing of equal importance—most powerfully to disagree with him."

When Meyer evolved, in the early nineteen hundreds, the concept that dementia praecox depended on a special personality and constitution and on habit-disorganization, he left the internal working and development of the structural and functional deficit "as possibly incidental and still to be worked out." Further developments were made on his principle by Dr. August Hoch, Dr. Smith Ely Jelliffe, Dr. William Alanson White, and other workers. Jung and Bleuler put strong emphasis on psychodynamic factors and mechanisms, although finally Bleuler went wholly over to a physiogenic cause: a lesion.

Tracing the evolution of the dementia praecox concept from the French school of Pinel in the 1790's, Meyer expressed his conviction at the 1925 meeting of the Association for Research in Nervous and Mental Disease that the steadiest line of progress lay in recognition of "the pluridimensional character of the facts involved." This attitude was "more largely nondogmatic, freely nosological, genetic-dynamic, with a formulation in which reaction-types, the factors entering into them, the prognosis, and the therapeutic aspects are given equal and relatively independent consideration." [46]

"There probably is today," he said,

a widespread preparedness to accept Meyer's formulation of parergastic-paranoid reaction-types based on a frankly pluralistic psychobiological integration concept, treating the susceptibility to special types of deterioration as an important issue, but making of the prognosis in general a special subaspect of the whole group problem.

The description of the picture brings out material of fancy and maladaptation with striking passivity reactions and disorders of fusion of the psychobiologically integrated functions, which express more clearly than any neurologizing or physiologizing formulation the actual state of the patient. At the same time it accepts the possibility of dynamic factors which may enter at several of the integrative levels. [See "Interrelations of the Domain of Neuropsychiatry," page 565.] It abandons frankly a dogmatic unitary treatment of the problem. It accepts a pragmatic frame and general "formulation" instead of a nosological diagnosis, and demands specific study of specific developments and factors entering into them. Its aim is to obtain definition of the events at hand and control of the synthetic and adjustive

542   The Commonsense Psychiatry of Dr. Adolf Meyer

factors and problems, and this, if possible, in terms which avoid the fatalistic presumption of an obligatory terminal state as the mark and inevitable fate of the whole set of facts.

The trend of interest turns more toward preliminary than toward final classification, and thereby toward developments and their management, and not exclusively toward the guessing of fatalistic end states. We do not like too much emphasis on a negative aspect in psychiatry. Considering the dementia praecox aspect of the problem looks like wanting to make bankruptcy the big chapter and issue of economics. The French today tend to ring the changes on schizophrenia, schizomania, and schizothymia. We do best to forget the words and to work more on the positive facts that may hint at deteriorative tendencies.[46]

For study, the most wholesome basis was the acceptance of work on "concrete, specific, narrowed topics and a frank recognition of there being a fairly large unclassified residuum." It was important to feel that psychiatric theory was in flux and was growing. In his presidential address before the American Psychiatric Association in 1928, Meyer welcomed the dawn of appreciation of "a real natural-history integration of man as opposed to a purely mechanistic or purely fantastic interpretation."

Psychoanalysis, he pointed out, was only a limited field within psychopathology and psychiatry—one set of methods for a very definite theory of disease, operating largely with a hypothetical unconscious. Dr. Clarence P. Oberndorf, of New York, observed at the meeting that Meyer had exercised a profound influence in the introduction of psychoanalysis into this country, especially at the New York State hospitals. But Meyer said that what had led him from the start to "open a very wide door" to psychoanalysis was its use of dynamic conceptions, and for the same reason he was keeping it open "to anything that psychoanalysis does." [47]

However, the sharing of things in common must not obscure the differences. For example, psychoanalysis taught that symptoms did not constitute the illness to be treated.

The dynamic theory that I use does not talk of symptoms; it talks of reactions that we want to understand and readjust in one way or another. We positively go for that which others discard because they want to treat only the transference reactions. I look upon symptoms, so-called, as manifestations, as reactions of the individual, which contain with reasonable certainty that which we want to go for. Therefore I like to pick out the abnormal reactions as I find them, with their setting and their content.[47]

A hypothetical system working with the erotic reaction of an individual on the ground of transference undoubtedly made use of a valuable asset; but only in the way that physicians used the reduction of pain with morphine and opium. That is, they did not assume that they thereby established a special method to reach the illness; they simply created conditions for easier adjustment. "It is one of the means of getting better access to the facts." [47]

When the cult of Émile Coué had its vogue in the early twenties, Meyer urged caution against drifting from a spirit of inquiry into one of dogmatic faith. "Sound conceptions of science are not merely a matter of talking and writing, but of familiarity with work and facts." The painstaking collection and testing of facts, needed for the development of correct ideas, was not as sensational and exciting as the autosuggestive chant of the French chemist's formula with twenty knots of string in hand. Like other healing cults, Couéism bespoke ignorance of pathology.

The recent wave of uncritical popularization of psychoanalysis has undoubtedly added to the inflammability of popular imagination and to the widespread notion that plausibility and desirability are sufficient evidence of truth and actuality. Everybody seems to be perfectly ready to think of the "unconscious self" as if its existence, in whatever form you might want to imagine it, could no longer be disputed. The concept of the "subconscious" is a convenient one because you make it out to consist of what suits your theory or wish. Freud makes it one thing, Morton Prince another, and Coué yet another, and nobody can give more than a pragmatic definition of the concept.[48]

To Meyer there was very little difference between the conscious and the unconscious.

The simple principle of crowding out all the other influences in ourselves by just repeating fast enough some well-meaning phrases will undoubtedly appear to work in many cases. If M. Coué had to deal with large numbers of patients who receive compensation for being sick and who resent any interference with their invalidism, he could come somewhat nearer the rank and file of so-called neuroses.[48]

In dealing with the complexities of human life, few physicians escaped from the delusion that intuitional revelation stood above objective inquiry and study. Nor could they profit by discussion of words when there was work to be demonstrated. Verbal concepts would have to be replaced by "orderly formulations of the most telling examples of experience and observation and experiment by the best workers." Some scientifically trained persons had a blind spot for the emotions as codeterminers of the human organism's health, happiness, and efficiency.

Those who complain that all psychiatry, psychopathology, and therapy have to resolve themselves into a smattering of claims and hypotheses of psychoanalysis, and that they stand and fall with one's feelings about psychoanalysis, are equally misguided.[1]

"I sometimes feel that Einstein, concerned with the relativity in astronomy, has to deal with very simple facts as compared to the complex and erratic and multicontingent performances of the human microcosmos." Psychiatrists were faced with "the most unruly and willful part or aspect of man, the very organ and function of self-assertion and self-concern and self-protection. Moreover, mankind would like to be free from scourges and their consequences without having to surrender the joys and habits that spread and engender them." Psychiatrists needed the patient's cooperation, as with the control of drugs, alcohol, and syphilis. They had the task of controlling and training "emotion and fancy that clash with reality, and the craving for self-realization at any price."[1]

Man must be seen as part of nature.

We emerge from the stream of life as individuals and then sink back into the larger flow of contemporaries and those who follow us in our family, our race, and our nation and whatever we are just a part or a more or less thoughtful representative of. It does not take much thought for us to realize the relativity, the dependencies, and the varying range of the sphere of action and influence of even the greatest of the individual entities in the larger flow of mankind.[1]

Besides behavior situations and life situations, Meyer saw in the problem of adjusting individual and environment the necessity of studying the patient's energy, endowment, capacity for constructive composure, ability to muster assets in emergencies (judgment), extent of the need of consistency (personality), inclusion of others, tendencies of action in vision, thought, fancy, play, work, prospect, retrospect, and the amount of socialization "as opposed to the mere self-concern and almost obsessive individualism so rampant today."

For all this there must be a simple formulation so as to make possible a sensing of the concrete work and achievement; of vistas that come with an effort to gain experience. "It is one of our great tasks to offer such vistas so that we may attract to our field healthy-minded and energetic and untiring workers with indomitable determination to attain the mastery of the simple and also the complex parts. For this we should from the outset be able to give the younger generation and the future leaders of our cause an outlook and a close contact with facts and methods which dawned upon us elders only after devious wanderings." Hope of progress did not depend on brilliant individuals, "but the success of these individuals and the continuity of their work will certainly also depend on a kind of atmosphere and a general base line of preparation with which we all have to work . . . and choose to work." [1]

The dedication of the New York State Psychiatric Institute and Hospital in 1929 brought to mind the concreteness of the psychiatrist's work as the great gain of this era—that and the workmanship and the surrender of "the 'absolutes' as goals of salvation, with a corresponding growth of courage." The Institute, created by the state and Columbia University, a fulfillment of the dream of Dr. Frederick Peterson, would do its best work by remaining free to concentrate on select types of investigation, besides serving as a center of teaching and training, and to devote itself to human beings open to complete study. Sample beings, of course; for "man can never bring into action at any one time and in any one setting all that may constitute the person."

Man is an evasive entity, only rarely caught in difficulties in which he would become willing to surrender to a complete and unreserved study as a personality. We are unfortunately too apt to plunge too one-sidedly upon the helpless child and perhaps upon the criminal, and are very one-sided with regard to the study of the as yet untamed and often undisciplined average adult, who still allows himself largely to be represented or misrepresented in novels and in the overspecialized accounts of special schools, rather than on the ground of thorough-going studies such as objective psychiatry of today would demand.[49]

While acclaiming the function of the Institute as a place for participation in work, Meyer expressed his deep conviction that there should be no invidious contrast with state asylums; instead, an ever-new stimulus to the various districts of the state. There had been a tendency to belittle so-called asylum practice and to picture psychiatry's glory in laboratory or extramural work, whereas the lack of hospital experience was a definite handicap. "I shall always be grateful," Meyer said on another occasion, "for the opportunities given me by the larger institutions, and I shall never cease working against any idea that admission hospitals and extramural work will make of the larger state hospitals a merely custodial affair." At the Institute exercises he declared that "the state institutions will continue to determine the sense and spirit of psychiatry in this country . . . by bringing their unique experience within the reach of the physicians and the public of their districts," and by revealing both the best of modern work and the failures of local civilization.

Communities have to learn what they produce in the way of mental problems and waste of human opportunities, and with such knowledge they will rise from mere charity and mere mending or hasty propaganda to well-balanced early care, prevention, and the general gain of health, efficiency, and happiness.

We cannot expect to change mankind completely. But we are learning to use experience and to avoid avoidable waste and avoidable unhappiness . . . helping not only the sick but those who now just drift, not knowing how much better off they might be.[49]

The Institute was an illustration of the spirit of the philosophy of America: Charles S. Peirce's philosophy of chance, William

James's pluralism, John Dewey's instrumentalism, "and all the basic confidence in the blending of practical achievement and contribution to the basic sciences and the formulation and command of the facts as found." Meyer called Dewey "our greatest shaper and exponent of American philosophical thought." Psychiatry had well kept up with the march from medievalism to the dawn of "vigorous and open objectivism of science and of life."

Psychobiology's place in science was brought out in the first Thomas W. Salmon Memorial Lecture at the New York Academy of Medicine in 1922. Meyer, given the honor of delivering it, outlined the new science of man that treats mind and body as an integrated entity and includes "all there is to a person," like any other object of natural history.

When we watch ourselves we see that in our commonsense attitude we really do recognize the really live man to a very great extent. But such a tremendous importance has been attached to the natural subjectivity of man, and that subjectivity has been so much described as something outside of nature, that there has been created the appearance that we are forced to study him from two sides—as a body and as a mind.

Behaviorism had striven for objectivity in eliminating the subjective with a confusing fear of getting involved in the so-called mental aspect. Psychobiology sought to understand man as a whole, in the way man knows himself and his fellows.

We therefore demand that we take the mental functioning as a general part of the functioning of the organism and have the courage to make ourselves responsible for the total functioning. Psychobiology claims that anything that is part of a person—his hopes and his fears, his motivations and urges, his attitude toward right and wrong, and even his religious conceptions and beliefs—is as much a property and quality of the person as anything that can be weighed in the scales or measured by the yard.

This was Meyer's acceptance of the challenge from the proponents of the test-tube view of science.

On the second evening of his lecture he decried the extension of psychoanalysis into a general psychopathology and general conception of man—"and perhaps even more than that, a special philosophy of life built around sex pathology." In the treatment of mental and nervous disorders, psychoanalysis by itself could not give the physician a complete account of the conditions causing the disturbances.

Psychoanalysis starts out from the stipulation of an unconscious and with the goal or promise of a normal sex life, as if anything as subtle as that could ever be absolutely perfect with an absolutely tenable pattern or an individual pattern quite safe enough to become a measure of life.

I prefer to treat psychoanalysis as a most noteworthy and incidentally highly fruitful venture in the development of medicine, with generalizations and analogies of great fascination, but not in any way, as such, as exclusive a way to salvation as the popularizing statements would seem to claim.

I prefer to keep to our broad psychobiological principle of considering the whole of man in terms accessible to one's ways and means, and to urge a broad foundation starting with what is generally accessible and at hand, rather than the exclusive subconscious, leaving us to extend our attention in every direction also to the less obvious, but with a sense of proportion that may best do justice to all our facts and opportunities.

No single approach or formulation could cover the nature of man, no matter at what phase of life. The facts and methods respecting subjectivity had to be supplemented by those of the non-mentally integrated sciences, including basic physics and chemistry in the study of the organism and the situation, the vegetative processes of growth, heredity, organization, metabolism, and reproduction.

The third part of Meyer's lecture was a plea for a return to commonsense methods of treatment; not to ignore the simple conscious acts of the patient; to take into greater account what he does rather than what he says.

We have suffered from an overmechanization of psychiatry, due to forty years' progress in the physiological studies of the brain and the nervous system and to the localization studies of the various functional centers in the brain. This led to reliance too much on chemistry and physiology as the cure-alls in psychic ills, while psychoanalysis, by laying too much emphasis on the subconscious and sex, has lost sight of the importance of the functioning of the conscious mind and has, in addition, disregarded the fact that man is subject to physical, chemical, physiological, biological, and social laws.

The following year Meyer delivered the Fourteenth Maudsley Lecture before the Royal Medico-Psychological Association in London, giving a further exposition of psychobiology and expressing his debt to British psychiatry. Said Dr. D. K. Henderson, who had become professor of psychiatry at the University of Edinburgh after his three years at Phipps: "If one man more than any other—I am not comparing him with Kraepelin and Freud and others—in recent years has helped to bring a working conception of mental disorders into actual practical life, that man is Professor Adolf Meyer." On behalf of the British graduates who had worked with Meyer, Henderson offered thanks.

While abroad, Meyer traveled to the Soviet Union for a visit to Kharkov, where he gave two talks, using material similar to that of the Salmon lectures. He spoke offhand, stopping from time to time to be translated, and the audience of Russian physicians seemed pleased with the dynamic approach of psychobiology. Illness prevented him from giving a third talk or seeing much of the people, and police surveillance hampered other contacts. Although appreciating the professional reception, a sense of relief came over Meyer when he left the country. Arriving at Constantinople, he was glad to be able to step into a store and talk to someone in free conversation.

In 1934 he received the honorary degree of doctor of science from Yale University at the same time that a degree was conferred upon President Franklin D. Roosevelt. At the exercises Professor William Lyon Phelps told an apocryphal anecdote which had grown out of the visit of Belgium's Queen to the Phipps Clinic. (It may as well be repeated, so that readers will recognize this wrong version.) According to "Billy" Phelps, she came into Meyer's office and said, "I am the Queen of the Belgians," and Meyer without looking up from his desk remarked, "Very interesting. How long have you thought so?" President Roosevelt threw his head back characteristically and laughed heartily. Afterward Meyer told the President that the Queen, properly announced, asked to make a tour of the Clinic with her suite, and Meyer offered to conduct it although, suffering from a leg injury, he had to be pushed in a wheel chair. "I was the only float in the parade."

By this time what was known as the American point of view in psychiatry was definitely acknowledged. Dr. John C. Whitehorn and Dr. Gregory Zilboorg, writing in *American Journal of Psychiatry* (13:303, 1933), stated that consideration of the whole character of an individual's life had become a tradition—"inaugurated by the contribution of Adolf Meyer." This emphasis of totality implied, they said, "a deeper individualization of our therapeutic efforts. It is only in the light of personal meaning that we are able to evaluate clearly a given life situation and the individual's reaction to it." They pointed out that Meyer's "constant reminder that a given psychopathological unit is an experiment of nature serves as a stimulus for the increased interest in the psychology of the so-called normal individual."

But with the lingering division of sciences into the mental and the natural, the difficulty of getting rid of "animistic residuals" of a special spark of life and mind—and with the contrast with matter "kept alive because of the apparent impossibility of understanding the rise of consciousness out of matter and even out of living matter"—it was not strange that investigators should think of needing a special approach to the material of psychiatry. "It was not until the concept of integration restated the situation that the hankering for the mystical stopgaps and reservations began to cease," said Meyer. The material of psychiatry required no special approach or special aspect foreign to medicine. Such things were merely the investigator's own response to different sets of relationships of facts. "We have only to learn what kind of facts we deal with and have in mind; the approaches will come quite naturally, and without confusing perplexities and disturbing obstructions in a pluralism with intrinsic consistency, rather than a dogmatic dualism or monism." [50]

In a symposium on the material of human nature and conduct, arranged by Meyer at the 1935 meeting of the American Psychiatric Association in Washington, he asked workers in various fields to tell what they considered their material to be, so that all might get on common ground. Responding to his invitation were Dr. Walter R. Miles of the Yale University School of Medicine, Dr. William Malamud of the Iowa State Psychopathic Hospital, Dr. Sandor Rado of the New York Psychoanalytic Institute, Dr. Stanley Cobb of the Massachusetts General Hospital, Dr. John C. Whitehorn of the McLean Hospital, and Dr. Lauretta Bender of the Bellevue Psychopathic Hospital.

Said Meyer in a summary of the symposium,

There is no doubt that we deal with a body of facts and methods that have a common ground and frame not completely handled by any one single "approach." There are many approaches used and at work. What we want to know is what the *facts as found* have in common and in what ways we may have to recast uncritical common-sense and uncritical tradition and also dogmatic science to obtain an unquestioned status for critical commonsense and our systematized psychobiology, or ergasiology, in the rank of the sciences.

It looks as if many of the data and materials discussed had little to do with what most of us have been taught to expect in psychology. Yet they represent very concretely the experience of those who are interested as observers and workers in the nature and functioning of human beings in health and disease.[50]

The varieties of data presented by the participants showed the "tremendous range of material that the psychiatrist has to cope with. To me they indicate the presence of something which calls for a very definite change in our general philosophy concerning science at large and particularly our philosophy concerning the science dealing with man and its relation to 'natural science.' "

The belittling of commonsense in matters of science had yet to be surmounted. In everyday life man was concerned with a person's actions and reactions, but these personal items were what the physician missed most in his teaching. Particularly in this country, science was subject to loose and dilettante exploitation that set it on a plane apart from ordinary life. Consequently the study of man seemed no concern, except for anatomy and physiology and their application in medical work; the rest was comfortably consigned to "man the unknown."

At the 1936 Conference on Psychiatric Education—devoted to undergraduate preparation of physicians, to enable them to deal with the person as well as with organs and disease—Meyer gave the background of his generation's effort to overcome the medical tradition of centuries and consider the pertinent facts in human nature from the angle of biology. The three American thinkers "who represent the finest upshot of the American pioneer spirit," Peirce, James, and Dewey, had developed concepts rooted in commonsense. Their work and thought

culminated in pragmatism and instrumentalism and in pluralism and a leaning toward objectivity and concreteness and respect for plain, everyday sense. These men laid the groundwork also for the use of principles of integration and relativity and of scientific history. This was a development not merely of philosophy, but of sound experience generally, and at the same time, we might say, a spontaneous and natural consideration of practical life, not merely of contemplative abstraction.[51]

The application of the natural-history method was consistent with the best formula of science, "the triad of observation, formulation, and obligatory test, together with the recognition of 'fact' as that which proves itself as a factor by performance, in history, experience, and experiment." Psychobiology emerged as the new discipline, grouping and studying the facts of man's behavior.

Mind—with the basic features of integration ("that which wields and keeps the component parts in units") and symbolization ("the use of signs and meanings as thought and feeling and expression and language")—was seen as mentation, a phase of behavior, in highly differentiated personality-organization.

This formulation gives us a new sense and direction also of pathology and of therapy, free from many of the artificialities that are apt to confuse the student and the worker. Instead of telling the student that he must add a new science to his curriculum, we teach him not to throw away, but to organize, those points of view and procedures which we all find of value in our work with man in life, in health, and in disease, what the physician of today has learned to respect and is beginning to utilize like his neighbors—the educator, the minister, the parent, and the practical man of affairs.[51]

Upon receiving a call for help, the physician did not stop short with the disease or distress but paid heed to the person who suffered it or conquered it.

This natural-history respect for the actual person is the most characteristic recognition in twentieth-century medicine, an old story that has come into its own and that is helping not only psychiatry but all of medical thought, that of the specialties included. We do well to forget theory, if theory should frighten us, and to turn to the plain facts of our work and experience, but sensibly and methodically and effectively, using all that the trained worker has to offer us.[51]

The patient's complaint was rendered as a complete picture of what had gone wrong, not a mere "fragment of discomfort." It was the story of a historical development. The facts were pulled together in a formulation of the case ready for action as a potentially modifiable experiment of nature. The types of disorder were set down not as diagnoses but as reaction-patterns or groupings of facts. Thus a case was not hastily categorized as manic-depressive psychosis or dementia praecox, recoverable or nonrecoverable, psychoneurosis or psychosis. The complaints were patterns of mistakes, blundering, mismanagement, disturbance of assets, inadequacy of function, to be redirected and adjusted.

Using *ergasia* as "local slang" at Phipps for mentally integrated activity, Meyer listed the array of possible happenings according to a simple arrangement with a different prefix for each type, again cautioning that they were not to be taken as diagnoses by themselves but as sets of facts occurring under varying conditions; thus

An-, meaning lacking or lost; *anergasia*, an organic reaction where behavior is modified by structural as well as functional defect, as in general paresis, senile conditions, and epilepsy.

Dys-, difficult; *dysergasia*, functionally determined disturbance, with structure not directly involved, nonneurological, the brain getting malsupport from toxic and infectious conditions or food deficiencies (deliriums, hallucinations).

Thymo-, affective; *thymergasia*, depressive or overactive mood, likely to be marked by anxiety or elation.

Para-, sidetracked; *parergasia*, distortion of content, essentially delusional or paranoid, including the disorganizing type known as schizophrenia and dementia praecox.

Mero-, part; *merergasia*, partial loss of function, conditional and temporarily interfunctionally disturbed part-disorder, such as so-called psychoneurosis, showing disappointment, frustration, anticipation, preoccupation, obsession, dissociation.

Kako-, bad; *kakergasia*, bad use of good enough organs, poor functioning or faulty behavior.

Oligo-, few or scant; *oligergasia*, constitutional structural deficiency, growth-determined, such as idiocy and imbecility.

Each reaction-type had to be qualified by consideration of the etiological factors. It was essential to distinguish depressions and elations tinged incidentally with delusions, from content disorders of delusional and hallucinatory nature and impure emotion. It was important to recognize that

. . . affective disturbances can be either the leading condition or just incidental to broader or deeper disturbances; they can be practically pure culture or they can be complicated; they can occur in situations that account for the reaction or without obvious explanation; in easily demonstrable situations or more difficult combinations of facts—some that are fairly directly corrigible, and others that are accessible only through very detailed work, in the course of the process or more in convalescence.[52]

If the student did not know that some content disorders were likely to occur in the affect disturbances, there could be confusion, "and ignorance can cause many diagnoses of dementia praecox that are absolutely unjustified."

Ergasiology did not escape gibes.

It is not, as some rather ungracious critics will have it, that one Greek word, psychology, is just being transferred into a supposedly stranger Greek word. It is the sense of that self-referring, responsibility-making type of action—not merely happening, but action—that the middle form of the Greek word is required. *Erg* is exactly the same root as *work*, and we all know it in *allergy* and in *energy* and as the unit of energy in physics. I rather think that this is the best word, born of and for responsibility and a goal.[53]

The few technical terms which Meyer introduced were meant to serve as a shorthand to express the necessary distinctions. Psychiatry had to keep away from jargon, yet the multiplicity of vocabularies was leading there. It needed to "debunk language irresponsibly used and irresponsibly taken." In correlating concepts with corresponding sets of facts—"always facts first"—any new word must be anchored in reality and not blurred by metaphor.

Meyer had no "a priori revulsion" from any term; if it gave the best generally intelligible characterization and reference, it would do its job.

I would not claim any merit for a word or a name unless it keeps us directly and as helpfully as possible in contact with the facts and their uses. When I use the word *thymergasia* I do not mean by that just any kind of emotional disturbance modifying human behavior. I use it in a technical way to denote a strictly defined sadness-elation pattern, and I would want my students to know what the difference is between speaking broadly of depression and excitement and using the more specific word *thymergasia*.[54]

"Regression" was used by psychoanalysts to designate a state where the individual was reduced to an earlier developmental level. Actually this term was a metaphor, a sometimes useful analogy. Preferring to stick to concreteness, Meyer said "regression" dodged the unpleasant fact that in sickness and senility one did not come up to the standards of ordinary living. "Conditioning" and "fixation"—they were not needed by Meyer, who spoke rather of habit-organization and disorganization.

One of civilization's biggest problems was to eliminate

. . . a false sense of competition which does not allow the human being to take himself as he is. He has to put up a bluff for himself and for everybody else, and so he may become a misfit in a certain place, interfering with the atmosphere of the place and frustrating his own happiness, while in a place more suited to him no difficulty would have arisen.

There will be some unhappiness and depression in the life of every one of us. We often come across problems that we would like to meet better than we can. After having tried very hard to do a thing and not succeeding well, we ought to be able to take ourselves as human beings and consider what we are able to do; the next time we may perhaps choose better both position and target, so that there will be a fair chance of a successful balance.[55]

A tribute to the inclusiveness and liberalism of Meyer's teaching was paid at a two-day celebration in Baltimore in April, 1937, marking the beginning of his twenty-fifth year as director of the Henry Phipps Psychiatric Clinic. Four hundred former pupils and coworkers gathered in the spirit of an alumni reunion, which incidentally observed also the passing of his seventieth milestone. Although Meyer had reached retirement age, the trustees of The Johns Hopkins University had refused his resignation. A map of the world, displayed before the celebrants at a banquet at the Belvedere Hotel, showed the far-flung distribution of the doctors he had trained; they included one hundred who were then teachers of psychiatry, seventy-nine of them in the United States.

"He has given medicine psychobiology, wherein lies the hope of a sound union of conflicting theories," wrote Dr. Franklin G. Ebaugh, director of the Colorado Psychopathic Hospital, in a special number of the *Archives of Neurology and Psychiatry* (37:4, 1937) dedicated to him.

Meyer has the courage to stress the influence of environmental factors in the pathogenesis of disease, while the bulk of European scholarship stresses the fixed genetic factor. Meyer is aware of the constitutional fraction of the integrated organism, but he prefers to put the primary emphasis on the possibilities for therapeutic modification and not on prognosis.

On this occasion the New York Psychoanalytic Institute and Society elected him to honorary membership. The Scottish Division of the Royal Medico-Psychological Association hailed his "original work which has proved so fruitful for the progress of psychiatry throughout the civilized world." Dr. C. Macfie Campbell, now director of the Boston Psychopathic Hospital, and toastmaster at the dinner, declared that Meyer's epoch was "a very important period of constructive work."

The presentation of scientific papers at the celebration showed a sense of dynamic understanding of points of concern, with elastic reconstruction of facts and pluralistic sorting out of opportunities. Omniscience and stereotypes were both avoided; so too were "hypothetical preoccupations about the brain or the assertion of events that either might not have existed at all or might be absolutely out of reach of one's attempt to bring about modification," as Meyer summed up. Physics and chemistry and the endocrines were "momentarily in the center of physiological investigation," but it was an illusion to think that everything should ultimately be expressible on that basis, as though all one needed to know about man was just more chemistry or just more endocrinology.

The Baltimore reunion heartened him, and he drew tremendous comfort from it.

One gets to a period of life where one has, more than in any other period, a need of confidence that while as an individual one will have to disappear, one wants the spirit to live and to grow; if so, it will always have to grow not in the abstract but through the actually living. . . . Individuals have to grow together and have to be able to rise sometimes to leadership, sometimes to service, to get back into the ranks again to give room to others, and to disappear.[21]

When he spoke at the dedication of the Adolf Meyer Building at the Rhode Island State Hospital for Mental Diseases, at Howard, in 1938, he regarded the symbol impersonally. The unit had been named after him to give patients awareness that his teachings were being followed to restore them to health. He said: "I still should like to efface myself as a person and think only of words that might say what is meant—'Dedicated to the will to get well.' "

As mental illness was the undeclared war of man and social forces, situations must be seen in terms of real life, everyday strain and stress; therefore, joint efforts must be undertaken in all the realms, economic, social, political.

If we want to create a safe ground for democracy and for a "fair-deal" and not merely just "new-deal" kind of life and government, we have to learn much from the revulsion of human nature seen in what costs us thousands and thousands in money and much more in anxiety and derangement of mind and of happiness. . . . Do we want to wait until doctrines of hate and brute power and the fear of concentration camps adorn our land? Have we the nerve and the will to succeed? [56]

In its broadening role, psychiatry had become a theory and practice of shaping happiness and correcting difficulties also of average life. What helped the ill could help those who merely got along with false props. The earlier centering on diseases which were segregated in unwholesome dread was slowly yielding to a general hygiene of individual and community life, leading to a concern in "the persons and forms of government determining the fate of nations and races."

Recognition of mental health as a major public-health problem and a major issue for American scientists came with a symposium brought before the American Association for the Advancement of Science in 1938 by Dr. Walter L. Treadway, Assistant Surgeon General of the United States. But the introduction given by Dr. Thomas W. Rivers, of the Rockefeller Institute, was a caricature of psychiatry. Rivers charged psychiatrists with isolating themselves from the mainland of medicine and with offering an "inundation of words" instead of a scientific discipline.

In a critique, Meyer took Rivers to task, along with other leaders in medicine, for indulging in the very isolation they deplored. Rivers displayed "a vicious circle of distrust derived from unfamiliarity and lack of curiosity as to what is actually being done." Meyer chided him for harking back to mind-body parallelism and leaving psychiatry to the internist, and wondered "whether he confuses the psychiatrist, who certainly has to be a well-trained physician, with a psychoanalyst, who might indeed keep aloof but today is increasingly less inclined to do so." Apparently Rivers, "a rehearser of anachronistic tradition," did not see psychiatry as a science of man-function.[57]

The symposium itself failed to tackle the question of how to get next to the crises and needs of the *patient*. It seemed to look upon the patient simply as the host of the ailment, ignoring him as a participant and center of the difficulty itself—"the live entity to be guided as well as helped and searched and researched and sampled and regulated—expected finally to regulate itself." Here was where psychobiology showed its fullest colors and the specific modes of dynamics on which amelioration turned and depended; and where the practitioner proved himself a good internist and sociologist, an expert in biotechnics.

The principal work and progress of the psychiatrist in this century and the greatest gift psychiatry can give in return for all it also gets from the rest of medicine is the fact of guidance in the sense of collaboration between the physician and the patient as a person . . . understanding the active as well as the passive role of the patient in the sickness and in the treatment.[58]

The idea no longer held that one had to dissect the person into detachable cells and elements before one could be scientific. Just as physics had undergone changes in its concepts and experimental methods and in the formulation of its data, so had biology. Just as physics had reached a reunion of space and time in space-time, biology had come to a respect for the interlocking of structure and function, whose separation would destroy the characteristics which gave them, when combined, their value as a unit.

If mind were split from body, neither could exist and operate by itself, but their union in a person obviously provides quite a different state. And so, the existence of units or integers in life can be taken directly out of experience, without having to be broken down by preliminary analysis. Such integral units have their specific organization which is more than the mere summation of their component parts. This is the commonsense groundwork in our dealings with man, based on the facts as they are, without the dogma of traditions or of statements that we must settle all problems in terms of their elements.[59]

In psychobiological integration the unit of integration was the person. In contrast: nonbiological units (crystal formation), lower biological units (osmosis in plant life), physiological units (cardiovascular function, nerve stimulus, reaction units, etc.).

Thus, the study of an isolated part-function, such as the knee-jerk, is physiological. But as soon as memory and consciousness enter in and that function becomes recognized as part of the total person, of the "he" or "she," then the physiological function becomes an essential part of the psychobiological functioning.[59]

But if psychobiological data were treated simply by physico-chemical analysis and synthesis, the study would be woefully inadequate.

The method of work Meyer taught at Phipps was summarized by him:

Take the facts we observe in actual experience. Under what conditions do they occur? What factors enter into them? How do they operate? With what range of results? With what possibility of control and modification? And, in general, one makes use of the methods of all science, choosing methods according to the nature of the data and being sure to fit the methods to the facts instead of forcing the facts into nonpertinent methods.

These facts appeared as attitudes, actions, and reactions, in a setting of genetic-dynamic emphasis, so that one saw the origins and ways of working together.

The principles of psychobiology and their applications in concrete cases are subject to trial, retrial, and the elimination of error, and they are tested by commonsense—that which any competent observer can subscribe to as fact.

Pathology and therapy were taken as correlates.

The one tests the other, and they have to be kept close together to remain true to nature's experiments and to give a real understanding of the dynamics at work.

In addition to being the science which deals with the person as a unit, psychobiology is also a biological philosophy, in which historical orientation is important. Psychobiology is open to the quest for progress and freedom of thought, with an honest and frank pluralism aiming at consistency. Pluralism implies the obligation to acknowledge unquestionably different and specific sets of units for the facts. It also calls for divisions in the field of science into specific spheres which cannot afford to be mixed up or substituted for one another. That sphere of science which pertains to behavior with mentation is psychobiology.[59]

Meyer's philosophy of science was one of action. Abjuring the habit of science of cutting up its material into smaller and smaller pieces to get the "final fact" (what he called learning "more and more about less and less"), so that the character of the thing one started with became virtually lost, he held: We must first determine what things are and what they do.

I start from the point of view of the person who picks up any kind of find and tries to orient himself. He does not want to pick it up hastily out of its setting. He wants to know what it is in itself and of what it is an immediate livable part. Out of consideration of what things belong to, what relations they have, we get some of the most important understandings that we really have to consider and get sense from. Only when we have that clear do we have a right to go into the most customary specifications by analysis, and even then not into particles and fragments which, Humpty Dumpty fashion, we would have difficulty to put together again.

Humpty Dumpty offers a very interesting unit concept. The symbol comes from the nursery, but the nursery very often is closer to an unprejudiced consideration of things than the preoccupations of complex erudition.[53]

With this perspective Meyer stressed the need to know the component factors and how they operated in a stream of events. "In this way all science becomes history," he said at a wartime conference on military psychiatry held at the University of Michigan in 1942. "I want from the start *action* as my frame; I want also the results in final performance, and then I have a complete picture, free of arbitrary and prejudiced classification." [53]

He told this conference that consideration of use does not make science unscientific. He urged a declaration of independence from dogmatism's strait jacket. He called for freedom from forcing "innocent but valuable facts into arbitrary channels, copied from other channels and lost for use." His declaration asserted the right to take from experience with actual problems all that was needed for inclusion in science; to deal "not only with the detail relationships of nerve-cells, nerve centers, and chemical ingredients, but also with the evaluations and interrelationships of history-making events." Opposing the exclusion of material essential to psychiatry, Meyer demanded "a free use of a free science."

After his resignation from The Johns Hopkins in 1941 at the age of seventy-five (he was succeeded by Dr. Whitehorn, who had moved from the McLean to a professorship at Washington University in St. Louis), Meyer continued at the task of "overcoming the rigidity of the scientific dogma according to which daily life has to be kept out of strict science." He pointed out:

> Just as in the development of the novel it took a long time before the ordinary individual and the simple situations received attention, so the respect for what is solid in the ways of conducting ordinary life was late in gaining the respect of the academic gowns, cultivating generality and the equivalent of "laws of nature." [60]

Bringing the person into science and medicine, and making it intelligible and productive, was the main goal of psychobiology. The movement was nonexclusive but not merely eclectic, Meyer reminded. Admitting that it was "not specific and glamourous enough to bid for the front page," he put it in contrast with "the rise of both practice and public response in the release theory of sex, and the escape phraseology, and the gift of courtesy called sublimation." [60]

However, he hailed the rescue of man's spirit from "the philosophical and theological heavens," where it had dwelt in the domain of abstraction. Man was now recognized as a person, "beginning to seem real to the understanding in intensive and concrete studies of actual life." And this was in keeping with the modern demand for a scientifically intelligible and fruitful view of life instead of "the age-long pondering over the fate in an eternity entered through death."

The change was toward a culture for a responsible life to take the place of a culture wrapped in eternity, with its rewards based on atonement for guilt and "the divine grace of sanctity." Supplanting the "dreary pessimism of fall from perfection and hope of redemption" there was a creative urge.

Without iconoclasm and surrender of ideals, instead with a sense of vital reality and inductive realism, a science of man as a reactive and creative entity with interest in progress, not merely in destruction, came to be our practical and ideal concern, and an inspiration to a constructive outlook of its science.[60]

The step had been long in coming. Benjamin Rush, the father of American psychiatry, had had no immediate successor to build on his teaching that the human individual was a dynamic unit, with mental and physical topics inseparably intertwined. "The birth of a biological concept of psychology was at work in Rush's mind," but the start he made was obscured by his persisting reputation as a bloodletter, and to this day the propriety of his title was being assailed by writers who merely repeated "reiterated gossip." [61]

Meyer told the hundredth anniversary meeting of the American Psychiatric Association in Philadelphia in 1944 that he had made an excursion into Rush's own writings and was richly rewarded with a realization of that forerunner's lifelong urge to see the psychological data on man and life included in medical training and perspective, even in a day when man was viewed "against a background of eternity rather than the plain life of man as person." If medicine and science had not shunned this contribution of Rush's, American psychiatry might have had the lead over the European development. "Science" might not still be standing in the way.

We talk glibly of democracy and the obligation toward the individual and the need of respect for self-government and basic education and organization of health, but we also realize that medical education has to include the person and not merely produce an army of specialists.[62]

Life, to Meyer, was an entity which passed through a long period "in which one is not completely made responsible" to a period where "full responsibility is expected and ought to be enjoyed and made effective"—and where one could be sure of the right to be respected.

He put his credo in these words:

We see ourselves as organisms that rise and bloom and pass and do their best under the ideal of ultimately making themselves in a way unnecessary through their own achievements—with various types of satisfactions as one goes along in one's fancy-endowed life. We do not so much aspire to eternity, but to leave when we pass the best opportunity for new times and new life. So it is with me. The goal of medicine is peculiarly the goal of making itself unnecessary; of influencing life so that what is medicine today will become mere commonsense tomorrow or at least with the next generation. The efforts of the worker today become so assimilated in the commonsense of tomorrow that it must be our pride to see that it has passed into the real objective nature of the world about us, no longer burdening our attention, but allowing us or those after us to do the same for ever-new problems with ever-new achievements and satisfactions.

It is in this sense and for this purpose that I advocate the genetic-dynamic formulation of the concrete facts of each case, and not only a nosological psychiatry.[63]

INTERRELATIONS OF THE

DOMAIN OF NEUROPSYCHIATRY

From presidential address by Dr. Meyer, American Neurological Association, Washington, May, 1922: Archives of Neurology and Psychiatry, 8:111 (*Aug.,* 1922).

How can we state clearly and simply what constitutes the field of neuropsychiatry? At this time there is especial need for clearness on this subject. Ours has always been a very responsible field, but today it is all the more responsible since the war has added large numbers of victims of neuropsychiatric disorders. Members of this organization, among them Thomas W. Salmon and our much-lamented Pearce Bailey, shaped a definite neuropsychiatric domain. For the first time in the history of the country psychiatrists and neurologists cast their lot together in a remarkable unitary organization. Noteworthy immediate services were rendered at the front and in this country during the war. Now, as lies in the nature of our field, we shall for years to come have to help maintain a worthy follow-up service for the country and for the men and women who rose to meet the great emergency. What can be held out to the public and to the medical profession as the foundation, scope, and goal of neuropsychiatry?

The task is not only the care of paralyzed legs and arms and troublesome nerve growths and brain lesions accompanied by impaired speech and other disorders; it is especially the so-called mental aspect, including the understanding of the *person;* of that aspect of the person which is likely to guide *or* misguide public opinion—that which constitutes the moods and morale of the patients, and the willingness and capacity to accept and use assistance, and to develop a real *conscience* about *health*. All this is the domain of neuropsychiatry.

Every domain of medicine has, generally speaking, two problems: the study and management of the special *organ or function* on its own ground, and the study and management of the patient as an *individual personality* and member of a group, as it affects the special organ or function.

Neuropsychiatry is quite specifically responsible in both lines, because the very organ of concern to us is also the principal organ for the integration of the individual as a personality. It is, however, equally essential that we should recognize that some familiarity with the science of man as a personality is as necessary for the gastroenterologist or surgeon or any physician or student of any problems pertaining to man, as it is for the psychiatrist and neurologist. But it behooves the neuropsychiatrist to know the psychobiological methods and facts especially well, because he deals with the principal integrating organ. Unfortunately, there are many who want to make a puzzle out of this simple proposition.

My principal claim is that there is no call for the traditional attitude of bewilderment over how to fit the personality facts into the scheme of objective sciences and practical medical data. The interesting reasons for the difficulty of physicians and laity resolve themselves into this: There is too much of the bad habit of expecting that the mental problems and mental conditions should be intelligible out of one's understanding of mere words and ponderings, when, as a matter of fact, one should have some firsthand experience with real and tangible human reactions and life factors and the methods of work with them.

It so happens that the leaders of medical organizations largely familiar only with other aspects, such as bacteriology, *i.e.,* facts outside of man, and with physiopathological part-functions, have treated with undue suspicion the effort of those who see in psychology frankly and directly the study of the patient as a unit or personality, and we find ourselves today confronted with the

demands of an intelligent public to furnish trained neuropsychiatrists fit to be social psychiatrists and neuropsychiatrists, with the
alternative that the public may have to go elsewhere, outside of
medicine, for help.

Neglect of the simple commonsense way of recognizing the study
of the function of the whole individual or the patient in addition to
the function of the parts is largely responsible for much confusion
on the part of the medical profession and the public, whereas, as
I hope to show, its recognition in terms of plain critical commonsense gives us a sound approach, scientifically and logically, on safe
ground and standing the test of direct and simple applicability,
objective and constructive.

Unfortunately, the public, and even the medical profession,
gropes for unsound types of psychology and many a would-be
neuropsychiatrist is apt to talk confusingly to the profession and
to the public. A frank acceptance of psychology as the study and
control of the functions and behavior of the individual organism
as a unit or personality gives us a perfectly sound objective basis
and sound methods of procedure. The concept of integration and
the understanding of the principle of symbolization gives us the
orderly natural-history view of man which allows us to do justice
to the whole personality and the parts, and to the demands of sound
medical and hygenic practice.

The principle is not difficult to grasp. We find that the universe
of which we are a part presents a vast problem of science, that is,
of systematic formulation and experimental and practical control.
The all-pervading realm of fact and of method of approach is that
of physics and chemistry. But the masses or entities we meet are
specifically integrated. From a certain level of complexity they
show more or less individuation and constitute finally what we
might call biological units and groups of units. The special types
of this whole large group can be presented in terms of a fraction,
the denominator being the formulation of the facts of life in
general—metabolism, growth, and organization and reproduction.
The numerator is one or another type or degree of development
of the general biological type: the purely vegetative type with only
limited and incidental motion; then the branch of life characterized

by motion and all that which goes with the animal type of life forming the numerator of our fraction. Within this we have, first, the forms with a type of behavior possible without a nervous system, and other forms in which the numerator crystallizes a definite nervous system with a literal *organization* of *reflex* process. It is within this that another specialization occurs, namely, that of symbol activity and what in ourselves we know and describe as integration in more or less of consciousness.

The swinging-in of a nervous system brings us an organ working essentially as an integrator, with no special meaning and value as such, remarkably economizing, little energy-consuming and with little fatigability, unable to live and work by itself but serving the task of unification in the form of reflexes and their combinations.

On this ground, among the many exigencies of life there expands a special type of *organization not only of structure but specifically of function*, an organization in what we know as more or less "conscious" *activity*. This organization takes place through that tremendous development which has as its essence the *use of symbols*, or symbolization, in the form of sensation standing for certain facts, perception and images, memories, picture formation, and language, all unified in subject-organization and psychobiologic integration. Thus human behavior becomes the behavior of an integrated individual brought into psychobiological organization with the help of all that which makes up man's specifically "mental" equipment and symbolizing or representative reactions hanging together in more or less consciousness. This realm of function is justly combined into a special topic of psychology or psychobiology, in contrast to or in addition to the science of *reflexes* which do not involve symbolization, and do not depend on integation with the help of signs. But in distinction from tradition we do not treat the "mental" or "conscious" data as a detached and special purely subjective realm of facts; we study them as a special incident of the objectively observable behavior.

As soon as sensations and perceptions, memories, images and ideas, fancy and reasoning, forecasting and deliberation, are involved in reaction and actions, we find a type of function or behavior which constitutes itself as "function or behavior of the individual," in what I call *subject-organization*, not merely as an abstract mind, as tradition has it, but as a specifically integrated type of activity of the cerebrally integrated organism; not as a part of a detached world but as the natural form of a psychobiologically integrated physics and chemistry, not only dealing with new words but with specific functions and coordinations and discriminations of behavior of definite kinds of organisms.

Psychobiologically integrated activity, or behavior with the help of mentation, or we might say in an even more telling manner, "behavior with the help of imagination," implies naturally and inevitably this new development: the inclusion or insertion, in the reflex type of function, of symbolizing functions of the highest possible saving in energy consumption; it implies the "mental" activity, which, however, is definitely recognized as cerebrally integrated activity of the organism, but making possible a new "state of function," the organization as an "individual in action as an agent or subject," as the "he" or "she," the "you" or "I" we know as a biological individual and social entity. Just as metabolism constitutes the special feature of the domain of physics and chemistry that makes up biology, so symbolization, the development of sign-function, establishes the psychobiologically integrated types of organism and function. Instead of acting as an ordinary mechanistic reflex-machine, the organism constitutes itself as a subject, with all the mind and soul that our anthropomorphic parlance chooses to emphasize, attained through the incorporation of symbolization among the other biological or life-dependent functions and activities.

The concept of symbolization, *i.e.*, treating the mentally integrated states and activities as brought about with the help of sign activity and its organization, is not difficult to grasp. It shows in the production of sign reactions from simple sensations up, that is, activity not necessarily of any special potency of effectiveness by itself through the actual physical energy-display it contains or implies, but getting its meaning and potency through its service in an associative system, a system which constitutes itself concretely as the variously adapted subject or personality. It shows in part individually and in part socially, as in the form of gesture, emotional display, and language and their silent forms, built up out of perceptive, cognitive-discriminative and affective and conative assets of response and construction. It brings about something that activity *not* integrated with this help could not produce with such a degree of differential adaptation. Just as logarithms and algebraic notations bring in simplifications and new possibilities of operation, so the introduction of the sensory-cognitive and conative and affective assets in overt form and overt behavior, or in their economizing so-called "mental" type experienced as mental activity or mentation, gives us means of psychobiological integration, so remarkably organized as using on the same level reality and fancy, past, present and future, one's own ideas and those of others, in overt effective and expressive action or in the specifically economizing form of implicit symbolization.

Jelliffe and White in their *Textbook of Neurology and Psychiatry* recognize this formulation and give us the data of neuropsychiatry in three long chapters on the physicochemical systems with the vegetative nervous system, the sensorimotor systems, and the psychic or symbolic systems. They give us a very concise and essentially American conception in a pithy paragraph (p. 21): "The hormone is the type of tool at the physicochemical level, the reflex at the 'sensorimotor' level, and finally the symbol at the psychic level." My own conceptions are very similar, only I prefer to speak outright of the vegetative, the reflex, and the psychobiological types of function or levels, and I prefer to claim as frankly unnecessary the confusing contrast of physical and psychic, as indicated in various older discussions of mine.

We have, then, a formulation of the facts we deal with that keeps us on the ground of objective data, with our eyes clearly open to the specific precautions needed in this field of relativities, with methods correspondingly adapted and safeguarded and without any call for mystical notions on the one hand or neurologizing psychophobia so confusing to commonsense on the other hand.

With such a philosophical and practical conception, one learns to subordinate the exaggerated contrast of mind and body, and to speak of reactions of the internal or visceral organs, the nervous segmental and suprasegmental organs and functions as such, or as parts of the reactions of the cerebrally integrated person. The nightmare of neuropsychiatric dilemma has no place. What the patient does, feels, and thinks ceases to be made a puzzle; one either finds objective facts calling for one's attention or one does not.

How do these general conceptions present themselves concretely? Our objective psychobiology expresses itself concretely and simply in certain definite aims in our medical curriculum. It is my ambition to organize the essentials as a science of neuropsychiatric work that will give us a right to insist on a comprehensive picture of the entire domain and on absolute clearness of the essential lines so that they may become usable in all medical practice. All our medical schools of today train the student to include a minimal number of neurological routine tests in any medical examination. But how many medical teachers of today and how many neurologists make it an acknowledged practice to include planfully the minimal number of questions and tests that will draw out the reactions disclosing at least the most tangible psychobiological problems? There is no difficulty in this. One simply has to be at least as familiar with some ordinary human problems and standards of adaptation as one is with the facts of reflexes, ataxia, tremor and palsies, anesthesias and decerebrate rigidity, and fits. After testing the principal reflexes, one should ascertain how the patient reacts and responds to a minimal number of simple questions: "What difficulties do you want help for? What is your work and how does it agree with you? Have you had any special experiences, or moods or fancies, fears or worries, or imaginations which you could not throw off? Does fate and everybody treat you all right? How does your memory serve you?" Wherever evidence calls for it, a small number of performance tests give us the memory data.

We add today to a reasoned scheme of working in anatomical and clinical neurology a gradual working-out of a general and special psychobiology and psychopathology for the student, beginning with the technique and practice of the simple life-study of an average person and average problems of psychobiology, and extending it to the work with the fundamental reaction-types and problems of psychopathology and psychiatry.

Instead of considering psychiatry a field of asylum diseases, let us see what we find wrong in behavior and mentation, without damning it at the outset by a terminology derived from merely possible terminal developments. The personality reactions present themselves to us concretely in terms of reaction groups: mood disorders, fears, obsessions, states of panic, seclusiveness, fancy states, simple or disorganizing, and memory, retention, judgment, and behavior disorders—plain facts which do not necessitate any very learned or bewildering vocabulary. We look for concrete mismanagement of home situations, for discrepancies of ambition and performance, existing difficulties and failures, problems of adaptation and problems of desensitization; and doing so, we shall be helpful to our patient instead of sacrificing him at the altar of vocabularies dealing with terminal states and with fixed fatalistic "constitutions" and too dogmatically fixed "disease entities."

We must get away from the idea that one examines only for some all-inclusive asylum diseases like dementia praecox and manic-depressive insanity and paresis. One examines primarily for the range of personal capacity to help in an examination and to co-operate in any plan for treatment, that is, assets as shown in plain life problems and successes and failures. If there are any failures, one determines whether there are any toxic or infectious intruders, any disorders of the internal organs and their functions, any neurological disorders (including the suprasegmental as well as the segmental symptoms); and finally any disorders of behavior or of mental reactions, not in the abstract but in terms of what the patient does with the jobs, with the family, with other people, and with his own worries and feelings and notions and moods, the thoughts he cannot throw off, the memory and judgment, and the speech and writing, and the management of his eliminative functions and sleep and appetite. One does not fish merely for a few so-called "frontal-lobe symptoms."

I am more concerned with having the best possible understanding of the condition and needs of the patient at the time, than with the customary relatively uncertain guesses as to the ultimate fate. I want to make sure that my attention is focused on all the points which might make a difference in the immediate treatment and guidance of the patient, without therefore losing sight of the long-term problems, the future and the ultimate fate. In some conditions, such as delirium, agitation, depression, or states of panic, the immediate problems are as clear and urgent as in any acute disease of general medicine; in other cases the broad long-term problems must lead us rather than the immediate appearance, as in the temporary spurts or temporary improvements of paresis or of paranoic or deterioration or psychoneurotic states. In all cases we need a sane elastic balancing of the facts, and I feel that we can show that this is possible with a theoretically and practically sound scheme, without leading the student first through a stage of dogmatic cocksureness of ultimately unattainable nosology and general pathological assumptions.

I am told that when I outlined a similar point of view at the Bloomingdale centenary, one of our colleagues turned to his neighbor with the remark, "How is this to help us in a case of brain tumor?" It is true I did not then discuss brain tumors specifically, but the "Contributions of Psychiatry to the Understanding of Life Problems." But does not the plan of attack bring a certain clearness into the study of any patient? Assume that even the brain-tumor patient, like E. W. Taylor's case, is one who has for years been troubled by obsessions; or that the condition is one of a Korsakoff-like callosal syndrome. In the former case we must know that the mental disorder is *not*, and in the latter that the mental disorder *is*, naturally accounted for by a focal disorder. In either case an examination and study of the facts as we find them in mental or psychobiological terms are necessary before we dismember the data.

It is clearly important that we should guide the public to recognize quite frankly a call for an obligatory practical pluralism in the use of the facts and methods required in the understanding and treatment of our patients. The layman understands at once what we mean by a study of the special organs and the study of general conduct and behavior and mentally organized functions. We study not an abstract "mind" but the functions and activities which constitute the facts of mind—just as we might study water and not "wetness," and living things and not life as a detached problem.

To be sure, the public with its ideas of a detached mind is today as much as ever under the influence of one-sided fads, all kinds of one-sided faith healing, and all kinds of temporarily successful cults; even physicians send patients deliberately and without further guidance to healing cults and to consultants and healers inadequately trained—apparently without knowledge of or trust in the conscientious efforts of physicians with all-round training. As a compensatory reaction, still others refer the public to a one-sided infection theory, or to a one-sided endocrinology, or the patient takes refuge with the osteopath or other types of chiropractor's work because of their grossly tangible display of curative efforts—their doing something with their hands, that which gives the surgeon his name. Our responsibility is great. As neurologists let us profess frankly that we are really neuropsychiatrists, that is, physicians with a comprehensive scope of interests and methods; and let us also see to it that the spreading of frank and intelligible views of the nature of the life problems and the psychobiological symbolizing level becomes a necessary and obligatory concern of the rank and file of physicians, appreciated in its right importance by both physician and patient.

There will but rarely be physicians who can cover the whole field, and each investigator will have his own choice of problems. But one thing is certain: we do demand of everyone a reasonable training in the entire domain, including the functions of the organism constituting the personality. We want neuropsychiatrists—not merely neurologists and not merely psychologists, but primarily physicians able to study the entire organism and its functions and behavior and more especially the share of the nervous system and of the problems of adaptation.

As we deal with the policy of the care of the war veterans, let us not enhance the inevitable traditional and personal difficulties and confusion among physicians and patients by overemphasizing a split between the neuroses, psychoneuroses, and psychoses, and the like. Let us remember that many psychoneuroses as problems of general adaptation are infinitely more problematic and difficult to treat than the frank psychoses. The maintenance of the necessary self-discipline and the practical use of judgment is often much more difficult to obtain in the so-called psychoneuroses. The actual

work of study and readjustment requires a high degree of cooperation on the part of the patient.

Let us do our best not to give cause for outcries of indifference
on the part of the physician through disregard of the personality
facts, and for the patient's untimely and arbitrary withdrawal from
experienced guidance. Let us see that the policies can be shaped by
those who are able to study and master the facts about the parts as
well as the personality, by those who know best and work most,
rather than by the sensational magazine literature and the exploiters
of dissension in the neuropsychiatric camps. To attain this we have
to be creative and constructive and in the front line, and we cannot
trust the old policy of mere following and drifting when we come
to the psychobiological problems. We must travel under one flag
and with a clear aim.

We consider it obligatory in the study of the reactions of man
not only to test the pupil and patellar reflex, but also a few essential
reactions to life problems and the essential ways of using and adapting oneself. Let us trust that such a conception of neuropsychiatry
may become a general one in practice and in teaching.

The public will then learn how to use the neuropsychiatrist, and
especially how to cooperate and what to expect. That the medical
profession appreciates the change is, I believe, adequately shown
by the frequency with which not only long-mismanaged cases but
acute cases are given the benefit of timely neuropsychiatric discussion and study among the junior members of our medical staffs.
Let us show the world that even we of the older generation have
some of the plasticity and vigor of ever-growing youth.

SPONTANEITY

From an address by Dr. Meyer before the Illinois Conference on Public Welfare, Mental-Hygiene Division, Chicago, October, 1933; A Contribution of Mental Hygiene to Education, p. 21.

I have had an urge to formulate what I considered a most needed characteristic feature of the human being apt to be neglected between rigid dogmatic science and traditional interests of life: a consideration of human spontaneity.

Being equally devoted to the study of the nervous system and to the study of patients in the clutches of mental disease and of the events in normal life, I have always sensed as unnecessary the zealous competition, if not intolerance, between a privileged, extremely mechanistic science that belittles spontaneity and the equally dogmatic intuitional and revelation-born conception of man that puts the emphasis on a principle extraneous to the self instead of on natural vital spontaneity.

All through science and throughout much of the popularized attitude toward man there is a peculiar tendency to a kind of mechanical conception of the nature of man. With an IQ, or intelligence quotient, and some ideas of conditioning and of reflexes and instincts and complexes, and an unconscious shaped according to a dogmatized psychopathology, many people consider the study and knowledge of man settled, and there develops a cut-and-dried attitude which threatens to hide from us very essential features of living beings and to prevent our attaining an adequate understanding.

It has also seemed strange to me that we should, after the fashion

of pathology and a defensive and narrow attitude of health interests, focus our attention so exclusively upon "what is wrong," upon
what calls for the surgeon and for antitoxins and for a search for
the enemy in the depths of one or another organ or function. Why
the lack of interest in the positive facts of life as found? Why
always the obsession of the "something else" in a panacea or in
exclusive salvation in the domain of physics and chemistry, or in
similarly life-shy histology or an unconscious or something ultrabiological?

The worker with the really live problems of the life of the
individual and community will always have a need of a sense for
the positively active and open constructive factors of nature, particularly of human nature. In contrast to a cold, mechanistic
conception of man with its insistence on the "mere" chemistry
and physics of it all—ignoring the fact that chemistry and physics
study only a limited range of the substantial relations of reality—
there is also an urge and a need of watching what I want to sum up
and discuss as spontaneity, not in any metaphysical or dogmatically
vitalistic sense, but as a feature not to be neglected where we find
and need it, and as it asserts itself as a special process of existence.

One hears frequent inquiries into the distinction between what
one is born with and what one acquires during life and through
living, a distinction between nature and nurture, very difficult to
disentangle but important from the angle of the educator and the
biologist. The far more accessible and far more important question
of what the person does with it all might draw much more profitable attention to the distinction between what man uses *sua
sponte*, out of himself and on his own, and what he is pushed into
as part of a wider setting. Without any disregard for the nature
and nurture issue, we have to turn with our heart and soul to what
is before us now and here, when we are confronted with the
problem of plasticity. To study this from a positive angle, to
occupy ourselves with the emergent person, with the range of the
individual's spontaneity, is the goal of this discussion.

There was a time when spontaneity was unquestioningly taken
for granted in a more sweeping sense, and actually exaggerated to
the point of being called "free" will or even the "divine spark,"

as if it could be something absolute, apart, and beyond nature and *physis*—beyond what is born or "is to be born" and grows. One spoke of spontaneous generation and spontaneous putrefaction until Pasteur put an end to that superstition merely by turning over the necks of his open flasks and avoiding the settling of contaminating dust. One does speak of spontaneous combustion. But any peculiarly spontaneous feature in man, especially anything voluntary, was to be kept outside the laws and consideration of nature, just because of a kind of all-or-none attitude.

The whole history of science has been such a necessary and strenuous war against magic, and such an iconoclastic reduction of all apparently occult forces to natural principles, that somehow the process has led to a thoroughgoing—shall I say—mechanistic materialism or, better, just untiring insistence on objectivity. It would almost seem as if there were in science almost as much exaggeration as has prevailed and still prevails in the antiscientific camps. Somehow the world likes extremes where at least some of us like to keep to a perspective for what can have common acceptance, a vision that need not blind us to realities that lie clearly before us. We are no doubt more willing to call a spade a spade and to allot to a consideration of spontaneity in nature and particularly in human nature its relative but positive position.

As we review the rising series of living beings in nature, from plant to animal and man, we see more and more the formation of active entities and more and more of what we properly shall call spontaneity, the function and working and acting with and from the subject's own nature and individual specificity. Whoever does not see and feel and respect that particular feature of a relative but actual "spontaneity" in nature and man has killed in himself a real part of human commonsense. Theoretically, we are reducible to physics and chemistry, but a physics and chemistry of a very remote future (which should also be ready to deal with products of integration, but still is far from exhausting, with the data and conceptions and methods of the physics and chemistry of today, the real essence of life as found) and without demanding that one pledge oneself to a vitalism making something out of nothing. A philosophy based only on the physics of the inanimate, trying to legislate a conception of the whole without respect for biology and psychobiology where they operate, is not an adequate guide for man.

If we enter a room where a dozen persons are gathered we cannot help noticing their different ways of reacting, their various types of relative spontaneity. We may naturally say they are "conditioned" to be and to do what they are and do, individually and differently. But the fact that counts most is what each is and does on his own, out of that which characterizes the person. The spontaneity of the person—that which he can do, and actually does, on his own and in his own way, without particular external prompting or coercion—is what interests us above everything, as I said, without our thereby pledging ourselves to any mystical vitalism. We deal with a product of organization and integration. What we need to know is that differentiation and integration are something different from a mere summation of parts and that the integrate has features and properties of its own, not present in the parts, and to be studied as found.

Even the elementalist will grant that he also recognizes compounds with specific properties, and that a certain group of these presents "relative spontaneity." To speak of spontaneity in this sense should not any longer be heresy.

Man's own creative imagination (and volition) is as much a force, of dynamic event, as anything produced by immediate and direct stimulation used in man's experiments. We may properly contrast reflex, volition, and spontaneity and consider the variable "use" of the "machine." The biological experiments of nature give us a world of positive growth and action to be studied for what it is and does and foretells—to be accepted and cultivated, without magic, but also without cause for belittlement. Our waking up is a positive process; so is our buoyancy as well as our dreams or our play. The philosopher who thinks that man will not act unless prompted by pain and conflict maligns nature and so does he who trusts only an arbitrarily hypothesized unconscious and any extranatural constructs of the mystic. We have a right to speak of a wider and perfectly natural uncomplicated spontaneity, just as we have a right to speak of natural growth as a differentiation of live individuals.

That is what we want to bear in mind as social workers and as educators and as physicians, and also when we want to function as spiritual guides of human beings. "Humans" with practically the same equipment do not prove equal nor the same all the time.

In these days, when the teacher, the social worker, the psychiatrist, are so eager to get the dependable and telling facts about a person, and when one speaks freely of instincts and hormones, of intelligence quotients, and the social setting and economics (for both consumers and producers) and earnings and employment and jobs, the degree and the kind of spontaneity become one of the most important items in the case—a commodity that differs widely from person to person and from time to time in most persons.

By the person's spontaneity I mean that which the person may be expected to rise to and to rise with on his own, *sua sponte*, with his "spons" and "response" and finally "responsibility." It is more than "muscle twitch" or reflex, an incorporation and integration of wider relationships. Certainly both in our practical and our scientific habits of dealing with persons—with one's own self and with the many others—we like to express the needs and possibilities in terms of what the person has and does and what can be expressed as resources and possessions. The individual cannot profitably come to be largely an abstract center treated like a mathematical point, for, as a matter of fact, it is the way the personality sums up as relatively active or inactive with its type of spontaneity that determines the probable success or failure according to adaptation. We want to know what we may expect of a person at any moment, and in the course of time, on his or her own initiative and integrated organization; this expectation may be relatively or largely unpredictable but surely does not result from "casual chance."

The type and the degree of emergent initiative and spontaneity become a most vital concern, in view of the fact that in the nature of the individual and group life there is always a setting, a past and a future, there are always the leaders and the led, and the fate of large numbers and of the various ranges of communities is usually largely dependent on a limited number of individuals and the working of their spontaneities and the morale of the rest. The history of the last twenty years has been full of disciplined and undisciplined centers of spontaneity. We have to choose between spontaneity of a revolutionary type and spontaneity of an evolutionary type. So much of human life and nature is influenced by specific contingencies and combinations of events that much depends finally on the individual's disciplined spontaneity.

The whole development of psychobiological integration is a growth and differentiation of structure and functions within the bonds of heredity and mutation but with organization and integration of spontaneity. More than ever we realize that every mother has to face a new entity in her baby with its own and specific range of spontaneity. There shapes itself an organism for action, guided by meaning-functions in a plastic flow of more or less grasp and inclusion of the realities with consciousness, and subject-function or personality-function. What we call mind or, better, mentation is the specifically integrated action itself and not merely action as the servant to an abstract self. To treat the action and integration facts as if they could be a special superentity is anthropomorphism. Each person proves to work as if with a constitutional government, a bundle of forces to be won for cooperative action or turned off into an army of revolt, with its energy and spontaneity in harmony or out of harmony with itself, in more or less biographic unity, and at the same time a not altogether predictable agency for success or failure in the familial, social, communal, and national units—with a capacity or inadequacy of foresight and with biological and sociological conscience and conscientiousness as well as consciousness.

It is spontaneity that I want to study and inquire into and cultivate and respect as the all-important characteristic quality of a person. It is the range of spontaneity, with its range of dependability and the capacity to rise to the various ranges of occasions and demands and opportunities of life. Call it psychology or behavior-study or, as one of my pupils suggests, ergasiology (using ergasia as the term for mentally integrated function)—organized common-sense allows us to reduce it all to terms of experiments of nature.

Whether we study the units or the group or the part, the questions are always the same simple questions of inquiring commonsense:

"What is the fact? The conditions under which it occurs and shows? What are the factors entering and at work? How do they work? With what results? With what modifiability?"

This is the formula which does justice to the factors of both elementalism and integration, to hindsight as well as foresight, and to the spontaneity of chance and purpose, individual and social.

If spontaneity is not an absolutely fixed quantity—only relatively constant—that is evidently the nature of this kind of fact and we must find the methods to do it justice.

Spontaneity covers the range of performance to which the individual is able to rise in the continual *status nascendi* [state of being formed] with the endless or at least ever-available "credits of time," within at least the range of expectancy of life, be it in mere waking up or in meeting any specific task or situation or opportunity.

In psychobiological study and work I should look for the capacity to see the problems and opportunities and to meet them constructively.

Our intelligence tests bring out "the spontaneity in the face of a multiplicity of questions." An intelligence test of life is much more a real spontaneity test than would be the case with any absolutely planned experiment; it is an experiment of nature with its mixture of necessity or determinism, chance and contingency, with law and order of growth, and choice under the evolution of ever-accumulating and self-maintaining experience, *i.e.*, etymologically and factually "that which one is from having gone through" (= *ens, peritus, ex*) function and performance in changing and yet more or less balancing processes.

Experimental psychology, with its demands for mathematical accuracy, has done much to make us neglect or underrate what needs also other methods of demonstration, analysis, and understanding and evaluation. One longs for direction of attention to what might revitalize the interests in man and bring them closer to what assures attention to the person and not largely some formulas favoring cut-and-dried or dogmatic conceptions of mechanization. A "science of life" without full respect for life where it lives and as it lives is not true science.

Spontaneity is not unscientific just because it may be too susceptible to misinterpretation by those biologically poorly trained. It is not just a concern of metaphysical reasoning and religious dogmatism, but the natural upshot of psychobiological integration or behavior open to critical obligatory observation and active planning in our work with human beings (including ourselves). It leads us far into social and political life, with the leaders and the led. It is that which we want to cultivate in its best disciplined and adjustable form.

We have many different types of pupils and teachers and homes and also of the communities ultimately becoming the consumers of the products of education. How can we assure a teaming of the constituent elements of the community? How can we attune the environment so as to attain the possibilities of contentment and satisfaction for the many varieties of fitness?

I shall never forget the discouraging and visionless description of this aspect of American education and ambitions given by former Secretary of Labor James J. Davis, now Senator Davis, when he told our City Club that there are occupations in this country which no American parent would want his children to be engaged in and for which we need "immigrants to do the dirty work." Any civilization that has no respect for the work it lives on and lives by is likely to keep both the conditions for work and the workers out of step with the general standards and principles of economic and social interrelations and obligations. We want to cultivate a reciprocity of spontaneity and attitudes, which must be disciplined and balanced, with due respect for the individual differences and the differently suited opportunities. Different settings have to be maintained with equal fairness and honor for the different spontaneities and capacities. There is a need of reciprocity between the satisfaction in the worker's life (*i.e.*, literally the duration of the organism) both as to dependability and worthwhileness, and the respect offered on the part of the social medium in which the individual has to live.

The following example of the working of spontaneity is one of special interest, considering the rigid system within which it asserts itself:

It was my privilege this summer to receive an invitation to visit Russia. One of my main interests outside of the special psycho-neurological and psychohygienic field was the evaluation of the educational system. Free of shackles from traditions, and familiar with the principles of Western progress, the Russian leaders put to a test the Dalton plan and the liberal principles to which Chicago, with its Colonel Parker and Professor and Mrs. Dewey and many others, has contributed so much.

The widow of Lenin, Madame Krupskaya, and Professor Pinke-vitch (whose most interesting book of *Education in Russia* is pub-lished by John Day, New York), and others outlined to me the basic principles and their evolution—a system of education con-stituting a remarkable respecter of spontaneity balanced by atten-tion to both the personal interests and the call for a "polytechnic" orientation; first a largely individualistic kind of project system under natural leaders, and of later years also a supplementing by systematic courses in order to assure standards of more universal greater dependability. There is every encouragement of personal initiative but a correction of the natural limitation of circumspec-tion by organized guidance. Education side by side with factory and other work, with equal pay for the work in the factory and that in the school, fosters a spirit of balance between needs and opportunities and elasticity. The plan is excellently suited to the five-year-plan attitude and the determination to bring home to a younger generation the opportunities of the locality and the various regions of that vast country.

The programs are not a "free-for-all" but the product of con-scientious discussion and decisions covering yearly periods, open to revision when the plans for the next period are made and out-lined anew for the rank and file and for the special conditions of the region involved. Education is a living and life-assimilating procedure, polytechnic in the sense of keeping both stimulus and the result in close contact with the variously pointed exigencies and opportunities of actual life; polytechnic not merely in the sense of vocational but definitely with intention to serve as a basis for further training and for practical use. For higher education a process of selection is practiced, strongly influenced by aptitude, not only in acquisition but also in performance.

What is done there in spite of regimentation seems to form a remarkable contrast to the difficulty of orientation of so many of our youth. The plan avoids the drawback of a loose system of elective courses. Initial consideration for spontaneity, clearness of the principles of appeal, a premium on work fitting into a scheme, and on health fitting for work and social action, are much simpler than with us.

Today, in talking with our own jobless college and university graduates caught in the prevailing unemployment, one is struck with the overspecialization of the sciences on the one hand and, frequently, aloofness from reality of "cultural" humanistics on the other. When teaching is too strongly attached to "research" often hardly worthy of the term but formally pretentious, and when degrees are the goal rather than evidence of maturity for self-directed work, the result seems to be not so much a preparedness too proud to take whatever job is available but often enough lack of fitness for any job actually wanted. We must admit quite frankly that even in the period of prosperity it had become exceedingly difficult for many people in our American environment to find the type of niche in which a satisfying and reasonably well-rounded life interest could be found outside of the get-rich-quick bond-selling—which is little more than a kind of magnified repetition of the variously safe and constructively helpful first pursuit in boyhood in the form of selling papers. In this respect the situation in Russia is much simpler. There is not the point of saturation and the competitive expectation that the earnings have to meet an artificially stimulated standard of living and expense.

Another gain in simplicity lies in the fact that the principles of both civil and criminal law in Russia are far more directly adjusted to present-day conditions and freed of often unintelligible procedure.

The spontaneous tendencies and reactions receive far-reaching attention in the handling of crime and of the transgressor of the law. Both in correction and in prevention more stress is put on the attitude and spontaneities of the subject than on the crime or the time allotted for punishment.

The experience with the "Loeb and Leopold" case showed glaringly the deplorable gap in an educational system that does not concern itself with the attitude of the pupil, *i.e.*, the spontaneity toward life going beyond mere erudition. That even in our ordinary school education there should be necessary a separation of ethical-religious and intellectual considerations is highly deplorable, something that leads to the apparent necessity of separate ("parochial") schools of different ritual interest, instead of the getting-together so desirable in the basic education for democracy.

We see in all this examples and evidence of how spontaneity comes to include getting closer to matters that one is apt to miss in the cut-and-dried science of man.

It calls for an active sense of subjectivity, but one protected against running away with itself if firmly implanted on a ground of sound critical objectivity. It shows a union and balance of what there is in the facts of energy, of life, of soul (*i.e.*, etymologically, the self-same?), of human nature as the active force it is. We come to ask, "Is it wholehearted and all there, or drifting and unformed? Is it wholeheartedly one with the self and also with what the self belongs to? Is it just in a fit, a squirming, like the first general reactions of an embryo or fetus, or nearer that final and highest attainment of a personal enthusiasm, elation, a force unified and harmonious and pointed? A harmonizable creative rise, urge and espousal? To what extent are the heart and the "sense" in it clear and whole-souled? illuminated by understanding and clearness of outlook and goal? an evidence of dependable spontaneity?"

We can readily see what ramifications we get into. Spontaneity is much more than a casual individual issue. It reaches far into the breadth and depth of human developments. It is far-reaching socially. We cannot get away from the continual interrelation of the individual and the various groups, from family to community and to state and government.

When we consider the limitation and variability of spontaneity we recognize how mankind finds itself confronted with a complexity of experience that makes one wish that the means of communication might for a time be cut and the news shut out so that the problems of life could be worked out in small intelligible groups and districts without the disturbing continual awareness of up- setting events and dangers. This must be attained by better ways than vain attempts to put back the clock. We have to attain a sense of responsibility in the exploitations of the infectious appeal of world-wide and local problems and interrelations, which are apt to become more than the average man can master. There is a call for orderly group formation, and for a very human kind of geography, a knowledge of soils and of their inhabitants, and aggregates of nationalities. There is a need of a certain simplicity and yet comprehensiveness with a grasp of controlling and con- trollable numbers, a wish to look for general dependables rather than exclusive salvation in ventures, or endless party conflicts devoid of clear and basic principles and of confidence in the sense of chosen representatives, which certainly should go beyond the interests in patronage of the ins and the outs, if we are not to be driven to highhanded and emotional dictatorships.

Spontaneity, if it is to constitute any smoothly running per- formance or adjustment, depends on a fitness and congruity of setting or environment which can never be anywhere near absolute. It requires proportion and plasticity and security of background and perspective of possibilities. It requires a certain morale and stability and continuity, which today are very seriously shaken up through surrender of false props, often without corresponding readjustments in the guidance and natural conditioning of the growing person or the one facing life, and a sense of a respected career with a balance of stimulus and contentment. One is staggered by the ease with which dictatorships can get a hold and the extent to which democracy is surrendered. This is explained only by serious malorientation under the pressure of ruthless propagation of patterns which are difficult to fit into the scheme of actual production and consumption and something like a code.

One realizes the need of a simultaneous cultivation of culture, self-dependence, and a balance of budget and its burdens, and of satisfactions from socialized life. The conditions affecting the balance of spontaneity and allegiance to the state and to law have to bring together the individual and the group in a reasonable and intelligible reciprocity of helpfulness. It should be obvious that adequate creative and planned attention should be given to the psychobiological needs and the balancing of the individual and group participants in the family, community, business and legal and political life. We need not only vocational advice but a morale and clearness of orientation and a place for the vocations; we need education of the individual and the groups, not merely as formal entities to be perpetuated but as time-bound personalities to live our span of life in our place in the procession of generations. We need our contact with actuality, but also with the spontaneities laid down in the human atmosphere.

What we need is the humanization of science generally and the influence of the regulating lawful procedure of science to digest man's human tendencies. We need balance; we need commonsense, a natural way of looking for what we can accept as common, in spite of all our individualism, and therefore respect for both individualism and social law and order. We need time for judgment and yet preparedness to act when the moment is at hand and decision is wanted. In the continual change and development of new conditions we need a balance of venture and consistency, and concentration and comprehensiveness, a capacity to use history and imagination for foresight. We need a balanced resourcefulness, a balanced spontaneity, the cherished good of humanly integrated life. When the spontaneity of leaders fails, there come waves of undisciplined spontaneity and the upshot yields the curves of dependability of our civilizations.

All this calls for a capacity in balancing education and medical work and economics and politics, which is not everybody's capacity but is sharable in spite of individual differences.

Thinking and working with and for man is thinking and working with and for a set of relations and realities nearest to us. But we also need perspective. There is not a boon that cannot also become a poison. Religion means to be the greatest aid to happiness and yet it has bred the most cruel inquisitions and still entails endless retardation of general progress by the holding back of its own adjustments. Law has been used by tyranny and through its hopeless obstinacy has made some turn to anarchy. Education has to be balanced or it creates a hotbed of discontent and armies of discontented learned fools and parasites. Modern life demands sense for work and sense for leisure.

With a growing sense for human spontaneity and its good and bad features, we need the philosophy of the now and here illuminated by history and by a cultivation of outlook and creative fancy.

We must learn to realize that life is history in the making.

To sum up, spontaneity is a quality that we have reason to pay specific attention to in order to get out of the purely static habit of disregarding the active and forceful features of our subjects, the human individuals and groups. Scientific objectivity does not imply disregard of human differences and especially that difference which we call spontaneity, and among the spontaneities those that pull together play, pleasure, and what one does *sua sponte*, as one's nature, response, and responsibility. In other words, we must treat man with and for that spontaneity that spells also responsibility as made up of ever-recurrent and disciplined spontaneity.

THE PSYCHOBIOLOGICAL POINT

OF VIEW

By the time a man can be expected to apply himself in a systematic and effective way to critical and systematic work and thought concerning man and all that is involved, he has acquired individual experiences and formed for himself ways of sensing and feeling and doing that cannot be pushed aside as unimportant, as in the sciences of physics and chemistry and anatomy and physiology, or replaced by an organized body of laboratory theory and practice of a prescribed and proved type.

In the struggle for a place in the attention (and also the tolerance) of man for the various sciences, various compromises and conventions were made in the way of delimiting the domains, and in our fields, especially those of physics and chemistry, biology (botany and zoology), anatomy, and physiology, with biology as the comprehensive concern with all living things and functions. On the other side there were the practical domains of training in religion, morality, and education, in law, in sociology and medicine, with tendencies to divide man into mind and body, or body and soul, as different sets of facts, entities, and functions, or as different aspects or mixtures of these divergencies. In medicine we find those who wish to reduce everything to physics and chemistry, or to anatomy, or to physiology, and within that to neurology or to endocrinology; but there is also an increasingly aggressive group that wants to emphasize the mind, either on the ground of common experience or on more or less highly specialized and systematized conceptions.

Our general formula for all the sciences urges a common point of view. Man meets a world of fact, to be studied for what it is and does, whether the inquirer is there or not; to be studied by observation of the material accessible to common experience, with a genetic-dynamic background and a willingness to accept and use all the facts according to their role and importance in working and thinking in terms of an experiment upon man or nature. Our chief aim in the study of man is the determination of the range of operation of man, affecting his own course of life and that of others and of our common background, and the determination and control of the special factors making for success and failure, for health, happiness, efficiency, and creativeness.

Psychobiology starts not from a mind and a body or from elements, but from the fact that we deal with biologically organized units and groups and their functioning. It occupies itself with those entities and relations that form, or pertain to, the "he's" and "she's" of our experience—the bodies we find in action, as far as we have to note them in the behavior and functioning of the "he" or "she." We are aware of a contrast between the activity of detached, or at least detachable, organs, such as the heart, stomach, or brain, and the activity of these same parts assigned to the "he" or "she" or "you" or "I."

We see the legs active in walking and dancing, but we also see the knee-jerk when, in proper position, we strike the slightly stretched tendon. We know that this can be produced on the detached reflex-preparation. Something similar can be shown in a psychoneurotic woman whose foot kicks out as soon as one comes near the knee with the hammer—evidently an anticipative response of the *person,* not a mere reflex, the operation resembling a delayed reflex, a reaction presupposing that *she* anticipated. What then is *she?* The person, the consciously or mentally or psychobiologically integrated woman or organism, functioning in a specific manner of subject-organization with the help of symbolizations, through pictures of past or of possible patterns of attitude, reaction and action and the so-called "content of consciousness," a special form of waking state, a state of function—orientative, perceptual, and dis-criminative-associative-affective-reactive-active, characteristic and essential for certain types of behavior adjustments. This behavior is what we have an understanding for, summary or detailed, correctly grasped readily or only with difficulty, *i.e.*, with chances of error and requiring effort and a personality state favorable to the correct association and mustering of resources. It is specific situations and their mastery, tasks, and solutions that interest us in what we call objective psychobiology.

It is behavior, overt and internal or implicit, that concerns us, so far as it works as the "he" or "she," that entity which is more than the body as found in a corpse, *viz.*, function including rises in *status nascendi*, in the now and here, as the reaction in and to the situation, including in the presentation also re-presentations of experience, past, remote, and anticipating, and general or abstract, through its organization as a subject or agent-and-reagent and its participating live resources. In order not to involve ourselves in unproved and possibly misleading hypotheses, we speak of functions of the organism as a unit, as the "he" or "she" (in contrast to what detachable parts can do) operating in a specific "state of function" or hanging together, in more or less consciousness and subject-organization.

Those who speak of mind seem to us to limit themselves unduly to the introspective data of consciousness (including an "unconscious" in the form of the less readily aroused assets) with implications apt to disregard the objective reality with which and by which we work, owing to their assuming too exclusively an egocentric view which science is trying to get away from, without, however, having to ignore it and the advantages of a personal study and amplification where it can be made accessible to common knowledge and work.

We rather speak of *ergasias*—actions and reactions and attitudes of the "he" or "she" or "you" or "I"—*i.e.*, mentally or more or less consciously integrated behavior, to be studied for the role they play in definable situations, from mere sensory and perceptual or affective to intentional-volitional performances, as opposed to the nonmentally integrated functioning. In the matter of food and nutrition we distinguish the personally integrated appetite and the finding and using of food and its incorporation. Digestion is attended to automatically, in nonmentally organized function, while the evacuation of the residue again becomes a "personality" function, personally and socially regulated.

As further instances I might point out the distinction between ordinary breathing and the psychobiologically integrated singing or speaking; or the acceleration of the heart in exertion or in emotion.

Other functions of obligatory consciousness are the dreams and the waking life. The processes holding them together are the subject-organization with representative movements, perceptions, and trends of what we may summarily call imagination or mentation. These processes are studied not merely as functions of the brain, but, in view of the many interdependencies, as functions of the individual.

The total-activity is indeed organized in a way that differs from the function of detached parts in that total-activity hangs together in terms of functions not only of direct effect but involving a flow of meanings which go much further than the mere physicochemical and physiological state and processes of detached structures. The integrated total-function represents an ever-new condition of *status nascendi* operating with meanings, with a system of symbolization making it possible to utilize the immediate orientation, together with re-presentation of experience of the past, and anticipations in the form of more or less consciousness and subject-organization.

This function constitutes the material for a science of psychobiology, a specific domain of study of specific persons (others or self) with specific facts and specific methods of study and control, open to observation as the function of the organism as a unit or individual, in the literal sense of this word, the "he" or "she," responding to varying situations, external and internal, and described in terms of function in a life record and biographical frame.

There is, a definite preference for the commonsense view that takes the individual organism as the entity, the total-function of which is mentally integrated life. Neither life, nor mind as a special part of life, or as it is sometimes represented, a special aspect, would receive special recognition as an independent detachable entity or fact (although naturally and unquestionably usable again in the human and spiritual relations of those who do carry on and can include the experience of the person, but definitely not in the magic sense). We deal with specific states of function of special organizations; these states of function do not exist without specific "content." They are characterized by a specific mode of hanging together and functioning inherent in the nature of the specific organisms and the nature of their functions. It is the picture of the organism or body in action that comes to mind when we speak of a person, very much as in the most authentic record we can make today, in a moving picture, with or without the additional sound record. The organism is a time-limited entity, starting as a bud from a kindred unit, a product of conception, reproduction, growth, and development characteristic of the species, with characteristic life and characteristic subject formation or "mind," which is not a new material substratum of the economizing symbolization, but is inherent in the structure, in structure formation and interfunctional activity.

Psychobiology is a frank and noncompromising formulation of "behavior with mentation" or ergasia, behavior integrated in a flow of economizing and yet amplifying system of signs or symbolization, constituting a specific set of facts and not only a special aspect, the mentally integrated functioning of the live human organism.

We recognize in the study of man certain discontinuities by no means limited to the step from matter to mind, or from the inorganic to the organic ("the emergence of life"), or from vegetative life to the appearance of consciousness, but best met with the general concept of integration. We find as the decisive principle of the specifically psychobiological fact of personality function the emergence of a system of symbolization and interrelations as meanings. All that which we know as thus integrated is to be studied for what it is and does. Taking this view, we are prepared to study the *facts* found in actual operation, the *conditions* under which they do or do not occur, the *factors* entering into the patterns, their *working* and the *results* and their *modifiability*, their *formulation* and their *reconstitution* as *"experiment of nature."*

How can psychobiology be presented and how does it make itself active?

In its strictest genetic procedure, psychobiology would start from the first evidences of reaction as a unit, in a stimulus-response pattern and in patterns of spontaneous total-function. It describes and analyzes the common traits of reactive and spontaneous functioning of the pertinent biological type, in terms of reflexes and delayed reflexes, the delays of which prove to be the inherent differentiation of total-function as primary pictorial and secondary verbal and conceptual symbolizations, implicit (economizing) or overt. Symbolization is made up of overt or economizing (pictorial) attitudes, reactions, and actions, implying or standing for what is intended or belonging together. It is this system of symbolization that constitutes the specific differentiation of the primitive biological response, the "content" of the delayed reflexes.

I start the description in terms of what is most likely to give me the distinctive and comprehensive account. I start with enough of a biography to put mistakes of identity out of the question; and I begin to study samples of function likely to bring me closest to the nature of what I aim to formulate in a way that might serve for reconstitution of the set of facts or events to be discussed, for reobservation and control of the formulations or hypotheses.

The question arises as to what type of science shapes itself in dealing with this type of occurrence and material.

The specific urge that makes me speak of psychobiology in contrast to the traditional psychology lies in the obligatory organismal time-bound nature of the material. The facts present themselves as the total-function of individuals and groups. Speaking with Madison Bentley of a separate "psychological organism" and a "biological organism" is definitely replaced by focusing on the total-function with but the one organism, and with function viewed in the light of the objective and subjective evidence of more or less consciousness, *i.e.*, a specific mode of integration or hanging together, constituting a solvent as it were, a flow of contacting in the form of sign-function or of symbolization holding together or integrating the attitudes, reactions, and actions making up our behavior.

I use the picture of subject-organization as government formation, allowing concrete activities or mere representative functionings or organized signs to have the lead as the very self, or a subordinate position in the temporary state or process. The question is one of formulation and delimitation. In my own mind I can operate with the experience of a tremendous relativity of overtness of the material, or mere referential or mere suggestive tendencies, in a gesture or word, without any obsessive need of overspecification. We can single out and describe or imply broad patterns or special components of emphases, operating with remarkable plasticity, and a principle perhaps best described as absence of fixed and binding rule such as mere structure would entail, a "rise," with varying order and temporary dominance of leading interests or drives or emotions or volitions, or purposes or reasons or whatever we may find as motivations or leading factors, in the main as a natural culmination of personality, character, temperament, as specific performance or agent in situations characteristic for the person. I speak of a natural system, as that which naturally shapes itself in a person or entity without necessarily a dominant and persisting boss. It would be the ideal democracy with the maximal individual freedom compatible with effective unity, but without God-ordained or fixed proprietary governmental representation, rather with a kind of natural self-regulating merit system within a reasonable regularity of happenings and outlooks.

In such a setting we are forced to work with samples. In order to be on the safe side, we choose our samples primarily from among the types of functions which express to the fullest extent what we consider specific for the field in which we work. We should prefer to choose complex samples which actually represent psychobiological function and on which we can bring to a test all the essentials of our conception, rather than give preference to what might appear simpler and at least logically detached and more definable as datum of introspection. It may be a great concession to necessity, but to my mind no great sacrifice and departure from the facts as they are, to deal with functions that cannot be detached from a good many implications and contingencies, but that after all constitute topics of concern and importance sufficient to deserve all the trouble we may have in working with them.

One of the great difficulties in psychology has been the relative futility of the matters chosen and often the merely logical detachment of the specific samples. Psychology has got away from the specific by putting more emphasis on the whole range of particular functions of special sense organs than on the total-function, that is to say, by discussing sensations, perception, image formation, rather than memory, ideation, association, affect, emotion, and activity tendencies. And to get rid of meanings and implicating inferences, it has taken up the ingenious device of working, for instance, with nonsense syllables but really thereby creating only particular new situations recalling the predicament of a man with an artificial nose: "Before I had it the kids shouted, 'There is the man without a nose,' and now, 'Look at the man with that nose.' "

Without any disregard for all these particular interests, an orientation in psychobiology would much rather start with the whole life record and then single out performances in particular situations, making sure that they are adequately specified and studied for the conditions that make them possible or impossible, the factors entering, their working, their effects and results and modifiability—realizing that we always deal with a fraction, the denominator of which is made up of the total personality record or potentiality of the person and the numerator of which is the particular sample of performance.

This may be tantalizing because the denominator evidently has what I would call an open definition, something unfinished (unless we deal with a dead object that can no longer change and must be tested in retrospect). And even with the numerator, the sample of performance, we have to recognize the relativity of the sample and the natural variability from day to day. If this is the nature of the material with which we have to work, it is best to adapt our methods rather than insist on methods devised for other material. If generalizations finally get more the character of a pattern than of a law, this also may be one of the characteristics of the science with which we deal.

The question arises, "How can such work be systematized and taught?" Being more or less in the beginnings of such work, it may be well to proceed with samples rather than with dogmatic categories, but also to use to best advantage what categories have proved dependable and suggestive so far. If we prepare a student to make examinations of sensibility, the experimental equation of the examination is relatively simple. We determine the range of responsiveness to the qualities and quantities of the special sensory field or perhaps merely the capacity to rise to the average standard. The same broad principle has been used for the wide range of sampling of such methods as were initiated by Binet and Simon, where we are satisfied with the question of success or failure. The utilization of these methods has made it clear that the issue finally is one of the extent to which the individual actually uses his or her capacities. This calls for a new type of inquiry, into the past record, and the trial under varying conditions. Here again we may be satisfied with the success or failure in relation to a conventional or special standard; but again we may be prompted to go further. We may turn the equation around and try to determine the conditions of existence and particular working of various factors and components such as attention, memory, endurance, foresight, intellectual and emotional "conscience," and whatever we may single out as a topic of concern.

In order to familiarize a group of students with the type of facts, topics, methods, presentation, and controls of the rank and file of facts in the psychobiological field, an equivalent of laboratory work has been worked out in the formulation of the personality-study, starting with a biographic sketch sufficient for a beginning and to be amplified where need occurs; next a brief survey of the judgments and prejudices more or less systematized in the evolution, from childhood up, of the student's spontaneous or taught formulations concerning mind, body, and the sciences that might come into question, and the dynamics and logic of the operation of the material.

This is done partly to arouse attention to one's habits of thought and to what they may be measured by or brought to an issue on, and it takes the place of, or enlivens, the impersonal review of the history of philosophic-epistemological concepts.

We next take up a survey of functions of the person beginning with the full-fledged performances and achievements and attempts that give an idea of the individual, the personal care, the jobs and hobbies, and the activations in various directions, such as family, sociability, public life, education, religious activity, etc. It is obvious that our commonsense leads us to specify also interests and ambitions, the ratio of one's preceptive life (sensual and esthetic gratifications), dreaming, thinking, acting, and what we speak of as the temperament. From the very start we make the student conscious of the fact that there are no absolute measures but that we recognize certain rhythms and orders in the functioning, activity, and rest phases, conditions of having enough and being in a state of composure or of unrest and nonsatisfaction. With such a preliminary occupation with concrete facts and their relations, the student can get his ideas straight with regard to the facts, formulations, and concepts, and relationships one has to be prepared to work with.

There may be some difficulty when we approach the next topic and have to meet the question whether, in the division of the field, we shall use the old concepts of cognitive, conative, and affective data. Inasmuch as we do not accept "elements in pure culture," we realize that a division is essentially a matter of emphasis and that it should be made along lines of what the functions serve and how they are logically grouped. I therefore make a division between topical (cognitive and conative) and essentially diffusely regulative (affective) functions, a division which falls into line with the emphasis on content and mood so important and helpful in the examination of pathological conditions.

It is doubtful whether speaking of sensing, acting, and feeling in the abstract, without a statement of specific quality and content, leads us very far either theoretically or practically. It would seem to me that in the field of psychobiology the "science" part in its strict sense should also concern itself with the specific content and meanings and not wash its hands of them. Those who want to see science only where there is generalization or formulation of laws can nevertheless get their satisfaction, although in many respects that ambition is more in the nature of proving the obvious than along the lines of any creative addition.

There is no belittling involved when we group together mathematics and logic and the other divisions of metaphysics (like esthetics and ethics) as necessarily based upon particular issues of data dependent on the nature of biological functioning and actually part thereof. On the other hand, there is no call for fanaticism and finding fault with those who, in concession to other issues, maintain a special province for these fields of preoccupation and study. I should only emphasize that when philosophy, religion, and the occupation with the formal sciences learn to recognize biology and its fullest scope and implications, they will have taken a very important, vital, and valuable step and they can do so in a system of relativities in which there is no particular emphasis on high or low, letting these valuations depend on wherever the valuator happens to stand.

The outline of the personality-study directs the questions so that there is every opportunity for the student to think and discuss special topics and problems connected with them, such as the range of simultaneous functioning, interaction and association, analysis and synthesis, etc. This leads us to the consideration of variations of the range of fitness, attention, fatigue, and the like, and it brings out quite emphatically the need of the recognition of the sets or levels of integration, physicochemical, structural-functional, and the function-functional (*i.e.*, interfunctional), and the general rule that no single set of integrations can be self-sufficient. Each of them studies specific data and sets of relations and not merely different aspects of the same thing, and certainly not the whole.

After discussion of what can as well be studied in the relatively detached individual, the student is led to consider the social relationships, the actual status and position in the family, and the dependencies and degrees of emancipation, the relations within friendships and broader social connections and all the modalities and concepts pertaining to these relations; and within this setting a study is made of the psychobiology of sex, again strictly based on concrete data, the study of concrete data being the main justification of psychobiology in contrast to discussion and debates about generalities.

Throughout the study we aim at an understanding of patterns, which ultimately are studied for their synthesis into a personality, with particular attention to the formation of types and the factors essential in determining them. After the collection and consideration of concrete samples pertaining to one individual as compared to dissimilar individuals within reach, the student is in a position to make a survey of the grouping of the sciences and fields of work as he sees them.

With a study of some outstanding differences and normal difficulties and reactions to disappointments, and the like, the capacity of students for the selection of facts, their specification, formulation, and control, is brought to a test; and the attention is led over to the methodology of general and special topics in the study of personalities and their functioning, such as may be used with the normal or with the sick.

The question naturally arises as to what theoretical and practical questions and inquiry we may wish to raise. Emphasis is put on the fact that we deal with objective data which are or are not present and functioning with or without integration with symbolizations, rather than on the question of whether they belong to what has so long been emphasized as the "physical" or the "mental" field. They inevitably belong to both when mentally integrated functions; they are then overt or implicit, largely objective or largely subjective. I do not erect any theoretical barrier to the inclusion of anything that pertains to the perhaps sometimes rather widely stretched range of the neighbor of the self-tormenter of Terence, *Homo sum; humani nihil a me alienum puto* [I am a man and deem nothing human foreign to me]. This does not interfere with my using some judgment as to what relations enter into the discussion of one or another problem or line of inquiry; but I should positively decline to close my eyes to any new problems of tact, esthetics, ethics, religion, or other issues if they figure as such, for instance, in the form of conscience, preferences, aversions, etc., in the problems of the person. On the other hand, the general outline and the sense and demands of the purposes have to weigh the sufficiency or insufficiency of our data.

The basic point in this attitude is the recognition of the number of discontinuities which justify the demarcations of the sciences. While I recognize the fact that in the study of any problem we have to face the interpenetration of various sciences, I most emphatically stand for as much differentiation of categories as practical sense concerning the nature of the material and the methods requires and as actual work may force us to recognize; but I repeat that, while we still might speak of a hierarchy of sciences, there is no distinction between high and low but only a logical grouping and grading according to the temporary and other importance for the specific questions under consideration.

This has many implications of considerable significance. In the first place, we do not assume or admit that any one science can exhaust the whole field and swallow up all the rest. A study of man, of any serious and responsible character, should presuppose reasonable dependability on general biology, psychology, and physiology, knowledge of the structures and, equally, knowledge of what is usually included under sociology. In order to deserve any degree of certificate of competency there should be evidence of an adequate training in these fields, and also in the formal sciences necessary for the correct formulation and interpretation of the data. When we come to the domains in the medical sciences, I should require a basic training in these fields as obligatory for all those who assume the responsibilities of the physician. No specialist should make himself exclusively responsible for merely one field. This means that the attitude of nonmedical workers does not measure up to what is required and considered desirable. The attitude of certain neurologists which makes of psychobiology a mere subordinated appendix, useful for diplomatic reasons, is not considered a wise and correct attitude to keep before the public. As a rule, one should recognize that whoever assumes responsibility for the patient must in the main be able to handle all the emergencies, at any rate with enough knowledge to serve until more competent help can be made available if necessary.

It is obvious that with the concept of psychobiology we imply essentially the fundamental perspectives which I trust give ample space and recognition to any specialized pursuits and methods even if they choose to develop any otherwise oriented foundations or principles. The chances are that the structuralist or physiologizing investigator or the Freudian analyst or the representative of individual psychology or the general biologist or anthropologist will in the main operate with methods that can be readily brought into psychobiological perspective. It may make a difference in the ultimate clearness whether there is any recognition of involvement of sign-functions and symbolization and subject-organization, which are particularly emphasized by this particular type of psychobiology.

A great deal of the work that is carried on under this system of concepts would not in its statements and reports voice specifically the tenets of the theory. As a matter of fact, the general conception and its use aims to be in line with the best critical commonsense so that in the actual rendering of the data there is nothing that would specifically bring out any exclusive characteristics. It is sensed as a desideratum that intrinsic allegiance should express itself by fact and act rather than by a conspicuous badge. After all, the virtue of a good deed does not depend on its being called "good" in the description.

The most fundamental and characteristic feature of the genetic-dynamic psychobiological viewpoint lies in the fact that there is perhaps too little conspicuousness on the part of the *principles* in the presentations of obligatorily concrete material. The principles have to show in what one does; and one has to bear with the appearance of the ordinariness of a large amount of the material. This appearance is inevitable and has to be met by order and perspective in the handling of the data and the capacity for obtaining brevity by a summary rather than by an arbitrary singling-out of essentially nondetachable items.

My attention is drawn to the fact that there is not enough analysis of the material and systematization of deductions. This is purely a question of what the human being is able to stand and to make useful. It does not, on the other hand, exclude a concentration on topics of particular temporary interest, although in the main one would feel happier if more generally digestible standpoints could be so favored rather than the psychoanalytic overemphasis which tries to make a transference situation the center of attention and of work in spite of the fact that we know that it is probably one of the most problematic and difficult foundations on which to bring the range of human capacities to a unitary measure and evaluation.

My earlier stand-by was that of habit formation and habit-deteriorations. In a period when our human institutions are conspicuously unstable, it also becomes difficult to specify groupings of habits which deserve categorical attention. Today growing attention is being paid to personality types and characterology, but it would seem that from the psychobiological point of view a collaboration with sociology would be particularly profitable in the direction of singling out critical relationships and patterns of the problems most frequently forming the determiners of matters requiring our attention. The difficulty there is also in the fact that social relations are considerably disorganized and in flux.

Among the interfunctional developments I recognize reaction sets forming relatively frequent and intelligible patterns. In the statement of the physician I want these expressed in concrete terms so that one can work with them in cooperation with patient, family, and home physician. The reaction set is not a diagnosis. It has to include a full statement of the causal and motivating components and the evidences of any possible lesions, somatic or situational disorders, and the factors inherent in the make-up of the patient on grounds of heredity and life record. I do not refer much to the standard "mechanisms" or "dynamisms" since they can be much more usefully expressed in the terms of the concrete case. I urge the student to accumulate a set of patterns, the systematized upshot of which shows in his procedure of examination and his sense for adequacy or insufficiency of the material and its formulation. The systematic organizations of the pathology and therapy consist of the teachable principles and generalizations by which the specific case can be checked up and allocated for statistical work.

The plan here outlined offers a satisfactory place for the upshot of practically every other scheme of pathology and therapy. It is nondogmatic but critically discriminating, although it frankly places itself on the ground of the best common experience and the best trained commonsense rather than authority derived from scientific system on ground of limiting theory.

Psychobiology explicitly is but one of the domains to be experienced and worked with in the study of man. For principles of collaboration it requires attention in all cases; for specific and essential attention it may be the strategic or only a subordinated domain. The common ground is the total experience with the case, the formulation of the complaint with utilization of all the corrections and directions offered by the work with the patient and his situation.

If I had to make a comparison between this approach and various other forms of psychology I should emphasize the definitely biological rather than physiological character of the problem and methods here described. What interests us is the functioning in a situation with content of varying bearing upon the *life-curve*. This does not exclude the other problems, such as the definitely physiological ones, or the localization issues. The recognition of integration sets allows us to study human nature as it is actually organized, and we are guarded against the old mistake of hasty and unjustified identification of parts of the mentation pattern with parts of the neurophysiological or the architectonic brain patterns. It becomes quite questionable whether aphasia studies will lead to more functional patterns in the psychobiological or the psychophysiological sense. For pharmacological and endocrinological studies the task is but slightly different, and we are likely to look for standardized behavior-functions by which to measure the effect of the drugs. We may be more interested in quantitative work with relatively easily comparable samples of psychobiological functioning. It is deplorable that centers of brain surgery have so little collaboration with services which are prepared to study the psychophysiological and psychobiological relations.

Interesting problems arise in connection with the foundations of mental hygiene which should follow a course quite different from that of pathology, as a study of variants not primarily medical and their conditions and management.

Concerning the correlation of psychobiology and psychopathology and the other sciences, we have to admit that collaboration is difficult to establish unless the workers are all well trained in psychiatry. Specialists not so trained are usually expensive guests and their work should be specially supported so as not to become a tax on the anyhow costly burden of the patients, their families, and the hospital.

A PLEA FOR THE CONCEPT OF

"SENSE" AS THE ESSENCE

OF CONSCIOUSNESS

From remarks by Dr. Meyer in Proceedings of the Fourth Conference on Psychiatric Education, *Baltimore, April,* 1936, *at p.* 213,
National Committee for Mental Hygiene, New York (1938).

The term *sense* appears in many connotations; but these connotations converge upon that which is most characteristic of our domain
and gives an important slant to the nature of "mind" and to all
mentally integrated function.

I refer to the obvious corollaries "meaning" and "participation"
as a necessary part of the characterization and definition of psychobiology and "sense." Speaking of sense points to function, including
both discrimination and direction and action. It directs attention
to the sensing of differentiations, not only of sensation and perception, but at the same time to the intrinsic tendency to result in
open action.

What interests us in mind and intelligence and its use is not only
knowledge, what the French specify as *connaître,* but it is the
savoir faire, the *savvy,* the doing, included in intelligence, desire,
and achievement and satisfaction. We want the story, the life in
the making, and if it becomes possible to define and to show the
operation of "sense" we may have just that essential condition—
rather than something suggesting itself as a thing or substance, as

has become the case with "mind"—and the equivalent of what is carried by the concept of metabolism in physiology.

In psychology the meaning of "sense" has been narrowed to the function only of the special receptor organs and to sensation, necessary for perception; but it also keeps the connotation of "feeling" and the original derivative meaning of the word, which includes the path and direction and action. During the transition period of emancipation of psychology from philosophy, most American psychologists were led to consider their output as "physiological psychology," and the "new" psychology at least as "functional," without, however, getting far beyond putting a more or less poor chapter on the nervous system and neurophysiology at the beginning of the old text and a meager chapter on personality at the end.

Titchener struggled with the two principles of his quest for psychological "elements," sensation and affect, keeping out Brentano's emphasis on the basic principle of action, and insisting on "trained introspection," and later on existentialism, while others, like Judd and champions of motility and behaviorists, tried hard to preserve their field from being treated as mere physiology. Ebbinghaus, working with nonsense syllables, did not make the study of memory more psychological but brought out certain laws along lines shared with physiology and the biological nature of mind and minding and memory, helping parallelism to the analogy of the inner and outer aspect of a shell. It was not till the "meaning" of these functions for life and for the sense and direction of the person was included again that commonsense could feel satisfied. We think and feel and act as we do with "sense" for the meanings of things for our life.

Even the unprejudiced dictionary gives the word "sense" the implication and meaning of significance and appearance, but also the meaning of general relations and of orientation (as in a "sense of locality; of distance"), of a capacity of perception and appreciation; or a natural "understanding" and "intelligence" as bearing on action or behavior, and of practical soundness of judgment, and of direction; further it implies "signification" (*i.e.*, sign-making and sign-serving) as when we speak of a special use of a word or thought or passage open to various interpretations (literal, mystic, moral) and evaluation.

Sense as understanding and a process in operation, prevailing and functioning in and between persons, is what we look for and appreciate and use, or what we may miss and aim to supply in ourselves and others and in our patients. We might in our work speak perhaps somewhat paradoxically of a "cultivation in ourselves and the student of our sense for sense," that which includes not only quantity and quality, but also *direction* of thought and *action*. We have too long isolated mind and soul in terms largely of sensation and its derivatives; the common denominator includes action and really constitutes a specific type of condition in action—*i.e.*, with the help of symbolizations or sign- and meaning-functions.

Meaning is an intermediary between related things, the pole between the poles. This is implied in the term *ergasia*, our concept of behavior—action, reaction, and attitudes, working with more or less sense, and as sense, with the help of sensations and their derivatives acting as sign-function and sign systems, with their sense, meaning, and driving force. Sense is the common medium of human function and interrelations and balance. It would seem best to think, speak, and work in terms of "person" and of "sense" or direction when we deal with human beings with "minds" and "souls." We are indeed dealing here with a central issue of the very essence and meaning of the person, of the human individual, and those animals similarly endowed although not to the same degree.

As a matter of routine in any kind of medical history taking and examination concerning the sense present and at work in the person or persons (in contrast to mere concern with the "body" or "organs"), in the behavior or function to be studied, in the complaint and in its treatment, the student might be advised to raise simple but essential and informing questions following the inquiry, "What do you want to get help for? What are you complaining about?" We should properly make it a rule to ask, "What do you think it is and how does it affect you?" The physician does not ask that often enough, largely because he considers it his professional privilege "to know" and his pride "to tell the patient," to be accepted without further question.

A good many patients are so accustomed to that point of view that they are very meek and say, "Of course, *I* don't know; you are the doctor." We want to break through that attitude of authoritarianism and to see that we get on common ground with the patient, who after all is at the same time the sufferer, closest to the complaint, and actually the most important collaborator in the study and in the actual carrying out of treatment and finally of preventive medicine. It is not merely "knowledge" but the attitude and fitness as a person that we want to heed and cultivate. We deal with the most fundamental step and achievement of twentieth-century medicine, the *inclusion of the patient in collaboratorship* in pathology and therapy and ultimate prevention, and a formulation of a "pathology" in the direction of such attainment—the respect also for what works in and through the sense of the participants, their meanings and their role, and the opening also to a sensible foundation for psychiatry.

I should follow up the patient's account of the complaint and appeal for help with such natural questions as these: "How does that affect you? What makes it better or worse? How does it affect your sleep, your appetite? Are there any worries and difficulties of yours that I ought to know about in order to save you trouble?" I look upon sleep and appetite as ergasias—*i.e.*, personality-functions—rather than as mere "physiology," because they are, for me and for the patient, functions of the person operating with corresponding meanings and attitudes and not only stimulus-reaction functions of some particular organ and also not merely a concern of psychiatry as a specialty. They are part of the concept of every man's nature and function or specific functioning.

Such questions as, "Does it worry you? What are the worries or burdens I should know about?" are the prototypes of what keeps our "finger on the pulse," on the sense that the patient has and shows and uses in the personal situation and in the direction of attitude, reaction, and action, and the sense that gives worker and patient the medium or common ground in working together.

This brings us very directly to the material with which we have to work most specifically in our special field, something apt to be side-stepped—for a long time it was tabooed—in academic psychology when it limits its interests and responsibilities while still claiming to govern the whole field. I have come more and more to the conclusion that the bulk of the psychology that we work with as physicians is very far from the dominating preoccupations of several now gradually passing types of psychologies, such as those of Titchener and many others, who focused their attention largely on the "structure" of their data of introspection with neglect of the meaning or sense. They seemed to me to occupy themselves with the ghost or shape of reality instead of the core and meaning, or at the other extreme, with its bones and static skeleton, or only its sense organs or muscles, as a physiologizing concern, something not close enough to the actual concrete and observable and really lived life we actually have to work with. This does not exclude an interest also in the special concerns for which we may be able to borrow methods also from other sciences.

For many problems we may take "meanings" for granted, but we cannot disregard them. That is why it set me questioning when I heard it said that "the psyche" with the one, or the reflex arc and conditioned reflex with others, should be the first principle from which we should start in "psychopathology." The concept of psyche with its abstractness and load of tradition is hard to make definite and a part of actual life, since it is too apt to detach itself from biological principles and material. When, on the other hand, I speak of the "he" or "she," and the person (implying also his or her sense) I know I am speaking of a "somebody" and a real biological object and its function on sure and real ground. When I mention a "person," everybody will promptly think of what he or she looks like and is as a body and what he *does* or may *not* be able *to do*. We are on perfectly objective ground which also does justice to the person's subjectivity. The inclusion of "sense" produces a science quite different from what used to be thought of as a quasi-histological psychology of introspection and microscopy in contrast to what in a way a good many of the special tendencies and schools would like to accentuate by including, if not actually starting from, behavior. If we can bring home what we mean by "sense" I should like to combine the two trends, the objective and the subjective, in a psychology of "sense" and "meanings," as when we state the facts deliberately in terms of a story.

The material with which we work is singled out for the "sense," which implies meaning and direction for action. There are those to whom it looks as if the elaborate technique and theory of "psychoanalysis" had been the first and the only system that sensed and appreciated and used the meanings of experiences. Undoubtedly it has done much and has incidentally produced a rich harvest. Some of us, however, have to give due credit to the original persistence and insistence of all critical commonsense, and to what we do and feel naturally under the guidance of meanings and the dynamics of reason and motivation, something we should never have allowed ourselves to be weaned from by a science too narrowly based on the mechanics of physics. We cannot help using it (critical commonsense) naturally and frankly, and it cannot be made unnecessary by our physics and chemistry and physiology. It is a necessary concern and consequence of critical commonsense that we accept the concept of man as person, as an integer, as the "he" or "she," a biographic entity.

When we consider what we deal with, we see the *facts as story and history and events in the making;* they are historical data of the actions and aptitudes and attitudes that exist at the time, always time- and sense-connected. That is why I speak, in history taking, of the history of the complaint *as a story*. It must be an *informing story* that forms the common link and material in any understanding of human life. We are not far from the real truth when we call natural science "natural history." Practically all that psychobiology and psychiatry occupy themselves with in their present mood and mode of progress is the study of the meanings and meaning factors and motivations in "personal history in the making," including also the performance in the special examinations and in application and therapy.

What is discussed as "the meaning of meaning" we might paraphrase as "the sense for sense." The account must bring concreteness, and the examination and continued contact must be headed toward "sense and its performance and disturbances." Those are the problems of psychiatry and psychopathology as I see them, and the basis of all collaboration and understanding between physician and patient, and the recognition of an active status also of the patient and person.

In all this, of course, we take up specific data and specific disturbances and consider them obligatorily for the facts constituting the "experiment of nature." For instance, it seems to be quite insufficient that anybody should be described without further question as depressed "without adequate cause." At any rate, we would say that there must be causes or determining factors when the "story" is made complete; therefore, if the patient's or my own formulation cannot give them to me offhand, I must look for a completion of the "story" beyond the immediate surface or range of consideration into a broader setting, including also the organism and what the event or development is part of. That is what actually happens in all sense and is essential in the psychiatrist's work.

I should like to offer this emphasis on "sense" as a challenge, as something to be heeded. We may properly ask, "Which are the types of psychology that do justice to the 'story in the making,' the life in the making, the person in the making, the 'he' or 'she' that is to be envisaged or formulated like an 'experiment in the making'?" I cannot get away from the fact that often enough a critical amplification of the layman's story makes the best "psychology"—and pathology—our best material and way for understanding and for action. We are dealing there with objective concepts and facts to be verified, and patterns in which the practical human being is closer to the factual reality than the erudite slave to traditional and stilted doctrine or too finical a division of labor, depriving the physician of the right and duty to include the person in his thought and work. In ordinary life, there may be too much of a traditional contrast between "mind as the person" and the "body as the tool." The layman naturally contrasts thinking and doing, although often forgetting that thinking is also a type of doing—*i.e.*, at least actual symbolization and not a mere "other aspect" or parallelism. Actually, in our stories these contrasts of the mental and the physiological cease to be mutually exclusive contrasts. The average person today is closer to a frank natural-history attitude than the dogmatic scientist, and he is therefore quite within his rights provided that he adjusts his concepts and responsibilities within his "critical commonsense."

All mentality that we see at work, even if we assume it to be as laid down in books and in culture and in what we mean by spirituality, can become effective only with a live body or person; hence, when we speak of mental processes, we are evidently singling out definite organismal functions. We call them mental because they imply "mind" *qua* "memory" and imagination and sense— *i.e.*, mentation, or symbolization or sign- and meaning-function, in a particular "state of function" (*i.e.*, more or less consciousness) but always functions of a person, of a specially unified live organism. When a person is knocked on the head, then that which we treat as a "state" of consciousness may be affected and even eliminated.

I use the term "more or less consciousness" unblushingly, as an objective as well as subjective "state of function" (in a sense analogous to our speaking of the "state of matter") notwithstanding the present habit of raising the specter of metaphysics as soon as consciousness is mentioned. I speak of consciousness where it proves itself, as a specific but varying mode of hanging and working together of assets and responsiveness and creative spontaneity in subject- and personality-organization, with evidences of presentative symbolization and subject-organization, with memories and anticipation and fancy and planning, choice and effective function as *action*.

We side with the critical-minded layman in presence of a patient or normal person and his questions. In the above case, we raise the question, "Is 'he' shamming or is 'he' knocked out?" In any practical situation we ask, "Is 'he' all there or not? Has 'he' his senses about him?" That is what I understand and look for and imply when I speak of the "state" of function we call consciousness. How much can he pull together? How acute is his discrimination, and how far can it be trusted and guided? How far does he need help?

The point is that actually we have to study, as a rule, the "human" facts in terms of the story in the making (or hanging-together of the situation) felt as intelligible, or as showing gaps, as static or as growing and modifiable and adaptable and creative.

The essential thing the student has to cultivate is his capacity of evaluation, the capacity to single out from the wealth and flood of data the facts that count. And then, inasmuch as facts are data about which we form ideas (or verbal and conceptual symbols) and toward which we form attitudes—that is to say, tendencies to action (as in the Spanish *actitud* rather than the English "aptitude") —we realize that our findings are data of observation which we formulate and test by the way we handle them and by the way they handle themselves.

There is a question then: "Can we expect the student to follow psychobiological events and formulations in a sensible way and with reasonable proficiency?" Evidently so, when presented in terms of the story, open to the dissection and analysis and scrutiny here suggested.

SUBJECT-ORGANIZATION

From remarks by Dr. Meyer in Proceedings of the Fourth Conference on Psychiatric Education, Baltimore, April, 1936, at p. 248, National Committee for Mental Hygiene, New York (1938).

The first condition for anything worth calling subject-organization is individuation or the formation of entities worth being called units or wholes in contrast to a mere accumulation of elements or particles.

In the nonbiological world, individuation is present at best only as crystallization (the assumption of shapes characteristic of the physicochemical make-up). This presupposes merely physicochemical integration or unit formation. We might speak of crystallization as balanced accretion, devoid as yet of the biological criteria.

Biological individuation occurs in vegetative organization as plants (in simple cells and cell colonies), and in the more highly specialized species of plants as units with vegetative biological integration, carried on and maintained by osmosis.

Zoological individuation obligatorily involves motility in part of the internal workings, such as the circulation, the ingestion and disposal of food, the locomotion, and the adjustment of sense organs.

Psychobiological integration appears, in this setting, wherever we find the differentiation of a special type of organization and function of the subject or agent with the characteristics best known as "more or less consciousness"—i.e., a contact and blending and a hanging-together of functions of the unit in subject formation with

616

meaning-function, as attention and attitudes and reactions and actions, overt and implicit. The specific feature lies in its working with the principle of symbolization—*i.e.*, sensations, pictures, ideas, thoughts, all of which are functions serving as signs with meanings (presentative and representative), implicit as well as overt (just thought or spoken and acted on); the implicit, the "contents of consciousness" in the narrower sense, constituting themselves the forerunner activity or vanguard in a series of functional gradients. We start with full-fledged overt activity as the standard perform-ance and attitudes and reactions, while the largely "unexpressed" implicit activity (sensations, perceptions, feelings, and conations) is best regarded as highly economizing and differentiated steps toward full-fledged performance.

Tradition singles out what is accessible to introspection as the supposedly unique and quasi-detached data of "mind" or "con-sciousness," the domain of actual and potential "awareness." The awareness-function is, however, the same for what happens within as for what happens without; introspection consists of amplifica-tion of states of consciousness, pictorial or conceptual, sensory or imaginative or verbalized, furnishing means of comprehension, a grasping together as well as differentiation, and used as full-fledged function or in more or less pure culture of symbolization or imagination.

The question arises whether what we observe in ourselves and "only infer" in others should be turned into a general division as a mental world as opposed to a physical world; or whether the facts so reached should be considered more vital than the methods and conditions of observation. Psychobiology or ergasiology prefers the study of the facts as found, and subordinates the distinction between immediate and inferred experience. It works with the sense and with the specific facts experienced and treats the ex-periencing as part of the mentally integrated performance to be studied in psychobiology or ergasiology.

This specific type of "mentally integrated functioning of the individual" comes out most distinctively in contrasts of sleeping and waking states—sleep being the period of maximal inactivity limited to little more than the anabolic vegetative processes; and waking states being comparable to a geyser of activity rising and again collapsing into itself, and made up of more or less "consciously" integrated activities hanging together in a system of individual and interindividual overt and implicit "symbolizations" or functions with meanings—*i.e.*, with differential association tendencies.

For example, assume that someone hands us an appeal for help in a disaster. We sense the request with its meaning in the form of varying pertinent imagination and general reaction, with the help of the "symbolizations" containing the request, and those that arise in us as we constitute ourselves in response to the appeal. The subject (the "he" or "she" or "you" or "I") as "personality of the moment" organizes itself out of the (conative) habit and activity resources and emotional (affective) responses with the help of "conscious" symbols for presentative-perceptual "cognative" material (for the facts present at the time to the sense organs); moreover, ideas and representative material of things and facts beyond the senses, memories of past experiences, and more or less constructive imagination, in imagery (primary symbolization) or in verbal form (secondary symbolization). These associative assets are knit together in variously focused attention and more or less "affective reaction," into pictorial or verbal anticipation, inference, and reasoning, and planning and choice, with action tendencies or conations, and emotions in expressive and effective overt activities. The functions of the organism constituting this type of integration are functions of the individual, or ergasias, in contrast to mere "part-functions" studied in physiology (as kinesis and vegetative function).

Each ergasia or psychobiological action phase or action unit (time period or special task) implies discriminative and associative, orientative, and constructive functions, and consists of topical (intellectual and conative) and regulative (affective) components. The specific peculiarity of this type of organization is the relative nondetachability of the components that receive distinctive emphasis. They appear as parts or topics of the stream of "behavior and mentation," and constitute functional facts of the world or reality and actuality, to be studied with the logic of all science for what they do, the conditions under which they occur as they do, the factors entering into their determination and working, the range of their effects and their modifiability.

We speak of subject-organization of the moment, and personality-organization of the lifetime of the person as an individual or a part of a group.

The fundamental and specific feature of psychobiological integration is the subject-organization with the help of symbolizing activity, bringing on the same level (with essential privacy, and with a remarkable range both of fusion and of differentiation) reference to reality and fancy, past, present and future, personal and social, as if it were all present now and here and with that one individual or group. It is the functional inclusion of a varying scope of relations reaching through its sign-function far beyond the static, physicochemically describable structural organism. Hence its tremendously economizing and at the same time comprehensive character. It is this "behavior with mentation," the functions of the "he" or "she" or "you" or "I" or "we" or "they" that we experience and consider as the personality and personality-functions, and as far as it becomes reasonably dependable, and not merely casual, as character. This personality goes through a series of characteristic steps of evolution from infancy to old age.

From the point of view of sets (rather than levels) of performance we contrast

1. The full-fledged objectively observable or overt performance, effective (producing a self-dependent result) or expressive (utterance or gesture, largely as carriers of meanings), always integrated by intraindividual economizing symbolizing activity (mentation). Janet speaks of *la fonction du réel* [reality-function] as concrete and effective performance. In its expressive socialized form of language and the arts and in the literary and historical and scientific and philosophical formations it constitutes the chief medium of human anticipation—and atmosphere of potentialities. Sensing is one of the functions, and sense the combination: the inclusion of a varying amount of the situation, internal and external.

2. The mentation or individual implicit economizing symbolizing and largely subjective and private activity, in pure culture as fancy and thought, and as perception and inference serving as orientative and forerunner activity. It has been singled out as the domain of introspection and psychology in its narrower—not a catching of something but rising to something, with something additional—sense. That man lives largely and in a leading manner in mentation is part of the principle of human biology. But it is obvious that mentation, like all of the life functions, is to be studied not only for its working and its results, but also for organization and components of the physicochemical and vegetative and animal anatomical and physiological components of the individual and the situations. Objective psychobiology or ergasiology concerns itself with the total-function of the other as well as of the self, including the organismal and the situational components of the events. The questions would be: "Who? Rising or functioning with what activity reaction or attitude in what kind of event?"

The overt and implicit functions are always fused in "mentally integrated behavior" and never in absolute pure culture such as the traditional division into mind and body implies for the sake of simplicity and abstraction. We rather contrast mentally integrated functions and nonmentally (merely "physiologically") integrated functions. The fact that we "live" in terms of consciousness does not do away with the fact that for "the other" our mentation, in the narrower sense of the term, is only an incidental part of the integral working of the performance or at least attitude of the individual organism or unit. We do well to consider, as contrasting and special phases and types, waking and sleeping, the personal and the social functioning, and also such special conditions as the Yogi experience of self-abstraction and the behavior under suggestion, etc.—submission reaction.

In every psychobiological attitude, tendency, or activity or event (or range of implication), we study the situation (*i.e.*, the condition or attitude of the subject as well as the "stimulus"), the reaction and the result, the contributing factors, their ramifications or upshots and their modes of working. We study the factors which have to be handled psychobiologically, those which we can handle neurophysiologically and neuroanatomically, and those accessible to a general and special physiology of functions or organs (metabolism and the endocrines and, in general, the "organogenic" factors assignable to special organs); and the independently controllable exogenic factors (infective and poisonous agents); and the physical and chemical data constituting the total situation.

Practically the physician makes it a rule, in formulating nature's experiments, to consider first the simplest integrations—physicochemical, general biological, anatomical, physiological—and to consider the psychobiological adjustments specifically where the physicochemical and the exogenic and physiological and neurobiological ones have been found inadequate or would be mere tautological formulations. As a matter of fact, through the naturalization of man it becomes mandatory that we should include all the psychobiological functioning in the biological consideration of the human individual, and do it in its own terms before we replace it by neurological or endocrinological physiologizing terms. Avoid neurologizing tautology—as much as psychologizing neurology.

We emphasize particularly the fact that each of the sets of integrations has to be studied for its own laws of working and that none of the integrative sets can make the study of the others unnecessary. Avoid the obsession of the "something else." Let anatomy be anatomy; physiology, physiology; the brain, brain; and the "mind," the "he" or "she," the organism in action.

Each integrative set (or level) is to some extent to be studied in its own right and terms, and to be treated as made up of fractions with different specific denominators; we have to beware of a hasty use of a fact or part of any set or level in another set, without watching the specific "denominator." Thus, the structural subdivisions of the nervous system (neurons and neuron chains) are not to be identified offhand with the subdivisions of the corresponding functional pattern—the special cells of a speech center cannot be identified with special words and the like. The relations of parts of the structure to parts of the functions are analogous to the relations of numerators of fractions of different denominators finally gathered as fractions of the total organism and personality. We do well not to puzzle over what we have no facts for. We may question; but not like a child.

Each science consists of (1) mastery and control of facts and of

(2) the proper verbal-conceptual formulations and (3) their trial and retrial. We therefore might speak of a logical-factual (or conceptual-factual) parallelism or correlation in all these events and spheres. We refuse to put any emphasis on a "psychophysical" parallelism. We form our verbal (logical-verbal) concepts in physics and chemistry and biology exactly in the same way as in psychobiology, and our introspectional data are experience like any other experience. We consider all the psychobiological functions as functions of the organism, but interwoven according to the principles of *integration, as opposed to mere summation.* We therefore do not speak of body plus mind, but of the organism studied for physiological part-functions, and mentally integrated attitudes, reactions and actions, *i.e.,* behavior with incidental more or less leading mentation. Let us develop the habit of focusing on what counts and works and should be known when we work with persons.

In the correlation of the actions of the various sets of integration (chemical, physical, physicochemical, biological, anatomical, physiological, psychobiological) we have no reason to object to "interaction," but it is an interaction of fractions of various denominators, interaction with interpenetration of the components and principles. Psychobiology or ergasiology may tell the best story of man and his nature, but for a mastery of the facts about man all the other sciences have their share.

THE CONCEPT OF WHOLES

From "*The Rise to the Person and the Concept of Wholes or Integrates*," written by Dr. Meyer for the centennial number of the American Journal of Psychiatry, 100:100 (*April*, 1944).

Before the present war Dutch psychiatrists had risen to the call to let judgment and intelligent effort come to their right in an actively democratic respect for the person and the peoples, before a life-and-death challenge would become the only way out. After having had a First World War with a worth-while goal—what we spoke of as making the world safe for democracy—we let the attempt to do our share in a real living-up to a sense of obligation be ship-wrecked. We failed to ask how we came to allow the distressing aloofness, and drifted into the *laissez faire* of orthodox tradition in our political and cultural efforts.

We may blame, in part, the undue trust either in the extreme of elemental detail or in a totalitarian grasp and power—both leading not only to the loss of respect for the dignity of man as a unit, but also to the lack of confidence in methods created to deal factually with the varied wholes of the individual and the groups. But our failure also hangs on the fact that our culture and language favors less our objective experience with and about man than it does a false dualism which lays the responsibility on a philosophy based on tradition or on specific atoms and molecules and more minute smallest entities.

When we deal with human conditions we do not want to operate with entities that lack the characters which are carried by the dramatis personae. It was a misfortune that the dogmatic philosophy

623

of Locke and Descartes, depending too exclusively on "sensation by sense organs," belittled so much of the essentials of human nature and life (such as emotions and propensities, and, in French psychiatry, the physical and the "moral" for mental).

Instead of drifting into a morbidly world-shy but actually sensation-loving culture, the history of the American Psychiatric Association and the *Journal* seems to encourage the actual endeavors toward a frank pluralism and empirical objectivity with an honest respect for the real person and group as units. As individual and group psychiatry has taught us, this requires the principle of dealing with individual wholes and group wholes, including also subunits and their parts, in harmony with good sense, science, philosophy, and religion: *first* and above all things, good sense, with its vigor of hygiene and meliorism and essential respect for relations; then *second*, science as intension and extension, with the smallest number of assumptions for search and research and reference to specific systems; *third*, philosophy, as concern for perspective, and recognition of a world of synonyms and antonyms, but operational principles of interrelations; and *fourth*, religion as a way of trust and reciprocal obligations as well as dependabilities in life.

The hundred years upon which we would like to bestow this our present commemoration have done a great deal to allow us to rise to the realization of persons with a gain in what we call knowledge, in the recognition that we should create our methods with respect for the facts, deliberately including the facts of man and bewaring the indiscriminate using of parts of different wholes or factors interchangeably.

In its way, the entrance of the "person" as the essential setting for all medical thought, surmounting as far as possible the residue of an arbitrarily dualistic culture in the medical language, so full of exclusive "physicalism" and "mentalism," frees us of the threat of a "psychiatric corner." While we may say with full right that the beginning of the Association's century brought the introduction of medical perspectives and methods into what was to become a broad and yet orderly psychiatry (instead of the division only of insanity or only of "analysis"), the fundamental development from the third phase on has been the presentation to medicine of the concept of the suffering of a *person*, a concept with curative importance for all of medicine, and reaching beyond medicine.

There is the entry of the individual and the family drama and the real dynamics of what families and human society can hardly think of any longer as too personal and too subjective to be given and understood. These facts and events are of special concern, today so clearly an issue that they neither overshadow the physiological and structure-functional preoccupation, nor tempt one to use the latter for concealment of the real facts and relations. The traditional urge of the physician to keep aloof from ethical implications and his cultural hesitation calls not for silence but that sense of tact and need of preparation that turns the physician-patient relation into more than technique, or at any rate, a technique and habit of deliberate consideration.

To do justice to facts essential in our human life, for our understanding and operation of the forces which we call causation and motivation, we have learned to respect *integrates* of special stability and with qualities of sometimes unassimilable character. We do not spend good time and good effort on such urges as "squaring the circle" or "making mind out of matter." We are coming to have a faith that the order we assume in our commonsense categories is the wholeness of stepwise integrates, *i.e.*, relative wholes, each whole or unit demanding concepts and methods consistent and necessarily specific for its own unique type of wholeness, within its operative formula and capacity to form specific sets or entities. Each set or level of facts has its new features, not a mere addition from the outside but a new amplification and recasting of the preceding level of integrate so as to constitute entities to be respected, even though not completely reducible to one type of element to be made the one "original" particle, disregarding the factor of organization.

By integrates we mean entities of a kind that may not stand unchangeable for eternity, but yet have a relatively enduring stability and may actually breed true. They present regularities often unpredictable and emergent. "Mutations" constitute the regularities which have come to modify supposedly eternal "laws."

We recognize wholes of intrinsic adherence, not explained by the nature of the component parts, but with total-functions resulting from organization.

Stable organizations attained and maintained are the main concern of the sciences, of physics, of chemistry, of biology, of the vegetative and the animal and finally the language- and history-forming human entities. It is not just one supreme whole of operation that we look to, but the operation of interpenetrating interdependent sets of wholes, each grade furnishing the foundation for new and more intimate blendings, with due respect for its remaining a whole itself and capable also of becoming a supporting subunit in larger sociological integrates.

Such intrinsically determined entities call for their own study in their own rights, with necessarily specific as well as generally consistent methods of observation, specification, and determination of intrinsic and extrinsic characters and relations. The entity "man," then, has to be treated and studied with respect to the unique whole of "personhood," with due attention also to his specific needs of human physics and chemistry and biology, but recognized especially as an entity in which a great organizing step has taken place.

Capacity for symbolization (shared, in various degrees, also with animals) has become relatively detached for social exchange (signs and language, spoken and finally written and printed). This intrinsically new unit of a cultural entity, with its supporting anatomical and physiological subunits, has its pragmatic independence and requires a scientific method adapted to its kind, *i.e.*, largely determined by and dependent on linguistics, and using, nonetheless, a common "logic of operation." The science of man the unit and the member of social and political superunits, as well as subunits, must work out courageously the specific principles not realized by less specific and less complex wholes, but realized with a capacity for choice in the light of wish, purpose, and motivation. The social unit or person alive or remembered is the unit of reference in our specific realms of culture and states of symbolization and the conditions and obligations of "belonging"—within groups of mutual responsibility.

Systems or plans founded on wrong principles will sooner or

later fall. There will be times and room for dispersion in discussions of man, but again, from time to time, a spirit and capacity to make for a coming-together. There is a need, however, of frank obligations to watch how low one can go with the analysis or cutting to pieces, lest one lose the essence, *i.e.*, what the specific entity requires in order to survive and maintain itself in progress. The remark, "It is just what we all do," is apt to drown the really important question of how "it" actually is used and fitted into plan and effort and result. Identification of intension without concrete enaction or extension is an ever-present danger in symbolization and generalization. Symbolization that does not adapt its culture and terms is bound to vitiate the selective process of intelligence, emotion, and action tendency, or ergasia (self-referred activity) generally. History has to single out data worth restating in forms of culture, effective in *specifications* and action rather than overconcern over systems of mere verbal definition.

We are all on the march to build the coming century. Life is history-in-the-making, in the historian Harvey Robinson's sense. Let us hope that the next century will really be the century of those wholes which we obligatorily envisage as "persons" and "social groups" and "political groups," at last in an active as well as decorative esthetic sense, for the study of health, and also of disease, but above all, a better hope for the varied cultures to respect each other's uniqueness and the range of equity, so as to work toward a sound relativity for the individual and group. Actual life has to become the point of reference. What works, what does not work so well, and what fails to work becomes the plain formula of the problem-pathology and work along the branches of science, with experience in both current life and the daily work of the psychiatrist and therapist and average person. Actual contact and responsibility, and leisure for the insertion of the component specialties, and trial and reciprocal respect, are the broad demands that regulate the play of symbolization (in the constructive sense of "illusion" in the nonrealities) and, resting on a consensus, make certain and objective the subjective grasp of the opportunities of reality.

RESPECT OF SELF AND OTHERS

AND EQUITY FOR PEACE

From a paper prepared by Dr. Meyer for the fourth symposium of the Conference on Science, Philosophy and Religion, New York, Sept. 10, 1943; *in* Approaches to World Peace, *edited by Lyman Bryson, at p.* 287, *Harper & Brothers, New York* (1944).

One often thinks of equality as essential to democracy. I naturally espouse pluralism and relativism.

What are the conditions for the building up of a democratic person? To what extent will a gain of regard of "self and the other" as individual and group under a fair deal bring us and maintain a lasting world peace in the face of all our differences?

It is my impression that above all things we need a realization that to satisfy general human need as well as special training, sound, common, general sharable sense demands not merely a "psych"-ology but a concrete concept of a science of the whole man and person, individual and group and unit, so disrupted by academic splits, a science of whole man and person in his pluralistic nature and setting, naïve as well as specified.

I respect the good work that is done on all sides but see, in the getting together among the scientists and philosophers and those in religious endeavor, a great need and call for a declaration of independence for inclusion in objectivity of the great domain of subjectivity.

In our human evaluation we know too well that no two human

beings are alike or able to be quite the same at all times, so that each must therefore be considered as a unique event, as a unique lifetime, with a unique fate to work out. The same holds for the *groups* we are part of, the same for the very different races and peoples that resolve to be the United Nations of our world, aiming to live peacefully side by side, partly mixed, but largely apart, yet working for lasting peace. Shall it be done with narrowly prescribed patterns, with blinders, or in an open world and its natural emphases?

A frank and correct "self-and-other" evaluation, a respect for man's dignity as a starting point and central issue, and each "human" as the resultant democratic person, is something to work on and to work for.

The primary condition toward which we work, therefore, is not just a utopia but the building up of a really democratic person, likely, in spite of the great differences, to maintain a reasonably objective self-estimation and self-respect commanding the respect of others, not underrated or overrated, and not forced into false equality standards. The reciprocity of respect—the finding one's place so as to be respected, in turn—is viewed as the very foundation of democracy, simple enough to be kept in mind by the participant, with an ultimate concept of equity rather than equality in the lowliest as well as the richly equipped. The human person stands evidently not as a mere "object" but a *personality as subject*, capable of growth and attainment with his or her own capacity and equipment among the coexisting specificities and range of differences and a clear demand of personal status under *responsible mutuality*.

From home and school days on, a relatively automatic but personal and more and more intentional self-standardization develops into a reasonably ingrained sense of one's own capacity to meet demands and to assume obligations and assignments. There evolves a feeling for mental grading according to competence and performance, with reciprocal appreciation or evaluation and an obligatory sense for proportions, which may be furthered by practical tests, not mere intelligence tests, but true capacity tests based on performance and a fair pragmatic record of achievement, including also the handicaps and failures. It should be one's open basis for plans and action, yet with due respect for what should be allowed to remain personal and private. Essential honesty and capacity of self-evaluation should be cultivated at the root, with a sound practice of self-respect in keeping with achievement, as individual and in the group. In my own experience I have found in the students' biographies a remarkable capacity to assume responsibility for what one is and does, exactly what one has to balance and cultivate as the problem of meliorism in one's work with patients.

A proper self-estimation is kept as free as possible from any one-sided and irrelevant influences or allegiances and "privileges" likely to mar the objectivity of the regard for self and others, involving as it does both approval and disapproval and ratings as "better" or "worse" or just "different-minded." As far as possible, the attitude is cultivated that differences as such are not considered a matter for conceit or shame, but to be positively evaluated as worthy of use in correctly respected categories. There is more of a need for a fundamental feeling of human relationships and mutual regard in the cultivation of internal freedom and spontaneity and its reciprocal responsibility and balance under equity than for sham equality.

In the natural formation of groups it is not degrading that one should defer to those in a better situation to judge or advise or help, if one cultivates an active regard and respect for actual differences in capacity to arrive at a solution, with a deeply rooted and well-earned feeling of *mutuality* and positive *reciprocity, responsibility, respect*, with uniform deep regard for the golden rule, and a definite and general disdain of an overrating or underrating of oneself or the others in the basic feeling of respect.

There should be a limit to any exclusive party pledges or feeling of being owned, and no narrowing of one's interest to only one side. A democratic loyalty stands for respect for differences as real specificities and for a knowledge of the otherwise-minded as well. It is excess of destructive assertion that needs concern, and unearned "privilege" that one objects to, not the differences of leadership and followership. Such a sweeping contradiction as a Sherman

Act, prosecuting as connivance both reasonable and unreasonable understandings in business, and, on the other hand, wholesale obligation to collective bargaining, and distinction into the "privileged" and "underprivileged" should not remain unresolved. They both try to hit abuses, but do not heed important real differences of effectivity of human specificities. To join a political or other "party" should demand a familiarization and knowledge also of the tenets and contentions of opposing parties, made as accessible and clear as possible, according to various levels of capacity of understandings and concern and interest. "Party" should cease to be party at the base and at the top, when it becomes mere belonging and being used as mere vote- and pressure-power through accumulated dues.

With regard to evils or dangers to be avoided, I put foremost, from the standpoint of commonsense and not merely as a psychiatrist, the confusion of equity with equality, the nonrecognition of our differences as specificity, and false comparisons; the separation into categories of the "privileged" and the "underprivileged," so blatantly used now even in official documents; the sabotage of democracy by the maintenance of a privately supported "machine" and boss government; the failure to inculcate the fact that laws will hold until they will be repealed or changed; the manipulation of the masses in the form of "benevolent" paternalizing, or actual despotism; the wholesale pauperization of personal initiative by giving party influence executive power; the techniques of secret police and secret proceedings; party regime with exclusive "domination" (the very word "danger" is derived from *dominiarium*) and failure of thinking in proportion; the inadequacy of cultivating competitive timber; and the unwillingness to return to the ranks when special assignments or tasks are done justice to. A rise to exclusive power by bluff and one-sided appraisal, such as that achieved by a Hitler or a Mussolini, must and can be made impossible.

With regard to "global consciousness," a union or balance of the two above points is essential: a frank recognition of real national and racial and personal specificities, and the obligation of any individual and group to treat itself and others with adequate self-understanding and evaluation and a good knowledge of its opponents, free of competitiveness and ruthless manipulation. Foremost stands the overrating and underrating of races and civilizations. It may be necessary to insist upon sufficiently widespread recognition and cultivation of proportional evaluation of differences and actual opposition, which without doubt must become a matter of serious work on the part of current person- and group-studies, also within the aggregates of populations. Improvements in voting regulations and techniques would go a long way toward teaching people a proportionate system of decision of what under a regimented "party system" can become unwarranted totalitarianism, with mere slogans in place of judgment and reasons. Unfortunately, the South inherits not only the race problem but the perpetuation of the poor white, and the North, its slums, and the whole country, the separation of the wage earner from natural partial self-support, which does violence also to human nature and the human person.

The determination to keep to the fore the above points, for one's individual sense of justice and for helpfulness to the social aggregates, will, I feel, be the condition of real success of what we speak of as democracy, or outright, as proportional responsibility. As one hears of the "escape from freedom" and from the burden of self-responsibility, because too exacting, there are undoubtedly those who prefer a cut-and-dried "totalitarian" regime, but most of us prefer self-chosen limitations under the heading of "freedom and discipline," the ideal of democracy.

Evidently we must watch not only in ourselves and the group, but between groups, the principle of "power" that has to be true to our time- and growth-bound nature and constitutes the essence of our "psychology" of the dynamics of personal and civic democratic life—not power from mere ganging-together, not power for and through coercion and destruction, but *con*structive, on the ground of balance of opportunity and capacity and proportion.

Constructive power will not primarily depend on party dominance, but on the development of "real persons," with a capacity for respect of self *and* the other and also for larger groups, with an expectation of working according to our different capacities in a balanced humanity, with regular current reports of needs and opportunities of open fields made available to the workers.

Our task is difficult and serious, and will require provisions for special needs and emergencies. It must be led to principles simple and direct to be effective. We deal with the fact that "facts" are not merely *facta*, things finished and of the past tense, but reaching into the present and dynamic with means requiring current accounting, as real life.

Nationwise and groupwise, but after all necessarily individualwise, we have to get as close as possible to the demand of self-evaluation and reciprocity and fair deal and a vision of possibilities and obligations—a principle in which science, philosophy, and religion have their contributive share and dynamic responsibility. We have to face the fact that we are different and "specific," in need of active self-building to become true to ourselves and able also to build on common and sharable principles, capable of being selves *and* groups and operating according to standards of capacity and performance. We have to guard against abuse of power and force by cultivating a balance of "good nature," of mutual respect and sense for proportion and relation, with principles of order, regularity, and reciprocity, to be a democracy without exclusive party striving and party rule, but with a natural grading according to capacity and need. If, by neglect in the mediating agencies, difficulties arise, they should be met according to need and provisions of a temporary nature.

The collaboration of common sharable sense, science, philosophy, and religion assumes or illustrates a freedom from embarrassing and overexplicit basic assertions of, in many instances, an exclusive dogma, excluding different-minded individuals from the implications and benefits of "belonging." This is contrary to the tenets of this outlook, and it becomes necessary, in harmony with the essentials of common ground, to limit oneself to a minimum of assumptions and stipulations. They are offered as a skeleton or pledge to consistent but liberal principles of method.

1. Legitimation as worth-whileness for actual discussion of particular facts and items requires only that their presence or absence, their working or not working, "makes a difference," with the obligation that we express the positive specificity that holds us to the topic that counts.

2. Scrutiny takes up the items for study (as the ragpicker does with his finds) and proceeds through the following steps: (*a*) The item under discussion may explain itself adequately in its setting or form as offered or found. (*b*) It may explain itself sufficiently only by what it belonged or belongs to. (*c*) Only after such sifting may or should one resort to "breaking down" the material in the usual "analysis or synthesis"—not into just any last elements as particles, but with clear distinction between what preserves the essential nature of the whole and can be reconstructed without one's having destroyed the integrate, such as the living being and its mentation, so that the results are recognized for their belonging to the unit through a specific kind of integration, such as its essence in structure and in function, in life, and in the human or living, using processes of symbolization. Hence the concern with integration of specific categories and the importance of types of specifications. To go further, and along other lines, to a "breaking down" will serve special purposes and special issues but, if not pertinent, may be a distraction and confusion for the problem at hand.

3. The operational formula grants the items and groups their history and position in the realm of possibilities, and asks without prejudice: (*a*) What special specific item (substance or function or occurrence) are *you* pointing to (the occurrence at hand, and those that have previously happened in the same or similar form in the life, as additionally important samples of the same or similar concrete experience, with statement of place and time, or what is needed to make it an intelligible statement)? (*b*) What are and were the facts and factors entering in? (*c*) How do and how did they work? (*d*) With what range of results? (*e*) With what modifiability? The total should give our best understanding for the whole problem.

It is *a science of man* that is wanted, with a historical and dramatic and physiological and voluntaristic causality, neither merely a narrow and dogmatic "psychology," nor merely an anatomy and physiology, but a broad science of man, with a declaration of independence asking for a frank permission to forget the old oversystematization which seems imposed on man in prejudicial rules, determined by other concerns, either "mental" or "physical," either of the soul or of physics and chemistry, which are two very multifarious masses of facts but do not specify what is both "mental" and "physical," but always "physical" in its general sense.

We stand here before an entity that does not fit into a test tube but, with its actual setting, is accessible to all of us in the biography and in formulations of the whole (anthropology, ethnology, history, biography, and civilization) and of the parts (anatomy and physiology), in each special chapter treated for the whole and its parts, or the emphasis that our issues and sense of economy demand.

It is not merely "science" in its narrow definition as particles that guides us, but also the organization of the essentials in the whole person and more, his relations, that we consider as examples and topics of a science of man. Within this setting we cultivate the material of the special sciences and special organs, for their own sake and also in the role of function and life of the parts. The whole and the special chapters thereof constitute man's broadest science, and only the whole can be a direct concern of religion, with knowledge and religion and its feeling of security together also as a concern of philosophy, and man the topic of "sense," and not only sensations.

Science is evidently that which special sciences have to deal with *in concreto* [concretely]. If it happens to be Humpty Dumpty, it is the science of what is of Humpty's kind—that "all the king's men," even if they are scientists, "cannot put together again." It is the science that sees in living entities "vitalism," but not as some thing, not as a superadded force—but inherent. The living and biological, growth- and time-bound being is no more a mystery but a state of nature, even if it is not what most religions hope it is, by associations, and filling of gaps, in what becomes to us a true moving urge of reality, actuality, and development or faith. We know many actual things, but that does not mean we are omniscient. The whole universe belongs together and carries with it its nature "according to its nature," including also its "as if's." "To be" is what proves itself to be with its properties as well as with its associations and representations. We carry "it" and may need more than one verb to carry the meaning. *Ferro, tuli, latum, ferre* [principal parts of Latin verb "to carry"] is not mere grammar but presents sense and meaning. We know what "integrate" means: no mere mystery, but real nature of specific combination. It is our task and opportunity to accept the orders and classes of nature and to *specify* them.

That this statement and outlook remains in a biologically valid form or frame of both individual and groups and contains not only what science demands but what philosophy and religion have to offer, as implication of growth and function, also as mentation, and the whole as essential to the universe, is what we have a right to look for, to work with, and, if necessary, to die for, if defense and fighting for one's conviction is the only way out.

REFERENCE NOTES

1. Thirty-five Years of Psychiatry in the United States and Our Present Outlook, *American Journal of Psychiatry*, 85:1 (1928).
2. *Aims and Plans of the Pathological Institute of the New York State Hospitals*, Ward's Island, New York (December, 1902).
3. A Few Demonstrations of the Pathology of the Brain, *American Journal of Insanity*, 52:242 (1895).
4. On the Observation of Abnormalities of Children, *The Child-Study Monthly*, 1:1 (1895).
5. Constructive Formulation of Schizophrenia, *American Journal of Psychiatry*, 78:355 (1921).
6. Psychopathology, *Clark University Decennial Celebration*, Worcester, Mass., p. 144 (1899).
7. *Proceedings*, American Medico-Psychological Association, discussion at p. 125 (1899).
8. British Influences in Psychiatry and General Medicine, *Journal of Mental Science*, 79:435 (1933).
9. Report of the Pathological Institute for the Year Ending Sept. 30, 1903, *Annual Report of the New York State Commission in Lunacy* (1903).
10. *Proceedings*, American Medico-Psychological Association, discussion at p. 380 (1903).
11. A Few Trends in Modern Psychiatry, *Psychological Bulletin*, 1:217 (1904).
12. The Anatomical Facts and Clinical Varieties of Traumatic Insanity, *American Journal of Insanity*, 60:373 (1903).
13. Arrest of Development in Adolescence, *Proceedings*, National Education Association, at p. 813 (1903).
14. The Extra-institutional Responsibilities of State Hospitals for Mental Diseases, *Proceedings*, Joint Board Trustees, State Hospitals of Michigan, p. 5 (1916).
15. Interpretation of Obsessions, *Psychological Bulletin*, 3:280 (1906).
16. Reviews and Abstracts of Literature, *The Journal of Philosophy, Psychology and Scientific Methods*, 4:79 (1907).

17. After-Care and Prophylaxis, *State Hospitals Bulletin*, 1:631 (1909).

17a. Reprinted from *Autobiography* by Sigmund Freud, by permission of W. W. Norton & Company, New York; copyright by the author (1935).

18. The Treatment of Paranoic and Paranoid States, *The Treatment of Nervous and Mental Diseases*, ed. by William A. White and Smith Ely Jelliffe, 1:614, Lea & Febiger, Philadelphia (1913).

19. Reception Hospitals, Psychopathic Wards, and Psychopathic Hospitals, *American Journal of Insanity*, 64:221 (1907).

20. The Present Status of Aphasia and Apraxia, *The Harvey Lectures* (1909-10) at p. 228, J. B. Lippincott Company, Philadelphia (1910).

21. *Contributions Dedicated to Dr. Adolf Meyer by His Colleagues, Friends and Pupils*, ed. by S. Katzenelbogen, at p. 47, Johns Hopkins Press, Baltimore (1938).

22. *American Journal of Insanity*, special number, vol. 69, remarks at p. 1079 (1912-13).

23. Organization of the Work of the Henry Phipps Psychiatric Clinic, *Transactions*, American Medico-Psychological Association, at p. 397 (1914).

24. Conditions for a Home of Psychology in the Medical Curriculum, *Journal of Abnormal Psychology*, 7:313 (1912).

25. Plans for Work in the Phipps Psychiatric Clinic, *Modern Hospital*, 1:69 (1913).

26. *Proceedings of the Fourth Conference on Psychiatric Education*, 1936, at p. 35, National Committee for Mental Hygiene, New York (1938).

27. The Justification of Psychobiology as a Topic of the Medical Curriculum, *Psychological Bulletin*, 12:328 (1915).

28. The Scope of Psychopathology, *Psychiatric Bulletin*, 1:297 (1916).

29. A Reconstruction Course in the Functional Anatomy of the Nervous System (Louis Hausman, collaborator), *Archives of Neurology & Psychiatry*, 7:287 (1922).

30. *American Journal of Psychiatry*, 87:327 (1930).

31. Historical Sketch and Outlook of Psychiatric Social Work, *Hospital Social Service*, 5:221 (1922).

32. Organization of Community Facilities for the Prevention, Care and Treatment of Nervous and Mental Diseases, *Proceedings*, First International Congress on Mental Hygiene, 1:237 (1930).

33. Growth of Scientific Understanding of Mentality: Its Relationship

to Social Work, *Proceedings*, National Conference of Social Work, at p. 192 (1923).

34. Freedom and Discipline, *Progressive Education*, 5:205 (1928).

35. Maturity, *Child Study*, 7:225 (1930).

36. The Meaning of Maturity, in *Our Children*, ed. by Dorothy Canfield Fisher and Sidonie Matsner Gruenberg, at p. 155, The Viking Press, Inc., New York (1932).

37. *Proceedings*, First International Congress on Mental Hygiene, vol. II, remarks at p. 469 (1930).

38. Discussion, Meeting of American Orthopsychiatric Association, *American Journal of Orthopsychiatry*, 2:229 (1932).

39. The Birth and Development of the Mental Hygiene Movement, *Mental Hygiene*, 19:29 (1935).

40. Mental Hygiene in the Emergency: A Symposium, *Mental Hygiene*, 25:1 (1941).

41. *Proceedings*, Association for Research in Nervous and Mental Disease, vol. 19 at pp. 14 and 357 (1938).

42. Growth of Scientific Understanding of Mentality: Its Relationship to Social Work, *Proceedings*, National Conference of Social Work, at p. 192 (1923).

43. Modern Conceptions of Mental Disease, in *Suggestions of Modern Science Concerning Education*, by Herbert S. Jennings et al., at p. 201, The Macmillan Company, New York (1925).

44. Review of "Psychopathology" by Edward J. Kempf, *Archives of Neurology and Psychiatry*, 5:782 (1921).

45. The Approach to the Investigation of Dementia Praecox, *Chicago Medical Record*, 39:441 (1917).

46. The Evolution of the Dementia Praecox Concept, in *Schizophrenia*, Proceedings of Association for Research in Nervous and Mental Disease, 1925, Paul B. Hoeber, Inc., New York (1928).

47. *American Journal of Psychiatry*, discussion at p. 939 (March, 1929).

48. Shall Couéism Spell Progress or Regression? *The Open Court*, 37:473 (1923).

49. Reminiscences and Prospects at the Opening of the New York Psychiatric Institute and Hospital, *Psychiatric Quarterly*, 4:25 (1930).

50. Symposium, "The Material of Human Nature and Conduct," *American Journal of Psychiatry*, 92:271 (1935).

51. *Proceedings of the Fourth Conference on Psychiatric Education*, 1936, at p. 5, National Committee for Mental Hygiene, New York (1938).

52. *Ibid.*, at p. 85.

53. Psychiatry: Its Meaning and Scope, in *Psychiatry and the War*, ed. by Frank J. Sladen, at p. 5, Charles C. Thomas, Publisher, Springfield, Ill. (1943).

54. *Proceedings* (see note 51), at p. 227.

55. *Ibid.*, at p. 230.

56. *Addresses of Dr. John E. Donley and Dr. Adolf Meyer*, at the Dedication of the Adolf Meyer Building, Oct. 18, 1938, State Hospital for Mental Disease, Howard, R. I.

57. Review of "Mental Health," *Science*, 92:271 (1940).

58. *Psychiatry*, discussion at p. 533 (Nov., 1940).

59. *Henry Phipps Psychiatric Clinic:* Fiftieth Anniversary Celebration, The Johns Hopkins Hospital (1939).

60. Historical Fragments on the Neurological and Psychiatric Specialties, *Journal of the Mt. Sinai Hospital*, 9:213 (1942).

61. Revaluation of Benjamin Rush, *American Journal of Psychiatry*, 101:433 (1945).

62. Introduction to *Psychiatry in Medical Education*, by Franklin G. Ebaugh and Charles A. Rymer, at p. xiv, Commonwealth Fund, New York (1942).

63. The "Complaint" as the Center of Genetic-Dynamic and Nosological Teaching in Psychiatry, *New England Journal of Medicine*, 199:360 (1928).

GLOSSARY OF MEDICAL AND
PHILOSOPHICAL TERMS
AS USED IN THE TEXT

ABDERHALDEN'S REACTION: test for infections, etc., by creating ferments in the circulation.

ABULIA: lack of ability to use the will; *adj.*, abulic.

AFFECT: emotionally charged motive; *adj.*, affective.

ALBUMINURIA: presence of albumin in urine.

ALCOHOLISM: unhealthy state due to addiction to drink.

ALIENIST: obsolescent term for psychiatrist.

ALLELOMORPH: in genetics, a character-unit in one of a pair of germ-cells, transmitted to descendants of a cross.

AMNESIA: loss of memory; *adj.*, amnesic.

ANABOLISM (see footnote, p. 236).

ANAMNESIS: prior history of a medical case.

ANATOMY: study of structure.

ANESTHESIA: absence of feeling.

ANIMISTIC: pertaining to the belief that objects in nature have conscious life.

ANTHROPOMORPHIC: in human form.

APATHETIC: lacking emotion.

APHASIA: loss of power of speech or writing; *adj.*, aphasic.

APPERCEPTION: use of perception in relation to previous knowledge.

APRAXIA: loss of coordination or of comprehension.

ARTERIOSCLEROSIS: hardening of artery walls.

ASPHYXIA: suspended animation due to interference with respiration.

ASSOCIATIVE PROCESS: interrelation of ideas, as by word-stimulus.

ASTHENIA: loss of strength, debility.

AURA: symptomatic sensation preceding an epileptic attack, as a feeling of cold air.

AUTOCHTHONOUS IDEAS: obsessive ideas springing out of harmony with one's trend; hallucinations.

AUTOEROTIC: sexually preoccupied with self.

AUTOINTOXICATION: poisoning due to bodily toxin.

AUTOPSY: medical examination of a corpse.

BEHAVIORISM: a theory of objective psychology excluding dynamic subjective functioning.

BILIOUS: pertaining to secretion of bile.

BIOCHEMISTRY: chemistry of living organisms.

BIOLOGY: study of the principles of living organisms.

BIOTROPIC: pertaining to the reduction of resistance to latent infection.

CALLOSAL LESION: lesion of the nerve tissue (*corpus callosum*) which unites the hemispheres of the brain.

CARDIOVASCULAR: pertaining to the system of heart and blood vessels.

CARTESIAN DUALISM: Descartes' separation of mind and body.

CATABOLISM (see footnote, p. 236).

CATALEPSY: temporary assumption of a posture with some rigidity.

CATATONIA: mental disorder in a state of immobility or lack of motor response; sometimes marked by excited action in a stereotyped pattern; *adj.*, catatonic.

CENTER THEORY: a system whereby nerve-cells and fibers govern a specific function.

CENTRAL NERVOUS SYSTEM: the brain and spinal cord; cerebrospinal system.

CEREBRAL: pertaining to the forebrain (cerebrum).

CEREBRASTHENIA: debility due to cerebral condition.

CEREBRATION: functional activity of the brain.

CEREBROSPINAL: pertaining to the brain and spinal cord.

CHARACTEROLOGY: theory of discerning character traits by physique, handwriting, etc.

CHOREA: nervous disease marked by involuntary irregular movements.

COGNITION: mental operation of awareness; *adj.*, cognitive.

CONATION: mental inclination toward action; *adj.*, conative.

CONDITIONED REFLEX: reflex action acquired in a situation after repeated association with the original nervous impulse.

CONSTITUTIONAL: inherent in make-up.

CORTEX: outer layer, as of the brain (gray matter); *adj.*, cortical.

CORTICAL SUBSTRATUM: underpart of the cortex; *pl.*, substrata.

CRETINISM: imbecility or idiocy associated with deformity and thyroid insufficiency.

CYCLOTHYMIC: pertaining to mood-swing, akin to manic-depressive state.

DECEREBRATE: adj., without cerebrum.

DEGENERACY: concept of deterioration to a lower type.

DELIRIUM: disoriented state with excitement and disordered speech; DELIRIUM TREMENS: a result of alcoholic excess, with marked hallucinations.

DELUSION (see footnote, p. 208).

DEMENTIA: deterioration of mental faculties.

DEMENTIA PARALYTICA: a form of brain syphilis.

DEMENTIA PRAECOX: term applied originally to an early or precocious dementia in contrast to senile dementia; a psychosis whose symptoms are now grouped under schizophrenia, evidencing a break with reality.

DIAGNOSIS: determination of a disease; DIFFERENTIAL DIAGNOSIS: distinguishing between similar diseases by comparison of symptoms.

DIALECTICAL: pertaining to logical analysis or disputation.

DIATHESIS: predisposition to a disease.

DIFFERENTIAL ANALYSIS: distinguishing between similarities; minute differences between consecutive values of a varying quantity.

DIFFERENTIAL DIAGNOSIS: see diagnosis.

DIFFERENTIATION: biological modification to perform special functions; acquisition of individual characteristics.

DIPSOMANIA: compulsive craving for alcoholic drink, to excess.

DISSOCIATION: disunion of mental activity; break in continuity of personality.

ECHOLALIA: automatic repetition of words heard.

ECHOPRAXIA: automatic imitation of actions seen, as of the examining physician's movements.

ECLAMPTIC: pertaining to a toxic condition in pregnancy (eclampsia).

EFFECTOR: nerve-ending within a muscle or gland, completing a reflex action.

ELEMENTALIST: believer in the supreme importance of elements or ultimate constituents.

EMPIRICISM: principle that knowledge derives from experience.

ENDOCRINOLOGY: study of ductless glands (endocrines).

ENDOGENOUS: originating within the organism.

ENURESIS: involuntary urination.

EPILEPSY: nervous disorder with convulsive seizures and loss of consciousness; EPILEPTIFORM, EPILEPTOID (*adjs.*): resembling epilepsy.

EPIPHENOMENON: phenomenon not in its own right but occasioned by another.

EPISTEMOLOGY: theory of the method or grounds of knowledge.

ERGASIA: mentally integrated activity.

ERGOTISM: poisoning due to the ergot fungus.

EROGENOUS: causing sexual excitement.

ESCHATALOGICAL: pertaining to the theological doctrine of the four finalities—death, judgment, heaven, hell.

ETIOLOGY: study of causes of disease.

ETYMOLOGY: derivation of words.

EUGENICS: study and development of conditions producing improvement of genes or transmitted character factors.

EUSTACHIAN TUBE: auditory tube.

EVISCERATION: removal of entrails (viscera).

EXANTHEMA: inflammatory skin eruption; *pl.*, exanthemata.

EXISTENTIALISM: philosophical doctrine predicating existence.

EXOGENOUS: originating outside the organism.

FACTOR: in genetics, an agent determining a hereditary character transmitted through the germ-cell; a gene.

FEBRILE DELIRIUM: delirium with fever.

FEEBLEMINDED: having mental deficiency but not to the extent of imbecility.

FETISHISM: emotional attachment to a symbolic object, as an erotic substitute.

FOCAL INFECTION: occurrence of disease germs at a focus, whence the infection issues to the blood stream.

FRONTAL LOBE: cerebral convolutions at the forehead, in front of the central fissure of the brain.

FUGUE: state of consciousness which is detached but purposeful.

GANGLION: nerve tissue massed as a center.

GASTRITIS: inflammation of the stomach.

GENERAL PARALYSIS: progressive deterioration due to syphilis of the brain; paresis.

GLIA: tissue supporting cerebrospinal nerves and cells; neuroglia.

GLOBUS: sensation of a ball in the throat, as in hysteria.

GRADIENT, FUNCTIONAL GRADIENT: in mathematics, determinant of the rate at which a function changes in value from point to point.

GRAVES' DISEASE: goiter with protrusion of the eyes.

GYNECOLOGY: study of women's diseases, especially of the genito-urinary system.

HALLUCINATION (see footnote, p. 208).

HALLUCINOSIS: psychotic state marked by hallucinations.

HEBEPHRENIA: subform of schizophrenia or dementia praecox.

HEMIPLEGIA: one-sided paralysis.

HEURISTIC: not demonstrable but helping to interpret; in education, training the pupil to find out for himself.

HISTOLOGY: microscopic study of tissue structure.

HOMOLOGY: correspondence in type of structure and function.

HUMORAL: relating to bodily fluids, such as blood, bile, lymph, and the ancient belief that they determined character.

HUNTINGTON'S CHOREA: hereditary, chronic form of chorea.

HYDROTHERAPY: treatment by means of water (baths, packs).

HYPEREMIA: unusual concentration of blood.

HYPERESTHESIA: excessive sensitivity.

HYPERTHYROIDISM: excessive thyroid secretion.

HYPERTROPHY: enlargement by diseased growth.

HYPNAGOGIC: leading to sleep.

HYPNOIDIZATION: induction of hypnosislike state.

HYPNOSIS: induced loss of consciousness with suggestibility.

HYPOCHONDRIASIS: morbid concern over one's health, with imaginary disease and apparent symptoms.

HYSTERIA: mental disturbance, often converted into manifestations of organic disorder; HYSTERIFORM (*adj.*), like hysteria.

ID: a Freudian concept, the cauldron of unconscious urges.

IDEALISM: in philosophy, a doctrine which identifies reality with mind.

IDEATION: process of forming ideas, especially of something not objective.

IDIOCY: mental deficiency rated at the two-year level.

IMBECILITY: mental deficiency rated at two to seven years.

INFRA-PSYCHIC: below the psychic (mental) level; reflex.

INSANITY: loose term for extreme mental disorders.

INTEGRATION: coordinated combination of components for a specific function; AN INTEGRATE: such an entity.

INTERNAL SECRETIONS: products of the ductless glands.

INTERNIST: physician specializing in internal medicine but not surgery.

INTERPAROXYSMAL: occurring between paroxysms or sudden revivals of symptoms.

INTROSPECTIONIST: adherent of the school of psychology which holds that mind can be studied only by examining one's own mental phenomena.

KNEE-JERK: see patellar reflex.

KORSAKOFF'S COMPLEX: organic psychosis (toxic, alcoholic) usually marked by lack of memory.

LEVEL OF INTEGRATION: type of integration or hanging-together of components of a function.

LESION: local injury of tissue.

LIBIDO: drive toward satisfactions (sex, etc.).

LOCALIZATION: determination of the area of activity (such as brain center) or the seat of an infection.

MANIA: state of morbid excitement, usually with a specific preoccupation; MANIC (*adj.*): akin to mania.

MANIC-DEPRESSIVE PSYCHOSIS: severe mental disorder with recurrent mood-swings.

MASOCHISM: tendency to obtain (sexual) pleasure by enduring pain.

MATERIALISM: in philosophy, doctrine that only matter is real.

MECHANISTIC: in philosophy, pertaining to the doctrine that phenomena are explained by mechanical causes.

MECHANOTHERAPY: treatment by mechanical means (electricity, massage).

MEGALOMANIA: delusion of grandeur.

MELANCHOLIA: deep depression.

MELIORISM: doctrine that improvement is possible by effort.

MENTAL HYGIENE: procedure of preserving mental health.

MENTATION: mental functioning.

METABOLISM (see footnote, p. 236).

METAPHYSICS: speculation concerning "first principles," such as being, essence, time.

METASYPHILIS: syphilitic deterioration without a local lesion.

MONISM: doctrine that reality is an organized whole.

MORBID: pertaining to disease.

MORPHOGENIC: producing growth or form.

MORPHOLOGY: study of the structure and form of organisms.

MYELASTHENIA: neurasthenia related to the spinal cord.

MYELINIZATION: supplying of substance sheathing the nerve fibers.

MYXEDEMA: thyroid deficiency in cretins, with swelling under the skin.

NATURALISM: in philosophy, a doctrine assuming the operation of natural forces and laws, as opposed to supernatural or spiritual.

NEGATIVISTIC: marked by resistance or opposite tendency.

NEISSER INFECTION: gonorrhea.

NEURASTHENIA: state of debility or exhaustion, emotional rather than organic.

NEUROGENIC: originating in the nervous system.

NEUROGLIA: tissue supporting cerebrospinal nerves and cells.

NEUROKYME: nerve-process energy.

NEUROLOGIZING TAUTOLOGY: use of a neurological term to repeat a statement as its own reason.

NEUROLOGY: study of the nervous system.

NEURON: nerve-cell and its processes.

NEUROPATHOLOGY: study of disorders of the nervous system.

NEUROPSYCHIATRY: branch of medicine combining neurology and psychiatry.

NEUROSIS: mental disorder; emotional disturbance without derangement; psychoneurosis; *adj.*, neurotic.

NEW THOUGHT: cult of optimism operating on so-called psychic powers.

NOSOLOGY: grouping of diseases.

NOUMENON: metaphysical concept of an object as a thing-in-itself.

OCCULTISM: doctrine assuming the use of knowledge of the supernatural.

ONANISM: seminal emission after interruption of coitus.

ONTOGENESIS: development of an individual life history.

OPHTHALMOLOGY: study of the eye and its diseases.

ORGANICISM: theory of organic origin of all symptoms according to the organ's special nature and lesion.

ORGANISMAL: pertaining to the organism.

ORGANOGENIC: originating within an organ.

ORTHOBIOSIS: hygienic way of life.

OVARIALGIA: ovarian pain.

OXALURIA: presence of oxalic acid in urine.

PANPSYCHISM: doctrine that all matter is spirit.

PARANOIA: derangement representing a morbid attempt at adjustment by (systematized) delusions; *adj.*, paranoic.

PARASYMPATHETIC: pertaining to midbrain fibers of the reflex nervous system.

PARENCHYMATOUS: pertaining to the essential tissue of an organ.

PARESIS: general paralysis; syphilis of the brain.

PARESTHESIA: disorder with abnormal sensations.

PATELLAR REFLEX: involuntary jerk of the leg after percussion of the kneecap ligament; knee-jerk; see also reflex.

PATHOGENESIS: development of a pathological condition.

PATHOGNOMONIC: evidencing a specific disease.

PEDIATRICS: branch of medicine devoted to children's development and their diseases.

PEJORISM: disparagement; belittling.

PELLAGRA: dietary disease affecting the central nervous and digestive systems.

PERICARDIAL: pertaining to the sac (pericardium) enclosing the heart.

PERIPHERAL NERVE: nerve on the peripheral part of the body transmitting impulses to and from a nerve center.

PERSEVERATION: involuntary, persistent repetition of a movement or an utterance; stereotypy.

PHARMACOLOGY: study of drugs and medicines and their effects.

PHARYNX: tube connecting the mouth and the esophagus.

PHOBIA: irresistible fear fixed on a specific fancied danger, with inhibition.

PHOSPHATURIA: presence of phosphates in urine.

PHRENOLOGY: assumption that mental faculties are localized on the skull.

PHYLOGENETIC: pertaining to the evolution of a species.

PHYSIOLOGY: study of bodily functions.

PINEAL BODY: ductless gland attached to the brain.

PLASTICITY: faculty of developing, being molded, adjusting.

PLURALISM: concept of many kinds of causation.

POLLUTION: discharge of semen without coitus.

POLYMORPHOUS: having several characters or forms.

POLYNEURITIS: multiple neuritis; inflammation of a number of nerves, as in Korsakoff's complex.

PRAGMATIC: having practical values.

PROGNOSIS: forecast of outcome.

PROPHYLAXIS: prevention of disorders.

PROTAGON DEGENERATION: degeneration of a specific brain substance.

PSYCHASTHENIA: mental disorder marked by anxiety, compulsions, obsessions, sense of inadequacy; PSYCHASTHENIC: a person in such a state.

PSYCHIATRY: branch of medicine concerned with mental behavior and personality disorders.

PSYCHOANALYSIS: any technique of analyzing mental function; specifically, the Freudian theory of repression and the unconscious.

PSYCHOBIOLOGY: study of mentally integrated behavior.

PSYCHOGENIC: originating within the mind.

PSYCHOLOGY: study of mental functioning.

PSYCHOMETRIC: measuring mental performance.

PSYCHOPATHIC: ill-balanced in personality.

PSYCHOPATHOLOGY: study of the processes of mental disorders.

PSYCHOPHYSICAL PARALLELISM: doctrine that mind and body, as separate organs, interact.

PSYCHOSIS: severe mental disorder; *adj.*, psychotic.

PSYCHOSOMATIC: pertaining to the influence of the psyche (mind) upon the soma (body); bodily changes caused by emotions.

RAPPORT: relation between physician and patient establishing sympathy and confidence.

RECEPTOR-FUNCTION: that part of a reflex action where stimuli are received at sensory-nerve endings.

REFLEX: involuntary action resulting from impulses conducted along a nerve path; REFLEX ARC: complete circuit of sensory nerve to nerve center to motor nerve (receptor-conductor-effector).

REGRESSION: reversal of development, a reaction of maladaptation.

RUMINATION: brooding; morbidly chewing the cud of one's own reflections.

SADISM: tendency to obtain (sexual) pleasure by inflicting pain.

SCATOLOGICAL: pertaining to examination of feces.

SCHIZOID: resembling a schizophrenic state.

SCHIZOPHRENIA: alternative term for dementia praecox; marked loss of contact with reality.

SEGMENTAL: pertaining to a segment, as of the spinal cord.

SENSORIUM: general state of awareness and orientation.

SENSORY-MOTOR (SENSORIMOTOR): pertaining to sensory impulses and motor responses.

SEROLOGICAL: pertaining to diagnostic study of serums (for syphilis, etc.).

SOLIPSISTIC: pertaining to the metaphysical theory that self alone exists and is therefore the only object of real knowledge.

SOMATIC: pertaining to the organs.

SOMATOGENIC: originating within organic cells.

SOMNAMBULISM: sleep-walking, a hypnoidal state.

SPINAL GANGLIA: enlargements of receptor nerves at the spinal cord.

STEREOTYPY: fixed pattern of behavior (by word, posture, gesture), as in schizophrenia.

STRUMOUS: pertaining to scrofula (tuberculosis of the lymphatic glands).

STUPOR: mute reaction to surroundings.

SUBACUTE: between acute and chronic.

SYLLOGISM: argument expressed in two premises leading to a conclusion inferred from them.

SYMBIOSIS: adoption of a symptom as an aspect of the personality.

SYMPATHETIC NERVOUS SYSTEM: reflex portion of the nervous system controlling automatic body functions; vegetative nervous system.

SYMPATHETICOTONIA (SYMPATHICOTONIA): state in which the sympathetic nervous system is overvigorous.

SYMPTOMATOLOGY: study of symptoms and indications of treatment.

SYMPTOM COMPLEX: set of symptoms at a given time; syndrome.

SYNCOPE: temporary loss of consciousness; fainting.

TABES: progressive syphilitic spinal-cord disease (locomotor ataxia).

TELEOLOGY: explanation of things by evidence of their purpose.

TERMINAL DEMENTIA: fatal deterioration as the culmination of mental disease.

THERAPEUTICS (THERAPY): procedure for restoring health.

THYROGENOUS: originating in the thyroid gland.

TOXIC AGENT: poisoning influence.

TOXICOSIS: diseased condition due to poisoning.

TRAUMATISM: condition due to an injury.

ULTRAPHENOMENAL: lying beyond the sphere of phenomena.

UNCONSCIOUS: characterizing absence of conscious functioning; an assumed embodiment of formerly conscious material; subconscious.

UNIT CHARACTER: in genetics, a transmitted trait.

UREMIA: condition resulting from urinary substance in the blood; *adj.*, uremic.

UROLOGY: branch of medicine concerned with the urinary system.

VAGOTONIA: condition where the pneumogastric nerve (vagus) is excessively active, bringing fatigue.

VASCULAR: pertaining to (heart and blood) vessels.

VASOMOTOR: pertaining to nerves controlling the action of blood-vessel walls.

VEGETATIVE NERVOUS SYSTEM: autonomic (nonvoluntary) nervous system as distinct from the cerebrospinal system; also called sympathetic nervous system, it acts automatically upon the lungs, heart, viscera.

VERBIGERATION: morbid reiteration, involuntary and voluble

VISCERAL ANESTHESIA: loss of sensation in an abdominal organ.

VITALISM: doctrine that a "vital force" (something nonmechanical, nonchemical) activates bodily functions.

VOLUNTARISTIC: having the nature of an intentional act.

Index

A

Abnormalities, mental, in children
(*paper*), 61–70
early prevention of danger
from (*paper*), 71–75
development of, 110–111, 150
hereditary predisposition for, 93
symptoms of, 97–98
Activity, concept of, 140–141
(*See also* Mental activity; Substitutive activities)
Addams, Jane, 49
Adenoids as cause of secondary
mental weakness, 64
Adjustments, social, 8, 235
Adolescence, arrest of development
in (*paper*), 117–120
common traits of, 240
Hall's work on, 228
importance of, 111
mental disorders of, 234
correction of, 240
Affective psychoses, 124
Affectivity, Bleuler's plea for, 125–
127
examples of, 127
and paranoia, 128–129
Affects, 131, 267, 272
After-care of mental patients, 150–
151, 288, 299, 313, 327–329, 363,
450–451
and discharge, 309
hospitals' role, 307, 310–311

After-care of mental patients, *paper*,
200–211
physicians' role, 308–311
After-care Committee, 301, 307, 311
Agoraphobia, 131
Alcohol, 6, 84
abstinence from, 19, 303, 307–308,
461–462
and mental disorders, 91, 117, 159,
278, 302–304, 323–324, 362,
460–461
(*See also* Insanity, alcoholic; Intoxication; Psychoses)
Alienists, 37–39, 46, 48, 54, 58
early, 90–91
Almshouses, 37, 40
Altgeld, John P., 46, 49–50
Amentia, 163
American Association for the Advancement of Science, 373, 558
American Board of Psychiatry and
Neurology, 377
American Journal of Insanity, 47,
81, 83
American Journal of Psychiatry, 550,
624
American Medical Association, 371,
373, 377, 397, 406
American Medico-Psychological
Association, 49, 56, 77, 81,
102, 145, 169, 278, 340, 398,
412, 540
(*See also* American Psychiatric
Association)

653

Soul, artificial, in Middle Ages, 2
  definition of, 1–2, 90
  real essence of, 6, 26
  (*See also* Psyche)
Southard, Elmer E., 370, 539–540
Southern Society for Philosophy
  and Psychology, 370, 379
Soviet Union, 476, 549, 584–585
Spinoza, quoted, 3
Spirochetes, and general paralysis,
  350
Spitzka, Edward C., 39, 45
Spontaneity (*paper*), 576–589
State, and care of insane, 55–56, 213–
  214
  paper, 320–329
Statistics, psychiatric, 149, 166, 217,
  428
  sham value of, 145
Stevenson, George S., 319
Stewart, Thomas Grainger, 20, 104
Stirner, Max, 525
Stokes, Anson Phelps, 313–314
Störring, Gustav E., 381
Stratton, George M., 144
Stream of consciousness, 140, 151,
  229
Strecker, Edward A., 376
Subconscious, 229, 543
Subject-organization, 447, 569, 593,
  596
  paper, 616–622
Sublimation of sex, 265, 267, 269,
  562
Substitutive activities, 228, 243, 272
  paper, 193–206
Suicide, resulting from depression,
  163
Suppressed desires, 449
  (*See also* Repressions)
Susceptibility, degrees of, 6
Swiss laws, 54–55
Switzerland, Meyer's early years in,
  17–22

Symbolism, 391
Symbolization, 31, 143–144, 260, 269,
  552, 568–570, 592, 594–596, 609,
  614, 617–619, 626–627
Symptom complex, 97–98, 181, 185,
  199
Syphilis, 250, 257, 269, 278, 304–305,
  324, 461–462

T

Tantrums, with imaginations, 6
Taylor, E. W., 573
Temperament, psychiatric classifica-
  tion of, 528–529
Temporary derangements, 74
Terence, 601
Terminal dementia, 83, 116, 184
Terminology, 189, 279, 553–555
Therapy (*see* Psychotherapy)
Thomson, J. J., 258
Thorndike, Edward L., 126
Thyroidism, 162, 251
Titchener, Edward B., 227, 608, 611
Toxicoses, 162
Toxins, 249, 255
  (*See also* Autointoxication)
Tranquilizing chair, 9, 40
Trauma, 205
Treadway, Walter L., 558
Treatment, 363, 365
  paper, 53–60
  (*See also* Psychotherapy)
Tufts, James Hayden, 44
Types of psychiatric case (*see*
  names of types, as Neurotic
  type)

U

Unconscious, 26, 35, 228–229, 543,
  592
  Freud's theory of, 228–229
  paper, 260–276
  (*See also* Psychoanalysis)